RADIOLOGICAL
PHYSICS

RADIOLOGICAL PHYSICS

By

M. E. J. YOUNG, M.Sc.

British Columbia Cancer Institute, Vancouver, B.C.

SECOND EDITION

With 244 illustrations

LONDON
H. K. LEWIS & Co. Ltd.
1967

First Edition, 1957
Second Edition, 1967

RM
847
Y6
1967

©

H. K. LEWIS & CO. LTD.

1957, 1967

PRINTED IN GREAT BRITAIN
AT THE UNIVERSITY PRESS, ABERDEEN

PREFACE TO THE SECOND EDITION

THE purpose and scope of this book remain essentially as stated in the preface to the first edition, but the text has been revised to take account of the changes in radiological practice which have taken place since 1957. These consist principally in a great increase in the use of megavoltage radiation in therapy and in the use of artificial radioactive isotopes, particularly for diagnosis. There has also been a considerable increase in the use of fluorescent image intensifiers and in the television and cinematic techniques which they make possible in diagnostic radiography. The main changes which have been made in the text are as follows. Sections upon semiconductor rectifiers and transistors have been added to the introductory chapter upon electronic devices. The production of artificial radioactive isotopes is discussed earlier in the book than previously (in Chapter V instead of Chapter XIII) so that isotope teletherapy units are described immediately after the high energy X-ray generators and artificial isotope sources for brachytherapy are described in the same chapter as radium sources. A separate chapter is now devoted exclusively to the diagnostic uses of artificial isotopes. In the chapters upon dosimetry, the definitions and recommendations adopted by the International Commission on Radiological Units and Measurements in 1962 are given and the problems of dosimetry with megavoltage radiation are considered in more detail than before. A section upon solid state measuring devices has also been included. The chapter describing some of the chemical and biological effects of ionising radiation has been completely rewritten to take account of recent developments in these fields. The chapter on diagnostic radiography has been expanded to include television techniques and cinefluoroscopy and the chapter on protection has been revised to accord with the 1966 amendments to the recommendations of the International Commission on Radiological Protection.

I wish to thank Dr. H. F. Batho of the British Columbia Cancer Institute for many helpful discussions and I am indebted

v

to him and to Dr. L. Young for reading either manuscript or proofs.   I also wish to thank Dr. D. A. Boyes, Dr. J. M. W. Gibson, Dr. B. G. Goodman, Mr. R. Allen, Mr. G. M. Kennelly and Miss K. Hoskin of the British Columbia Cancer Institute and Dr. A. F. Holloway of the Manitoba Cancer Institute for supplying material for figures for this edition.

M. E. J. YOUNG

January, 1967

PREFACE TO THE FIRST EDITION

THIS book has been written with the object of providing a short text-book of Radiological Physics suitable for students working for either the Diplomas in Radiology of the Royal College of Physicians of London and the Royal College of Surgeons of England or for Membership or Fellowship of the Society of Radiographers. It is also hoped that physicists just starting hospital work will find it useful as an introductory survey of the field.

No discussion of classical electricity is included. However, two introductory chapters contain a brief account of the basic assumptions of modern physics and an elementary account of electronic valves respectively, since the author has found that the older students in particular find the inclusion of this material helpful. Megavoltage X-ray generators and isotope teletherapy units as well as more conventional X-ray and radium equipment have been described and a fairly detailed discussion is given of the ways in which X- and γ-rays of different energy are absorbed. The measurement of ionising radiations by means of Geiger-Müller and scintillation counters as well as by ionisation chambers is discussed. A chapter upon the chemical and biological effects of ionising radiation has been included to give some indication of the processes which may occur when such radiation is absorbed in a living organism and to indicate the nature of the problems which modern research in these fields is attempting to elucidate. Typical examples of treatment planning and dose calculation in therapy are given. The use of artificial radioactive isotopes for both diagnosis and therapy is described in some detail and chapters upon diagnostic radiography and upon radiological protection are also included.

Since considerable differences in previous knowledge of both physics and mathematics are to be expected amongst readers, sections in small print have been added when it was

vii

felt that further elucidation of the text might be desirable for a particular category of reader.

A list of references is appended at the end of each of the later chapters. The general references are to books or reviews upon related topics, while the numbered references are intended to provide points of entry to the current literature.

I wish to thank Dr. B. Daniels-Hunt, Dr. W. A. Leyshon, Dr. G. J. Neary, Dr. M. D. Waller and Dr. L. Young for reading parts of the book in manuscript or in proof. I am also indebted to Dr. L. A. W. Kemp, Mr. N. W. Ramsay, the General Electric Co., Philips Industries Ltd., The High Voltage Engineering Corporation, and the publishers mentioned in the text for supplying material for figures, and to the Examining Board in England by the Royal College of Physicians of London and the Royal College of Surgeons of England and to the Society of Radiographers for permission to include questions set in their examinations.

M. E. J. YOUNG.

January, 1957.

CONTENTS

ix

CONTENTS

RADIOLOGICAL PHYSICS

CHAPTER I

INTRODUCTION: FUNDAMENTAL CONCEPTS

In order to understand the effects of X-rays and nuclear radiations upon both living and non-living matter, it is necessary to consider the nature of both electromagnetic radiation and of the atoms of which all matter is composed. This chapter contains a very brief description of the modern conception of the extra-nuclear structure of an atom and of the quantum theory of radiation. The structure of atomic nuclei is discussed in Chapter V.

1.01. Atoms

All atoms consist of a small but massive, positively charged nucleus, around which move a number of very light, negatively charged electrons. The radius of the nucleus is of the order of 10^{-12} cm. Since the radius of the atom is of the order of 10^{-8} cm., the nucleus is small compared with the atom as a whole. Normally a nucleus, having a positive charge Z times the charge upon an electron, attracts Z electrons into its vicinity so that the atom as a whole is electrically neutral. The chemical properties of an atom are determined almost entirely by Z and the value of Z is therefore characteristic of a particular element. When the elements are arranged in order of increasing Z, the chemical Periodic Table is obtained, i.e. Z is the atomic number of the element.

The principal experiments which led to this concept of atomic structure were those of J. J. Thomson which established that all atoms contain identical negatively charged constituents (1897), and those of Rutherford and his co-workers which led to the conclusion that the massive positively charged part of the atom is small compared with the atom as a whole (1911).

1

Thomson examined the phenomena occurring in a gas discharge tube (i.e. a tube containing two electrodes with a high potential difference between them and gas at low pressure) and concluded that the " cathode rays " to which the phenomena were attributed, consisted of negatively charged particles moving across the tube from cathode to anode. By observing the deflection of these particles in electric and magnetic fields, he was able to determine the ratio of the charge to the mass of the particles and found this ratio was always the same whatever the nature of the gas or the electrodes which he used. The ratio was about 1,800 times as great as the charge/mass ratio for the hydrogen ion as determined by electrolysis. Thomson assumed that the charge/mass ratio for the cathode particles was high because their mass was very small and since identical particles were produced whatever materials he employed, he concluded that these particles must be constituents of all atoms. Later experiments by Thomson upon thermionic emission (1899) and by Lenard upon photo-electric emission (1900) established that particles having the same charge/mass ratio as the cathode particles could be released from metals by the action of heat or light. These particles were recognised as being identical with the cathode particles and all such particles are now called electrons.

Rutherford's nuclear theory of atomic structure was developed to explain the observation that when energetic α-particles (which were known to be helium atoms which had lost two electrons each and were therefore positively charged) fell upon a thin metal foil, although most particles were deviated only slightly in passing through the foil, some particles were deviated through very large angles and a few were even reversed in direction. To produce such large deflections of the α-particles, a very intense field of force is necessary (an encounter with a neutral atom would not be adequate) so Rutherford assumed that the mass and positive charge of the atom must be concentrated in a small volume (the nucleus), producing in its immediate vicinity an intense electrostatic field, while the electrons moved around the nucleus some distance away. An α-particle being a helium nucleus was small but fairly massive and could therefore pass through the extra-nuclear regions of the foil atoms without being deviated, but was strongly repelled if it passed near the nucleus of a foil atom. With these assumptions, it was found possible to account quantitatively for the observed scattering. Results obtained with foils of different elements suggested that the nuclear charge increased approximately proportionally to the atomic weight and later experiments have shown that the nuclear charge is an integral multiple (Z) of the electronic charge.

1.02. Electromagnetic radiation

The various types of electromagnetic radiation, e.g. radio waves, radiant heat, light, ultra-violet radiation, X- and γ-rays

2

are forms of energy which are propagated by wave motion. In a vacuum the different types of electromagnetic wave all travel with the same velocity of approximately $3 \cdot 0 \times 10^{10}$ cm. /sec. (usually referred to as the velocity of light and denoted by c). The different kinds of radiation differ, however, in wavelength and therefore also in frequency since for any wave, the velocity (v), frequency (ν) and wavelength (λ) are related by the equation

$$v = \nu\lambda \qquad . \qquad . \qquad . \qquad (1)$$

For electromagnetic waves in a vacuum, therefore

$$\nu\lambda = c = 3 \times 10^{10} \text{ cm./sec.}$$

The wavelength of an electromagnetic wave may be of the order of 10^{6} cm. as in long radio waves, or less than 10^{-12} cm. as in cosmic radiation. (See table 1.01.)

TABLE 1.01

ELECTROMAGNETIC RADIATION

Type of radiation	Approximate range of wavelengths	Corresponding frequency (c./s.)	Corresponding photon energy
Radio and Hertzian waves	3×10^{6} cm. to $0 \cdot 01$ cm.	10^{4} to 3×10^{12}	$4 \cdot 1 \times 10^{-11}$ eV.* $1 \cdot 2 \times 10^{-2}$ eV.
Infra-red rays .	$0 \cdot 01$ cm. to 7×10^{-5} cm. (i.e. 7000 Å) †	3×10^{12} $4 \cdot 3 \times 10^{14}$	$1 \cdot 2 \times 10^{-2}$ eV. $1 \cdot 8$ eV.
Visible light . .	7000 Å to 4000 Å	$4 \cdot 3 \times 10^{14}$ $7 \cdot 5 \times 10^{14}$	$1 \cdot 8$ eV. $3 \cdot 1$ eV.
Ultra-violet light .	4000 Å to 100 Å	$7 \cdot 5 \times 10^{14}$ $3 \cdot 0 \times 10^{16}$	$3 \cdot 1$ eV. 124 eV.
X- and γ-radiation .	100 Å to 10^{-4} Å	$3 \cdot 0 \times 10^{16}$ $3 \cdot 0 \times 10^{22}$	124 eV. 124 MeV.
X- and γ-rays used in medicine are usually in the range .	1 Å to 10^{-3} Å	$3 \cdot 0 \times 10^{18}$ $3 \cdot 0 \times 10^{21}$	12·4 keV. 12·4 MeV.

* The electron-volt is defined as the work done when an electron is accelerated by a potential difference of 1 volt.
    One electron-volt (eV.) = $1 \cdot 601 \times 10^{-12}$ erg.
    † The Angstrom unit (Å) = 10^{-8} cm.

At any point P in space, in the path of an electromagnetic wave, there exist electric and magnetic fields which are mutually perpendicular to one another and to the direction of propagation and vary periodically with the frequency ν which is characteristic of the wave. (See fig. 1.01.) Thus if the wave is incident upon a charged particle, the particle will experience

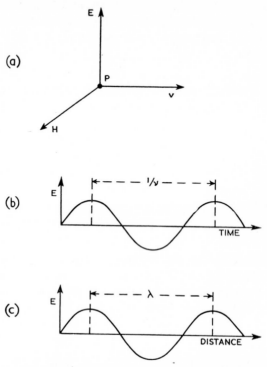

(a)

(b)

(c)

FIG. 1.01. (a) Fields in an electromagnetic wave. The electric field E and the magnetic field H are both perpendicular to the direction of propagation.
(b) Variation of electrical field with time at a particular place.
(c) Variation of electrical field with position at a particular time.

a periodic force and if free to move may be set into vibration by the wave, thus absorbing energy from the radiation.

Before 1900 it appeared that it would be possible to describe all phenomena by means of the classical concepts of mechanics or by the classical concepts of electromagnetism. In these classical theories, matter and energy were regarded as distinct entities and it was assumed that energy could be absorbed or radiated by matter in infinitesimally small amounts. In 1901, however, Planck found that the distribution of energy amongst the different wavelength radiations emitted by hot solids, which could not be explained satisfactorily by the classical theory, could be accounted for if it was assumed that the energy was radiated, not continuously, but in discrete quanta, the size of a quantum being proportional to the frequency of the radiation emitted, i.e.

$$\text{the energy per quantum } E = h\nu . \qquad . \qquad (2)$$

where h is a constant known as Planck's constant.

In 1905, Einstein suggested that if Planck's theory was correct, then it should apply in other processes also. For example, in the photoelectric effect where the absorption of energy results in the emission of electrons from a metal, only one quantum of energy should be given up to any particular electron. Consequently, (1) an electron is emitted only if the energy per quantum exceeds the minimum energy required to liberate the electron from the metal, so that there is a lower frequency limit below which emission does not occur whatever the light intensity; (2) at higher frequencies, the maximum kinetic energy with which electrons are emitted increases as the size of the quanta increase, i.e. as the frequency of the illumination increases. These predictions were subsequently verified in a series of experiments culminating in those of Millikan in 1916. Millikan's experiments enabled Planck's constant h to be evaluated. The modern value is 6.6256×10^{-27} erg sec. The value of h is such that the discontinuous nature of the interaction of radiation with matter becomes apparent only in the case of high frequency radiation, but is of considerable importance in considering the effects of X- and γ-radiation. It is frequently more convenient to treat high-energy electromagnetic radiation as a stream of elementary units of energy rather than as a wave. When the radiation is regarded in this manner, the individual units of energy, the quanta, are usually referred to as photons. The energy of the photons associated with different types of electromagnetic radiation are shown in table 1.01.

Another fundamental alteration in the classical views of matter and energy was brought about by the development by

5

Einstein of the theory of relativity (1905). Introduced in order to explain the apparent impossibility of detecting motion relative to the ether, Einstein's theory includes the assumption that no measured velocity can exceed the velocity of light. If an object is accelerated until its velocity nears that of light, the increase in kinetic energy appears as an increase in mass, rather than as an increase in velocity. Einstein deduced that the mass (m) of a moving object is related to its velocity (v) by the equation

$$m = m_0/\sqrt{(1 - v^2/c^2)} \qquad . \qquad . \qquad (3)$$

(where m_0 denotes the rest mass, c the velocity of light) and that mass and energy are related by the equation

$$E = mc^2 \quad . \qquad . \qquad . \qquad . \qquad (4)$$

The velocities of material particles normally encountered are much less than that of light, but using high-energy electrons, an increase in mass with increasing velocity was detected experimentally by Kaufmann in 1906 and the exact form of equation (3) has since been confirmed by other workers.

TABLE 1.02

VARIATION OF ELECTRON MASS WITH VELOCITY

Energy	Velocity (cm./sec.)	Mass as fraction of rest mass
1 keV.	$1\cdot87 \times 10^9$	$1\cdot002$
10 keV.	$5\cdot85 \times 10^9$	$1\cdot020$
100 keV.	$1\cdot68 \times 10^{10}$	$1\cdot196$
1 MeV.	$2\cdot82 \times 10^{10}$	$2\cdot957$
10 MeV.	$2\cdot99 \times 10^{10}$	$20\cdot58$

The rest mass is equivalent to 0·511 MeV.

Since $c^2 = 9 \times 10^{20}$ (cm./sec.)^2, it follows from equation (4) that a very large amount of energy is equivalent to a very small mass. In chemical reactions the energy released or absorbed is only a few electron-volts per atom and is too small for any detectable change in mass to result. In nuclear reactions, however, several million electron-volts of energy may be absorbed or released and from such reactions, when the masses of the reacting nuclei have been known with sufficient accuracy, experimental confirmation of Einstein's equation (4) has been obtained.   Electromagnetic radiation can also be converted into " mass ", provided the photons have sufficient energy.   Thus a photon of energy greater than 1 MeV. can produce an electron-positron pair.   This is discussed in Chapter VI.   (A positron resembles an electron but is positively, not negatively charged.   Positrons were first detected by Anderson in 1932.)

1.03. The emission of radiation by atoms.   Bohr's theory of atomic structure and optical spectra

The nuclear model of the atom accounts for certain experimental observations, such as the scattering of α-particles, but the question immediately arises as to how atoms so constructed can persist, for on account of their opposite electrical charges there must be a force of attraction between the nucleus and the electrons.   If the electrons are at rest, they will be pulled in to the nucleus directly by this force.   If they move in orbits about the nucleus, although an uncharged body can persist in a stable orbit under the action of a centrally directed force, according to classical electromagnetic theory a charged body such as an electron must radiate energy under the action of such a force and hence gradually spiral into the nucleus.   The energy so radiated would be distributed continuously over a range of wavelengths.   Bearing in mind the experimental observation that the light emitted by atoms consists of a series of discrete lines and is not a continuous spectrum, and also the fact that Planck had already assumed that energy was radiated in discrete quanta and not continuously, in 1913 Bohr suggested that (despite the laws of classical electromagnetism), the electrons in Rutherford's atomic model, did not radiate continuously but only when they " jumped " from one stable orbit to another. He was able to show that this assumption would not only permit the existence of stable atoms but would also, with the aid of an additional assumption about momentum, account in remarkable detail for the observed regularities in the spectra emitted by hydrogen and ionised helium.

Consider the energy possessed by a single extra-nuclear electron (charge e, mass m) moving about a nucleus (charge Ze) with velocity v, in a circular orbit (radius r) assuming the electron does not radiate. The potential energy of the electron = charge on electron × potential of nuclear field,

$$= - e Ze/r = - Ze^2/r.$$

The kinetic energy of the electron = $mv^2/2$, but for an electron moving in a circular orbit under the attraction of the nucleus,

$$mv^2/r = Ze^2/r^2$$

∴ The kinetic energy = $Ze^2/2r$.

∴ Total energy of the electron = $- Ze^2/r + Ze^2/2r = - Ze^2/2r$.

Thus if the electron jumps from an orbit of radius r_1, to another of radius r_2, the change in energy will be

$$- Ze^2(1/r_2 - 1/r_1)/2 = Ze^2(1/r_1 - 1/r_2)/2$$

i.e. energy is *emitted* if $r_1 > r_2$, energy is absorbed if $r_2 > r_1$.

Suppose the energy is emitted as a single quantum of magnitude hv,

then $\qquad hv = Ze^2(1/r_1 - 1/r_2)/2$

or $v = Ze^2(1/r_1 - 1/r_2)/2h$ . . . . . (5)

It had already been discovered empirically that the light emitted by hydrogen in a discharge tube consisted of a number of lines, whose frequency could be obtained by substituting integers in formulae of the form

$$v = Rc(1/n_1^2 - 1/n_2^2) \qquad . \quad . \quad . \quad . \quad . \quad . \quad (6)$$

(R denotes a constant known as Rydberg's constant, c denotes the velocity of light.)

Thus with $n_1 = 1$ and $n_2 = 2, 3, 4 \ldots$ a series of values of v are obtained which correspond with the frequencies of a set of lines in the ultra-violet known as the Lyman series. With $n_1 = 2$, $n_2 = 3, 4, 5 \ldots$ the values of v give the frequency of a set of lines known as the Balmer series and so on.

Comparison of equations (5) and (6) suggests that " permitted " orbits (i.e. those in which an electron can move without radiating) are restricted to those whose radii are the square of integers. Bohr showed that not only this relation, but also the correct numerical value for R is obtained if it is assumed that the electrons are restricted to orbits in which their angular momentum is an integral multiple of $h/2\pi$ (where h is again Planck's constant). For if $mvr = nh/2\pi$ and $mv^2/r = Ze^2/r^2$, where n is an integer (called the principal quantum number), then $v = 2\pi Ze^2/nh$ and $r = nh/2\pi mv = n^2h^2/4\pi^2 mZe^2$.

Hence $v = Ze^2(1/r_1 - 1/r_2)/2h = Z^2e^42\pi^2m(1/n_1^2 - 1/n_2^2)/h^3.$ (7)

∴ For hydrogen where $Z = 1$

$$R = 2\pi^2me^4/ch^3 \qquad . \quad . \quad . \quad (8)$$

As already stated, substituting numerical values in equation (8) leads to a value of R in good agreement with that obtained directly from spectroscopic data.

Only the simplest type of electronic orbit, a circle, has been discussed above. This suffices to explain the general features of the spectrum of hydrogen, the simplest atom. By considering elliptic orbits also, and allowing for the relativistic change of mass with velocity and for the possibility that the electron spins upon its own axis, it is possible to account for the finer details of the hydrogen spectrum.

According to Bohr's theory, energy is emitted by an atom when an electron moves from an outer to an inner orbit. Normally electrons will occupy the innermost stable orbit so that the atom is in the lowest possible energy state. Thus before an atom can radiate it must receive energy in some way (e.g. by collision with another fast moving electron).

For atoms other than hydrogen, Kossel first suggested that the electrons arrange themselves in regular shells within the atom, the number of electrons in any one shell being limited. As the atomic number increases, shells are usually filled from within outwards. This enables the periodicity of chemical properties to be explained by postulating that elements in the same group of the periodic table have the same number of electrons in the outermost shell (e.g. the alkali metals all have one electron in the outermost shell), it being these outermost electrons which take part in chemical reactions and whose " jumps " result in the emission of visible light. According to this scheme, the innermost or K shell can contain up to 2 electrons, the next shell (the L shell) can contain up to 8 electrons, the M shell can contain 18 electrons in all, the first 8 of which can be regarded as a subshell and so on. (See fig. 1.02 and table 1.03.)

Using these models for atoms other than hydrogen, the main features (but not the finer details) of the optical spectra emitted by these more complicated atoms can be accounted for by Bohr's theory.

Since the electrons in the inner shells of heavy atoms are much more strongly attracted to the nucleus than is the case with light atoms (the nucleus carrying a greater positive charge) the energy required to remove an electron from an inner orbit in a heavy atom is greater than in the lighter atoms. Correspondingly (since $E = h\nu$), the radiation which is emitted if an

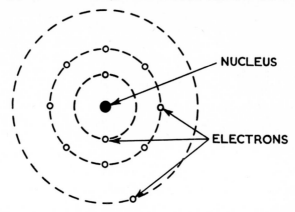

FIG. 1.02. Conventional diagrammatic representation of sodium atom (*not* to scale), showing 2 electrons in K shell, 8 electrons in L shell and 1 electron in M shell. See also Fig. 1.04.

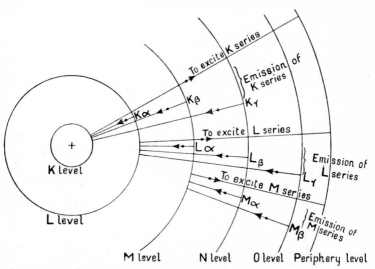

FIG. 1.03. Simplified diagrammatic representation of energy levels in a heavy atom with the corresponding X-ray emissions.

By permission from *The Structure of the Atom* by E. N. de C. Andrade. (G. Bell & Sons Ltd., London.)

electron jumps from an outer to an inner orbit in a heavy atom is of higher frequency or shorter wavelength than in light atoms

TABLE 1.03

THE ELECTRON STRUCTURE OF THE ELEMENTS NEAR THE BEGINNING OF THE PERIODIC TABLE

Group	I	II	III	IV	V	VI	VII	VIII
Number of electrons in	*Hydrogen*							*Helium*
K shell . .	1							2
Total (Z) .	1							2
	Lithium	*Beryllium*	*Boron*	*Carbon*	*Nitrogen*	*Oxygen*	*Fluorine*	*Neon*
K shell . .	2	2	2	2	2	2	2	2
L shell . .	1	2	3	4	5	6	7	8
Total (Z) .	3	4	5	6	7	8	9	10
	Sodium	*Magnesium*	*Aluminium*	*Silicon*	*Phosphorus*	*Sulphur*	*Chlorine*	*Argon*
K shell . .	2	2	2	2	2	2	2	2
L shell . .	8	8	8	8	8	8	8	8
M shell . .	1	2	3	4	5	6	7	8
Total (Z) .	11	12	13	14	15	16	17	18

11

and instead of visible light, X-radiation is emitted. Since the frequency is characteristic of the emitting atom, this is known as characteristic X-radiation. The radiation emitted when an electron jumps into the innermost shell is usually referred to as K-radiation, the radiation emitted when an electron jumps to the next shell is called L-radiation and so on. (See fig. 1.03.) The square-root of the frequency of any particular X-radiation (e.g. the shortest K-radiation) is approximately proportional to the atomic number of the emitting atom. This is predicted by Bohr's theory (eqn. 7 modified for heavy atoms) and was verified experimentally by Moseley in 1913. Characteristic X-radiation is of course only produced when an electron has first been removed from one of the inner shells of an atom.

1.04. Wave mechanics

Despite its initial success in the interpretation of optical spectra, when Bohr's theory was extended to atoms other than hydrogen, the details of the fine structure of the lines predicted by the theory were not in exact accord with experiment. Also Bohr's basic assumption that electrons could persist only in orbits in which their angular momentum was an integral multiple of $h/2\pi$ was felt to be a rather arbitrary hypothesis which for no very obvious reason had to be combined with the classical equations of motion when the behaviour of electrons in atoms was considered. After about 1927 Bohr's theory was superseded by a theory of atomic structure in which the classical equations of motion were abandoned and the behaviour of the electrons was predicted from a quite different set of equations, the equations of wave mechanics or the mathematically equivalent matrix mechanics.

These equations were developed between 1924 and 1927 by a number of scientists, including de Broglie, Schrödinger, Heisenberg, Pauli, Born and Dirac. The method of formulation most frequently used and which will be discussed here is that due to Schrödinger. Schrödinger was stimulated by a paper published in 1924 by de Broglie in which the latter suggested that if Planck's relation $E = h\nu$ represents a fundamental relation between energy and frequency, not only should radiation which was normally regarded as a wave of frequency

ν sometimes behave as if composed of particles having energy $E = h\nu$ (as had already been observed for example in the photo-electric effect), but conversely a particle having energy E should sometimes behave like a wave (or set of waves), of frequency E/h. If a set of waves is considered and their group velocity equated to the velocity of the particle, de Broglie pointed out that the wavelength of the waves (λ) would be h/p where p denotes the momentum of the particle. Since $h = 6\cdot6 \times 10^{-27}$ erg sec., this wavelength is so small for any macroscopic particle that there is no means of detecting any wave-like behaviour, but for elementary particles of extremely small mass such as electrons, the wavelength should be great enough for wave-like properties to be detected. This prediction was confirmed experimentally by G. P. Thomson and by Davisson and Germer in 1927 who showed that a beam of electrons could be diffracted by a crystal just as a wave of length h/p would be.

With the recognition that particles could exhibit wave-like properties in addition to the acceptance of the quantal or particle-like properties of radiation, it became obvious that neither classical electromagnetic theory nor classical mechanics were really adequate to explain the behaviour of electrons. The older quantum theory of radiation and Bohr's theory of atomic structure attempted to explain new phenomena by using the old laws and adding certain rather arbitrary restrictions when the laws were applied to the interaction of radiation with matter or to the motion of electrons in atoms. The equations of wave mechanics on the other hand were developed from the start to include both wave-like and particle-like properties of both matter and radiation, the classical equations of electromagnetism being obtained as an approximation valid for long wave-length radiation and the classical equations of mechanics as an approximation valid for massive particles.

Now mathematically each type of wave-motion is described by a particular type of differential equation. (For example, the electric field (E) due to a plane electromagnetic wave obeys the equation $\partial^2 E/\partial t^2 = c^2 \partial^2 E/\partial x^2$ where c is the velocity of propagation along the x axis.) If the value of the dependent variable E at one particular place at a given instant of time is known, then by solving the equation, the value of E at any other place at any later time can be calculated. The equations of wave mechanics are differential equations which resemble differential equations for wave motion. By solving the appropriate equation, for given initial conditions, it is possible to determine the value of a function ψ at any place at any later instant of time. ψ itself has no direct physical significance, but the value of ψ^2 represents the probability that a particle will be found at a particular place at a given time.

Thus when the motion of electrons in atoms is considered, the solutions of the appropriate wave equations determine the probability that an electron will be found in a particular position. (See fig. 1.04.) Each solution of a wave mechanical equation can be specified by a set of quantum numbers which (as in Bohr's theory) are the values of certain parameters introduced in the process of solving the equations. In wave-mechanics the parameters have to be restricted to integral or half-integral values in order that the solutions of the equations shall be physically acceptable, e.g. continuous, single-valued and finite. The restrictions therefore seem very reasonable when introduced in wave mechanics instead of being introduced arbitrarily as in Bohr's theory. Since the wave equation for an electron contains in one of its terms, the total energy of the electron, the restrictions required for physically acceptable solutions mean that such solutions are only obtained if the total energy has particular values, i.e. it follows that an electron can only exist in an atom in one of a number of discrete energy states. If the electron changes from one state to another, energy is radiated or absorbed. One of the earliest successes of wave mechanics was that it predicted correctly the finer details of the energy levels and therefore of the frequencies of the spectral lines emitted by helium as well as by hydrogen. (Bohr's theory gave the correct result for hydrogen but not for helium.)

As a simplified illustration of the way in which it may be necessary to restrict a particular parameter to (say) integral values in order to obtain an acceptable solution of an equation, consider the following hypothetical case. A particle of mass m, travels with velocity v around a circular orbit. If it is assumed that a wave of length $\lambda = h/mv$ accompanies

14

the particle, then in order that the amplitude of the wave shall have a single finite value at each point of the orbit, it is necessary that the length

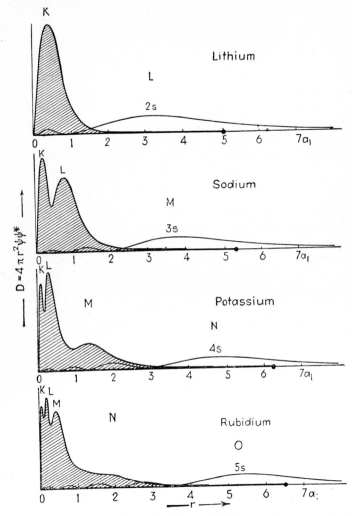

Fig. 1.04. The relative probability of finding an electron plotted against distance from the nucleus for the alkali atoms. In each case the core is shown by one curve and the valence electron by another.

By permission from *Introduction to Atomic Spectra* by H. E. White. (McGraw-Hill Publishing Co. Ltd., New York and London.)

of the orbit shall be an integral multiple of the wavelength, i.e. $2\pi r = n\lambda$ where n must be restricted to integral values. Substituting for λ gives

$2\pi r = nh/mv$ or $mvr = nh/2\pi$, i.e. the momentum of the particle must be restricted to integral multiples of $h/2\pi$.

Since the mathematics required for the solution of the equations of wave-mechanics (and particularly for the relativistic forms of the equations due to Dirac) is not easy, in later sections of this book we shall usually use the concepts and methods of the older quantum theory, which in most cases give results which are a sufficiently close approximation to those obtained by wave-mechanics. In some instances, however, we shall require to quote the more accurate results which can be derived by solving the equations of wave-mechanics (for example, the Klein-Nishina formula for Compton scattering coefficients).

EXAMINATION QUESTIONS

1. What is electromagnetic radiation? List the types of radiations in the electromagnetic spectrum in order of wavelength and give a brief account of the general properties of electromagnetic radiations . . . . .
(Part question.) M.S.R. (R. & T.), 1963.

2. Describe briefly the structure of a simple atom, explaining carefully the meaning of the terms atomic number, mass number and isotope. State how this accounts for (a) the emission of monochromatic light, (b) the emission of X-rays.

M.S.R. (R. & T.), 1962.

CHAPTER II

THERMIONIC VACUUM TUBES AND SEMICONDUCTOR DEVICES

2.01. Thermionic emission

IN 1899 J. J. Thomson showed that when a metal is heated in a vacuum, electrons are set free. This process is known as thermionic emission and its main features were established by

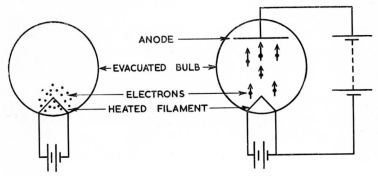

FIG. 2.01.   Thermionic emission.

O. W. Richardson by about 1903.   The experimental observations can be accounted for by assuming that electrons can leave a metal when their energy exceeds a certain minimum value. At room temperature, the number of electrons with sufficient energy is very small, but as the temperature is raised, the number of electrons with sufficient energy increases very rapidly (varying as $T^2 e^{-b/T}$ where T denotes the absolute temperature and b is a constant for a given material). Normally even the electrons which have sufficient energy to leave the metal do not escape from its vicinity, because as soon as electrons leave the metal it becomes positively charged and attracts them back again. Thus at any particular temperature, an equilibrium is attained at which the number of electrons leaving the metal equals the number which return.   If, however, the heated metal is enclosed

17

in an evacuated bulb which also includes a second plate maintained at a positive potential with respect to the first, then the electrons which leave the heated metal will be attracted to the positive plate instead of returning to the emitter. Such an arrangement is known as a two-electrode thermionic vacuum tube or diode. The electrode which emits electrons, the cathode, is usually heated by passing an electric current either through the electrode itself (which is then usually called the filament) or through an adjacent coil of wire.

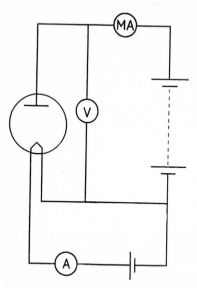

If the diode is included in a circuit such as that in fig. 2.02, which enables the variation in anode current with the anode voltage and

FIG. 2.02. Circuit for determining the characteristics of a diode.

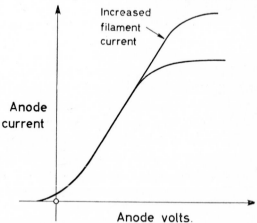

FIG. 2.03. Characteristic curve for a diode.

with the cathode heating current to be measured, it is found that for a given heating current, the anode current increases

18

with increase in anode voltage up to a certain limiting value and then becomes constant (fig. 2.03). The value of the maximum or saturation current increases if the heating current is increased. When the anode current attains its maximum value, all the electrons released from the cathode are being collected by the anode, and the value of the saturation current is therefore determined by the electron emission from the cathode, i.e. by the nature and temperature of the cathode. To obtain complete collection of all the electrons released from the cathode it is necessary to have a potential upon the anode which is sufficiently positive to produce near the cathode a field greater than the negative field produced by electrons which have already left the metal and are in the space between the anode and cathode. (These are usually referred to as the space-charge.) If the anode is not sufficiently positive some electrons return to the cathode and the number so returning and therefore the magnitude of the anode current depends upon the anode voltage. A diode which is operated with the anode voltage at a value less than that required to produce saturation is said to be " space-charge limited ". Diodes which are used as rectifiers are normally operated under these conditions, whereas X-ray tubes (which are a special form of diode) are operated with such high voltages upon the anode that the anode current is saturated and can only be appreciably increased by raising the temperature of the filament. (See Chapter III.)

2.02. Vacuum diodes as rectifiers

Electrons can only cross a diode from filament to anode when the latter is at a positive potential with respect to the filament. If the anode becomes negative, electrons are repelled by it and since the anode itself cannot supply any appreciable number of electrons so long as it remains unheated, no current crosses the tube. This fact enables diodes to be used as valves or rectifiers of alternating current.

If an alternating voltage is applied to the electrodes of a single diode, as shown in fig. 2.04, current only flows across the tube during those half-cycles when the anode is positive. This is known as half-wave rectification.

By the use of two or more diodes it is possible to obtain full-wave rectification. For example, with the arrangement shown in fig. 2.05a, electrons will flow across valve 1 when *A* is positive with respect to *C* and across valve 2 when *B* is positive with respect to *C*. Thus there is current in the circuit *ADEFC* when *A* is positive and in the circuit *BDEFC* when *B* is positive, i.e. current flows through *EF* in the same direction every half-cycle. A double diode having two anodes and a

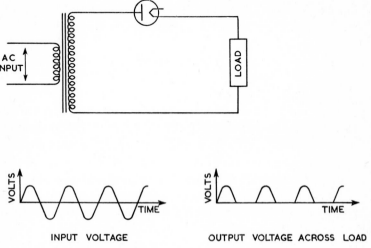

INPUT VOLTAGE   OUTPUT VOLTAGE ACROSS LOAD

FIG. 2.04. Single diode used as half-wave rectifier.

cathode within the same envelope can be used as a full-wave rectifier in a similar manner.

An alternative arrangement which is often employed is the so-called bridge rectifier or Grätz circuit, in which four diodes are connected as shown in fig. 2.06. Current flows in the circuit *ADEFGHB* when *A* is positive with respect to *B* and in the circuit *BHDEFGA* when *B* is positive with respect to *A*.

The two diode or double diode circuit with a centre-tapped transformer is widely used when an output of the order of a few hundred volts is required, for example, for the operation of amplifiers. The bridge circuit is preferred when a high output voltage is required, as in the anode circuit of an X-ray set, since the peak value of the output voltage is approximately

20

equal to the full voltage developed by the transformer, instead of being approximately one-half of that voltage as in arrangements

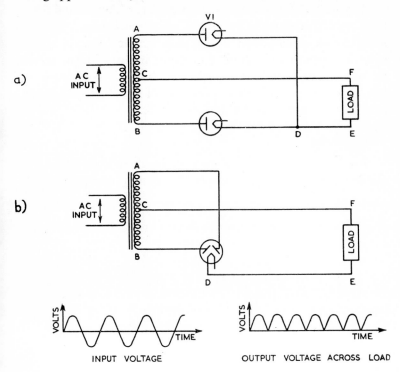

FIG. 2.05. Full-wave rectifier circuits. (*a*) using two diodes; (*b*) using double diode.

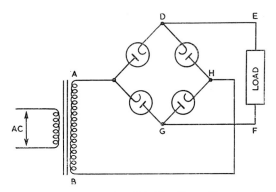

FIG. 2.06. Four valve, " bridge " rectifier circuit.

2

21

using a centre-tapped transformer. In each arrangement the diodes have to withstand the full inverse voltage.

The output from a full-wave rectifier, although unidirectional, still fluctuates in magnitude, so " smoothing " circuits must be used in conjunction with these rectifiers if a voltage of constant magnitude is required. A Grätz bridge with condenser smoothing (as used in some cine-radiographic equipment) is illustrated in fig. 3.17. Special features of high voltage vacuum rectifiers are also discussed in Chapter III.

2.03. Triodes

A triode as its name implies, contains three electrodes. An open network or spiral of wire called the grid is inserted between

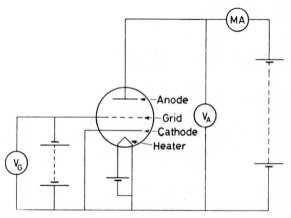

FIG. 2.07. Circuit for determining the characteristics of a triode.

the cathode and anode. The grid is normally maintained at a potential near that of the cathode and is usually a few volts negative with respect to the cathode. Under these circumstances most of the electrons which leave the vicinity of the cathode pass through the interstices of the grid and reach the anode. The number of electrons which leave the cathode and are not recaptured by it, and therefore the magnitude of the anode current (since the grid captures very few electrons) depends upon the resultant field produced near the cathode by the combined effect of the anode, the grid, and the space charge. The magnitude of the unsaturated anode current can therefore be changed by altering the potential of the grid as well as by altering the potential of the anode. The effect of any change in the grid potential upon the anode current appears almost instantaneously, since an electron requires only about 10^{-10} sec. to travel from the cathode to the anode.

Fig. 2.08 shows a series of curves in which the current to the anode is plotted against the potential of the grid for a series of values of the anode potential. A small change in the grid potential produces the same change in the anode current as a

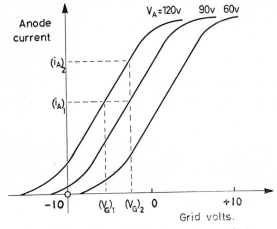

FIG. 2.08. Characteristic curves for a triode.

much larger change in the anode potential. The grid is more effective than the anode because it is nearer the cathode. The ratio of the change in the anode voltage producing a given change in the anode current to the change in the grid voltage producing the same change in the anode current is called the amplification factor of the valve. It is usually denoted by μ.

One of the most important uses of the triode is as a voltage amplifier. For this purpose the valve is usually operated with the grid at a small negative potential with respect to the cathode and the voltage to be amplified is superimposed on the negative grid potential. The anode current (i_A) varies with the grid potential (V_G) and hence the potential difference across a high resistance (R) in the anode circuit varies likewise. If Δi_A

23

denotes the change in the anode current produced by a change ΔV_G in the grid volts, and R_A is the effective resistance between anode and cathode in the valve (i.e. $R_A = \Delta V_A / \Delta i_A$ for constant V_G), then $\Delta i_A = \mu \cdot \Delta V_G / (R + R_A)$, and the change in voltage ΔV_R across the resistance $R = R \cdot \mu \cdot \Delta V_G / (R + R_A)$. Thus the voltage amplification $(\Delta V_R / \Delta V_G) = \mu R / (R + R_A)$ which is less than the amplification factor of the valve, because $R / (R + R_A)$ is less than 1. Typical values which might be obtained in practice would be $R = 10^5$ ohm, $R_A = 2 \cdot 5 \times 10^4$ ohms, giving $R / (R + R_A) = 0 \cdot 8$ and $\Delta V_R / \Delta V_G = 80$ for $\mu = 100$.

Triodes are particularly useful for the measurement of small voltages from sources of high internal resistance. Such voltages cannot be measured by ordinary voltmeters, since unless the resistance of the measuring instrument is very much greater than that of the source, the voltmeter effectively short-circuits the voltage to be measured. If the source is connected between the cathode and grid of a triode with the grid at a negative potential, however, very little current flows between the grid and cathode, but the applied voltage may be deduced from the change in the anode current. Thus the triode can be used as a voltmeter of high internal resistance. The magnitude of the internal resistance of the source that can be measured in this way, is limited by the grid current in the valve. When the grid is negative, the grid current is mainly due to positive ions which are produced when residual gas in the tube is ionised by the electrons crossing the tube. In an ordinary triode, the grid current is usually of the order of 10^{-10} ampere but in electrometer valves which are specially constructed so that the grid current is small, the grid current may be as little as 10^{-15} ampere. Electrometer valves are commonly either triodes or space-charge grid tetrodes (see below) although occasionally a pentode may be used. Such valves are usually operated with low electrode voltages so that the electrons do not acquire sufficient energy to ionise the residual gas. They are widely used in radiology for the measurement of small voltages produced across resistances of the order of 10^{11} ohm by the currents from ionisation chambers. Further details are given in Chapter VII.

24

The use of triodes as switching tubes in cine-radiographic units is described in Chapter IX.

2.04. Tetrodes and pentodes

For some purposes, the operation of a triode can be improved if additional grids are introduced into the tube, producing tetrodes or pentodes. The action of these valves is essentially the same as that of a triode but the extra grids are used to modify certain features which interfere with the satisfactory operation of the valve for particular applications.

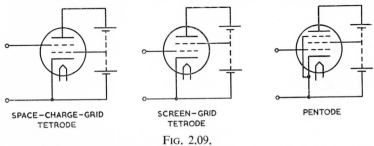

SPACE–CHARGE–GRID
TETRODE

SCREEN–GRID
TETRODE

PENTODE

Fig. 2.09.

Tetrodes are of two types, (1) space-charge grid tubes and (2) screen grid tubes. In a space-charge grid tube, the extra grid is placed between the cathode and the control grid and is maintained at a potential which is slightly positive with respect to the cathode. The additional grid enables the tube to be operated with a lower voltage upon the anode, so that electrons crossing the tube do not acquire sufficient energy to ionise residual gas in the tube, and also repels any positive ions formed in its vicinity. The introduction of the space-charge grid thus reduces positive ion current to the control grid. This device is frequently used in electrometer valves.

In a screen grid tetrode, the additional grid is introduced between the control grid and the anode and is normally maintained at a positive potential only slightly less than that of the anode. Most of the electrons from the filament pass through the interstices of the screen grid and reach the anode, but the screen grid shields both the control grid and the filament from the electrostatic field of the anode. The introduction of the screen grid therefore prevents the undesirable interaction of

25

anode and grid circuits which occurs if a triode is used for the amplification of radio-frequency voltages. It also means that when the screen grid is kept at a constant potential, the anode current is determined almost entirely by the potential of the control grid and varies only slightly with the anode voltage. Thus the amplification factor which can be obtained with a screen-grid tetrode is much higher than with a triode.

Pentodes. If a screen grid tetrode is required to supply a fairly large anode current with a high resistance load in the anode circuit, the voltage drop across the load may be sufficiently great to cause the anode voltage to fall below that of the screen grid. In this case, any secondary electrons which are ejected from the anode are attracted to the screen grid. (Normally such electrons return to the anode.) The anode current then depends upon the anode voltage and the advantage of using a screen grid is lost. To prevent secondary electrons reaching the screen, another grid called the suppressor grid may be introduced between the anode and the screen grid, thus producing a pentode valve. The suppressor grid is normally connected to the cathode. The electrons from the filament have sufficient energy to pass the suppressor grid and reach the anode, but secondary electrons from the anode are repelled by the negative potential gradient between the suppressor and the anode and return to the latter.

2.05. Gas-filled thermionic tubes

The previous discussion has been concerned with highly evacuated tubes. Tubes are also constructed which contain a small quantity of gas. Mercury vapour is frequently used. The purpose of the gas is to permit a larger current to flow across the tube.

The action of a gas-filled diode is as follows. At low anode voltages, only a small thermionic current flows. As the anode voltage is increased the velocity of the electrons crossing the tube increases until a point is reached at which an electron colliding with a gas atom has sufficient energy to eject another electron from the atom. This process is known as ionisation by collision. (The gas pressure must be correctly selected, it is usually between 0·001 mm. and 0·05 mm. of mercury.)

The positive ions which are produced, travel fairly slowly to the cathode and have the effect of neutralising the negative space charge, which in high vacuum tubes limits the anode current. Consequently, as soon as ionisation occurs the anode current is greatly increased. If the anode becomes negative with respect to the filament the current is stopped, so that gas-filled diodes can be used as rectifiers just as can highly evacuated diodes.

Gas-filled triodes are sometimes called thyratrons. In addition to passing larger anode currents they differ in one other important characteristic from evacuated triodes. The onset of ionisation and therefore the growth of the anode current can be controlled by the potential of the grid, but once ionisation is taking place the anode current becomes independent of the grid voltage and cannot be reduced by making the grid more negative, but only by removing (or sufficiently reducing) the anode voltage. The ineffectiveness of the grid, once ionisation is occurring, is due to the positive ions which collect around the grid and counteract its electric field.

For examples of the use of gas-filled tubes in radiology see Chapters III and VII.

2.06. Semi-conductor devices; junction diodes

For many purposes, thermionic vacuum tubes are being displaced by semi-conductor devices. In order to understand the operation of these devices it is necessary to consider briefly the conditions which determine the conductivity of solids.

In materials such as metals which are good conductors, the valency electrons of the atoms are free to move through the material under the action of an electric field. In insulators, the valency electrons are normally confined to the vicinity of a nucleus and they cannot move through the material under the action of an electric field unless they first receive a relatively large increment of energy. In pure semi-conductors, the valency electrons are normally confined to the vicinity of a nucleus as in insulators but a relatively small increment in energy is sufficient to enable them to move under the action of an electric field. At room temperature, a few electrons in semi-conductors acquire

27

the necessary energy, but as the temperature is raised, the number of electrons acquiring the requisite energy increases rapidly and the conductivity of pure semi-conductors therefore increases rapidly with increase in temperature. The conductivity of semi-conductors is also markedly influenced by the presence of impurities and in the materials used in the semi-conducting devices to be discussed in this chapter, impurities are deliberately added to obtain desired characteristics. In these devices the base material is commonly germanium or silicon.

Both germanium and silicon are tetravalent and in the pure materials, each valency electron is " shared " between two atoms, forming what is known as a covalent bond. At room temperature in the pure materials, a few electrons acquire sufficient thermal energy to break the chemical bond. This results in a few electrons, which, as already described, are free to move under the action of an electric field. At the same time, an equal number of empty bonding states of " holes " are produced. In an electric field, the holes move across the crystal in the direction in which positive charges would move and also contribute to the conductivity. If a penta-valent atom such as phosphorus, arsenic or antimony is substituted for a germanium or silicon atom, only 4 of its 5 electrons are required to complete the covalent bonding of the material. The extra electron is free to move under the action of an electric field. A material in which the impurity atoms increase the number of mobile electrons (negative charges) compared with the parent material is called an *n*-type semi-conductor. If a trivalent atom is substituted for a silicon or germanium atom, then the three valency electrons of the impurity atom form co-valent bonds, but there is no electron to form the fourth bond of the normal lattice. Thus the addition of the impurity increases the number of holes. This type of material is called a *p*-type semi-conductor. Electrons in *n*-type and holes in *p*-type material are referred to as " majority carriers ". Electrons in *p*-type and holes in *n*-type material are " minority carriers ".

A junction diode consists of an *n*-type and a *p*-type semi-conductor joined together along a plane boundary. In the absence of any external applied voltage, electrons and holes in the immediate vicinity of the common boundary tend to diffuse

28

across the boundary and neutralise each other. Thus there is a region in the p-type material close to the boundary which (due to the filling of holes) becomes negatively charged, while in the n-type material (due to the loss of electrons) there is a positively charged zone. This results in the creation of a potential barrier

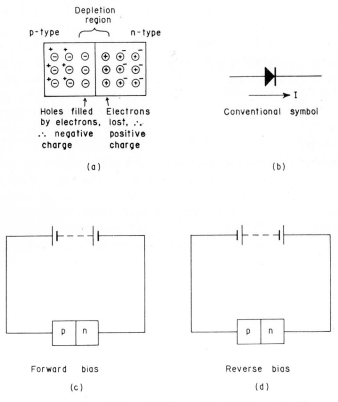

Holes filled by electrons, ∴ negative charge

Electrons lost, ∴ positive charge

(a)

Conventional symbol

(b)

Forward bias

(c)

Reverse bias

(d)

FIG. 2.10. A junction diode. (a) Charge distribution and (b) conventional symbol showing direction of easy (positive) current flow. (c) forward and (d) reverse biased junctions.

at the junction which opposes further diffusion of the majority carriers. (See fig. 2.10). If an external potential difference is applied across the junction, this may either augment or counteract the potential barrier. If the external potential difference is applied so that the p-type material is positive with respect to the n-type and the potential barrier is annulled, then electrons from the n-type material can move across the boundary into the p-type material. As the electrons fill the holes in the p-type material, more electrons cross the boundary and an appreciable current is readily maintained. If, however, the external potential difference is applied in the reverse direction so that p-type material is negative with respect to n-type, the potential barrier for the majority carriers is increased. The only current flow across the boundary in this condition is due to the minority carriers. Since the number of such carriers is small, however, the current is small and it remains constant at a given temperature over a wide range of voltage. Thus the p-n junction acts as a rectifier, permitting a relatively large current flow when the p-material is positive with respect to the n-material but only a very small current flow in the reverse direction. If, however the reverse voltage applied across the junction is sufficient to produce an electric field which will either disrupt co-valent bonds or give the minority electrons sufficient energy to produce ionisation by collision, then the reverse current suddenly increases and " breakdown " of the diode is said to occur.

Combinations of junction diodes can be used in the same way as vacuum diodes. For example four junction diodes arranged in a bridge circuit are commonly used as a meter rectifier which enables a direct current measuring instrument (suitably calibrated) to be used for the measurement of an alternating voltage or current.

2.07. "Barrier-layer" rectifiers

In addition to the p-n junction diodes discussed in section 2.06, there are a number of other devices, in which rectification takes place at the junction between a metal and a semi-conductor or between two semi-conductors. For example, in point-contact diodes, a wire of gold or tungsten makes contact with n-type germanium or silicon (these diodes are used in high frequency applications) and copper-copper-oxide rectifiers were used in some early X-ray sets. More recently cadmium-selenium rectifiers have begun to be used quite extensively in X-ray equipment and a typical selenium rectifier is illustrated diagrammatically in fig. 2.11.

The rectifier is constructed as follows:

A thin film of selenium is supported on a metal base plate (commonly, nickel, iron or aluminium) and a cadmium alloy is sprayed onto the selenium. An alternating voltage is then applied across the device and this probably causes the formation of a layer of cadmium selenide at the cadmium-selenium interface. The mechanism of the rectifying action is not fully understood but it almost certainly takes place at the junction between the two semi-conductors, selenium and cadmium selenide.

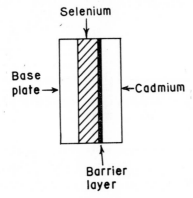

FIG. 2.11.   Construction of a selenium rectifier.

When these materials are in contact, there is a potential barrier at the junction which permits electrons to pass readily from the cadmium selenide to the selenium but not in the reverse direction. Thus the direction of easy (positive) current flow is from the base metal, through the selenium to the cadmium electrode.

For a description of the selenium rectifiers used in X-ray circuits see Chapter III, section 3.09.

2.08. Transistors

The junction transistor is a semi-conductor triode consisting of either a *p*-type material between two *n*-type materials as shown in fig. 2.12 (*a*) or alternatively a *n*-type semi-conductor between two *p*-type materials as shown in fig. 2.12 (*b*). For simplicity we will restrict our discussion to the *n-p-n* transistor.

FIG. 2.13 shows the commonest way of using *n-p-n* transistors in amplifiers. The lower junction is biased in the forward direction so that electrons from the *n*-type material, called the emitter, move readily across the junction into the *p*-type material, called the base. Most of these electrons cross the base, which is very

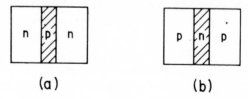

(a)   (b)

FIG. 2.12.   Junction transistors.   (*a*) *n-p-n*.   (*b*) *p-n-p*.

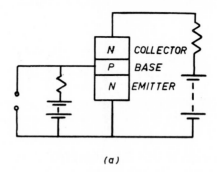

(a)

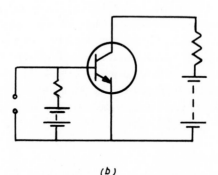

(b)

FIG. 2.13.   *n-p-n* transistor circuit.   (*a*) diagrammatic and (*b*) conventional representation of transistor.

thin, and enter the upper *n*-type material, called the collector. Some electrons are neutralised by holes in the base region but the number lost is small as the base is very thin. Holes in the base move across the base-emitter junction. The ratio of the number of electrons from the emitter which cross the first junction, to the number of holes from the base which cross the junction, is determined primarily by the ratio of the impurity concentrations in the emitter and the base and remains approximately constant over a wide range of currents. Emitter and base materials are selected so that the emitter contains a greater concentration of impurities than the base so the current across the emitter-base boundary is carried mainly by electrons. A change in the potential across the emitter-base junction produces a change in the number of electrons crossing the junction. Hence it changes the number of electrons reaching the collector, i.e. the collector current. In this respect, the transistor behaves like a vacuum triode with the base controlling the collector current as the grid controls the anode current. However, it differs in that an appreciable current flows to the base whereas in a vacuum triode the grid current is extremely small. The base current is due to the recombination of electrons and holes in the base and to the holes from the base which flow into the emitter. In the so-called common-emitter configuration shown in fig. 2.13, the operation of the transistor is described in terms of a current amplification factor β which gives the ratio of the change in the collector current to the change in base current which causes it. β is usually between 50 and 200.

Only a relatively low input impedance can be obtained with the junction transistor. This means it cannot replace a vacuum tube in those applications which call for an electrometer valve. Also random fluctuations in current (noise) may be more troublesome with transistors, and their characteristics are very sensitive to temperature. Transistors have the advantages, however, of robustness, smallness, lightness, longer life and the absence of filament heating requirements. In radiology, vacuum tubes will usually be found in the amplifiers used with ionisation chambers for X- and γ-ray dosimetry (where a high input impedance is essential) but in most of the instruments using Geiger-Müller or scintillation counters and in portable monitoring equipment, transistors are now employed. See Chapters VII and V III.

There are two types of transistor, known as field effect transistors, (1) the Shockley type and (2) the metal-oxide-silicon

33

type, which have a higher input impedance than junction transistors. These may eventually replace electrometer valves but have not yet done so.

2.09. Photo-electric devices; vacuum phototubes and photo-multipliers

As mentioned in Chapter I, electrons can be set free from metals by illumination with visible or ultraviolet light. This is known as photo-electric emission and is utilised in vacuum phototubes and photomultipliers to detect or measure light. The essential elements of a vacuum phototube are a cathode surface of large area covered with a material which emits electrons readily when illuminated and a collecting electrode, maintained at a positive potential with respect to the cathode, contained in a glass envelope. For a given light source and given voltage on the collecting electrode, the photo-electric current is proportional to the light intensity. For the detection or measurement of very weak flashes of light, photomultiplier tubes are used instead of a simple vacuum photo-tube. In photo-multiplier tubes, a series of electrodes (usually called dynodes) are included with the cathode in an evacuated tube and a potential difference of 100 or 200 volts is maintained between successive electrodes. Electrons liberated from the cathode by the photo-electric effect are accelerated by the potential difference between the cathode and the first dynode and arrive there with sufficient velocity to eject other electrons from the dynode. These electrons are then accelerated to the second dynode and in their turn produce more electrons. Thus the number of electrons is increased at each dynode so that the final pulse of charge arriving at the anode or collector plate is large enough to be readily measured. The photo-cathode usually consists of a film of antimony-caesium (which gives a large photo-electric but small thermionic emission) deposited either on a nickel plate or on the glass envelope. The dynodes may be solid curved metal plates arranged in two approximately circular arrays so that the electrostatic field focuses electrons on to successive plates as shown in fig. 2.14 (a), or alternatively they may consist of a set of parallel metal strips arranged longitudinally in a Venetian blind fashion, fig. 2.14 (b), so that the secondary electrons can pass through the gaps between adjacent strips to the next dynode.

Applications of photo-multipliers in radiology are described in section 3.14, and section 8.03.

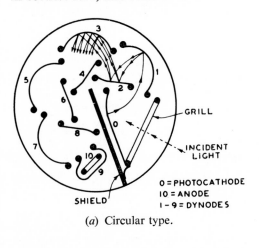

GRILL

INCIDENT LIGHT

0 = PHOTOCATHODE
10 = ANODE
1 – 9 = DYNODES

SHIELD

(a) Circular type.

Fig. 2.14. Diagrammatic representation of photomultiplier tubes.

By permission from *Scintillation Counters* by J. D. Birks. (Pergamon Press Ltd., London.)

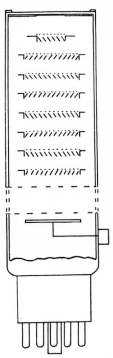

(b) Longitudinal type.

2.10. Semi-conductor photo-electric devices

When semi-conductors are illuminated, energy absorbed from the light, increases the number of electrons able to move under the action of an electric field and therefore additional electron-hole pairs are generated. This effect is utilised in a number of semi-conductor photo-devices. Thus the increased conductivity produced in a single material by illumination may be measured and used as a measure of light intensity. Alternatively the effect of irradiation on a *p-n* junction or a barrier layer may be used. In the latter cases the junction or barrier

35

layer is operated with either a small reverse voltage or with zero external voltage across the junction and the current which flows upon illumination (due to the additional electron-hole pairs generated by the light) is used as measure of the light intensity.

EXAMINATION QUESTIONS

1. Give an account of the phenomenon of thermionic emission. Why is tungsten usually used for the filament of an X-ray tube?
   Show graphically how the anode current in a diode varies with anode voltage and with filament temperature.

   M.S.R. (R. & T.), 1962.

2. Describe the phenomena of " the thermionic emission of electrons " as exhibited by a vacuum diode valve.
   Illustrate your answer with graphs which show how the current flowing through the valve depends upon (a) the filament temperature, and (b) the anode-filament (cathode) voltage. Hence explain how such a diode is able to act as a rectifier.

   M.S.R. (R. & T.), 1965.

3. Describe how a diode valve is able to act as a rectifier. Draw and explain the operation of any high voltage rectifying circuit used in X-ray practice.

   M.S.R. (R. & T.), 1961.

4. Describe the principle of the selenium rectifier. Discuss its place as a high tension rectifier in comparison with a hot cathode valve. What other materials may be used instead of selenium?

   F.S.R., 1962.

5. Discuss the phenomenon of thermionic emission and describe the mode of action of a thermionic triode valve. Indicate briefly how the device can be used as a voltage amplifier.

   F.S.R., 1963.

6. Give brief accounts of (a) thermionic emission, (b) photo-emission. Discuss either (a) the characteristic curves of a high tension diode rectifier and X-ray tube or (b) the construction and action of a barrier layer photocell and a photomultiplier.

   D.M.R., 1962.

7. Describe the construction and characteristics of (a) a diode valve, (b) a triode valve.
   Explain the use of a diode in X-ray equipment.

   D.M.R., 1964.

8. Explain the action and construction of a triode valve and describe its use, (*a*) as a switching valve and, (*b*) as a voltage amplifier.

D.M.R., 1962.

9. Summarise the properties of free electrons as used in electronic devices. Give accounts of any *two* electronic devices (other than X-ray tubes) in common use in radiological apparatus.

D.M.R., 1963.

CHAPTER III

THE PRODUCTION OF X-RAYS UP TO ABOUT 400 keV. IN ENERGY

3.01. The discovery of X-rays

IN 1895, the German physicist Roentgen was carrying out experiments using an evacuated discharge tube. He observed that a barium platino-cyanide screen beyond the anode end of the discharge tube glowed when the tube was operating, even when the latter was covered in black paper and when the screen was as far as two metres from the tube. Objects held between the discharge tube and the screen threw shadows upon it, but were not usually completely opaque to the radiation. The darkness of the shadow increased with the thickness and with the density of the object interposed. He also observed that wrapped photographic plates in the same position as the screen were blackened. Roentgen concluded that these effects were due to some form of radiation coming from the discharge tube. He found that the radiation was not deflected by a magnet. Because of this and because of its penetrating power, he concluded that the radiation could not consist of charged particles such as cathode rays. After further experiments Roentgen decided that the X-rays (as he called them) emanated from that part of the wall of the discharge tube which was struck by the cathode rays. He tried to obtain evidence of refraction and interference to establish the wave-like nature of the radiation, but in this he was unsuccessful. These effects were difficult to observe with the existing methods because of the extremely short wave-length of X-radiation, but in 1912 von Laue suggested that the regular arrangement of atoms in crystals might act like a very closely spaced diffraction grating and diffract X-rays as a grating does light. At von Laue's suggestion, Friedrich and Knipping tested his theory experimentally and succeeded in detecting X-ray diffraction. The measurement of the wavelength of X-rays using crystals is discussed further in section 3.15.

Roentgen also discovered that charged objects lose their charge in the presence of X-rays. He showed that this is due to the conductivity acquired by the air through which the X-rays pass.

3.02. Modern X-ray tubes

The modern method of generating X-rays for medical use differs from that discovered by Roentgen in that the electrons

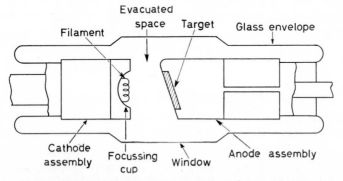

FIG. 3.01.   Schematic diagram of a modern X-ray tube.

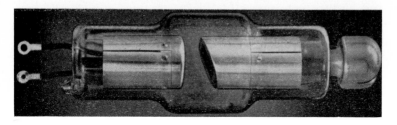

FIG. 3.02.   A modern X-ray tube, designed for operation up to 100 kVp.

By permission from *Medical Radiographic Technic* by G. W. Files (Charles C. Thomas, Springfield) and of the General Electric Co., Milwaukee, U.S.A.

whose bombardment of a target produces the X-rays are obtained from a heated filament instead of by a gaseous discharge. The essential features of a typical modern X-ray tube are shown diagrammatically in fig. 3.01.

The cathode assembly comprises (1) the heated filament, which is usually a spiral of tungsten wire, and (2) a shield or focusing cup, which screens the adjacent parts of the tube and is usually shaped so that electrons from the filament are focused by the electrostatic field on to the target.[1] Tungsten is used for the filament because it has a high melting point and there is appreciable thermionic emission at a temperature at which the filament is mechanically strong.

Electrons are accelerated across the evacuated space within the glass envelope under the action of the electric field which is established between the anode and cathode and strike the target with high velocity. The targets of both diagnostic and therapeutic X-ray tubes are usually made of tungsten. This metal is used because it has a high atomic number, a high melting point and adequate thermal conductivity (see below). The tungsten may be a solid block but is usually a disc set in the end of a copper rod which forms the anode.

The potential difference maintained between the anode and cathode depends upon the purpose for which the X-rays are to be used. In diagnostic and superficial therapy tubes, the maximum potential difference used is about 150 kVp., whereas in deep therapy tubes the potential difference is usually between 200 and 400 kVp. (The abbreviation kVp. is used when the peak value of a kilovoltage which varies in magnitude is specified.) The tube walls which support the electrodes must provide sufficient insulation to withstand this potential difference and sparking over the outside of the tube must be prevented. Hence the tube walls are usually of glass and the tube is immersed in a fluid which has better insulating properties than air. The most usual insulator is oil, which can also be used to cool the tube (see below), but has the disadvantage of making the set heavy. In some designs, a highly insulating gas, sulphur hexafluoride, is used.[2] A window of thinner glass or of beryllium [3, 4] is frequently provided in the tube in the direction of the X-ray beam. Such a window is essential in superficial therapy tubes operated at low kilovoltages since otherwise the long wavelength X-rays which are used in these treatments are absorbed in the tube walls.

X-ray tubes are enclosed in an outer case or " housing " of lead impregnated plastic, or lead impregnated porcelain, or of metal, which is usually provided with a shuttered window. The case is earthed to protect the user from the high voltage. It also acts as a shield to reduce the intensity of X-rays leaving

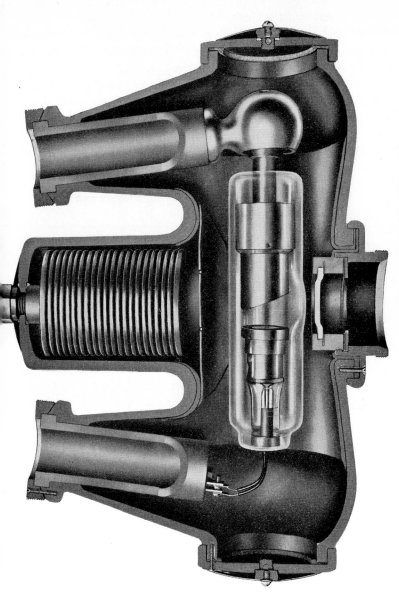

FIG. 3.03. Oil immersed X-ray tube and housing.
By permission from *X-rays* by W. E. Schall. (John Wright and Sons Ltd., Bristol.)

the tube in directions other than the window. For the safety of the operator, it is desirable that the X-ray intensity should be reduced as recommended by the International Commission on Radiological Protection. (See Chapter XIV.) The case also acts as a container for the insulating fluid.

The electrical connections to X-ray tubes are usually carried in shock-proof cables. These cables have an outer flexible metal sheath which is earthed and insulated from the high voltage conductor. If the main high tension transformer is enclosed in the same case as the X-ray tube, however, only low voltage wiring is needed outside the tube housing.

3.03. Processes occurring at the X-ray tube target and details of target and anode construction

When the electrons from the filament arrive at the X-ray tube target, they are rapidly slowed down as they interact with the atoms in the surface layer of the target material. Electrons with an initial energy of the order of 100 keV. lose energy principally in interactions with the outer electrons of the target atoms. However, X-rays are only generated when an electron passes near the nucleus of a target atom or collides with an electron in an inner shell of the target atom. Hence only a small fraction of the energy of the incident electrons is converted into X-ray energy, the remainder is converted into heat.

Fig. 3.04 illustrates diagrammatically the possible inter-actions between an incident electron and the target atoms. In (*a*) the high-speed electron displaces an electron from an outer orbit of the atom, but this electron subsequently returns to its original position. This process is known as excitation and requires the transfer of only a few electron volts of energy from the incident electron to the excited atom. In a solid the excitation energy normally appears as heat. In (*b*), the incident electron again displaces an outer electron from its orbit, but sufficient energy is transferred to enable the displaced electron to escape from the parent atom, i.e. the atom is ionised. The displaced electron may in its turn produce further ionisation. The energy given up by the incident electron again ultimately appears as heat. In (*c*), the incident electron has also ionised the target atom but the electron has been ejected from an inner shell of the atom.

In this case the incident electron must lose energy in excess of the binding energy of the particular shell of the target atom and the process is therefore only possible if the incident electrons have energy in excess of the particular binding energy concerned. (The difference in energy between that lost by the incident electron and the binding energy is carried away by the inner shell electron and will be dissipated in ionisation and excitation). In this case, an electron from an outer shell of the target atom will move in to fill the vacancy in the inner shell and in the process will emit X-radiation characteristic of the target atom

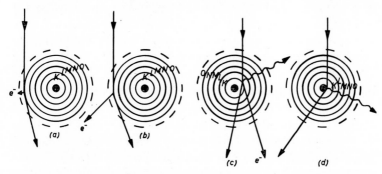

FIG. 3.04. Diagrammatic representation of interactions between electrons and target atoms. (a) Excitation, (b) ionisation, (c) ionisation and production of characteristic X-radiation, (d) Bremsstrahlung production.

(as described in Chapter I, section 1.03). In (d), an incident electron has passed close to the nucleus of a target atom and has been strongly deflected by the attraction of the multiply charged positive nucleus. In this process the electron is suddenly decelerated and loses a considerable amount of energy which is emitted as X-radiation. (The German name Bremsstrahlung which is sometimes applied to this type of X-radiation is literally translated as " braking radiation ".) The amount of energy which is converted into X-radiation depends upon the closeness of the electron path to the target nucleus and can take any value from zero to the total energy of the electron. There is therefore a continuous distribution of X-ray wavelengths above a certain minimum in " Bremsstrahlung " and this radiation is also often described as the continuous X-ray spectrum. (See section 3.15 for further details of wavelength distributions.)

The relative probability of these different processes depends upon the energy of the incident electrons and the nature of the target atoms. At energies of the order of 100 keV., excitation and ionisation are very much the most probable processes in all materials. The probability of these processes decreases to a shallow minimum about 1 MeV. and then increases again slowly. The probability of X-ray production on the other hand increases with increasing energy of the incident electrons. Thus for a tungsten target, with an accelerating voltage of the order of 100 kVp., less than 1 per cent. of the incident energy is converted to X-radiation and the remainder appears as heat, but as the accelerating voltage is increased the efficiency of X-ray production increases until above about 10 MeV. more X-rays are produced than heat. The efficiency of X-ray production also varies approximately proportionately with the atomic number of the target material. Hence an X-ray tube target should have a high atomic number and it must also have a high melting point and good thermal conductivity. Tungsten (Z = 74, M. Pt. 3370°C.) is commonly used for X-ray targets below 400 kVp. but gold (Z = 79, M. Pt. 1063°C) or platinum (Z = 78, M.Pt. 1773°C.) is used in some megavoltage tubes. The conductivity of tungsten (0·4) of gold (0·7) and of platinum (0·17) is less than that of copper (1·0) so apart from the target itself, the anode as a whole is usually made of copper.

In a modern X-ray tube, the heat generated may be of the order of 1,000 calories per second. This heat is lost partly by radiation from the target face to the tube envelope (and hence by conduction and convection to the surrounding fluid) and partly by conduction from the target through the anode stem to the surrounding fluid. The rate of heat removal can be increased by providing the anode stem with a metal radiator (in the form of fins or a rounded ball) outside the tube. (See fig. 3.05 (*a*) and (*b*).) In some sets, air is blown over the radiator to accelerate cooling. If the tube is immersed in oil, the oil expands when it becomes heated and to allow for this expansion a bellows is included within the tube shield (see fig. 3.03). These devices are usually sufficient for diagnostic tubes and for superficial therapy tubes. In therapy tubes operated in the 200 kVp. to 400 kVp. range, the cooling that can be obtained in this way is not sufficient and the insulating oil may be circulated through a water cooler or a hollow anode may be used through which oil (or water if the anode is at earth potential) is circulated to cool the target. (See fig. 3.05 (c).)

The heat which is generated in the target imposes a limit upon the power at which a tube can be operated. For short exposures there is not enough time for the heat generated to be conducted away from the focal spot, so the total heat produced must not exceed that required to raise the temperature of the focal spot above its melting point. To obtain a sharply defined X-ray beam it is necessary for the area of the focal spot to be small. This is particularly important in diagnostic tubes since the sharpness of the radiographic image de-

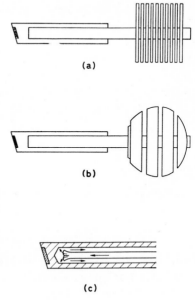

(a)

(b)

(c)

FIG. 3.05. Alternative methods of cooling X-ray targets.

creases as the size of the X-ray source increases. However, the smaller the focal spot, the greater is the rise in temperature produced by a given amount of heat, and, in practice, it is necessary to compromise between a focal area small enough to give a clear radiograph and one large enough to permit operation of the tube at high power without melting the target. The average tungsten target can withstand an energy dissipation of about 200 watts per square millimetre of actual focal area for exposures of the order of 1 sec. Somewhat higher rates can be tolerated for shorter exposures and for full-wave instead of half-wave rectification.

To enable tubes to be operated at higher power without increasing the effective size of the focal spot, the face of the X-ray target is usually inclined at a fairly small angle to the X-ray beam. By using a cylindrical filament coil and oval

45

focusing cup, a focal spot is produced which appears as a narrow rectangle when viewed at right angles to the target face. When this rectangle is viewed at right angles to the tube axis, however (i.e. in the direction of the X-ray beam), the projection of the focus is a small square. (See fig. 3.06.) In diagnostic sets the angle θ between the target face and the X-ray beam is commonly between 15° and 20°, which gives an effective focal area between 1/4 and 1/3 of that of the actual (rectangular)

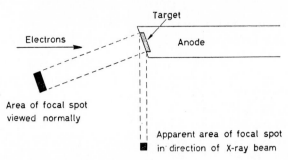

FIG. 3.06. Method of obtaining small apparent focus.

area. (The effective area $=$ actual area $\times \sin \theta$.) Inclining the target at a small angle to the X-ray beam has the disadvantage that the intensity of the X-rays in a plane parallel to the tube axis, is less at the anode side than at the cathode side. This is because the X-rays which are generated at a depth in the target have to traverse progressively greater thicknesses of the target, the more obliquely they emerge from the target face. It also limits the area of the X-ray beam. In diagnostic sets it is more important to have a small focal spot than a uniform distribution of intensity across the X-ray beam, but in therapy sets it is desirable that the variation in intensity across the beam should be as small as possible, and a wide X-ray beam is sometimes desirable. Angles between 20° and 40° are therefore commonly used in therapy sets. (Factors other than the target angle which affect the distribution of intensity across the X-ray beam are discussed in section 3.05.)

A second method of obtaining high energy dissipation with a small focal area, which is used in diagnostic tubes, is by rotation of the target. Rotating anode tubes are discussed in the next section.

The effective area of the focal spot can be measured by producing a " pin-hole image " of the target. A sheet of lead containing a small pin-hole $(00')$ of known diameter is placed between the X-ray target (TT') and an X-ray film in a cardboard holder (i.e. the film is used without intensifying screens). Since X-rays travel in straight lines, the size of the focal spot can

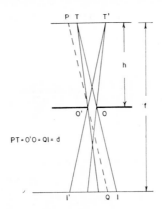

FIG. 3.07. Determination of apparent target size from a pin-hole image.

be determined from the size of the image $(II']$ produced on the film provided the target film distance (f), the target pin-hole distance (h) and the pin-hole diameter (d) are known. In fig. 3.07, the line $PO'Q$ has been drawn parallel to the limiting ray TOI so $PT = 00' = QI = $ d.
From the similar triangles $PO'T'$, $I'O'Q$,

$$\frac{PT'}{h} = \frac{I'Q}{f-h}$$

i.e. $$t + d = \frac{h}{f-h} \ (I'I - d)$$

II' is the diameter of the total image on the film (i.e. including the penumbra). If the pin-hole is placed midway between the target and the film, so that $h = f - h$ then $t + d = II' - d$ or the target diameter t is given by $t = II' - 2d$.

For therapy tubes operated with accelerating voltages of 200 kVp. or more, it is now customary to use " hooded " anodes (fig. 3.08). A hollow metal tube or hood is placed around the target to shield the glass walls of the tube from secondary electrons which are emitted from the target and which at these energies may reach the tube walls. This is undesirable since if secondary electrons strike the tube walls (1) an electric charge may build up on the walls sufficient to distort the focusing of the primary electrons on the target, (2) X-rays are generated in the tube walls, and (3) the glass envelope may be punctured. The hood is usually constructed of copper to absorb the secondary electrons, surrounded by a thin tungsten sleeve to

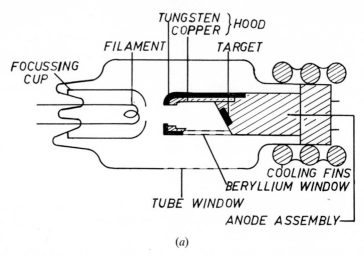

(a)

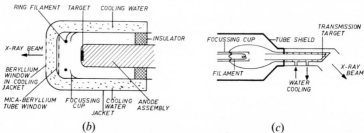

(b)   (c)

FIG. 3.08.   (a) Therapy X-ray tube with hooded anode.
(b) Contact therapy tube with circular filament.
(c) Contact therapy tube with transmission target.

absorb any X-rays produced in the copper. A thin beryllium window which will stop electrons but not absorb X-rays appreciably is provided in the hood in the direction of the X-ray beam.

X-ray tubes designed for contact or intracavitary therapy, i.e. so that they may be placed in contact with the skin or introduced into body cavities, differ somewhat in construction from ordinary therapy tubes. The electrical connections to both anode and cathode usually enter at the same end of the tube and the X-radiation is emitted from the opposite end of the tube in the direction of the tube axis. The X-radiation may be emitted from either the cathode or the anode end of the tube. In the former case a circular filament is used, and the X-rays pass through the centre of the circle (fig. 3.08 (b)). In the latter case a very thin target of copper is employed, and the X-rays pass through the target (fig. 3.08 (c)). The X-ray beam at the tube surface is commonly 1 or 2 cm. in diameter, but diverges rapidly so that larger areas can be treated if the tube is held a short distance from the skin surface.

3.04. Special features of diagnostic X-ray tubes

In diagnostic radiology, it is usually desirable to keep the duration of the X-ray exposure as short as possible to prevent blurring of the radiograph due to movement of the subject. Hence it is necessary to use high currents during the exposure and the instantaneous rate of heat production is large although the average rate of heat input per hour (say) is not as great as in therapy tubes. Since, as already explained, it is also desirable that the size of the focal spot shall be as small as possible, in order that sharply defined radiographs be obtained, the chief problem in the design of these tubes is how to avoid momentarily producing excessively high temperatures at the focal spot. It is usual for diagnostic tubes to be constructed with two separately mounted filaments, the electron beams from which fall upon different regions of the target and form focal spots of different sizes, thus permitting a choice of focal area.

Since heat is lost more rapidly from the edges than from the centre of the target area, it is also common practice to design the filament and focusing devices so that somewhat fewer electrons strike the centre than the edges of the target area. (The effect of this design feature upon radiographic detail is discussed in Section 9.05.)

Even with these design features and using an inclined target face as already described, heating of the target still places an undesirable limit upon the maximum tube currents which can be used with a given focal spot size, so long as the anode is stationary. To obtain higher energy dissipation with a small focal area, it is now customary to use rotating anode tubes. In these tubes the target is a thin disc of tungsten supported by a rod which acts as the rotor of an induction motor, the windings of which are outside the glass tube. (See fig. 3.09.)

The electrons are focused on to a small area near the periphery of the target but they impinge upon a different region of the target as it rotates and each element of the target surface is only in the electron beam for a fraction of the total exposure

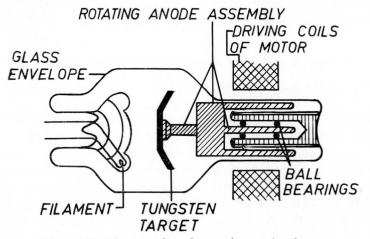

FIG. 3.09. Cross-section of a rotating anode tube.

time. Thus the heat generated by the electrons is spread through an area approximately equal to the circumference of the anode ($2\pi\lambda$ say) multiplied by the length (l) of the focal spot, while the effective focal area is a square of side l sin θ (where θ is the target angle) and of course remains stationary with respect to the tube as a whole. The speed of rotation is commonly of the order of 3,400 revolutions per minute. For the same effective focal spot size and exposure time, the maximum permissible current is commonly 7 or 8 times as great with a rotating as with a stationary anode. (See Table 3.01.)

In cine-radiography, so-called " grid-controlled " X-ray tubes are used. These tubes are usually similar in construction to regular X-ray tubes except that the filament is well insulated from the focusing cup, so that any selected potential difference can be maintained between the filament and cup. When the latter is at a sufficiently negative potential with respect to the filament, no electrons cross the tube (just as when the grid of a vacuum triode is sufficiently negative no electrons cross the triode), but when the cup is at the same potential, as that of the filament, the cup merely focuses the electrons onto the target in the usual manner. In cine-radiography, regular voltage pulses

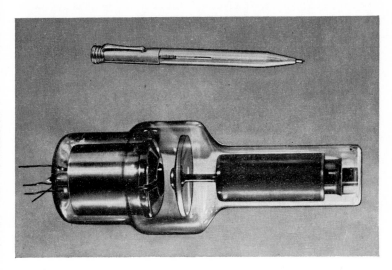

FIG. 3.10.   A rotating anode tube.

By permission from *X-Ray Research and Development*.   (Philips Electrical Ltd., London.)

are applied to the focusing cup, so that electrons only cross the tube to generate X-rays when the camera shutter is open. (See Chapter IX.)

Manufacturers of diagnostic X-ray sets usually supply rating charts which show the maximum permissible combinations of tube current and exposure time for different kilovoltages for each size of focal spot for a given type of tube and given type of rectification. Fig. 3.11 shows a typical chart. The use of such a chart is made clear by the following example. Suppose that to obtain X-rays of sufficient penetrating power it was desired to operate at 100 kVp. and that to reduce the possibility of blurring due to movement it was desired to limit the exposure time to less than 1 second. Then the chart shows that with the small focal spot, the maximum permissible tube current is 155 mA. If the resulting radiograph is not sufficiently dense then it would be necessary to change to the larger focal spot before increasing the tube current. With the large focal spot, the maximum permissible current is approximately 275 mA.

In addition to keeping the heat input to the target per exposure within safe limits, it is also necessary to consider the number of exposures which can be made in rapid succession and the tube current for continuous operation.

TABLE 3.01

TYPICAL X-RAY TUBE RATINGS FOR FULL-WAVE RECTIFICATION

Type of set	Target	Apparent area of focal spot (sq. mm.)	Anode volts (kVp.) *	Max. current for 1/10 sec. exposure (mA.)
Diagnostic	Stationary	4	80	60
„	„	20	80	200
„	Rotating	4	80	450
				Max. current for continuous operation (mA)
Diagnostic	Stationary	4	80	5
„	„	20	80	5
Therapy	„ (oil-cooled)	40	200	25

* The abbreviation kVp. is used to denote the peak kilovoltage applied to the tube.

Rotating anode tubes have the disadvantage that both the heat storage capacity and the cooling rate of the anode are rather low. (This is because the anode is of relatively light construction and is carried on bearings so that it can rotate easily.) This means that although the permitted heat input per exposure can be large, the total number of exposures which can be taken in rapid succession (determined by the storage capacity) and the maximum permissible current for continuous operation (determined by the cooling rate) are less for rotating than for stationary anode tubes and are limited by the design of the anode. In stationary anode tubes the transfer of heat from the anode to

52

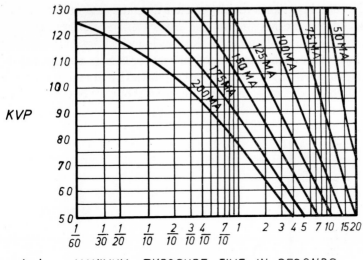

(a) MAXIMUM EXPOSURE TIME IN SECONDS
SMALL FOCAL SPOT

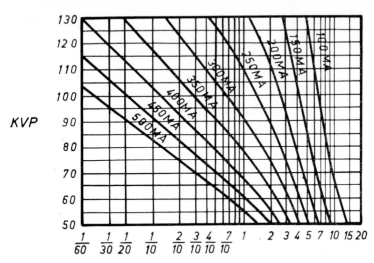

(b) MAXIMUM EXPOSURE TIME IN SECONDS
LARGE FOCAL SPOT

FIG. 3.11. Diagnostic X-ray tube rating chart.

the tube housing is usually greater than the rate of removal of heat from the housing and in this case it is the heat storage capacity and cooling rate of the housing which limit the number of exposures per hour and the current for continuous operation. Information about heat storage capacities and cooling rates are usually given by the manufacturers in arbitrary but convenient units called " heat units ". The energy dissipated in heat units is

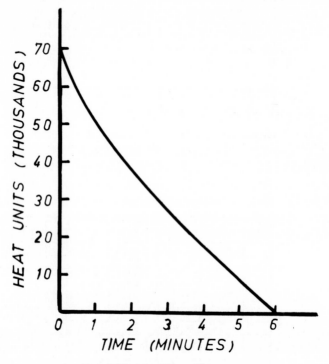

FIG. 3.12.   Anode cooling curve.

measured by the product of the peak accelerating voltage in kilovolts, the mean anode current in milliamperes and the exposure time in seconds. (The size of a heat unit is not constant but varies with the wave form of the accelerating voltage, but the units are very convenient and quite adequate for specifications restricted to a given machine.) Thus an exposure of 1 second duration made at 100 kVp. and 100 mA. would contribute 10,000 heat units. If the storage capacity of the anode of a given rotating anode tube were (say) 70,000 heat units, then after seven such exposures in rapid succession it would be necessary to permit an interval for cooling before making another exposure. The time interval required can be calculated from a cooling curve such as that of fig. 3.12. For example another 100 kVp, 100 mA, 1 second exposure could be made when the anode had cooled to a temperature corresponding to 60,000 heat units, i.e. after about half a minute. For continuous operation, the tube current is restricted to a value which produces a heat input less than the maximum cooling rate of either the anode or the tube housing, whichever is the smaller. Typical values of tube current for continuous operation are also listed in Table 3.01.

3.05. The angular distribution of X-rays around a target

X-rays are not emitted equally in all directions from a target. There is a preferential direction for the emission of X-rays relative to the direction of retardation of the incident electrons. When the velocity of the electrons is low, the radiation is emitted mainly at right angles to the direction of retardation. As the velocity is increased the maximum intensity shifts in the forward direction. This spatial distribution is most marked when thin targets are used. With thick targets the extra scattering makes the angular distribution more uniform. If the X-ray window is placed so that the central axis of the X-ray beam is at right angles to the tube axis (as is usual for X-rays generated up to 400 kVp.), then at the higher voltages, in a plane parallel to the tube axis, the X-ray intensity will increase from the cathode to the anode side on account of the angular distribution. However, if the target face is inclined at a fairly small angle to the X-ray beam, absorption in the target of X-radiation generated at a depth, reduces the intensity at the anode side more than at the cathode side (as already described in section 3.03). These two effects therefore tend to cancel out and by a suitable choice of target angle it is possible to obtain an approximately symmetrical distribution of intensity across the X-ray beam for a particular radiation quality. (An angle of 27° has been suggested [7] as the optimum for radiation generated at about 200 kVp.) When X-rays are generated at 1 MV. or more, it is usual to design the X-ray tube so that the X-rays transmitted through the target in the forward direction are used. (See Chapter IV.)

3.06. Electrical supplies for X-ray sets

The essential supplies required for an X-ray set are a small heating current of a few amperes supplied at about 6 volts for the filament and a large potential difference of the order of hundreds of kilovolts, to maintain the accelerating field between anode and cathode. Fig. 3.13 shows the basic elements in the simplest form of X-ray circuit (using ordinary single phase a.c. mains).

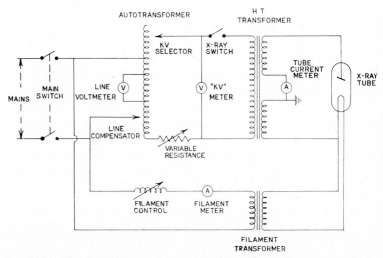

FIG. 3.13.   Simplified diagram to show basic features of X-ray tube circuit.

The small voltage for the heating current is obtained from a step-down transformer (the filament transformer), the large accelerating voltage is obtained from a step-up transformer (the anode or high-tension transformer). The primary of the high tension transformer is supplied from an auto-transformer to enable the input voltage to be varied. Notice that all switches and controls are in low voltage circuits, controlling the currents to the primaries of the transformers. Also the milliammeter in the anode circuit is connected at the earthed point of the circuit.

For a particular X-ray tube the range of wavelengths of the X-radiation generated (the " quality " of the radiation) depends upon the energy with which the electrons impinge upon the target. This is determined by the potential difference between the anode and the cathode. The intensity of the radiation depends upon both the accelerating voltage and the number of electrons reaching the target per second, i.e. upon the accelerating voltage and the tube current. The tube current varies slightly with the anode voltage, but is determined mainly by the electron emission from the filament, which in turn is controlled by the current heating the filament. (An X-ray tube is essentially a thermionic diode operated with a very high anode voltage so that the anode current is saturated.) In operation it is therefore necessary to know and to be able to control the anode voltage (to obtain a given quality of X-radiation) and to know and to be able to control the tube current (to obtain different intensities at a given quality). The control of the tube current is achieved by making appropriate changes in the filament heating current. The supplies and control circuits are discussed in detail in the following sections.

3.07. The filament circuit

The potential difference required to maintain the filament current is obtained from a step-down transformer. An X-ray tube may be operated with the filament at earth potential or at 100 kV. or more negative with respect to earth. In the latter case the primary and secondary windings of the transformer must be suitably insulated from one another.

The magnitude of the current in the filament circuit is usually controlled by adjustable resistances or inductances in the circuit of the primary of the filament transformer. When the filament is at earth potential, the magnitude of the filament current may be indicated by an ammeter in the filament circuit itself, but when the filament is at a negative potential with respect to earth, the " filament current meter " is usually an ammeter indicating the current in the primary circuit of the filament transformer.

The primary of the X-ray filament transformer may be supplied either directly from the mains as in fig. 3.13 or from a section of the autotransformer as shown in fig. 3.14. The former arrangement can be used in therapy equipment where there is time during an exposure to make manual adjustments of resistance or inductance to maintain a desired filament heating current despite changes in the line voltage. In diagnostic equipment, the controls normally have to be " pre-set " and no adjustments can be made during the very short time of the actual exposure. In order to maintain a desired filament heating current in these conditions it is more convenient to supply the X-ray filament transformer (and also rectifier filament transformers where these are used) from a section of the autotransformer as shown in fig. 3.14. In diagnostic sets the autotransformer is usually tapped on both the input and output sides. A voltmeter is connected across a fixed section of the autotransformer and the input taps adjusted by the line compensator switch until a standard reading is obtained on the voltmeter. The voltage at each output tap of the autotransformer then has a fixed value.

Since small changes in the filament heating current produce a large change in the electron emission from the filament and hence in the X-ray tube current (see section 2.01 and fig. 2.03), automatic voltage regulators, shown in fig. 3.14 but not in fig. 3.13, are usually included between the supply and the primary of the filament transformer to ensure that the potential difference across the latter remains constant. There are two main types of regulator: (1) booster transformers, which are introduced to prevent the operation of the anode circuit causing a drop in the voltage input to the filament transformer, and (2) stabilisers, which compensate for rapid transient changes in the line voltage such as are caused by the starting or stopping of other electrical equipment.

A booster transformer is a step-up transformer in which the primary coil is connected in series with the mains and the auto-transformer, while the secondary coil is connected in series with the filament transformer. The total potential difference across the primary coil is of the order of 1 volt and varies with the current taken from the mains by the auto-transformer.

The number of turns and the resistance of the secondary coil is adjusted so that the voltage induced in the secondary by current in the primary is just sufficient to compensate for the drop in the line voltage caused by the current taken by the autotransformer. If vacuum tube rectifiers are used, the booster transformer is usually connected so that it controls the current to the primaries of the valve filament transformers as well as the X-ray filament transformer. (See fig. 3.14.)

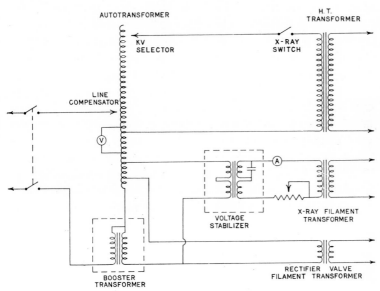

FIG. 3.14. Typical arrangement of X-ray filament transformer supply circuits in a diagnostic X-ray set.

Voltage stabilisers are rather more complicated than booster transformers. They usually depend upon the use of chokes or transformers whose inductance is not a constant but depends upon the magnitude of the current. For example, if the core of the inductive element is nearly saturated magnetically, an increase in the current results in a decrease in the inductance. This property can be used to obtain a constant voltage for the primary of the filament transformer in two ways. (1) A saturated core transformer and an unsaturated transformer are used in series. The primary coils are connected to the input and the secondary coils are connected so that the output voltage, which is supplied to the primary of the filament transformer, is the difference between the voltages generated by the two secondaries, the saturated transformer supplying the greater voltage. If the input voltage increases, the saturated transformer supplies proportionately less voltage, so that in a properly adjusted system, the output can be kept nearly constant. (2) If a saturated inductance and a condenser form the secondary circuit of a transformer, the resonant frequency of the secondary circuit increases if the inductance decreases. The effective inductance of the transformer primary is a maximum when the resonant frequency is the same as the input frequency, so that by a suitable choice of the initial frequency of the resonant circuit, it is possible to arrange that the impedance of the transformer primary increases if the input voltage increases and decreases if the input decreases. Details of the voltage stabilisers used in practice vary in many respects, but they are usually based on one or other or a combination of both of the above methods. A variation of $\pm$ 15 % in the input voltage can thus be reduced to about $\pm$ 1 %, provided that the frequency remains constant.

As already mentioned, the magnitude of the filament heating current is normally controlled by the magnitude of the inductance or resistance in the primary circuit of the filament transformer, the controls being adjusted continuously throughout an exposure in therapy, but " pre-set " in diagnostic work. Now the X-ray tube current, although determined principally by the temperature of the filament of the X-ray tube, (and thus controlled primarily by the X-ray filament heating current) does vary somewhat with the kilovoltage across the tube (fig. 2.03), so that to obtain a given tube current a somewhat lower filament heating current is required as the kilovoltage is increased. To avoid the necessity of considering the kilovoltage when presetting the filament controls on diagnostic equipment, some sets include a " space-charge transformer " whose function is to introduce into the filament circuit a voltage sufficient to reduce the current by the requisite amount as the kilovoltage is increased. The primary is connected through the kilovoltage selector to the auto-transformer while the secondary is connected in series in the filament circuit. In many modern X-ray sets (both diagnostic and therapy sets) a " milliampere stabiliser " is used to maintain the X-ray tube current at a desired value. If this is done then the space-charge transformer is not necessary. Milliampere stabilisers are discussed in section 3.13.

3.08. The anode circuit

The high potential difference required between anode and cathode is obtained by means of a step-up transformer. The step-up transformer must be carefully insulated. The entire transformer is usually immersed in oil, although sulphur hexafluoride gas is also sometimes used as an insulating medium. The high tension transformer is frequently connected to earth at its mid-point so that the insulation of the cables to the X-ray tube need only withstand one-half of the full voltage. With this arrangement the filament is at a high negative potential with respect to earth and as mentioned earlier the secondary of the filament transformer must then be adequately insulated from its primary.

The primary of the step-up transformer is supplied from an auto-transformer so that any selected voltage can be applied to the primary by adjustment of the kV. selector switch. In most diagnostic and in some therapy sets, it is arranged that a constant voltage is developed across each section of the auto-transformer by adjusting the line compensator switch to obtain a standard reading on the line voltmeter. A particular setting of the kV. selector switch should then always result in the same input voltage to the primary of the high tension transformer. In some therapy sets, the line compensator switch and line voltmeter are omitted and the line is connected across a fixed portion of the auto-transformer. In such therapy sets, however, the actual voltage input to the primary of the high tension transformer is measured directly on a voltmeter, which may be called the " kV. meter ". (kV. meters are sometimes included, sometimes omitted on diagnostic sets). The setting of the kV. selector cannot normally be changed without breaking the circuit so in therapy sets a variable resistance is sometimes included in series with the primary of the step-up transformer to enable minor adjustments of the high voltage to be made while the set is running. In some designs a similar resistance is used to enable the voltage across the step-up transformer to be built up gradually to its maximum value.

The voltage generated by the secondary of the step-up transformer is seldom measured directly. The so-called " kV. meter " normally measures the voltage input to the primary of the transformer although it may be calibrated in terms of the voltage developed across the X-ray tube. Since the ratio of the output voltage from the transformer to the input voltage depends upon the current flowing through the X-ray tube, it is necessary to calibrate the kV. meter for each value of the tube current. Therefore the kV. meter is frequently provided with several scales, each labelled with the tube current for which it is appropriate. In some sets the necessity for a series of scales is avoided by the inclusion of a compensating transformer and variable resistance in parallel with the voltmeter. The operation of the filament current controls is then arranged so that as the filament heating current (and hence the tube current) is changed the appropriate shunt resistance is also introduced into the voltmeter circuit to cause it to indicate the correct kilovoltage.

The calibration of the kV. meter is normally carried out by the manufacturers of the X-ray set. The high voltage across the transformer secondary may be measured by means of a high resistance voltage divider, but it is more usual to use either a spark gap or a rotary or generating voltmeter. In the spark-gap method, the voltage is applied across two polished insulated spheres which are initially well separated from one another. The distance between the spheres is gradually reduced until the insulation of the air breaks down and a spark passes. The separation of the spheres when this occurs is noted and is used as a measure of the maximum voltage which has been applied. For example, with 25 cm. diameter spheres in air at 25° C. and 760 mm. pressure, spark-over occurs at a separation of 1·68 cm. for 50 kVp., and at 2·51 cm. for 100 kVp.

In one common form of generating voltmeter,[5] a sheet metal cylinder, (fig. 3.15) split in half longitudinally, is rotated at constant speed between two electrodes connected to the terminals between which the potential difference is to be measured. Alternating electrostatic charges are induced in the two sectors of the cylinder. These charges are picked up by brushes on a commutator as shown and flow through a galvanometer. The magnitude of the current (I) through the galvanometer is directly proportional to the high voltage (V) between the electrodes. ($I = 2CVn$ where C is the capacity formed by either sector of the cylinder and the electrode adjacent to it when the plane of the splits is vertical, and n

denotes the number of revolutions per second.) Such voltmeters are normally calibrated by observing the galvanometer current for a known voltage.

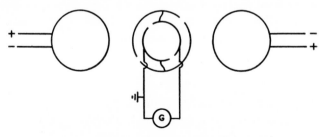

FIG. 3.15. The principle of a generating voltmeter.
(After Kirkpatrick and Miyake[5].)

The mean value of the current flowing in the anode circuit is usually indicated by a milliammeter connected in that part of the circuit which is near earth potential. In diagnostic sets where exposures less than 1/10 sec. may be employed, a ballistic milliamp-second meter is used. This is necessary since during a very short exposure an ordinary milliammeter does not have time to indicate a true mean value of the current. The moving part of a ballistic meter has a large moment of inertia, and a long periodic time of oscillation. It therefore requires a time which is long in comparison with the exposure time, to reach its maximum deflection. Under these circumstances, the deflection is proportional to the total quantity of electricity which has passed through the meter. In self-rectified and half-wave rectified equipment, d.c. measuring instruments can be connected directly to the transformer as shown in fig. 3.13. With fully rectified equipment, the transformer current is alternating. In this case it is usual to connect the primary coil of a small " instrument transformer " at the earthed point of the high tension transformer and a d.c. milliammeter is then connected in series with a rectifier and the secondary of the instrument transformer. (See section 3.09 and fig. 3.20).

Most X-ray sets are provided with circuit breakers to prevent damage to the tube in the event of a momentary surge in the mains voltage or of failure in the cooling, etc. These circuit breakers may be electromagnetic relays which open contacts in the primary circuit of the high tension transformer when the current through the relays exceeds a certain value, or they may be thermally operated tripping devices which break the circuit when a certain temperature is exceeded. On therapy sets, relays are usually arranged to break the transformer circuit if the door of the treatment room is opened.

3.09. Rectification of the anode voltage

It is possible to operate an X-ray tube (as shown in fig. 3.13) without first rectifying the high voltage supply, since the X-ray tube itself acts as a rectifier. This is known as self-rectification. In a self-rectified set, the X-ray tube can be connected directly to the secondary of the high tension transformer and both tube and transformer can then be readily insulated by immersion in the same oil or gas filled container. Such sets are simple and compact but have a number of disadvantages. Thus no X-rays are generated for the half-cycle when the anode is negative with respect to the cathode but during this half-cycle, since no current flows, the inverse voltage across the X-ray tube exceeds that during the positive half-cycle. The X-ray tube insulation must therefore withstand a voltage rather greater than is actually used for the production of X-rays. If the anode should become unduly heated and emit electrons, X-rays may be produced at the cathode end of the tube during the negative half-cycle. The high inverse voltage across the X-ray tube (and cables) during the negative half-cycle may be reduced by either (1) the inclusion of an " inverse suppressor " in the primary circuit of the high tension transformer or (2) the use of rectifiers in series with the secondary of the high tension transformer. The use of an inverse suppressor in the primary circuit has the advantage that it does not increase the weight and size of the X-ray head, and is used in some low power portable diagnostic equipment and in some therapy equipment. The suppressor consists of a rectifier in parallel with a resistance as shown in fig. 3.16 (b).

The rectifier may be either a gas-filled diode or a semiconductor, but both rectifier and resistance must be able to carry the relatively large currents which flow in the primary circuit of the high tension transformer. The size of the resistors required and the amount of heat generated in them limits the use of inverse suppression to relatively low powered units.

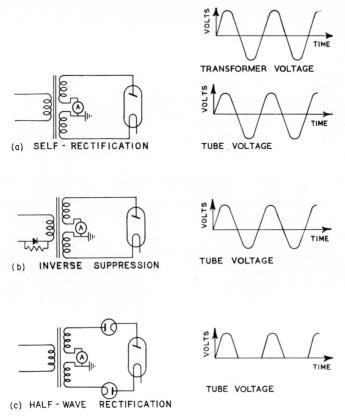

FIG. 3.16. Alternative forms of anode circuit; (a) self-rectification; (b) inverse suppression; (c) half-wave rectification.

Inverse suppressors fail to protect the X-ray tube from the emission of X-rays by the cathode if the anode becomes heated. To accomplish this as well as to reduce the inverse voltage across the X-ray tube, rectifiers may be included in series with the secondary of the high tension transformer as shown in fig. 3.16 (c).

X-rays are still produced during only one-half of each cycle, however, and this is less efficient than the use of full-wave rectification. For the same mean anode current, the peak current is halved with full-wave rectification, since there are twice as many pulses per second. This means that (1) the filament can be run at a lower temperature, and (2) since the rate of heat input to the target *per pulse* is reduced, a smaller focal spot may be used. Alternatively, if the same filament

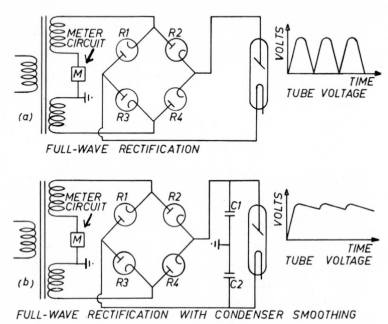

FIG. 3.17. Alternative forms of anode circuit; (*a*) full-wave rectification using a four-valve bridge rectifier; (*b*) full-wave rectification with condenser smoothing.

heating current and focal spot size are used, an increased mean tube current will be obtained with full-wave rectification, permitting shorter exposure times. One of the commonest types of full-wave rectifying circuit used is the four-valve bridge or Grätz circuit already described in section 2.02. This circuit is almost invariably employed in high power diagnostic sets (fig. 3.17 (*a*)).

Even full-wave rectification has the disadvantage that when the accelerating voltage is low, there are few X-rays produced (see fig. 3.18) and those produced are insufficiently penetrating to be useful. The most efficient circuit is one which produces a voltage which is not only unidirectional but also constant in magnitude.

The output from the Grätz bridge circuit is sometimes " smoothed " by connecting condensers in parallel with the X-ray tube as shown in fig. 3.17 (b). The smoothing action of the condensers arises as follows. Suppose C_1 is charged to a voltage $+ V/2$ and C_2 to a voltage $- V/2$ at the end of the first quarter-cycle when the rectifiers R_2 and R_3 are conducting. Electrons cannot flow back across the rectifiers during the second quarter-cycle so the voltage of the condensers decreases only on account of the loss of charge which occurs through the

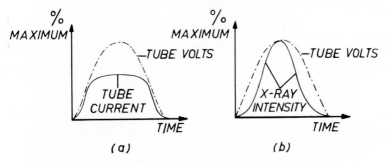

Fig. 3.18. The relationship between tube voltage, tube current and X-ray intensity.

X-ray tube. In the third quarter cycle, when the transformer voltage exceeds the condenser voltage the condensers are recharged through the rectifiers R_1 and R_4. In the fourth quarter-cycle, the condenser voltage again falls only on account of the charge flowing through the X-ray tube. The magnitude of the voltage " ripple ' is proportional to the current drawn by the X-ray tube (see the calculation in connection with the Greinacher circuit).

The rectifiers used in these circuits must be designed so they will withstand voltages of the order of 100 kV. in the reverse direction and so that when passing current in the forward direction, the resistance of the rectifier is small in comparison with that of the X-ray tube (so that the voltage drop across the X-ray tube is nearly the full transformer voltage and so that X-rays are not generated by the rectifiers). If vacuum diode

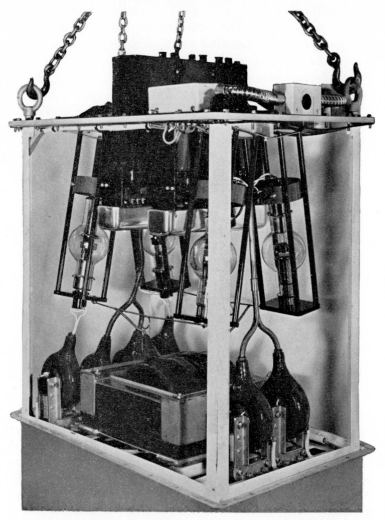

FIG. 3.19. Typical arrangements of the components of the high tension circuit (the components are shown withdrawn from the oil-filled container for clarity).

(*a*) four valve bridge unit using vacuum diode rectifiers. The high tension transformer (centre) and the transformers for the X-ray filaments and diode filaments can be seen below the rectifiers.

FIG. 3.19. (*b*) Selenium barrier-layer rectifier unit. The high tension transformer is below the rectifier. The smaller transformers beside the rectifier unit are for the X-ray filaments.

(Courtesy Siemens-Reiniger-Werke AG, Erlangen.)

rectifiers are used, they are constructed with heavy tungsten filaments which give a copious emission of electrons. " Thoriated " tungsten, i.e. tungsten covered by a surface layer of thorium is commonly employed since this gives a higher (although less constant) emission than pure tungsten. The anode is of large area (frequently a cylinder surrounding the filament) so that the heat generated is readily dissipated. The filaments of such rectifiers usually require a heating current of the order of 12 amperes supplied at 12 volts. This is readily obtained from a step-down transformer but the transformer secondary must be suitably insulated, since the valve filaments may be 100 kV. or more from ground potential. The life of vacuum diode rectifiers is appreciably increased when the X-ray set is equipped with a booster transformer to maintain a constant line voltage, since otherwise it is necessary to operate the rectifier filaments at a sufficiently high temperature to ensure that, when a drop in line voltage occurs, the filament temperature still remains high enough to produce the necessary electron emission. If selenium rectifiers are used instead of vacuum diodes, then several thousand individual units are required. A single selenium " cell " will carry a current of about 300 mA. per square inch and will withstand a reverse voltage of about 30 or 40 volts. In X-ray applications, 100 or 200 such cells are commonly mounted in series in a procelain or bakelite tube about 1 inch in diameter and 6 inches long and are held in contact by a spring. Some assemblies include cooling fins. As many tubes are used in series as are necessary to withstand the operating voltage. Compared with vacuum tube diodes, the main advantages of selenium rectifiers are, (1) no filament transformers are required, (2) they are mechanically robust and theoretically should have an infinite life. The main disadvantages are, (1) increased costs, (2) a higher resistance when passing current in the forward direction. The increased resistance means there is a rather large voltage drop across the rectifiers when the tube current is large, i.e. if they are used for diagnostic sets of high rating. On the other hand, where voltage surges are anticipated, (e.g. in three phase equipment), it is claimed that the resistance of the selenium rectifiers is an advantage in damping out transients.

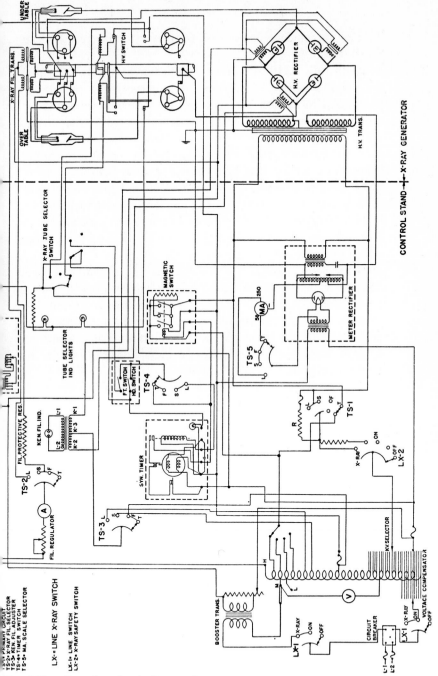

FIG. 3.20. Complete circuit diagram for a fully rectified diagnostic X-ray set.

permission from *Medical Radiographic Technic* by G. W. Files (Charles C. Thomas, Springfield) and of the General Electric Co., Milwaukee, U.S.A.

71

Typical arrangements of transformers and rectifiers are illustrated in fig. 3.19.

With fully rectified equipment, the current flowing through the high-tension transformer is alternating. As already mentioned in section 3.08 a small "instrument transformer" and "meter rectifier" are therefore connected at the earthed point of the transformer in order that a d.c. meter can be used to measure the current flowing in the X-ray circuit. The meter rectifier may be a double vacuum diode (as shown in fig. 3.20) or a Grätz bridge using semi-conductor components as described in Chapter II. D.c. meters are preferred to a.c. meters because the scale of the latter is not uniform. It is necessary to avoid measuring as tube current, the current which charges up the cables to the X-ray set (these have appreciable capacity). A compensating transformer and condenser are therefore also required to provide a current equal and opposite to the X-ray cable charging current. The primary of the compensating transformer is connected in parallel with the primary of the high-tension transformer so that the input to both transformers is controlled by the kilovolt selector.

The complete circuit diagram for a fully rectified diagnostic X-ray set is shown in fig. 3.20.

3.10. Three-phase high voltage circuits

We have so far assumed that the mains supply of electricity is alternating and of single phase. It is also possible, however, to obtain three-phase alternating supplies. With a three-phase supply, the power is transmitted over three lines which are connected to three different coils of the a.c. generator, so that the maximum e.m.f. is produced in the second coil, one-third of a cycle after the maximum is produced in the first coil and in the third coil the maximum e.m.f. is produced one-third of a cycle later still. (See fig. 3.21.)

By connecting the output from each branch of a three-phase high tension transformer in series with two rectifiers and the X-ray tube, as shown in fig. 3.21, a unidirectional potential difference is obtained across the tube which never drops to zero although it fluctuates to a certain extent about the mean value. This results in more efficient production of X-rays than with most single-phase equipment. For example the average kilovoltage is about 95 per cent. of the peak kilovoltage instead of about 70 per cent. Thus to obtain the same quality of radiation (or the same contrast in a radiograph), the set will be operated at a lower kVp. Also the same mean tube current can be obtained with a reduced filament heating current and there is reduced heating of the target " per pulse". Alternatively, if the filament heating current is unchanged, the

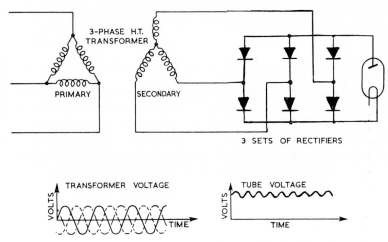

FIG. 3.21.   Anode circuit with three-phase voltage supply.

mean tube current is increased (about 20 per cent) with three-phase compared with single-phase equipment, so shorter exposure times can be used. Three-phase equipment has the disadvantage that it is more complicated than single-phase equipment. Three auto-transformers are usually required and the timing circuit must either make and break three circuits in sequence or else circuits will be opened or closed when the current flow is not zero. For this reason selenium rectifiers, which can absorb voltage surges, are usually pre-ferred to vacuum diodes in three phase equipment. Three line cables (instead of two) are also required but the current per cable and hence the size and cost of each cable is less than for single-phase units. Three-phase equipment is required by some electrical distributors who object to the heavy load placed on a single phase by high powered diagnostic X-ray sets.

3.11. Voltage doubling circuits and resonant transformer circuits

Any of the circuits discussed in sections 3.09 and 3.10 may be encountered in either diagnostic or therapy equipment. The Villard and Greinacher voltage doubling circuits and the resonant transformer circuit to be discussed in this section, however, are used primarily in therapy sets.

Some X-ray tubes are supplied from transformers which generate only one-half of the potential difference required between anode and cathode. This is made possible by the use of a voltage doubling circuit. Two types of voltage doubling circuit commonly used to produce voltages of a few hundred kilovolts are described below. (The Cockcroft-Walton voltage multiplier circuit which is used for higher voltages is described in the next chapter.)

The Villard Circuit was devised in 1901 but is still widely used. It produces an unidirectional but not a constant potential difference across the tube. The form of the circuit most generally employed is shown in fig. 3.22 (*a*).

Initially T_1 and T_2 are at the same potential. Suppose T_1 first becomes negative and T_2 positive. In this condition electric current can flow through R_1 and R_2 but not across the X-ray tube. During the first quarter cycle, therefore, the potential of the " transformer plates " of C_1 and C_2 becomes that of T_1 and T_2 ($- V/2$ and $+ V/2$ say), the potential of the " rectifier plates " is approximately zero since each is connected through a rectifier which is conducting to earth. During the second quarter cycle, the transformer plates of the condensers return to ground potential. The rectifier plates must retain their charges (since the electrons cannot flow back across the rectifiers) and therefore the rectifier plate of C_1 attains a positive potential $V/2$, and the rectifier plate of C_2 a negative potential $- V/2$. During the third quarter cycle, the transformer plates of the condensers are again charged and reach a potential of $V/2$ and $- V/2$ respectively, but, since in this part of the cycle the rectifiers cannot conduct, there is no flow of electrons between the rectifier plates of the condensers and thus the potential of the rectifier plate of C_1 becomes approximately $+ V$, and that of C_2 becomes $- V$. The potential difference across the X-ray tube is thus approximately $2V$ or twice the transformer voltage. The voltage across the tube is slightly less than $2V$ because of the

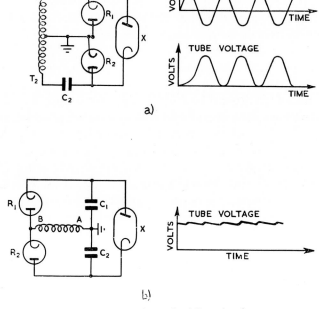

FIG. 3.22. Voltage doubling circuits.
(a) The Villard circuit.
(b) The Greinacher circuit.

passage of current through the X-ray tube itself as soon as the anode becomes positive with respect to the filament. During the fourth quarter cycle the potential of the "transformer plates" of the condensers return to zero and that of the rectifier plates to something less than $V/2(C_1)$ and $- V/2(C_2)$. During the first quarter of successive cycles, the potential of both plates of C_1 falls while that of C_2 rises. No current can flow through the rectifiers until the rectifier plate of C_1 is negative with respect to the rectifier plate of C_2, but then electrons flow from

75

C_1 to C_2 as already described and the cycle is repeated as above. The circuit has the advantage that because of the voltage doubling feature, the transformer cost is reduced. The accelerating voltage, however, varies in magnitude. In modern sets, a smoothing circuit may be combined with the Villard circuit to produce a nearly constant voltage.

The *Greinacher Circuit*, like the Villard, is a voltage doubling circuit, but as the transformer must be end- not mid-grounded, no great saving in transformer cost is obtained from the voltage doubling feature. The Greinacher circuit has, however, the advantage that the voltage supplied to the X-ray tube is nearly constant in magnitude.

Suppose that initially B (fig. 3.22 (*b*)) is negative with respect to A, so that R_2 is conducting. Then the rectifier plate of C_2 becomes negatively charged and at the end of the first quarter cycle will be at a potential of $-V$ while the transformer plate of C_2 is at earth potential. During the second quarter cycle the potential of B returns to zero but electrons cannot flow across R_2 from C_2 so the potential of the rectifier plate of C_2 remains $-V$. During the third quarter cycle B becomes positive with respect to A, the rectifier R_1 becomes conducting and the potential of the rectifier plate of C_1 rises to nearly V. Thus the voltage across the X-ray tube is approximately $2V$, twice the transformer voltage (except for the slight reduction due to current flow across the X-ray tube itself). During the fourth quarter cycle the potential of B returns to zero but the rectifier plates of C_1 and C_2 remain near V and $-V$ respectively. In succeeding cycles the potentials of the rectifier plates of C_1 and C_2 are boosted to V and $-V$ respectively, each cycle and the potential difference across the X-ray tube remains nearly constant close to $2V$. Essentially in this circuit, each condenser is charged during the favourable part of each cycle, when the appropriate rectifier becomes conducting and the condenser is then isolated from the transformer for the remainder of the cycle. The magnitude of the potential drop in each condenser caused by loss of charge through the X-ray tube may be calculated as follows :

Suppose the tube current is 10 mA. In one cycle $\left(\dfrac{1}{50} \text{ sec.}\right)$, the charge lost by the condenser $= \dfrac{1}{50} \times 0{\cdot}01 = 2 \times 10^{-4}$

coulomb. If the capacity of each condenser is $0{\cdot}5$ μf., the charge stored in each condenser when charged to 100 kV.

$$= 100 \times 10^3 \times 0{\cdot}5 \times 10^{-6} \text{ coulomb,}$$
$$= 5 \times 10^{-2} \text{ coulomb,}$$

i.e. per cent. loss of charge due to tube current

$$= \frac{2 \times 10^{-4}}{5 \times 10^{-2}} \times 100 \text{ per cent.} = 0{\cdot}4 \text{ per cent.}$$

∴ Voltage drop $= 0{\cdot}4$ per cent.

Since the condensers are charged alternately the tube voltage actually fluctuates by only $0{\cdot}2$ per cent. twice per cycle.

Resonant transformer circuits

In some therapy equipment, the usual iron-core, high tension transformer using 50 or 60 cycle/sec. alternating current is replaced by a resonant transformer operated with current alternating at a higher frequency. Such resonant transformers were first used in X-ray sets designed to operate at 1 or 2 MV. (see Chapter IV) but their use has now been extended to the 200-400 kV. range. There is little or no iron in these transformers and more compact and lighter equipment can be obtained in this way.

The high frequency current is obtained from a motor generator. The frequency is chosen so that it is equal to the so-called resonant frequency of the secondary circuit of the transformer (this is determined by the inductance and capacity in the circuit). When this condition is satisfied, a higher voltage may be developed across the secondary coil than that which would be obtained solely on account of the turns ratio. Sometimes the primary circuit is also " tuned " so that the voltage developed across the primary coil exceeds that delivered by the motor generator. In these units the transformer is usually end-grounded and the X-ray tube is connected directly to the transformer (there is no rectifying system). The tube and transformer are both included in the treatment head, producing a relatively compact unit requiring no high voltage cables. A gas under pressure (sulphur hexafluoride or dichlorodifluoro-methane) is commonly used as the insulating medium to reduce the weight of the equipment.

3.12. Condenser discharge apparatus

X-ray diagnostic equipment is occasionally encountered in which a set of condensers (of effective capacity about 1 μf.) is first charged by the high voltage supply and then subsequently discharged through the X-ray tube. The condensers can be charged relatively slowly and then discharged rapidly and this enables a power supply of limited capacity to be used without unduly prolonging exposure times. The method has the advantage that the energy dissipated during the exposure is predetermined, so overloading is unlikely, but the disadvantage that the initial voltage and tube current cannot normally be varied independently and that the choice of operating conditions is very limited. It is not usually employed in medical radio-graphy if there are adequate electrical supplies for ordinary equipment. (Condenser discharge apparatus is sometimes used industrially to obtain very short exposure times for the radiography of rapidly moving objects such as bullets in flight.)

3.13. Milliampere and kilovoltage stabilisers

Many X-ray sets are now provided with milliampere and/or kilovoltage stabilisers. The function of a milliampere stabiliser is to maintain a constant value of the X-ray tube current. The stabiliser is arranged so that any change in the X-ray tube current causes a change in the current to the primary of the filament transformer which so modifies the filament heating current as to annul the change in X-ray tube current which causes it. The function of a kilovoltage stabiliser is to maintain a constant value of the accelerating voltage across the X-ray tube. This is achieved by arranging that any change in the accelerating voltage causes a change in the voltage to the primary of the high tension transformer which annuls the change causing it.

One of the earliest types of milliampere stabiliser to be used was the Kearsley multivibrator. In this stabiliser, the

X-ray tube current operates one or more relays which determine the resistance in the filament circuit. Thus in fig. 3.23 if the tube current through the coil W increases (note that W is connected at an earthed part of the X-ray circuit), the relay S is opened and additional resistance R is introduced into the filament transformer circuit thus decreasing the filament heating current and hence the tube current. When the tube

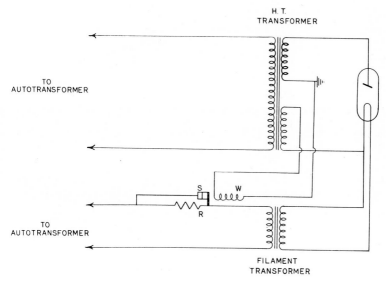

FIG. 3.23. Simplified circuit diagram to show the principle of the Kearsley milliampere stabiliser.

current decreases, the relay S closes and shortcircuits R increasing the filament heating current and hence the tube current.

The relay S vibrates as it opens and closes the shortcircuit across R, hence the name multivibrator which is often used.

Most modern stabilisers employ electronic circuits.

Fig. 3.24 illustrates the principle of an electronic milliampere stabiliser, which is shown in this instance as used in conjunction with a Grätz full wave bridge rectifier. The current in the X-ray tube circuit determines the voltage applied to the grid of a triode valve. The anode current of the triode flows through the primary of a transformer whose secondary is in series

79

with the primary of the filament transformer and thus it modifies the filament heating current. In fig. 3.24 V is the triode valve. When there is no current flowing across the X-ray tube, the key K_1 is closed, K_2 is open, so that the voltage on the grid of the valve V is that determined by the bias battery B (there is no voltage drop across the resistor R_s). When the X-ray tube is energised K_1 is opened and K_2 closed so that

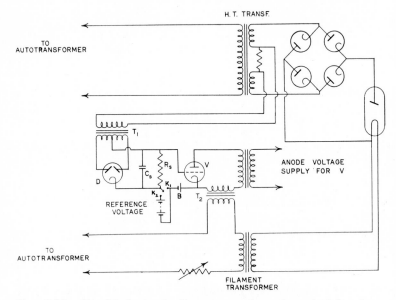

FIG. 3.24. Simplified circuit diagram to show the principle of an electronic milliampere stabiliser.

a reference voltage which would tend to make the grid of V more positive is introduced in series with the bias voltage. At the same time however a voltage is developed across R_s which tends to make the grid of V more negative. The voltage across R_s is obtained as follows. When current flows across the X-ray tube a voltage is developed across the fixed resistance which is introduced at the earthed point of the X-ray tube circuit. This voltage is alternating and its magnitude is determined by the X-ray tube current. It induces an alternating voltage in the coupling transformer T_1. The voltage across R_s is the voltage output from the secondary of this transformer after it has been rectified (by the double diode D) and smoothed. If the X-ray tube current increases, then the voltage across R_s increases making the grid of V more negative. This reduces the anode current and therefore reduces the voltage which the coupling transformer T_2 introduces

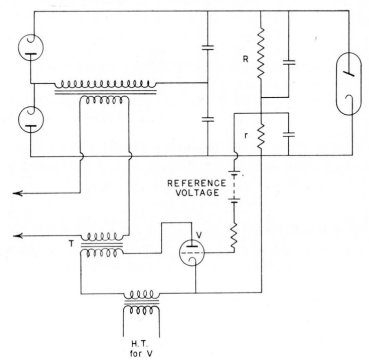

FIG. 3.25. Simplified circuit diagram to show the principle of a kilovoltage stabiliser.

in the filament transformer circuit, which in turn reduces the filament heating current and hence the X-ray tube current. In practice the single valve V is usually replaced by several stages of amplification but the principle of operation is essentially as above.

Kilovoltage stabilisers

Fig. 3.25 shows a Greinacher circuit to which a kilovoltage stabiliser has been added. In this circuit the accelerating voltage has been applied across a high resistance in parallel with the X-ray tube. The voltage developed across a small section (r) of this resistance is tapped off and when the X-ray tube is energised, the difference between the voltage across r and a reference voltage is introduced into the grid circuit of the valve V. The potential of the grid determines the magnitude of the current flowing in the anode circuit and hence in the coupling transformer T which is so arranged that the voltage input to the primary of the high-tension transformer is increased when the voltage drop across r falls and is decreased when the voltage drop across r rises. In practice the single valve V may be replaced by several stages of amplification but the principle of operation is essentially as above.

Kilovoltage and milliampere stabilisers can of course be used simultaneously. They have only been shown separately in the previous examples for the sake of clarity.

3.14. Exposure timers

The duration of an X-ray exposure is usually controlled either by the time during which a high voltage is applied to the anode or alternatively by the time during which a lead shutter over the window of the X-ray tube is open. The former method is used in diagnostic sets. In most modern therapy sets a shutter is opened to start the exposure, but the anode circuit may be opened or a shutter closed to end the exposure. The " exposure time " is measured by the time during which there is high voltage on the anode and the shutter (if any) is open, although useful X-rays may be generated for only a part of this time (depending upon the waveform of the voltage applied to the anode). For exposures of 1/5 second or more, the time interval may be determined by a clutch timer driven by a synchronous motor. When the operator starts the exposure, a relay is energised which causes an initially stationary disc (C) (figs. 3.26, 3.27) to be engaged by a second disc (B) (the clutch plate), driven by a synchronous motor (A). At the start of its travel, an arm on the disc C closes a relay circuit, (KI closes, fig. 3.27). This closes the anode circuit or opens the shutter.

The disc *C* then advances along an axle until an arm on the disc encounters a contact *J* which opens the relay circuit and thus switches off the high tension and/or closes the shutter. The disc is returned to its initial position by a spring or other

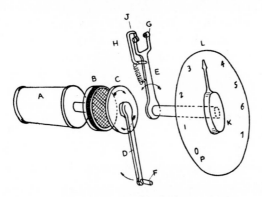

FIG. 3.26.   A clutch timer.

By permission from *X-Rays* by W. E. Schall.   (John Wright & Sons Ltd., Bristol).

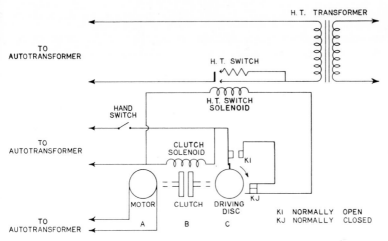

FIG. 3.27.   Simplified circuit diagram of clutch timer.

mechanism so that it is ready for the next exposure. The closing of the transformer circuit is usually made with a high resistance in series with the transformer. The resistance is shortcircuited a fraction of a second later. This method reduces initial voltage surges in the transformer. (See fig. 3.27.)

For the shorter exposures used in diagnostic radiography (less than 1/5 sec.), impulse timers or electronic timers are used. A synchronous impulse timer is so designed that the relays open or close the high tension circuit when the applied voltage is zero. Thus the exposure time is always an integral number of cycles or half-cycles. The accuracy of such timers may be conveniently checked by exposing a film behind a revolving metal disc in which a hole is cut off-centre. After development, the number of spots on the film will equal the number of cycles,

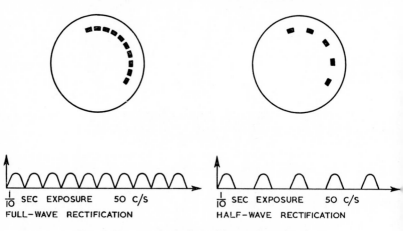

FULL-WAVE RECTIFICATION

HALF-WAVE RECTIFICATION

FIG. 3.28. Method of checking an impulse timer.

for half-wave rectification, or the number of half-cycles, for full wave rectification, which have elapsed. (See fig. 3.28.)

In electronic timers, the duration of the exposure is determined by the time taken for charge to build up on or to leak away from a condenser. The charge on the condenser determines the potential of the control grid of a gas-filled triode (i.e. a thyratron or " trigger tube ", see section 2.05). When this potential reaches a critical value, the valve " fires ", i.e. current flows through the valve and operates a relay which terminates the exposure. Thus in fig. 3.29 when the operator closes the hand switch to start the exposure, current flows through the thyratron and switch solenoids. The switch solenoid closes the high tension circuit (or opens the shutter); the thyratron solenoid closes the key KI_1 (normally open) so that there is a positive potential on the thyratron anode and also closes KI_2 and opens KL, thus removing the short-circuit across the condenser C and permitting it to charge up from the battery. The potential on the grid of the thyratron becomes more positive as C charges up, until the thyratron " fires ". Current then flows in the anode circuit passing through the timer solenoid (T), which opens the key KJ and ends the exposure. The time taken to charge or discharge the condenser (the exposure time) is controlled by the value of the resistance in series with the condenser

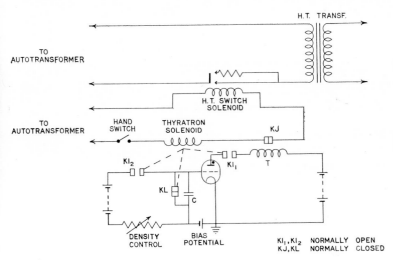

FIG. 3.29.   Simplified circuit diagram of electronic timer.

which is selected by the operator. If it is desired that the exposure shall be started at an instant when the current in the high tension circuit is zero, then instead of the hand switch controlling the current flow to the thyratron and switch solenoids directly (as in fig. 3.29) the hand-switch is used to actuate another thyratron, the " starter thyratron " which only fires at the peak of the voltage cycle. The current in the anode circuit of the starter thyratron then actuates a relay which closes the circuit allowing current to flow through the switch and thyratron solenoids. The time taken for the relay to operate is adjusted so that the high tension switch is actually closed when the voltage is zero, the " starter thyratron " ensures that the closing is always at the same instant in the cycle. The exposure then proceeds as before.

In photo-timers, an electronic timer is used in conjunction with a photomultiplier tube (see section 2.09) viewing a fluorescent screen. A condenser is either charged or discharged by the current from the photomultiplier. With suitable

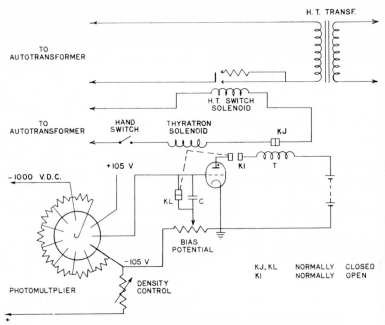

FIG. 3.30.   Simplified circuit diagram of phototimer.

precautions, it can be arranged that the photo-current is proportional to the intensity of the X-radiation producing the fluorescence. Changes in intensity then alter the rate at which the condenser is charged or discharged. Variations in X-ray intensity such as are produced by different body-thicknesses are therefore automatically compensated for by alterations in the length of the exposure. A simplified circuit diagram of a photo-timer is shown in fig. 3.30. The condenser C is initially short-circuited (key *KL* is closed). When the operator closes the hand switch, current flows through the switch and thyratron solenoids. The switch solenoid closes the high tension transformer circuit and the thyratron solenoid closes *KI* and opens *KL*. The condenser then begins to charge up and the potential of the upper plate which is connected to the ninth dynode of the photomultiplier tube (not the anode) becomes more positive as the exposure proceeds. When the potential of the condenser plate and therefore of the control grid of the valve becomes sufficiently positive, the valve fires and current flows through the timer solenoid (*T*). This opens the key *KJ* and terminates the exposure.

In order that the photomultiplier current shall be proportional to the X-ray intensity, it is necessary that the cathode views the same area of fluorescent screen regardless of the size of radiograph to be taken. To achieve this a lead scanning disc is placed between the fluorescent screen and the photomultiplier. The disc is usually divided into three segments, containing one fairly large, four medium and sixteen small holes respectively. The total area of the four medium and sixteen small holes is the same as that of the single hole, but they are spread out so that when a large radiograph is taken, the light reaching the phototube does not come from a particular region. This is clearly necessary when a large region containing small opaque and non-opaque parts (e.g. the gastro-intestinal tract) is to be radiographed.

3.15. The distribution of wavelength (or energy) in an X-ray beam

X-ray wavelengths range from about 10^{-4} Å. to 100 Å., corresponding to photon energies from 100 eV. to 100 MeV. The longer wavelengths, corresponding to photon energies less than 100 keV., can be measured by a crystal spectrometer, using a method first employed by W. H. and W. L. Bragg. In this method, the distribution of wavelength in an X-ray beam is determined by observing the relative intensity of the X-rays scattered at different angles from the regular array of atoms that make up a crystal (the spacing of atoms in the crystal must be known). This method was used extensively in the early investigations of X-rays but cannot be employed to investigate the shorter wavelength, higher energy radiations.

The distribution of wavelength in the latter formerly had to be calculated from absorption or secondary electron energy measurements (see Chapter VI). More recently scintillation spectrometers have been developed and most investigations of the spectral distribution of the X-ray beams used in medicine, which have been made in the last few years, have been made using these instruments.

Scintillation counters are described in detail in Chapter VIII. Briefly, the essential components are a phosphor (a material which emits light when irradiated) and a photomultiplier. Each X- or γ-ray photon absorbed in the phosphor produces a light flash which in turn produces a pulse of electrons in the photomultiplier. The pulse size is approximately proportional to the energy absorbed from the photon, so (after amplification) analysis of the distribution of " pulse heights " from the photomultiplier enables the distribution of energy amongst the incident photons to be determined.

Fig. 3.31 and 3.32 show the relative intensity of X-rays of different photon energy in typical X-ray beams. In these figures the continuous lines represent the intensity measured experimentally under the conditions stated. The dotted lines in fig. 3.31 represent the theoretical distribution of intensity in the continuous spectrum of radiation from a thick target in the absence of filtration and the arrows show the energies of the characteristic X-radiation from a tungsten target.

The continuous spectrum is emitted (as already explained in section 3.03), when the electrons impinging on the target pass close to target nuclei and are rapidly retarded. If the electrons are accelerated by a potential difference V, they strike the target with energy eV (where e denotes the electronic charge). If all the energy of an incident electron is converted into electromagnetic radiation and emitted as a single quantum, then the emitted radiation will have the maximum energy (E say). Planck's equation gives

$$E = h\nu = hc/\lambda \text{ (Chapter I, equation 2)}$$

$\therefore$ The wavelength (λ) of the radiation emitted is given by

$$\lambda = hc/E = hc/eV.$$

This is the shortest wavelength which can be produced when the accelerating voltage is V. The short wavelength limit therefore varies inversely as the voltage across the tube. This is sometimes referred to as the Duane-Hunt law.

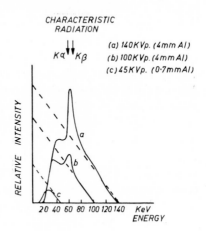

FIG. 3.31. The distribution of energy in X-ray beams. The continuous lines represent the energy distribution measured experimentally with the kilovoltage and filters stated, the dotted lines represent the theoretical distribution without filtration.

FIG. 3.32. The effect of increasing the filtration upon the distribution of energy in a typical therapy X-ray beam. The beam is filtered initially by 3·2 mm. Be + 3·2 mm. bakelite + 1 mm. Al. + 0·25 mm. Cu. To this is added
(a) 0·2 mm. Sn. to give H.V.L. 1·77 mm. Cu.
(b) 0·4 mm. Sn. to give H.V.L. 2·63 mm. Cu.
(c) 1·2 mm. Sn. to give H.V.L. 3·14 mm. Cu.
(after Cormack et al.[8])

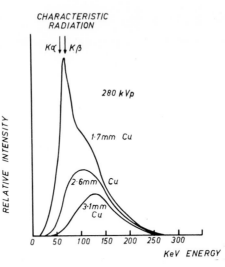

To calculate the minimum wavelength of X-radiation produced by a given accelerating voltage, it is convenient to remember that if V is the voltage in kilovolts and λ the wavelength in Ångstrom units, then $\lambda = 12\cdot4/V$. The constant 12·4 is obtained by substituting $h = 6\cdot62 \times 10^{-27}$ erg-sec.,

89

$c = 3{\cdot}0 \times 10^{10}$ cm./sec., $e = 4{\cdot}80 \times 10^{-10}$ e.s.u., 1 kV. = 1000/300 e.s.u. and 1 Ångstrom unit $= 10^{-8}$ cm. in the equation $\lambda = hc/eV$.

Most of the electrons in the cathode beam strike the target in such a way as to convert only a part of their energy into X-ray photons. Hence most of the X-radiation produced is of lower energy or longer wavelength than the limit. For a thick target, it can be predicted that the intensity of radiation of energy E will be proportional to $E_{max} - E$, and the dotted lines of fig. 3.31 represent this relationship. The total intensity summed over all energies (represented by the area under the dotted lines) is therefore proportional to E^2_{max} or V^2. The low energy radiation however is strongly absorbed in the target itself, in the tube walls, in the insulating fluid and in any added filter. Thus for the radiation emerging from the tube, the minimum energy (or maximum wavelength) is determined by the filtration and the spectrum does not extend to zero energy. The maximum intensity usually occurs at an energy rather less than $\dfrac{E_{max}}{2}$.

Further, since increasing the accelerating voltage increases the proportion of radiation which can penetrate the filter, etc., the total intensity of the emerging radiation increases as V^n where n is greater than 2, (n is commonly between 3 and 4).

Superimposed upon the continuous spectrum, is the characteristic radiation from the target. For tungsten targets, transitions from the L shell to the K shell produce the $K\alpha$ lines of energy 59.31 and 57.97 KeV. and transitions from M or N shells to the K shell give the $K\beta$ lines of energy 67.24 and 69.09 KeV. Transitions to the L shell from outer orbits produce lines between 8 and 11 KeV. in energy. The intensity of the characteristic radiation increases approximately as the difference between the accelerating voltage and the binding energy of the shell considered (i.e. as $(V - 69.51)$ KeV. for the K lines of tungsten). For a lightly filtered X-ray beam, the characteristic radiation may represent 30 or 40 per cent. of the total energy, but in therapy beams the heavier filtration normally used means the characteristic radiation is only a few per cent. of the total energy emitted.

REFERENCES

1. BEESE, N. C. (1937). *Rev. Sci. Instr.* **8**, 258.
2. GROSS, M. J. (1951). *Amer. J. Roentgenol.* **65**, 103.
3. BRACKNEY, H. and ATLEE, J. (1943). *Rev. Sci. Instr.* **14**, 59.
4. JENNINGS, W. A. (1953). *Brit. J. Radiol.* **26**, 193.
5. KIRKPATRICK, P. and MIYAKE, I. (1932). *Rev. Sci. Instr.* **3**, 1 and 430.
6. MORGAN, R. H. (1942). *Amer. J. Roentgenol.* **48**, 220.
7. FARR, R. F. (1955). *Brit. J. Radiol.* **28**, 364.
8. CORMACK, D. V., DAVITT, W. E., BURKE, D. G. and RAWSON, E. G. (1958). Brit. J. Radiol. **31**, 565.

OTHER REFERENCES

SPROULL, W. T. (1946). *X-rays in Practice.* New York, McGraw-Hill.
SCHALL, W. E. (1961). *X-rays,* 8th edn. Bristol, Wright.
FILES, G. W. (1951). *Medical Radiographic Technic.* 3rd edn. (1965) edited by BLOOM, W. L., HOLLENBACH, J. L. and MORGAN, J. A. Illinois, Thomas.

EXAMINATION QUESTIONS

1. Describe with the aid of graphs how the magnitude of the anode current passing through a diode valve depends upon (a) the filament temperature and (b) the voltage between the anode and the cathode. Both a rectifying valve and an X-ray tube may be regarded as diodes. Explain briefly the differences in their operation and construction.

M.S.R. (R. & T.), 1964.

2. How does the efficiency of conversion of electron beam energy to X-ray energy in an X-ray tube vary with the voltage applied to the tube? What happens to that part of the electron beam energy which is not converted to X-rays? How is an X-ray tube designed to deal with this unwanted energy?

M.S.R. (T.), 1964

3. Describe and explain the construction of an X-ray tube and shield, making special reference to any *three* of the following points: (i) dissipation of heat at the target, (ii) size of focal spot, (iii) radiation safety, (iv) electrical safety.

M.S.R. (R. & T.), 1963.

4. Describe a rotating anode X-ray tube and explain its radiographic advantages. Illustrate your answer with a suitable diagram showing the features of the tube.

M.S.R. (R.), 1963.

5. Discuss the reasons for using a line focus in a diagnostic X-ray tube and describe how you would determine the size of the effective focal spot.

    The angle between the central ray of the X-ray beam and the anode surface is 15°, and the electron beam is focused along a strip 2 mm. wide. If it is required to have an effective focal spot 2 mm. × 2 mm. calculate the length of this strip (sin 15° = 0·059).

    M.S.R. (R. & T.), 1962.

6. Why is it necessary to cool the target of an X-ray tube? What could be the results of inefficient cooling?

    Describe with the aid of a diagram, the manner in which heat is dissipated from the target of *either* a tube used for diagnostic radiography *or* a tube used for radiotherapy at 250 kV.

    M.S.R. (R. & T.), 1963.

7. What information do you get from a tube rating chart?

    Give two examples of radiographic procedures which could result in overheating of the X-ray tube.

    M.S.R. (R.), 1963.

8. In an X-ray set why is the mains compensator voltmeter important? How does the compensator function?

    What does a filament voltage stabiliser do, and why is it necessary? Illustrate your answer with diagrams where appropriate.

    M.S.R. (R.), 1963.

9. Why is it necessary for a radiographer to be able to vary the kilovoltage at which the X-ray tube operates?

    Explain how a kilovoltage control functions, illustrating your answer with a simple diagram.

    M.S.R. (R.), 1964.

10. What is meant by the terms:

    (*a*) self rectified; (*b*) half wave rectified, and (*c*) full wave rectified, as applied to a high tension circuit? Illustrate your answer by drawing one cycle of the voltage waveform in each case. Draw the basic circuit used to obtain full-wave rectification and briefly explain its operation.

    M.S.R. (R. & T.), 1964.

11. Certain equipment provides the X-ray tube with " constant potential " What are the advantages of this? Give a description illustrated by a simple diagram of the operation of a circuit which would provide " constant potential " for the X-ray tube.

    M.S.R. (R.), 1963.

12. List the different types of timer you are likely to encounter in a large X-ray department. Describe an electronic timer, including a simple diagram in your answer.

M.S.R. (R.), 1965.

13. Describe how X-rays are produced at a tube target, giving the main features of the spectrum.
What is the peak voltage of a tube emitting X-rays with a short wavelength limit of 0·155 Å?

M.S.R. (R. & T.), 1953.

14. An X-ray tube having a tungsten target is operated at 80 kVp without additional filtration. Show graphically how the intensity of the radiation emitted varies with wavelength, and explain the main features of your diagram. How would your diagram be changed if, (*a*) the kV where increased to 150 kVp, (*b*) a copper filter were inserted in the beam?

M.S.R. (R. & T.), 1961.

15. Describe the way in which the radiation is distributed around the target of an X-ray tube. How does this spatial distribution of intensity vary with the voltage applied across the tube?
In what way is the target design influenced by the distribution of intensity and how does the target design itself influence the distribution?

M.S.R. (T.), 1965.

16. With the aid of a circuit diagram, describe the main features of the electrical supply for an X-ray tube filament. How can such a supply provide compensation for the effects of space charge and mains voltage fluctuation?

F.S.R. (R.), 1963.

17. What factors govern the choice of target material and of focal spot size in an X-ray tube? How can the effective focal spot size be measured?

F.S.R., 1965.

18. *Either* (*a*) Describe and explain the construction of a rotating anode diagnostic X-ray tube. Describe how you would investigate (i) the size and shape of its focal spot, (ii) whether the X-ray field in the plane of the film is uniform.
Or (*b*) Describe and explain the construction of a conventional (250 — 300 kV) therapy X-ray tube. Draw a diagram of a high tension circuit which can deliver a smoothed voltage to the tube and explain the functions of the principal components. How would you investigate the variation of dose across an X-ray field on the skin of a patient?

D.M.R., 1963.

93

19. Explain why the voltage supply to an X-ray tube needs to be rectified and show how this can be achieved in, (a) a half-wave circuit, (b) a full-wave circuit.
Draw circuit diagrams and graphs to show the relationship between voltage and current in each case.

D.M.R., 1961.

20. Describe the electrical equipment necessary to activate the X-ray tube and to control its output for *either* diagnostic *or* therapeutic radiology. Explain the function of each important component.
How would you investigate the waveform of the voltage across an X-ray tube?

D.M.R., 1964.

21. Discuss the theory of the production of X-rays in the target of a tube. Explain the relation between the peak kilovoltage on the tube and the shortest wavelength emitted.
Describe one method of determining the peak voltage of an X-ray generator.

D.M.R., 1962.

22. Draw graphs of the radiation spectra emitted when an X-ray tube with a tungsten target is operated at, (a) 50 kVp, (b) 100 kVp.
Explain the difference between the two spectra.

D.M.R., 1964.

CHAPTER IV

THE PRODUCTION OF HIGH ENERGY
X-RAYS

X-RAYS with an energy up to a few MeV. may be produced by methods similar to those described in the last chapter (i.e. by accelerating electrons obtained from a heated filament towards an anode maintained at a high positive potential with respect to the filament so that they strike a target with high velocity). However, special features, to be described below, must be introduced into the design of the tubes and special high voltage generating equipment is necessary. For very high energies, such high voltage equipment becomes very bulky and although X-rays are still generated by causing fast electrons to strike a target, different methods of accelerating the electrons are used. These are discussed in sections 4.05-09.

4.01. Multi-section X-ray tubes

At one time it appeared that tubes for generating X-rays of the order of 1 MeV. or more in energy would have to be continuously evacuated, since gas, occluded in the envelope and the electrodes, was released on application of the high voltage and caused electrical breakdown. Improved methods of " degassing " sealed tubes and of distributing the electrical stress uniformly have now made continuous evacuation unnecessary. Most modern high voltage tubes are sealed tubes constructed with intermediate accelerating electrodes between the filament and the anode. In this way a uniform potential gradient is maintained between anode and cathode (in tubes without intermediate electrodes the potential gradient is ordinarily non-uniform) and corona effects are avoided. The X-radiation is obtained as a narrow beam in the forward direction, i.e. it is transmitted through the target, which may be gold or platinum. The anode is frequently earthed and water-cooled and the filament is maintained at a high negative potential. The tube is normally insulated by immersion in a gas under pressure because the volume of oil required would make the equipment too heavy. Air, nitrogen, or gases with better insulating properties such as dichlorodifluoromethane (freon 12) or sulphur hexafluoride [1] are used.

4.02. High voltage generators, voltage multiplier and resonant transformer circuits

Some of the laboratories standardising radiological equipment use high voltage generators which consist of either a succession of Greinacher voltage doubling circuits or of a Cockcroft-Walton voltage multiplier. (The circuit of the latter is shown in fig. 4.01. A potential difference twice the peak transformer voltage is developed across each of the condensers C_2, C_4 and so on.) It is of interest that some of the earliest megavoltage X-radiation to be used clinically was obtained using a Cockcroft-Walton voltage multiplier [2, 3]. The equipment is bulky, however, and hence is not installed in hospitals now that more compact generators are available.

Voltages up to 2 MV. can be obtained from a resonant transformer [4,5]. As already explained in Chapter III, this is a transformer operated with current alternating at a higher frequency than the usual 50 to 60 c.p.s. so that the frequency of the alternating current supplied to the primary circuit is equal to the resonant frequency of the secondary circuit. In the megavoltage equipment, the frequency is usually a few hundred cycles per second. Intermediate voltage taps on the transformer are connected to the intermediate electrodes of the multi-section X-ray tube which is normally mounted along the

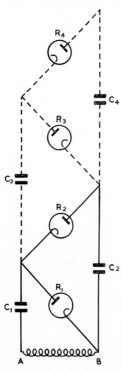

FIG. 4.01. Cockcroft-Walton voltage multiplier circuit.

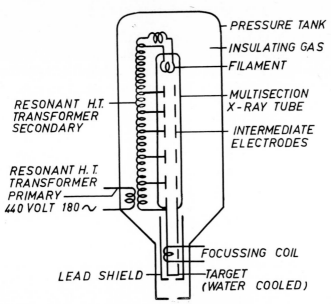

PRESSURE TANK

INSULATING GAS

FILAMENT

RESONANT H.T.
TRANSFORMER
SECONDARY

MULTISECTION
X-RAY TUBE

INTERMEDIATE
ELECTRODES

RESONANT H.T.
TRANSFORMER
PRIMARY
440 VOLT 180 ∿

FOCUSSING COIL

LEAD SHIELD

TARGET
(WATER COOLED)

FIG. 4.02. Schematic diagram showing cross-section of 1 or 2 MV.
resonant transformer X-ray unit.

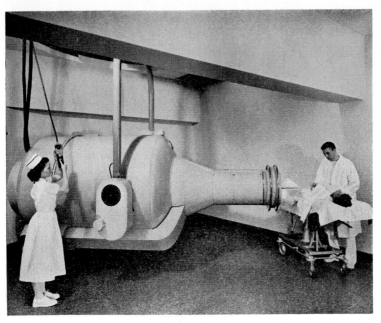

FIG. 4.03. General view of 2 million volt resonant transformer X-ray unit.

Courtesy of the General Electric Co.

97

axis of the transformer (fig. 4.02), X-rays are, of course, only
generated when the filament end of the transformer is negative
and the electron emission is, in fact, deliberately restricted
to that part of the half-cycle when the voltage is near its peak.
Resonant transformer units are more flexible than voltage
multiplier sets and 1 or 2 MV. units are in use in a number of
medical centres. The equipment is still cumbersome, however
(see fig. 4.03), and these sets also are less frequently installed
now that more compact sources of megavoltage radiation are
available.

4.03. The Van de Graaff generator [6, 7]

The Van de Graaff generator is the most compact of the
million volt generators. A 2 MV. unit is about 2 ft. in diameter
and 5 ft. high. It also has the advantage of producing a

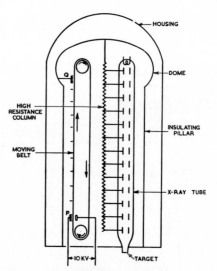

FIG. 4.04.   Schematic diagram of Van
de Graaff electrostatic generator.

constant potential. It is an electrostatic generator based upon
the principle of transferring mechanically many small electrostatic charges to an insulated conductor until the conductor is
raised to a very high potential. A large metal dome is supported on an insulating pillar as shown in fig. 4.04. Within

98

the pillar a continuous belt runs between pulleys. Near its lower end the belt passes between a set of needle points (*P*) at a high negative potential with respect to a rounded surface. A negative discharge takes place from the points at *P* and negative charges are therefore collected by the belt as it passes by *P*

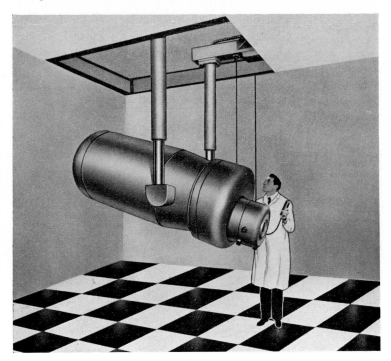

FIG. 4.05. A Van de Graaff generator for medical use.
Courtesy of High Voltage Engineering Corporation, Cambridge, Mass., U.S.A.

and carried by it up to the dome. Within the dome another set of points, maintained at a positive potential, collect the charges from the belt which then travel to the outside of the hollow conductor. By running the moving belt at sufficiently high speed, very large charges can be built up. When the equipment is used to generate a high voltage for the production of X-rays, the X-ray tube is usually placed to one side of the belt, within the generator column. The intermediate accelerating electrodes are connected to appropriate points on a high resistance column between the generator dome and earth. The

99

entire equipment is normally gas insulated and as is usual for high energy X-ray tubes, the filament is at a high negative potential, and the target is earthed and water-cooled.

4.04. Particle accelerators

The particle accelerators to be discussed in the following sections were developed for experiments in nuclear physics. For this work, machines were required which would accelerate light nuclei and protons as well as electrons. Electron accelerators are a special type of particle accelerator and have frequently been developed from machines designed to accelerate heavy particles.

In these accelerators no source of very high voltage is maintained, but the particles (light nuclei, protons or electrons) are nevertheless given very high energies comparable with those which would be produced by direct acceleration through several million volts. This is usually achieved by giving the particles very many repeated small increments of energy. The accelerators may be divided into two groups according as to whether the particles travel in a straight line or in a circular or spiral orbit during acceleration.

4.05. Linear accelerators [8, 9, 10]

The early linear accelerators consisted of a series of hollow cylindrical electrodes of increasing length, connected alternately to a source of high-frequency alternating potential as shown in fig. 4.06.

The particles were injected down the axis of the system and the lengths of successive electrodes were adjusted so that a particle accelerated at the first interelectrode gap reached the second gap one half-cycle later, and was therefore again accelerated and so on. With the frequencies available in the 1930s, this device was only suitable for the acceleration of heavy particles, since excessively long electrodes would be required for electrons. However, with the development during the last war of very high frequency (microwave) generators for radar, it became possible to design linear accelerators suitable for the acceleration of electrons. We shall discuss here only the travelling wave type of linear accelerator which is used in medical units.

In the travelling wave linear accelerator an electromagnetic wave is propagated down a cylindrical wave-guide in such a

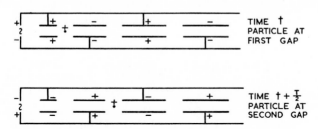

FIG. 4.06. Principle of early type of linear accelerator.

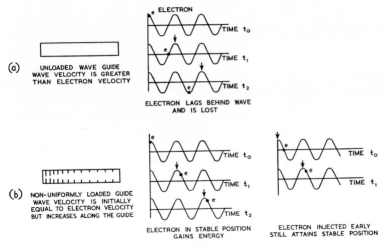

FIG. 4.07. Principle of travelling wave linear accelerator.
(After Newbury.[8])

way that there is an axial electrical field down the guide. Electrons are injected down the axis of the tube. Suppose that the wave and an electron are injected so that the electron starts at the peak of the wave when the field direction is such as to accelerate the electron. Then the electron will gain energy from the field. It is necessary to keep the wave velocity equal to the electron velocity if the electron is to remain in an accelerating field. If the wave velocity is much greater than the

101

electron velocity the electron will lag behind the wave and ultimately experience a retarding field. The initial wave and electron velocities must therefore be equal and the wave velocity must increase as the electron gains energy, and therefore velocity, until the electron has such an energy that its velocity approaches that of light and remains nearly constant. The variation in the wave-velocity along the guide is achieved by the use of circular irises of varying dimensions. This is illustrated diagrammatically in fig. 4.07(b).

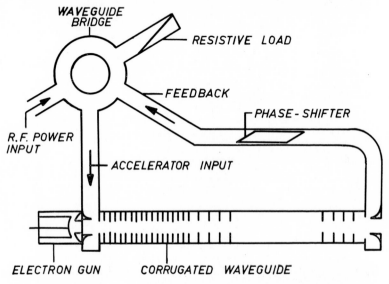

FIG. 4.08.   Schematic diagram of linear accelerator with feedback bridge.

In the travelling wave accelerator, an appreciable amount of wave power reaches the end of the guide. In some units this power is absorbed in a copper load; in other units, to avoid wasting power, it is returned by means of a bridge circuit to the input end of the guide (fig. 4.08).

It should be noted that the electrons are emitted from a linear accelerator in short bursts, being bunched together during the initial period of velocity change. In a typical accelerator, there are 500 pulses per second of about 2 μsec duration.

For medical use, microwave linear accelerators are particularly valuable for the generation of X-rays with energies

102

between about 3 MeV. and 20 MeV. Above 3 MeV. most high-voltage generators become bulky due to insulation difficulties, and there are no convenient γ-ray sources. There are now a large number of linear accelerators in routine clinical use operating at either 4 MV. or 6 MV., which are sufficiently compact for the accelerator to be mounted on a movable framework permitting rotation of the unit about the patient

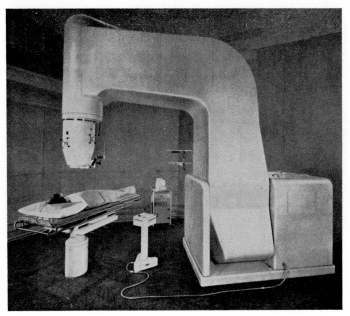

FIG. 4.09.   A linear accelerator for medical use.
Courtesy Vickers Ltd.

(see fig. 4.09). A limited number of accelerators are in use at higher energies, but most of these are fixed units and positioning of the patient is not as convenient. Above 20 MeV. the length of accelerator required becomes excessive for hospital use, and X-rays are generated more efficiently by a betatron or synchrotron.

4.06. Cyclic accelerators

In the 1930s it was not possible to accelerate particles to a very high energy in a linear accelerator of reasonable length.

103

Lawrence therefore suggested that the particles be constrained to move in a spiral by a magnetic field. The first machine to be designed upon this principle was the cyclotron. The cyclotron itself is *not* suitable for the production of high energy electrons but will be briefly described since (*a*) it is used for the production of certain artificial radio-active isotopes and (*b*) it was the forerunner of the betatron and the synchrotron, which are used to accelerate electrons.

The machine is shown diagrammatically in fig. 4.10.

In the space between the pole pieces of a large electromagnet,

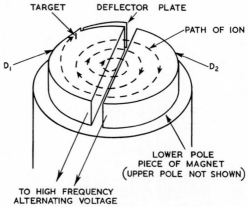

FIG. 4.10. Schematic diagram of cyclotron.

ions, generated near the centre, travel over a spiral path within two hollow evacuated hemicylindrical chambers (known as the dees because of their resemblance in shape to the letter D). A high-frequency alternating voltage is applied between the dees. Consider the forces upon an ion of charge q, mass m, and velocity v. The ion will be accelerated into one or other dee by the electrical field. Within the dee the force due to the magnetic field acts at right angles to the field itself and to the initial direction of motion of the ion, and causes the ion to move in a circular path of radius r where r is determined by the equation

$$Hqv = mv^2/r$$

(force due to magnetic field) = (mass × acceleration)

i.e. $$r = mv/Hq \qquad . \qquad . \qquad . \qquad (1)$$

When the ion again reaches the space between the dees it is again accelerated by the electrical field so that its velocity and hence the radius of its subsequent path is increased. Thus the ions travel in paths of increasing radius as they gain energy.

In order that the ion shall be accelerated each time it reaches the space between the dees, the electric field must change direction during the time taken by the ion to travel round one dee, i.e. the half-period $(\tau/2)$ of the alternating electrical voltage between the dees must equal the time required for transit round one dee.

i.e. $\qquad \tau/2 = \pi r/v.$

Since $\qquad r/v = m/Hq$ from equation (1)

$\qquad \therefore \tau/2 = \pi m/Hq.$

The same frequency of field is satisfactory for all ions of the same mass whatever their individual velocities. The faster ions travel in larger arcs and require the same time as the slower ions moving in paths of smaller radius. But if the mass of the particles changes, the particles will get out of step with the accelerating voltage. This is the reason why cyclotrons are not suitable for the acceleration of electrons to high energies. Electrons, on account of their smaller mass, attain much larger velocities than nuclei and an electron with an energy of 1 MeV. travels with a velocity approaching that of light. According to the theory of relativity, the mass then increases with increase in the energy. (See Chapter 1, eqn. 3.)

4.07. The betatron [9, 11, 12, 13, 14]

The betatron is designed to accelerate electrons. The electrons are constrained to move within a hollow ring or " doughnut " by the action of a guiding magnetic field (as in the cyclotron), but the magnitude of the field is increased as the electrons gain energy in order to keep them in the same orbit. The electrons are accelerated by changing the magnetic flux, i.e. the number of lines of magnetic force, passing through the doughnut. (This is the same effect, electromagnetic induction, as produces an induced current in a closed conductor such as a loop of wire, when the magnetic flux through the circuit is changed. In a metallic conductor, however, forces are brought into play which oppose and limit the electronic motion, so the conductor has a finite resistance. In the betatron the resistance is reduced to a minimum by evacuating

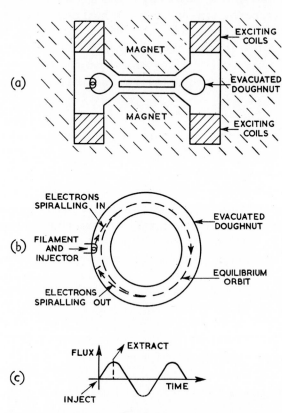

FIG. 4.11.   Diagrams illustrating the construction of a betatron.

(a) Longitudinal section showing doughnut and magnet.

(b) Transverse section through doughnut.

(c) The operating cycle.

the doughnut.)   The magnetic field thus fulfils two functions, both guiding and accelerating the electrons.   To do this the pole pieces of the magnet and the iron core (if used) must be carefully designed to give a distribution of lines of force obeying certain conditions.   The guiding effect is a function of the field strength at the orbit, i.e. of the number of lines of force per unit area at the orbit, whereas the accelerating effect is a function of the flux through the orbit, i.e. of the total number of lines of force going through the orbit. The following calculation shows that the change in flux must be just twice what it would be if the field throughout the doughnut were equal to the field at the orbit.

Let m_1, v_1 denote the mass and velocity respectively of an electron at any instant and let m_2, v_2 denote the corresponding values t seconds later when the electron has gained energy. (For high energy electrons m as well as v changes with increase in energy as already explained.) If the radius of the orbit r, is to remain constant, the guiding field must change from H_1 to H_2 where

$$H_1 e v_1 = m_1 v_1^2/r \text{ and } H_2 e v_2 = m_2 v_2^2/r$$

i.e.
$$(H_2 - H_1)er = m_2 v_2 - m_1 v_1. \qquad . \qquad . \qquad (1)$$

The change in mass and velocity are related to the flux by which they are produced as follows:

According to the laws of electromagnetic induction, the electromotive force (E) generated in a closed circuit is equal to the rate of change of the flux through the circuit, i.e. $E = (N_2 - N_1)/t$, where the flux changes from N_1 to N_2 in time t. For an electron moving around a circle of radius r, if the electromotive force is E, the work done in taking the electron once around the circle is Ee. But the work done is also $2\pi r F$ where F is the mean force acting tangentially upon the electron;

i.e.
$$Ee = 2\pi r F \text{ or } F = Ee/2\pi r$$

Substituting for E $\therefore F = e(N_2 - N_1)/2\pi r t$.

But a force F acting for a time t will produce a change in the momentum of the electrons given by

$$Ft = m_2 v_2 - m_1 v_1$$

i.e.
$$e(N_2 - N_1)/2\pi r = m_2 v_2 - m_1 v_1. \qquad . \qquad (2)$$

Combining equations (1) and (2), we obtain as the condition that electrons shall remain in the equilibrium orbit when accelerated by a change in flux from N_1 to N_2,

$$(H_2 - H_1)er = e(N_2 - N_1)/2\pi r$$

i.e.
$$N_2 - N_1 = 2\pi r^2(H_2 - H_1)$$

107

Betatron magnets are normally energised by alternating current with a frequency of between 60 and 600 c./s. The electrons are injected from a heated filament when the magnetic field is beginning to increase and are accelerated during one quarter cycle. They initially spiral inwards or outwards until the equilibrium orbit is reached. The orbit radius varies from

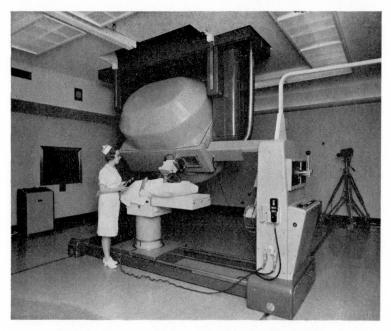

FIG. 4.12. A 35 MeV. betatron for medical use.
Courtesy the Manitoba Cancer Treatment and Research Foundation, Winnipeg, Canada.

6 in. or so for 10 MeV. electrons to several feet for higher energies. Electrons may travel several hundred thousand times around the orbit before the field reaches its peak value. As the magnetic field reaches its maximum value, the electrons are pulled from the equilibrium orbit, and either extracted from the doughnut for use as an electron beam or allowed to fall upon a target to produce X-rays. At energies above about 20 MeV., most of the energy of the incident electrons is converted into X-radiation and not into heat. At these energies therefore it is not necessary to make special arrange-

ments to cool the target. The output from a betatron is of course intermittent with a pulse of electrons or X-rays of 1 or 2 μsec duration each cycle.

4.08. The synchrotron [9, 11, 15, 16]

The synchrotron resembles the betatron in that electrons are constrained to move in a circular orbit within an evacuated ring by the action of a guiding magnetic field which is increased as the energy of the electrons is increased. The main acceleration of the electrons, however, is produced by a radio-frequency

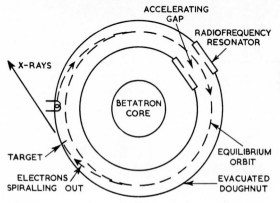

FIG. 4.13. Schematic diagram of a synchrotron.

field with electrical component tangential to the orbit instead of by changing the magnetic flux through the orbit. This radio-frequency field is applied over a small section of the doughnut which acts as a resonant cavity. Most synchrotrons have a small magnetic core and the initial acceleration of the electrons is produced by the betatron principle. Only when the electrons have reached about 2 MeV. in energy, when their velocity approaches that of light and therefore becomes nearly constant is the radio-frequency accelerating field switched on. Its frequency is adjusted so that a single cycle takes the same time as an electron requires to go once around the doughnut. This time is constant when the orbit radius is kept constant and the electrons have sufficient energy to be travelling with constant velocity. Electrons crossing the resonant cavity at the appropriate instant in the radio-frequency cycle gain energy

(E say) but remain in an orbit of the same radius since the magnetic field is also increased. (As in the betatron $r = mv/He$ and remains constant if mv and H are increased proportionally.)

Electrons crossing the resonator gap either earlier or later in the cycle do not receive the appropriate increment of energy. They therefore move into an orbit of different radius and reach

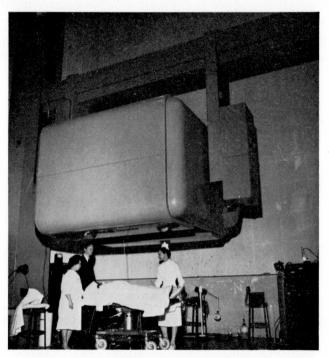

FIG. 4.14.   A 70 MeV. synchrotron for medical use.
By permission of G. D. Adams and *Radiology*[16]

the resonator the next time at a different instant in the cycle. This results in the electrons becoming bunched together in such a way that they cross the resonator at the favourable part of the cycle, and therefore remain in the equilibrium orbit and receive repeated acceleration.

The radio-frequency field is switched off just before the magnetic field reaches its maximum value. The final increase in the magnetic field may be used to cause the electrons to move into a smaller orbit where they strike a target for the production of X-rays, or a subsidiary field may be applied to extract the electron beam or deflect it on to a target.

Both betatrons and synchrotrons tend to be noisy in operation and care in design is necessary if the noise level close to the machine is to remain within tolerable limits. The main bulk of the machines is due to the magnet. Up to about 25 MeV., betatrons are rather simpler to operate than synchrotrons but for higher energies, machines can be made smaller and lighter by changing to synchrotron acceleration.

REFERENCES

1. GROSS, M. J. (1951). *Amer. J. Roentgenol.* **65**, 103.
2. COCKCROFT, J. D. and WALTON, E.T.S. (1931). *Proc. Roy. Soc. A.* **136**, 619.
3. INNES, G. S. (1946). *Brit. Med. Bull.* **4**, no. 1, 51.
4. CHARLTON, E. E., WESTENDORP, W. F. and DEMPSTER, L. E. (1939). *J. Appl. Physics*, **10**, 374.
5. CHARLTON, E. E. and WESTENDORP, W. F. (1944). *Electronics*, **17** (Dec.), 128.
6. VAN DE GRAAFF, R. J. (1931). *Phys. Rev.* **38**, 1919.
7. TRUMP, J. G. and VAN DE GRAAFF, R. J. (1939). *Phys. Rev.* **55**, 1160.
8. NEWBURY, G. R. (1949). *Brit. J. Radiol.* **22**, 473.
9. FRY, D. W. and WALKINSHAW, W. (1949). *Reports on Progress in Physics*, **12**, 102.
10. MILLER, G. W., BEADLE, R., KELLIHER, M. G. and McGINTY, G. K., (1962). *Brit. J. Radiol.* **35**, 182
11. FRY, D. W. (1949). *Brit. J. Radiol.* **22**, 462.
12. KERST, D. W. (1941). *Phys. Rev.* **60**, 47.
13. PITTET, L. (1962). *Brown Boveri Review*, 5.
14. KERST, D. W. (1943). *Radiology*, **40**, 115.
15. BOHM, D. and FOLDY, L. L. (1946). *Phys. Rev.* **70**, 249.
16. ADAMS, G. D. (1964). *Radiology*, **83**, 785.

EXAMINATION QUESTIONS

1. Describe an equipment producing high energy (greater than 1 MeV) radiation which is suitable for therapy work. Discuss the advantages of such equipment.

F.S.R. (R. & T.), 1961.

2. Give brief accounts of . . . . . *Either* the Van de Graaff machine *or* the linear accelerator for producing megavoltages. . . . .

(Part question). D.M.R. 1964.

CHAPTER V

RADIOACTIVITY

5.01. The discovery of natural radioactivity

WHEN Roentgen described his discovery of X-radiation, he reported that the radiation seemed to come from those parts of the discharge tube which were bombarded by the cathode rays. (See Chapter III.) Since the cathode rays also cause fluorescence of the walls of the discharge tube, it occurred to several other scientists to try to find out whether fluorescence was always accompanied by X-radiation. This is not the case, but the idea led Henri Becquerel to investigate the fluorescence produced by sunlight in various uranium compounds and in 1896 he discovered that these compounds emitted penetrating rays (which could affect wrapped photographic plates) not only when they were fluorescing but even when kept in the dark. Also a charged electroscope was found to lose its charge and zinc sulphide fluoresced when in the vicinity of the uranium compounds. Schmidt and Madame Curie subsequently showed that thorium compounds produced the same effects and all such compounds were called radioactive. Later Madame Curie noticed that crude pitch-blende seemed more active than could be accounted for by its uranium content and she was able to isolate compounds of two other radioactive elements which were named polonium and radium.

It was gradually realised that the radiations from radioactive materials were of several different types. Some of the rays were deflected in electric and magnetic fields as if they were positively charged and were stopped by a few sheets of paper or a few centimetres of air. These were called α-rays. A second type behaved as if negatively charged and were more penetrating than the α-rays but were stopped by a few millimetres of aluminium. These were called β-rays. A third group, called γ-rays, remained undeflected by electric or magnetic fields and were very much more penetrating than the

112

α- and β-rays, several centimetres of lead being required to reduce their intensity by an appreciable amount.

γ-rays, because they could not be deflected by electric or magnetic fields were assumed to be an electromagnetic radiation of the same nature as light or X-rays but of very short wavelength. (The first wavelength determinations were carried out by Rutherford and Andrade in 1914.) β-rays were shown to consist of high energy electrons by determining their charge/mass ratio using an electromagnetic deflection method (Kaufmann 1902). α-rays were found to be more difficult to examine

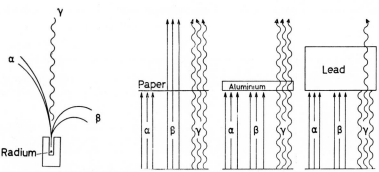

Fig. 5.01. Magnetic deflection of radiation from a radium source.

Fig. 5.02. Relative penetrating power of α-, β-, and γ-radiation.

than β-rays because the deflections obtained in electric and magnetic fields were much smaller. However, in 1903 Rutherford devised a modification of the electromagnetic deflection method and showed the charge/mass ratio to be one-half of the value obtained for the hydrogen ion in electrolysis. Thus if the α-rays consisted of singly charged particles their mass must be twice that of the hydrogen ion, if the particles were doubly charged, their mass would be four times that of the hydrogen ion and so on. In order to determine whether the particles were singly or multiply charged, Rutherford and Geiger measured (1) the rate at which charge was transferred by the α-particles from a known quantity of radioactive material (Radium C) to an electrode nearby (the source and the electrode both being within an evacuated vessel), and (2) the rate at which α-particles were emitted by radium C. The total charge

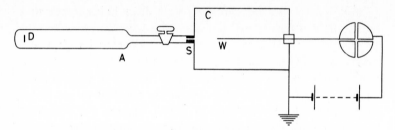

FIG. 5.03. Apparatus of Rutherford and Geiger for " counting "
α-particles.

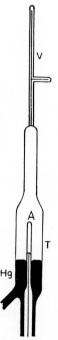

FIG. 5.04. Apparatus of
Rutherford and Royds to
demonstrate that α-particles
are helium nuclei.

By permission from *Radioactivity and
Radioactive Substances* by J. Chad-
wick. (Sir Isaac Pitman and Sons
Ltd., London.)

transferred per second divided by the number of particles emitted per second gave the charge on each particle as twice the electronic charge. Thus the mass of the particles was four times that of hydrogen, and it was concluded that the α-particles were doubly charged helium atoms.

The α-particles were counted using the apparatus shown in fig. 5.03. The radioactive source was enclosed in a highly evacuated vessel A, with an aperture of known area at S, covered with mica sufficiently thin to allow α-particles to enter the chamber C. The latter was partially evacuated and contained an insulated central wire maintained at a positive potential with respect to the walls of C. Each time an α-particle entered C, a momentary passage of current took place between the wire W and the chamber walls. This could be detected by an electrometer and hence the number of α-particles entering C in a given time observed. Knowing the angle subtended by S at D, the number of particles emitted in all directions by the source could be calculated. (A more detailed account of the processes taking place in the counting chamber and a description of modern forms of Geiger counter is given in Chapter VIII.)

114

That α-particles are doubly charged helium atoms was confirmed directly by Rutherford and Royds in 1909 by introducing radioactive material into a thin-walled tube (A) (fig. 5.04) contained within an outer evacuated tube (T) connected to a discharge tube. The α-particles could pass through the walls of the small tube A into the evacuated tube. After six days, when the gas which collected in T was compressed into the discharge tube and a high voltage was applied between the electrodes, the glow showed the characteristic lines of the helium spectrum.

5.02. Radioactive transformations

If the nuclear theory of atomic structure is accepted, then the positively charged α-particles emitted by radioactive materials must come from the nucleus. This view is also suggested by the fact that radioactive properties are independent of the chemical state of the radioactive element. It does not matter, for instance, whether radium chloride or radium sulphate is observed, the radioactive properties are the same, those characteristic of radium, although the chemical properties of radium chloride and radium sulphate are not identical. When an α-particle is emitted by an atom, the atomic mass is reduced by 4 atomic mas units. (An atomic mass unit is approximately equal to the mass of a proton or neutron; it is defined as $1/12$ of the mass of the most abundant isotope of carbon. $1 \text{a.m.u.} = 1.66 \times 10^{-24} \text{g.}$) The emission of an α-particle reduces the nuclear charge by 2 electronic charge units. The atomic number is therefore reduced by 2. Since the emission of two β-particles entirely annuls the chemical effects of the emission of an α-particle, it follows that the β-particles also come from the nucleus. The emission of a β-particle leaves the mass almost unchanged but increases the nuclear charge and therefore the atomic number by one unit. The suggestion that radioactivity was an actual disintegration of the nucleus, was first made by Rutherford and Soddy in 1913.

The disintegration series of uranium. The disintegration of uranium occurs as follows. The parent element has an atomic number of 92 and an atomic mass of 238 m.u. It decomposes by emitting an α-particle producing an element usually called

115

uranium X_1, having atomic number 90 and atomic mass 234. Uranium X_1 is also radioactive, emitting a β-particle (accompanied by γ-radiation) to give uranium X_2, another β-emitter which produces uranium II. Uranium II has the same atomic

TABLE 5.01

THE URANIUM-RADIUM SERIES

Usual name	Atomic number	An isotope of	Atomic mass	Half-life	Radiation emitted. Energy in MeV.		
					α	β	γ
Uranium I	92	U	238	4.5×10^9 yr.	4·21	—	—
Uranium X_1	90	Th	234	24·1 d.	—	0·13	0·09
Uranium X_2	91	Pa	234	1·14 m.	—	2·32	0·80
Uranium II	92	U	234	2.5×10^5 yr.	4·75	—	—
Ionium	90	Th	230	8.0×10^4 yr.	4·66	—	γ
Radium	88	Ra	226	1620 yr.	4·79	—	0·19
Radon	86	Rn	222	3·825 d.	5·49	—	—
Radium A	84	Po	218	3·05 m.	5·99	β	—
*Radium B	82	Pb	214	26·8 m.	—	0·65	0·24 to 0·35
†Radium C	83	Bi	214	19·9 m.	5·50	3·15	0·6 to 2·2
Radium C¹	84	Po	214	1.6×10^{-4} s.	7·68	—	—
Radium C¹¹	81	Tl	210	1·3 m.	—	1·80	—
Radium D	82	Pb	210	21 yr.	—	0·025	0·047
Radium E	83	Bi	210	5 d.	—	1·17	—
Radium F (Polonium)	84	Po	210	139 d.	5·30	—	
Radium G (lead)	82	Pb	206	Stable	—	—	—

* For details of the γ-radiation emitted by Radium B and Radium C, see table 5.03.

† Radium C may disintegrate *either* by emitting a β-particle to form Radium C¹ *or* by emitting an α-particle to form Radium C¹¹. The latter occurs in only 0·04 per cent. of disintegrations. Both Radium C¹ and Radium C¹¹ produce Radium D.

number as the parent uranium (92) but a smaller atomic mass (234 instead of 238). Atoms such as make up these two kinds of uranium which have the same atomic number but differ in atomic mass, are called *isotopes*. Their existence was first noted by Soddy in 1906 when he was investigating another radioactive material ionium. Soddy found ionium to be

116

chemically indistinguishable from thorium although the two substances differed in radioactive properties.

Radium, which is the radioactive element which has been most widely used in hospitals, is isolated from uranium ores in which it has probably been formed by the slow disintegration of uranium II. The complete series of disintegration products formed from uranium is shown in table 5.01.

The first disintegration product of radium is an inert gas (radon). The final product, radium *G*, is an isotope of lead

TABLE 5.02

THE THORIUM SERIES

Usual name	Atomic number	An isotope of	Atomic mass	Half-life	Radiation emitted energy in MeV.		
					α	β	γ
Thorium	90	Th	232	1.41×10^{10} yr.	4.20	—	—
Mesothorium 1	88	Ra	228	6.7 yr.	—	0.053	—
Mesothorium 2	89	Ac	228	6.13 h.	4.5	1.55	—
Radiothorium	90	Th	228	1.9 yr.	5.42	—	γ
Thorium X	88	Ra	224	3.64 d.	5.68	—	—
Thoron	86	Rn	220	51.5 s.	6.28	—	—
Thorium A	84	Po	216	0.16 s.	6.77	β	—
Thorium B	82	Pb	212	10.6 h.	—	0.36	—
Thorium C	83	Bi	212	60.5 m.	6.05	2.26	γ
Thorium C¹	84	Po	212	3×10^{-7} s.	8.77	—	—
Thorium C¹¹	81	Tl	208	3.1 m.	—	1.82	2.62
Thorium D	82	Pb	208	Stable	—	—	—

with atomic mass 206. Thorium and actinium also produce series of radioactive products terminating in isotopes of lead, having atomic masses of 208 and 207 respectively. The prediction that lead found in uranium, thorium and actinium ores would differ in atomic mass was confirmed by experiment and was one of the early successes of Rutherford and Soddy's theory of radioactive decay.

5.03 The ionising properties of nuclear radiations

α-particles

When a relatively massive, positively charged α-particle passes through matter, it frequently passes sufficiently close to the outer loosely-bound electrons of atoms to attract these electrons from their shells. Thus the particle causes ionisation of the atoms of the material through which it passes. The tracks of individual α-particles through gases can be observed in a Wilson cloud chamber. The cloud chamber usually consists of a glass cylinder closed by a piston and containing a gas saturated with water vapour. If the piston is suddenly withdrawn, the gas is cooled and is then supersaturated with water vapour. If there are any ions in the chamber these act as nuclei upon which the water vapour condenses and forms droplets and the distribution of the ions is thus made visible. A cloud chamber photograph showing the track of an α-particle is reproduced in fig. 5.05.

FIG. 5.05. Track of an α-particle.

By permission from *Ions, Electrons and Ionising Radiations* by J. A. Crowther. (Edward Arnold Ltd., London.)

It will be noticed that except near the end, the track is approximately rectilinear and that the ionisation is so dense that the individual droplets have coalesced. The number of ions produced per cm. (the specific ionisation), is of the order of several tens of thousands of ions per cm. in air and increases towards the end of the track. This increase is explained by the fact that the α-particle is moving more slowly near the end of its track. It therefore spends more time in the vicinity of each gas atom and has a higher probability of producing an ionisation.

The early experimenters noticed that the α-particles from any one isotope all produce tracks of very nearly the same length and must therefore be emitted with the same energy. The range was also found to be related to the rate of decay of the emitting nucleus. (This is expressed mathematically in the Geiger-Nuttall law.) In gases the range is usually a few centimetres whereas in liquids and solids it is a fraction of a millimetre (see figs. 5.06 and 5.07). The range varies inversely as the number of electrons per cc. of the

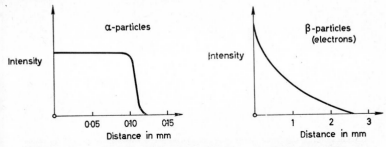

FIG. 5.06. The " range " of α- and β-particles. Typical absorption curves.

absorber and also depends upon the ionisation potential of the atoms of the absorber. It therefore varies inversely as the density of the absorber but depends also upon the atomic

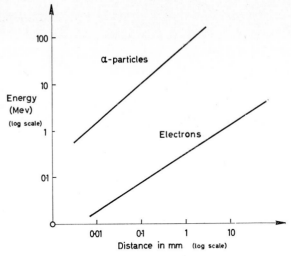

FIG. 5.07. Approximate ranges of α- and β-particles in water.

number. (The number of electrons per cc. = number of electrons per atom × number of atoms per gm. × number of gm. per cc. = $ZN\rho/A$, where Z denotes atomic number, N Avogadro's number, A atomic weight and ρ density).

119

β-particles

The track of a *β*-particle in a Wilson cloud chamber is shown in fig. 5.08. The specific ionisation is much less than that produced by an α-particle. The specific ionisation produced by fairly high energy electrons (say about 1 MeV.) is about 50 ion pairs per cm. in air. Electrons of very high energy produce slightly more ionisations per cm. (this is a relativity effect), while below 1 MeV. the specific ionisation increases fairly rapidly with decrease in energy because the electric field of the *β*-particle has a longer time in which to

FIG. 5.08. Track of a *β*-particle.

By permission from *Ions, Electrons and Ionising Radiations* by J. A. Crowther. (Edward Arnold Ltd., London.)

interact with the orbital electrons when the particle moves more slowly.

β-particles differ from α-particles in that the energies with which the *β*-particles are emitted from any one isotope are spread over quite a wide range. As a result of this energy spread and also because the *β*-particles are more readily deflected and travel more devious paths than α-particles, *β*-particles do not have as well defined a range as α-particles. If the number of *β*-particles passing through an absorber is plotted against absorber thickness a curve of the form shown in fig. 5.06 is obtained. The curve is not a simple exponential curve but can usually be divided into parts each of which is approximately exponential with a different coefficient. The maximum range of the *β*-particles depends upon the maximum initial energy of the particles and is of the order of several metres in gases and a few centimetres or less in liquids and solids (see fig. 5.07 for ranges in water). The range varies inversely as the number of electrons per cc. of the absorber but depends also on the ionisation potential of the atoms of the absorber.

γ-rays

A cloud chamber photograph of a gas traversed by X- or γ-rays shows numbers of short tracks which resemble those

FIG. 5.09. "Tracks" of X-rays.

By permission from *Ions, Electrons and Ionising Radiations* by J. A. Crowther. (Edward Arnold Ltd., London.)

produced by β-particles. (See fig. 5.09.) These tracks are due to electrons ejected from the gas atoms by the radiation by processes which are discussed in detail in the next chapter.

5.04. The structure of atomic nuclei

The phenomenon of radioactivity raises the question of the nature of atomic nuclei, and suggests that the nuclei of different elements may contain the same components. Also the discovery of the existence of isotopes, having the same atomic number and chemical properties but differing in atomic mass explains the fact that the atomic weights of different elements as determined by the chemists are not simply related to the atomic weight of hydrogen. Before 1913 this fact had been the chief objection to any theory which suggested that the atoms of all elements were built up from the same elementary components. It was then realised that the atomic weight of an element might be determined by the masses of several isotopes present in constant proportions. The existence of stable isotopes was first demonstrated in 1913. J. J. Thomson showed by an electromagnetic deflection method that positive ions of neon consisted of two components with masses in the ratio of 20 : 22. Shortly afterwards Aston showed that almost all elements consist of a mixture of isotopes, the atomic mass of any one isotope being approximately an integral multiple of the mass of the hydrogen atom.

In view of these experiments, it was at first suggested that the nuclei of all elements were made up of protons (i.e. hydrogen nuclei) and electrons, with the α-particle as a secondary unit made up of four protons and two electrons relatively firmly bound together. The mass of the nucleus was determined by the number of protons and the charge by the excess of protons over electrons. (The emission of protons from a nucleus was detected in 1919 when Rutherford bombarded nitrogen with α-particles.) However, there are several difficulties in the suggestion that electrons are nuclear constituents. The relative sizes of the electron and the nuclei of the heavier elements are not compatible with the idea that the latter contain large numbers of electrons and the value of the nuclear spin cannot be satisfactorily explained. These difficulties were resolved in 1932 by the discovery of the neutron.

The neutron is a particle of mass approximately equal to that of the proton but carrying no charge. Its existence was first postulated by Chadwick to explain the production of a very penetrating radiation which had been observed by Bothe and Becker when lithium, boron or beryllium were bombarded by α-particles. Bothe and Becker established that the radiation was undeflected by magnetic or electric fields and hence regarded it as γ-radiation. Curie and Joliot then noticed that it was readily absorbed by light materials such as paraffin which contain hydrogen and that in the process protons were emitted. γ-radiation would not be absorbed in this way, hence Chadwick suggested that the radiation consisted of neutral particles, of mass comparable with that of the proton.

With the discovery that neutrons could be ejected from nuclei, it became necessary to modify the concept of nuclear structure outlined above and it was possible to avoid postulating that electrons were nuclear constituents.

Nuclei are now considered to contain protons and neutrons. The number of protons is equal to the atomic number, and determines the nuclear charge. The number of protons plus the number of neutrons together determine the nuclear mass. (The term " nucleon " is sometimes used to designate either protons or neutrons. Thus the number of nucleons determines the nuclear mass.) It is usual to denote a particular nuclear type or " nuclide ", by using the chemical symbol for the appropriate element with the atomic number as a subscript and the mass (in atomic mass units) as a superscript, e.g. $_6C^{12}$ denotes a nucleus containing six protons (and therefore carbon) with a mass of 12 units. It must therefore contain six neutrons. $_6C^{13}$ denotes an isotope of carbon with a mass of 13 units, a nucleus of this isotope must therefore contain seven neutrons in addition to the six protons. The subscript is not strictly necessary and is frequently omitted, since all nuclei of a particular element contain the same number of protons, but it is sometimes convenient to show the atomic number explicitly. The neutrons and protons are usually considered to be in rapid movement but they normally remain within the confines of the nucleus because of a strong force of attraction which operates between all the nucleons at short distances. In the naturally occurring elements of low atomic number, the nucleons never acquire sufficient energy to leave the nucleus and the elements are stable, but in the naturally occurring elements of high atomic number, a nucleon or group of nucleons may occasionally acquire sufficient energy to escape and these elements are radioactive.

The electrons which form the β-radiation emitted by radioactive nuclei are now believed to be produced by the conversion of a neutron into a proton. The emission of β-particles is accompanied by the emission of neutrinos, which are elementary particles carrying zero electrical charge and having a mass which is very small, even compared with that of the electron. (These properties make neutrinos very difficult to detect but fairly direct experimental evidence of their existence was obtained by Reines and Cowan in 1953[1].) The idea that neutrinos participate in β-emission was developed by Fermi about 1934 to explain the fact that the electrons

123

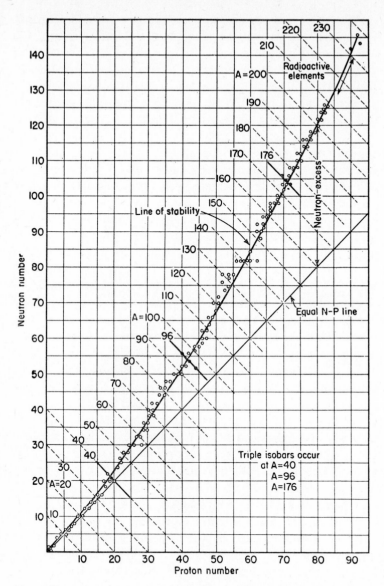

FIG. 5.10. A neutron-proton plot of natural nuclides. (Only those nuclides that have a relative abundance greater that 20 per cent. are shown.)

By permission from *Nuclear Radiation Physics* by R. E. Lapp and H. L. Andrews. (Prentice-Hall, Inc., New York.)

124

emitted from a particular nuclide do not all have the same energy, but may have any energy up to a certain maximum value, which is characteristic of the nucleus. This can be explained if the energy lost by the nucleus when a neutron changes to a proton is shared between the emitted electron and the neutrino. The reaction is usually written as follows

$$n_0{}^1 \rightarrow p^1 + e_{-1}^{\,\circ} + v_0{}^\circ$$

The converse process, the transformation of a proton into a neutron results in the emission of positrons and anti-neutrinos

$$p_1{}^1 \rightarrow n_0{}^1 + e_{+1}{}^\circ + v_0{}^\circ$$

Positrons are emitted by some artifically produced radioactive isotopes (see below) but are not emitted by naturally occurring radioactive elements.

In fig. 5.10, the number of protons per nucleus is plotted against the number of neutrons per nucleus for the more abundant stable nuclides. On this graph the points cluster about a line, suggesting that for a given number of protons a certain number of neutrons is required for stability. For the elements of low atomic number the numbers of protons and neutrons in the stable nuclei are approximately equal (so that the atomic weight is approximately twice the atomic number). For the heavier elements the number of neutrons exceeds the number of protons. There are also far more nuclei with an even number of both protons and neutrons than with an odd number of either type of nucleon and there are very few stable nuclides with an odd number of both protons and neutrons.

5.05. Nuclear Reactions and Artificial Radioactivity

If stable nuclides are bombarded with atomic particles such as α-particles, protons or neutrons, a proportion of the bombarded nuclei may capture one of the incident particles. Positively charged particles can enter the target nuclei only if they have sufficient energy to overcome the electrostatic repulsion. Neutrons on the other hand, being uncharged, do not have to overcome electrostatic repulsion and are often most readily captured when moving fairly slowly. When an incident particle enters a target nucleus, the compound nucleus which is formed must dissipate the extra energy it receives from the incident particle if it is to persist. In most elements, the greater part of the excess energy is dissipated immediately (within 10^{-12} sec.) either as electromagnetic radiation or by the emission of one or more other atomic particles. Such nuclear reactions are frequently described by the nature of the incident and emitted radiation. If the target nucleus is bombarded by neutrons, for example, and the compound nucleus emits γ-radiation, this is described as an (n, γ) reaction. If the incident radiation consists of α-particles and the compound nucleus emits protons, it is an (α, p) reaction and so on. The product nucleus which remains after the initial reaction is completed is not in general in a stable state. If the number of neutrons in the product nucleus is greater than in the stable isotopes of the same atomic number, there is a definite probability that the product nucleus will emit (negative) electrons since this reduces the neutron-proton ratio. If, on the other hand, the product nucleus has an excess of protons, either positron emission or K-capture is probable. (K capture consists in the absorption into the nucleus of an orbital electron from the K shell and is discussed further below). Artificially produced nuclides are therefore in general radioactive and the greater the difference between the neutron-proton ratio in the new nuclide and in corresponding stable isotopes, the more rapidly does the artificial nuclide decay. Methods of producing artificial radioactive isotopes * and the particular artificial isotopes which are of medical interest are discussed more fully in 5.13 and the following sections.

*The word " isotope " literally translated means " in the same place " (i.e. in the Periodic Table). It is therefore used correctly in a sentence such as " Radium G is an isotope of lead " but some writers consider it should not be used unless a particular " place " (i.e. element or atomic number) is mentioned. However, since the use of " isotope " as if it were synonomous with " nuclide " in such phrases as " artificial radio-active isotopes " is very well established and does not appear to cause any confusion, we have followed common usage in this respect, in these phrases.

5.06. The exponential decay of radioactivity

The early experimenters with radioactive materials observed that the emission from most materials decreased with time and it was soon realised that when a single isotope was isolated, the rate of decay was characteristic of the particular isotope being studied.

Consider a particular radioactive isotope and suppose there are N_t atoms present at some time t. Then during a small interval of time Δt, a certain number ΔN_t of these atoms will disintegrate so that there will be $N_t - \Delta N_t$ atoms present at time $t + \Delta t$. The quotient $\Delta N_t/\Delta t$ is the average value of the disintegration rate during the time interval from t to $t + \Delta t$. Provided the sample of the isotope considered contains a large number of atoms, however, as Δt is decreased, the quotient $\Delta N_t/\Delta t$ approaches a limiting value which is not appreciably altered by further reduction in Δt. This limiting value is called the disintegration rate or *activity* of the source at time t.

If the activity of a source is plotted against time, then it is found that the activity decreases exponentially with the time, i.e. the activity A_t at time t is related to the activity A_0 at time $t = 0$ by the equation $A_t = A_0 e^{-\lambda t}$ where λ is a constant known as the transformation or decay constant. The characteristic feature of an exponential decay curve is that in equal intervals of time, the activity decreases by a constant fraction. This is illustrated in fig. 5.11 where the time required to reduce the initial activity from 100 to 50 per cent is 3·83 days. It will be observed that in a further 3·83 days, the activity falls from 50 to 25 per cent., in another 3·83 days from 25 to 12·5 per cent. and so on. The time required for the activity to decrease to one-half its initial value is called the *half-life* of the particular isotope considered. (The half-life is usually denoted by the Greek letter τ.)

It can be shown mathematically that the exponential decay of radioactivity is to be expected if the probability that any particular atom will decay in unit time is the same for all atoms of the same isotope, and is independent of the age of the particular atom. Let this probability be λ. Then for each atom the probability of decay in time Δt is $\lambda \Delta t$. For a sample

127

containing a large number of atoms N_t, the total number decaying in time Δt will be $N_t . \lambda . \Delta t$. But the number decaying is $-\Delta N_t$, the decrease in N_t

$$\therefore \qquad -\Delta N_t = \lambda . N_t . \Delta t$$

$$\therefore \qquad \frac{\Delta N_t}{\Delta t} = -\lambda . N_t$$

As $\Delta t \to 0$, $(\Delta N_t / \Delta t) \to (dN_t/dt)$, the disintegration rate at time t. Therefore the disintegration rate at any instant is proportional to the number of atoms present.

Also $$\frac{1}{N_t} \frac{\Delta N_t}{\Delta t} = -\lambda$$

Integrating* $$\therefore \quad \Big[\log_e N_t \Big]_{N_0}^{N_t} = \Big[-\lambda t \Big]_0^t$$

or $$N_t = N_0 e^{-\lambda t} \qquad \ldots \ldots \quad (1)$$

where N_0 denotes the number of atoms present initially when $t = 0$.

*Those who are not familiar with the calculus may derive the relation $N_t = N_0 e^{-\lambda t}$ as follows: The equation $-\Delta N_t = \lambda N_t . \Delta t$ implies that in equal intervals of time a constant fraction of the atoms present decay. If t denotes a number of time intervals, as t increases by equal amounts, the number of atoms present decreases each time in the same ratio. Suppose for example that after one day a fraction f of the atoms (originally N_0 in number) have disintegrated

Then $N_1 = N_0 - fN_0 = (1 - f)N_0$

After two days, $N_2 = N_1 - fN_1 = (1 - f)N_1 = (1 - f)^2 N_0$

After three days, $N_3 = N_2 - fN_2 = (1 - f)N_2 = (1 - f)^3 N_0$ and so on. In general after t intervals of time

$$N_t = (1 - f)^t N_0$$

Taking logarithms to any base

$$\log N_t - \log N_0 = t \log (1 - f)$$

If logarithms to base e (natural logarithms) are used

$$\log_e (N_t/N_0) = t \log_e (1 - f)$$

Writing $\log_e (1 - f) = -\lambda$,

$\therefore \qquad \log_e (N_t/N_0) = -\lambda t$

or $\qquad N_t = N_0 e^{-\lambda t}$

In the above development both λ and t are pure numbers. If t is used to denote time, λ must be given the dimensions of the reciprocal of time.

Thus the number of atoms present decreases exponentially with time and since the disintegration rate is proportional to the number of atoms present, the disintegration rate or activity also decreases exponentially with time, i.e. $A_t = A_0 e^{-\lambda t}$.

It should be noted that in the above derivation we have assumed that the sample considered contains a large number of atoms. This is usually the case, but because radioactive disintegration is in fact a discontinuous process, if this condition

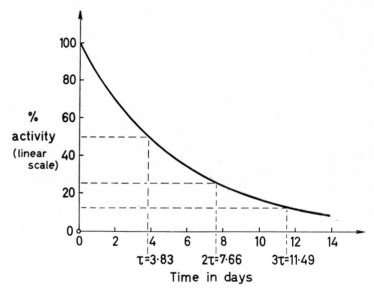

FIG. 5.11. The decay of radon (an exponential decay curve). The half-life of radon is 3·83 days.

is not satisfied, N_t cannot be treated as a continuous function of the time and problems arise in determining the limiting value of $\Delta N_t/\Delta t$. In this chapter and elsewhere except when the contrary is explicitly stated, we shall always assume a large number of atoms is taking part in any of the processes discussed.

Instead of plotting the activity of a radioactive isotope against time (as in fig. 5.11) it is more usual to plot the logarithmic of the activity against time. This is more convenient because a plot of log activity against time gives a straight line (see fig. 5.12) since $\log_e A_t - \log_e A_0 = -\lambda t$ or $2 \cdot 3$ $(\log_{10} A_t - \log_{10} A_0) = -\lambda t$ since $\log_e A = 2 \cdot 3 \log_{10} A$. To avoid the

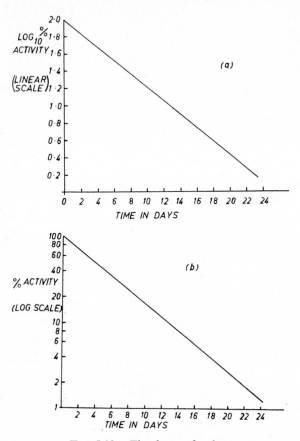

FIG. 5.12. The decay of radon.

(a) $\log_{10}$ per cent. activity on a linear scale is plotted against time on a linear scale.

(b) Per cent. activity on a logarithmic scale is plotted against time on a linear scale.

In each case a straight line is obtained.

labour of looking up tables of logarithms, special graph paper is available in which the separation of the lines denoting integers is proportional to the difference in the logarithms of the numbers concerned, not to the difference between the numbers themselves. Plotting activity on such a logarithmic scale against time on a linear scale is equivalent to plotting both log activity and time on linear scales and also yields a straight line (fig. 5.12 (b)). If the half-life of an isotope is known, then its decay can be readily represented on such graph paper by simply drawing a straight line through points representing 100 per cent. and 50 per cent. of the initial activity which are separated on the time axis by the half-life.

The relation between the decay constant λ and the half-life τ is obtained by substituting $N_t = \frac{1}{2} N_0$ in the equation $\log_e (N_t/N_0) = -\lambda t$. Then

$$\log_e \tfrac{1}{2} = -\lambda\tau$$

or
$$\log_e 2 = \lambda\tau$$

$\therefore$
$$\tau = \log_e 2/\lambda = 0\cdot693/\lambda$$

Equation (1) is sometimes written in terms of τ as

$$N_t = N_0 e^{-0\cdot693t/\tau} \qquad \ldots \ldots \quad (2)$$

5.07. The curie

The activity of a radioactive source is usually measured in units known as curies. A source is said to have an activity of 1 curie if $3\cdot70 \times 10^{10}$ disintegrations take place per second. The number $3\cdot7 \times 10^{10}$ was chosen because this is approximately the number of disintegrations occurring per second per gram of radium. (Experimental determinations of the disintegration rate carried out in 1937 by Guenther[2] and in 1947 by Kohmar et al.[3] give values of $3\cdot67 \times 10^{10}$ and $3\cdot61 \times 10^{10}$ respectively.) The curie was originally introduced as a measure of radon but the original definition has now been superseded by the one given above which can be applied to any radioactive material and which is independent of any revision in the estimate of the number of disintegrations occurring per second per gram of radium. The abbreviation for curie which has been commonly employed for many years to denote the unit is c. However, in their most recent publications[21] the International Commission on Radiological Units have adopted the abbreviation Ci, which is therefore used below. At the present time, either abbreviation may be encountered in the literature.

For *radium* sources, the activity in curies is numerically equal to the mass of the element in grams.

Illustrative Problem

A radioactive material has a half-life of 3 days. If the initial activity was 10 mCi., what will be the activity (1) 6 days, (2) 7 days later?

Six days is exactly twice the half-life of the source. After three days, the activity will be $\frac{1}{2} \times 10$ mCi = 5 mCi., after 6 days it will be $\frac{1}{2} \times \frac{1}{2} \times 10$ mC$_1$ = 2·5 mCi. Alternatively using equation (2),

$$N_t = N_0 e^{-0.693t/\tau}$$

or

$$\log_e \frac{N_t}{N_0} = -0.693 \ t/\tau$$

∴

$$2.3 \log_{10} \frac{N_t}{N_0} = -0.693 \ t/\tau$$

When $t = 6$ days and $\tau = 3$ days

$$t/\tau = 2$$

$$\log_{10} \frac{N_t}{N_0} = -0.693 \times \frac{2}{2·3} = -0.602.$$

From log tables (using $-0.602 = -1 + 0.398$)

$$\frac{N_t}{N_0} = 0.25$$

∴

$$N_t = 10 \times 0.25 = 2·5 \text{ mCi.}$$

When $t = 7$ days

$$t/\tau = 7/3$$

$$\log_{10} \frac{N_t}{N_0} = -0.693 \times \frac{7}{3} \times \frac{1}{2·3} = -0.70$$

From log tables (using $-0.7 = -1 + 0.30$)

$$\frac{N_t}{N_0} = 0.2$$

∴

$$N_t = 2·0 \text{ mCi.}$$

5.08. Radioactive equilibrium

The half-life of radium is so long (1620 years) that a very small fraction decays each day and for most purposes, the total amount of radium present may be regarded as constant. If radium is placed in a sealed vessel, the amount of radon in the vessel (initially zero) gradually increases. If radon were stable, the amount of radon would increase until all the radium

132

was converted into radon. But radon is itself disintegrating. Moreover, radon disintegrates more rapidly than radium. Fairly soon, therefore, the number of radon atoms disintegrating per second equals the number formed per second When this occurs the amount of radon present remains effectively constant. (See fig. 5.13.) In this condition the radon is said to be in equilibrium with the radium. In general any daughter element with half-life less than that of its parent, will come to equilibrium with the parent substance and the number of atoms of the daughter material will then decrease

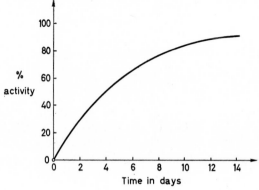

FIG. 5.13. Growth of radon.

with the same half-life as that of the parent. When there are a number of disintegration products, all of which have shorter half-lives than the parent material, the series as a whole reaches a state of equilibrium in which the amount of each substance decreases with the half-life of the parent. The relative amount of each substance is proportional to its own half-life, substances which decay rapidly being present in relatively small quantities and those which decay more slowly in greater amounts. In the radium series, this means that when radium is kept in a sealed container, radium B and radium C which emit penetrating γ-radiation, are also present and the amount of these substances decreases with the same half-life as radium. Thus radium can be used as a source of γ-radiation although the parent radium itself emits mainly α-radiation. Similarly, radon in a sealed container may be used as a γ-ray source,

133

since again radium B and radium C are produced. These products quickly come to equilibrium with the radon and the amount of each substance then decreases with a half-life of 3·83 days, the half-life of radon. Thus both radium and radon sources emit γ-radiation of the same quality (that emitted by radium B and radium C), but radium sources have such a long half-life that for practical purposes the activity can be regarded as constant, whereas radon sources rapidly decrease in strength.

TABLE 5.03

THE RELATIVE ENERGIES OF THE LINES IN THE RA (B + C) SPECTRUM

	Energy of γ-ray (MeV.)	Relative number of disintegrations (per 100 α-ray disintegrations of radium)	Energy of line as per cent. of total energy
Radium B	0·241	11·5	1·55
	0·294	25·8	4·26
	0·350	45·0	8·82
Radium C	0·607	65·8	22·4
	0·766	6·5	2·79
	0·933	6·7	3·50
	1·120	20·6	12·9
	1·238	6·3	4·37
	1·379	6·4	4·93
	1·761	25·8	25·4
	2·198	7·4	9·13

(Because radium D has a much longer half-life than radon, radium D does not come to equilibrium with the radon but the γ-activity of radium D is weak in comparison with that of radium B and radium C.)

The energies of the main γ-rays emitted by radium B and radium C are given in Table 5.03. For some purposes (e.g. for estimating the shielding required around radium sources), the spectrum can be regarded as approximately equivalent to two lines of energy, 0·55 and 1·65 MeV.

5.09. Exposure to short-lived isotopes; average life

When a patient is treated with radium it is usual to record the treatment in terms of the product, source-strength × time.

134

This is normally expressed in mg.-hours. When the exposure is to radon, the patient is exposed to the same quality of radiation, but the source is decreasing in strength throughout the exposure. With any short-lived isotope, the source strength and therefore the exposure rate decreases as the treatment proceeds.

Suppose a source of short half-life has an activity A_0 initially and is left permanently in the tissues (this is the most usual method of using isotopes of short half-life). The complete destruction of 1 mCi. of activity gives rise to $3 \cdot 7 \times 10^7$
$$\int_0^\infty e^{-\lambda t} dt$$ disintegrations, where λ is the decay constant

but
$$\int_0^\infty e^{-\lambda t} dt = 1/\lambda$$

∴ The complete destruction of 1 mCi. of activity produces a total of $3 \cdot 7 \times 10^7/\lambda$ disintegrations and the destruction of A_0 mCi. produces $A_0 \cdot 3 \cdot 7 \times 10^7/\lambda$ disintegrations.

A source of *constant* activity A_0 would disintegrate at the constant rate of $3 \cdot 7 \times 10^7 A_0$ dis./sec. and in a time t would give rise to the same total number of disintegrations as the short-lived source if

$$t = \frac{1}{\lambda} = \frac{\tau}{0 \cdot 693}$$

Thus a treatment with the short-lived isotope is equivalent to a treatment of $A_0 (\tau/0 \cdot 693)$ mCi-hours from a similar source of constant activity A_0.

For example, for radon $\lambda = 0 \cdot 181$ per day and $(1/\lambda) = (\tau/0 \cdot 693) = 5 \cdot 52$ days or $132 \cdot 4$ hours. A permanent implant of a radon source of initial activity A_0, therefore gives the same γ-irradiation of the patient as would an exposure of $132 \cdot 4$ hours duration using A_0 mg. of radium.

$\tau/0 \cdot 693$ is called the *average* life of the short-lived isotope since the same value is obtained for the sum of the lifetimes of all the atoms in a source if it is assumed every atom exists for a time $\tau/0 \cdot 693$ as is obtained by summing the actual lifetimes of all the atoms. If a treatment with a short-lived isotope is discontinued when some activity (A_F say)

135

still remains, the radiation delivered can be estimated from the activity $(A_0 — A_F)$ which is completely destroyed.

Methods of estimating the dose delivered in therapy treatments using radioactive sources are discussed in Chapter XII.

5.10. Natural radioactive sources used in medicine

In most medical treatments with radioactive sources, it is the γ-radiation which is used to produce the desired effect. In the treatment of certain dermatological cases, however, α- or β-radiation may be employed, since γ-rays may damage underlying healthy tissues. γ-rays are used clinically in two rather different ways. In teletherapy large sources are used to provide a γ-ray beam which is used in a similar way to an X-ray beam. By this method, it is possible to obtain high energy radiation with relatively simple equipment. In surface, cavitary and interstitial γ-ray therapy, it is the small size and accessibility of the sources which are the important features, since these enable the sources to be placed close to or within the tissues to be treated, so that these tissues can be readily given a dose which is large compared to that received by more distant normal tissue.

For use as a γ-ray source, radium in the form of one of its salts, most frequently the sulphate, is enclosed in a thin metal sheath and one or more of the cells so formed are then included in an outer metal covering in the form of a tube or needle. (See fig. 5.14.) The metal most commonly employed is an iridium-platinum alloy (90 per cent. Pt, 10 per cent. Ir) which is almost invariably referred to as " platinum ". Occasionally steel, monel metal or gold alloys are used. Needles are used mainly for implantation into tissue which it is desired to irradiate and are therefore made as thin as is compatible with mechanical strength. The wall thickness which gives sufficient rigidity depends upon the length of the needle.[4] Needles up to 4 cm. in length usually have a wall thickness of 0·5 mm. iridium-platinum and an overall diameter of about 2 mm. It has been found that 0·5 mm. of iridium-platinum is sufficient to absorb all but a few per cent. of the β-radiation from a radium source, so the effect of such needles is due almost entirely to γ-radiation.[5] Needles rarely contain more than

1 mg. of radium per cm. length. Radium tubes are used on moulds applied to the skin surface or accessible cavities and are usually of greater diameter and may be of greater wall thickness than needles. The linear density of the radium is normally greater in tubes than in needles. The radium in both tubes and needles should be uniformly distributed. The distribution can be checked by placing the sources on wrapped photographic film. After development, the blackening of the film produced by the radiation indicates the distribution of the radioactive material.

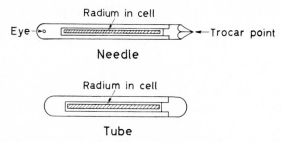

FIG. 5.14.   Radium containers.

The radium sources used in teletherapy units are usually made up from sets of radium tubes of considerably greater diameter (typically about 0·5 cm.) and radium content (200 or 250 mg.) than those used for moulds. Twenty or more such tubes are then mounted in a movable treatment head made of steel encased lead or tungsten alloy. Tungsten alloy is approximately one and a half times as dense as lead and therefore makes a more compact shield. The head screens the source except in the direction of the treatment beam. In some units, the source is normally stored in a safe remote from the treatment head and is only introduced into the head at the commencement of the treatment. The source is blown through a pipe into the treatment head by compressed air, and is sucked or blown back into the safe at the end of the treatment. This has the advantage that the amount of shielding which is included in the head can be reduced making the head lighter and easier to manipulate. In the past, radium was the only material available for γ-teletherapy sources. The usefulness of the equipment was restricted by the fact

137

that only limited amounts of radium could be used. The size of the sources was limited by (1) the high cost of radium, (2) the fact that in a large source a high percentage of the radiation is absorbed in the source itself. The development of nuclear reactors has now made available artificial γ-emitting radioactive materials and modern γ-ray teletherapy units use artificial radioactive sources. These units are described in section 5.15.

Radium was formerly also used as a source of β-radiation. In radium β-plaques, the salt is spread in a layer 1 or 2 mm. thick in a shallow, vacuum tight container. The front surface is usually a metal foil, thin enough to transmit most of the β-particles. Although at the surface, the clinical effects of a plaque are due primarily to β-rays, the simultaneous emission of penetrating γ-rays from radium-B and radium-C is a disadvantage. To avoid this, β-applicators were sometimes prepared containing radium-D isolated from the earlier members of the series. However, although radium β-plaques may still be encountered, most centres now prefer to use plaques containing artificial radioactive isotopes (see below).

For medical use, radon is obtained by pumping off the gas from a solution of a radium salt.[6] After purification the gas is passed into a fine capillary tubing of either glass or gold. In the former case the glass is sealed off into 3 or 4 mm. lengths by a micro-flame and then enclosed in a gold or platinum casing with a wall thickness of about 0·3 to 0·5 mm. If the gas is passed directly into gold tubing, the tubing is both cut and sealed by snipping with pliers.

Thorium X (see table 5.02), an α-emitter of short-half-life was formerly used in dermatology (an aqueous solution was painted on the skin surface) but this is now obsolete.

5.11. Nuclear stability

Most of the *artificial* radioactive isotopes which are used in medicine are produced in nuclear reactors or " piles ". In order to understand the operation of a nuclear reactor, it is necessary to consider the relative magnitude of the attractive forces which exist between nucleons in different nuclei. The magnitude of these forces in a particular nucleus is indicated by the value of the binding energy per nucleon for that nucleus. The total binding energy of a nucleus is measured by the work which would have to be done to separate the nucleons, against the attractive forces holding the nucleus together. The binding energy may be calculated for any particular nuclide by comparing the mass of the nucleus with the sum of the masses of its components.

For example, for helium, the measured mass of the helium nucleus $= 4{\cdot}0015$ m.u.

The measured mass of the proton $(m_p) = 1{\cdot}00728$ m.u.

The measured mass of the neutron $(m_n) = 1{\cdot}00866$ m.u.

The sum of the masses of the constituents of the helium nucleus

$$(2m_p + 2m_n) = 4{\cdot}0319 \text{ m.u.}$$

$\therefore$ Mass of components $-$ mass of

$$\text{nucleus} = 4{\cdot}0319 - 4{\cdot}0015 \text{ m.u.}$$
$$= 0{\cdot}0304 \text{ m.u.}$$

Since the energy (in ergs) associated with a mass m (in gm.) $= mc^2$ where c is the velocity of light, the total binding energy

$$= 0{\cdot}0304 \times 1{\cdot}66 \times 10^{-24}$$
$$\times 9 \times 10^{20} \text{ ergs.}$$
$$= 4{\cdot}54 \times 10^{-5} \text{ ergs}$$
$$= 28{\cdot}3 \text{ MeV.}$$

$\therefore$ The binding energy per nucleon $= 28{\cdot}3/4 = 7{\cdot}07$ MeV.

Now, if the binding energy *per nucleon* of the stable nuclides is plotted against atomic mass, the curve shown in fig. 5.15 is obtained. It will be observed that the binding energy per nucleon is greatest for elements of intermediate mass and is approximately constant for these elements, but it decreases slightly for the heaviest elements and very sharply for the lightest elements. Thus the elements of intermediate mass are the most tightly held together and the most stable. It follows that, if it were possible to rearrange the nucleons in two nuclei of intermediate mass and combine them into a single nucleus of greater mass, work would have to be done against the greater cohesive forces in the smaller nuclei. Conversely if a heavy nucleus is split into two or more parts, the excess energy of the nucleons in the more loosely bound heavy nucleus is released. This method of generating energy, by nuclear fission, is the

139

process employed in nuclear reactors. It is considered in more detail in the next section. It should be noted that energy can only be obtained by fission for the heavy nuclei. In the case of nuclei of low atomic mass, the nucleons in the lighter nuclei are less tightly bound and have more energy than the nucleons in the nuclei of intermediate mass and consequently in order to release energy the light nuclei must be caused to combine.

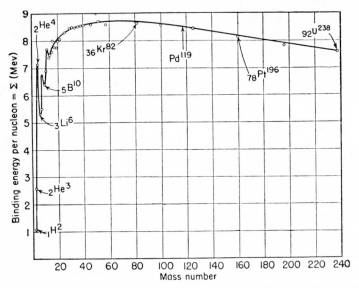

Fig. 5.15. The variation of binding energy per nucleon with mass number.

By permission from *Nuclear Radiation Physics* by R. E. Lapp and H. L. Andrews. (Prentice-Hall, Inc., New York.)

The general form of the curve of fig. 5.15 can be explained as follows : Suppose the nucleons are uniformly distributed through a small sphere and are in rapid movement, so that they make many collisions per second and thus have approximately the same energy. (This is comparable with the state within a drop of liquid.) Then the total binding energy of the nucleus will depend mainly upon the cohesive forces between the nucleons and the total number of nucleons and thus will be proportional to the atomic mass A. Corrections must be made, however, for (1) the " surface tension " forces between nucleons at the surface of the " drop ", which will be less tightly bound

140

than those in the interior (this effect will be most important in small, i.e. light, nuclei), and (2) for the electrostatic repulsive force between protons (which will be most important where there are large numbers of protons, i.e. in heavy nuclei). Thus the total binding energy per nucleus may be written as $a_1A - \left(a_2A^{2/3} + a_3\dfrac{Z^2}{A^{1/3}}\right)$. The first term represents the contribution due to the cohesive forces. Therefore it is proportional to A. The second term represents the correction for the surface tension effect. It is proportional to the surface area, i.e. to $A^{2/3}$. (For a nucleus of uniform density A must be proportional to the cube of the radius (r). Hence r is proportional to $A^{1/3}$ and the area ($4\pi r^2$) to $A^{2/3}$.) The third term represents the correction for the electrical repulsion between the protons. This is proportional to the square of the charge and inversely proportional to the radius of the nucleus. Hence it is inversely proportional to $A^{1/3}$. a_1, a_2, a_3 are constants which can be determined empirically.
Thus the binding energy per nucleon

$$= a_1 - \frac{1}{A}(a_2A^{2/3} + a_3Z^2A^{-1/3}).$$

Thus, as already stated, the numerical value of the binding energy per nucleon is low for the very light nuclei because a high proportion of the nucleons are at the surface and the surface effect introduces a large correction ; it rises for nuclei of intermediate mass when the surface effect is less important, and then begins to fall again as the term representing the mutual repulsion of protons increases.

The above explains only the general features of the binding energy curve. To account for some further facts concerning the stability of nuclei, namely (1) that stable nuclei tend to have equal numbers of protons and neutrons, and (2) that nuclei with even numbers of both protons and neutrons are more plentiful and therefore presumably more stable than those with odd numbers of either type of nucleon, two further terms are added to the expression for the binding energy. The first additional term is a function of the excess of either neutrons or protons over the number of neutron-proton pairs, i.e. it is a function of $A/2 - Z$. The second correction term, usually denoted by δ, is zero if the number of either neutrons or protons alone is odd but is negative if both numbers are even, positive if both numbers are odd (so that the binding energy is greatest for the most stable nuclei). Thus the expression for the total binding energy becomes :

$$a_1 A - \left\{ a_2 A^{2/3} + a_3 Z^2 A^{-1/3} + a_4 \left(\frac{A}{2} - Z \right)^2 A^{-1} + \delta \right\}$$

or for the binding energy per nucleon

$$a_1 - \frac{1}{A} \left\{ a_2 A^{2/3} + a_3 Z^2 A^{-1/3} + a_4 \left(\frac{A}{2} - Z \right)^2 A^{-1} + \delta \right\}.$$

5.12. The fission of uranium

In section 5.05 it was pointed out that when naturally occurring nuclides are irradiated with atomic particles, those nuclei which capture an incident particle must dissipate the energy contributed by the incident particle (this includes both binding energy and kinetic energy) if they are to persist. In most elements, the excess energy is dissipated by the emission of γ-radiation or atomic particles, but in the heaviest nuclei, the excess energy may make the compound nucleus so unstable that it splits into two (or occasionally more) fragments, i.e. nuclear fission occurs. If fission does take place, free neutrons are produced as well as the heavy fragments, since the neutron-proton ratio is greater in the heavy elements than in elements of medium atomic weight. Because two or three neutrons are released during each fission, once fission is initiated a chain reaction can take place. This may be self-sustaining or may increase rapidly so that energy is released with explosive violence. The progress of the chain reaction depends upon the fraction of the neutrons generated by each fission which themselves cause fission in other nuclei. This in turn depends upon the nature of the fissile material and its distribution among non-fissile material. If an explosive reaction is required, then as many neutrons as possible must strike fissile material so that once fission starts, the number of fissions increases rapidly. If the reaction is merely required to be self-sustaining, as in nuclear reactors, then only one of the neutrons released in the fission process is required to produce fission in another nucleus and the other neutrons are available for other purposes, e.g. for the production of artificial radioactive isotopes.

There are several types of nuclear reactor. Most radioactive isotopes are produced in " thermal " reactors, containing natural uranium. In these reactors, the uranium is mixed with a moderator to slow down the neutrons to " thermal " energies, i.e. about 0·1 eV. The reason for this is as follows : Uranium consists of three isotopes of mass 238 m.u. (the most abundant), mass 235 m.u. (there is approximately 1 part of U^{235} to 140 parts of U^{238}), and mass 234 m.u. (the least abundant). When U^{235} captures a neutron, U^{236} is formed. This is a nucleus with an even number of both protons and neutrons and the binding energy to be dissipated is 6·8 MeV. 6·8 MeV. makes the U^{236} nucleus so unstable that fission takes place. When U^{238} captures a neutron, U^{239} is formed. This has an odd number of neutrons and the binding energy to be dissipated is therefore less, namely 5·3 MeV. 5·3 MeV. is not sufficient to cause fission in U^{239}. In order to produce fission of this isotope, the neutron must be able to give up kinetic energy to the nucleus. Thus whereas fission can be produced by exposing U^{235} to bombardment by slow neutrons, fission can only be produced in U^{238} by bombardment with fast neutrons with energy about 1 MeV. Insufficient of the neutrons released during the fission of U^{238} have sufficient energy to cause further fissions in U^{238} nuclei. Therefore when natural uranium is used in a reactor, the reaction is sustained by fissions in the U^{235} nuclei. The probability of neutron capture followed by fission in U^{235} is greatest for low energy neutrons. The purpose of the moderator is to slow down the neutrons by elastic collisions, so that the probability of capture by U^{238} (without fission) is reduced and the probability of capture by U^{235} (with fission) is increased. The moderator is commonly either graphite (in which case the reactor consists of a " pile " of graphite blocks interspersed with rods of uranium) or heavy water. The number of neutrons and thus the rate of production of energy in the reactor is controlled by inserting or withdrawing rods carrying a material such as cadmium which absorbs neutrons very readily without fission.

Two isotopes which do not occur naturally but can be prepared artificially, U^{233} and Pu^{239}, resemble U^{235} in undergoing fission very readily. They are therefore potential sources of nuclear energy. Pu^{239} is obtained as a " by-product " in any reactor using natural uranium, since it is formed when neutrons are captured by U^{238} without fission. The reactions are

$$U^{238} + n \to U^{239}$$
$$U^{239} \to Np^{239} + e_{-1}$$
$$Np^{239} \to Pu^{239} + e_{-1}$$

Reactors designed so that as much of the U^{238} is converted into Pu^{239} as is possible without stopping the chain reaction, are usually referred to as " breeder " piles, since the amount of fissile material (Pu^{239}) which can be produced exceeds the amount of fissile material (U^{235}) which is used up in maintaining the reaction.

5.13. The production of artificial radioactive isotopes

There are two principal methods of producing artificial radioactive isotopes; the target nuclei are either bombarded with high energy atomic particles in a cyclotron, or the target nuclei are irradiated in a nuclear reactor. The great majority of the isotopes which are used clinically are produced in (thermal) nuclear reactors. Since most of the neutrons in such reactors have been slowed down, these isotopes are produced mainly by (n, γ) reactions, e.g. $Co^{59} + n \to Co^{60} + \gamma$, $Au^{197} + n \to Au^{198} + \gamma$, etc. (see Table 5.04). A few isotopes can be produced by (n, p) or (n, α) reactions, e.g. $S^{32} + n \to P^{32} + p$, but such reactions usually require more energetic neutrons than are available in thermal reactors. Whether produced by (n, γ) or (n, p) reactions, however, the product nuclides have an excess of neutrons. Fission fragments which can be extracted from the uranium when it is removed from the pile, are usually radioactive and are also nuclides with an excess of neutrons. Reactor produced isotopes are therefore normally $\beta-$ emitters. Isotopes which are $\beta+$ (positron) emitters usually have to be produced in a cyclotron, where the target nuclei may be bombarded by protons, deuterons or α-particles, e.g. $_{12}Mg^{24} + _1H^2 \to _{11}Na^{22} + _2He^4$.

The production of artificial radioactive materials resembles the production of a radioactive daughter from a long-lived parent in that the radioactive material is formed at a constant rate but decays at a rate proportional to the number of radioactive atoms present. The activity therefore increases initially but cannot be increased indefinitely by prolonging the irradiation time since a limiting or saturation activity is reached when the rate of decay is equal to the rate of formation. For isotopes of long half-life it is usual to irradiate for about two half-lives of the element concerned when 75 per cent. of the possible activity is reached.

The rate of production of radioactive atoms during irradiation of N_p parent or target atoms in a region where the flux of irradiating particles is F particles/cm.^{2}/sec. can be represented by the product $N_p F \sigma$ per sec. where σ is a constant called the atomic cross-section for the particular reaction which produces the radioactive material. σ is a measure of the probability that the particular reaction will occur when the parent atoms are irradiated with specified particles of a particular energy. Each atom can be regarded as presenting an area σ to the incident particles such that a particle incident upon that area is absorbed and produces the specified reaction. The cross-section for a nuclear reaction is frequently measured in units called barns. 1 barn $= 10^{-24}$ cm.^{2}/atom. (The term cross-section is also used in connection with the absorption of X and γ-radiation. See section 6.01.)

The saturation activity (when the number of atoms disintegrating per second is equal to the number formed per second) is therefore $N_p F \sigma / (3.7 \times 10^{10})$ curie.

Assuming that a negligible fraction of the target atoms are transformed during the irradiation, the activity produced after a time t when the radioactive product has a disintegration constant λ is $N_p F \sigma (1 - e^{-\lambda t})/(3.7 \times 10^{10})$ curie.

If the target material has atomic weight A, the specific activity, i.e. the activity per unit mass, is given by

$$6.02 \, F \, \sigma \, (1 - e^{-\lambda t}) \, 10^{23}/(3.7. \, A. \, 10^{10}) \text{ Ci./g.}$$

(since there are $6.02 \times 10^{23}/A$ atoms per g.).

145

Illustrative Problem

The cross-section for the production of Ta^{182} by the bombardment of Ta^{181} with slow neutrons is 20 barns. Calculate the specific activity producted by irradiation to saturation in a flux of 10^{11} neutrons/cm.^{2}/sec.

$$\text{Saturation specific activity} = \frac{6\cdot02.\ F.\ \sigma 10^{23}}{3\cdot7.\ A.\ 10^{10}}\ \text{Ci./g.}$$

Writing $F = 10^{11}$ neutrons/cm.^{2}/sec., $\sigma = 20 \times 10^{-24}$ cm.^{2}/atom, $A = 181$.

$$\text{Saturation specific activity} = \frac{6\cdot02.\ 10^{11}.\ 20.\ 10^{-24}.\ 10^{23}.}{3\cdot7.\ 181.\ 10^{10}}\ \text{Ci./g.}$$

$$= 180\ \text{mCi./g.}$$

It is to be noted that in all (n, γ) reactions the product has the same atomic number, and is therefore chemically identical with the parent material. Hence it is impossible to separate the radioactive material from the parent material chemically, and the specific activity, the radioactivity per gram, of the product is usually rather low. For clinical investigations in which it is desired to keep the total quantity of the element which is administered to a minimum, this is a disadvantage. Occasionally a radioactive isotope may be prepared by an (n, γ) reaction which is followed by fairly rapid decay. Thus I^{131} is prepared from tellurium

$$Te^{130} + n \rightarrow Te^{131} + \gamma$$

Te^{131} is a β-emitter and decays to give I^{131}

$$Te^{131} \rightarrow I^{131} + e_{-1}$$

The final product (I^{131} in this case) can then be extracted chemically and a higher specific activity can thus be obtained. In other cases, it is possible to incorporate the parent isotope in a chemical compound of such type that when the (n, γ) reaction occurs, the recoil momentum given to the nuclei emitting γ-rays is sufficient to break the chemical bonds. The product of the reaction is thus obtained in a different chemical state from the parent material and can be separated chemically. (This is known as a Szilard-Chalmers reaction.)

There is of course, no difficulty in obtaining a high specific activity for those isotopes which are produced in reactions in which the product nucleus differs from the target material in atomic number.

146

The artificial radioactive isotopes which are commonly used in medicine are listed in Table 5.04. This table shows the method by which the isotope is produced, its half-life, the mode of decay (by negative electron and neutrino emission $\beta-$, by positron and antineutrino emission $\beta+$ or by electron capture E.C.), and the principal radiations emitted.[7,8]. It is frequently possible for a radioactive isotope to lose energy by more than one process and therefore the percentage of the total number of disintegrations in which a particular radiation is emitted is indicated in Table 5.04 for the more probable processes. (Where no percentage is given, the radiation is produced in less than 20 per cent. of the disintegrations.) Although the emission of an electron may be sufficient to produce a stable nucleus (e.g. the emission of negative electrons (and neutrinos) from P^{32} produces the stable nucleus S^{32}), it is more usual for the nucleus still to retain excess energy (i.e. to be in an excited state), and this energy is commonly emitted as γ-radiation. Thus Co^{60}, for example, emits negative electrons with an energy of 310 keV. (0·31 MeV.) producing Ni^{60}, but a further 2·5 MeV. is emitted as two γ-ray photons of energy 1·17 MeV. and 1·33 MeV., before a stable state is reached. In some cases, particularly in heavy nuclei, " internal conversion " may replace γ-emission. In this process the excess energy of the nucleus is transferred to one of the orbital electrons (commonly a K shell electron), so that electrons with energy equal to the excess minus the shell binding energy are emitted. Characteristic X-rays are then also produced, as outer electrons move in to fill the vacancy left by the conversion electron. (Internal conversion is denoted by I.C. in Table 5.04.) Thus following the disintegration of Au,[198] for example, a γ-ray photon of energy 412 keV. (0·412 MeV.) is usually emitted, but in 4·5 per cent. of the disintegrations internal conversion takes place instead. Normally the γ-ray photons or conversion electrons are emitted within a fraction of a microsecond of the original disintegration. If the product nucleus remains in an excited state for a measurable period of time, it is usually referred to as a metastable isomer of the final stable nucleus. For example, Cs^{137} decays to a metastable isomer of Ba^{137} which has a half-life of 2·6 minutes. Isomeric

TABLE 5.04

RADIOACTIVE ISOTOPES USED IN MEDICINE

Element	Isotope	Production Process	Physical half-life	Made of decay	Electron energies (Max. in MeV)	γ-ray energies (MeV)
Arsenic	As^{72}	Ga^{69} (α, n)	26 h.	E.C. (22%) $\beta +$ (78%)	2·50 (56%) 1·84, 3·34,	0·51 from $\beta +$ 0·835 (78%) 0·63
	As^{74}	Ga^{71} (α, n) Ge^{74} $(d, 2n)$	18 d.	$\beta -$ (33%) $\beta +$ (30%) E.C. (37%)	0·72, 1·36 0·91 (26%) 1·51	0·51 from $\beta +$ 0·596 (62%) 0·635
	As^{76}	As^{75} (n, γ)	26·5 h.	$\beta -$	2·97 (56%) 2·41 (31%) 0·35, 1·20, 1·75,	0·56 (45%) 0·66, 1·21, 1·44 1·79, 2·08
Bromine	Br^{82}	Br^{81} (n, γ)	36 h.	$\beta -$	0·44 (100%)	0·55 (75%), 0·62 (42%) 0·70 (28%), 0·78 (83%) 0·83 (25%), 1·04 (29%) 1·32 (28%), 1·48
Caesium	Cs^{134}	Cs^{133} (n, γ)	2·19 y.	$\beta -$	0·09 (20%) 0·65 (75%) 0·28, 0·89	0·57 (24%), 0·605 (98%) 0·80 (90%), 0·48 1·04, 1·17, 1·37
	Cs^{137} parent of Ba^{137}M	U $(n, \text{fission})$	30 y. 2·6 m.	$\beta -$	0·51 (92%) 1·17	0·662 (82%)

Element	Isotope	Reaction	Half-life	Decay		
Calcium	Ca^{45}	$Ca^{44}(n,\gamma)$	165 d.	β –	0·25 (100%)	1·31 (77%) 0·48, 0·83
	Ca^{47}	$Ca^{46}(n,\gamma)$	4·7 d.	β –	0·66 (83%) 1·94	
Carbon	C^{14}	$N^{14}(n,p)$	5760 y.	β –	0·155 (100%)	
Cerium	Ce^{144} parent of Pr^{144}	U (n, fission)	285 d.	β –	0·32 (76%) 0·19, 0·24	0·934 to 0·133
			17·5 m.	β –	2·98 (97·7%) 0·80, 2·29	0·69, 1·49 2·18
Chromium	Cr^{51}	$Cr^{50}(n,\gamma)$ $V^{51}(d,2n)$	27·8 d.	E.C. (100%)		0·323 [0·005 — V X-rays]
Cobalt	Co^{56}	$Fe^{56}(d,2n)$ $Fe^{56}(p,n)$	77 d.	β + (18%) E.C. (82%)	1·5	0·51 from β + 0·845 (100%) 1·24 (70%) 1·03, 1·36, 1·75, 2·02, 2·60, 2·99 3·24, 3·47
	Co^{57}	$Fe^{56}(d,n)$ $Ni^{60}(p,\alpha)$	270 d.	E.C. (100%)		0·122 (88%) 0·014 (6% + 83% I.C.) 0·136
	Co^{58}	$Ni^{58}(n,p)$	71 d.	E.C. (85%) β + (15%)	0·47	0·81 (100%) 1·62 0·51 from β +
	Co^{60}	$Co^{59}(n,\gamma)$	5·27 y.	β –	0·31 (100%) 1·48	1·17 (100%) 1·33 (100%)
Copper	Cu^{64}	$Cu^{63}(n,\gamma)$	12·8 h.	β – (38%) β + (19%) E.C. (43%)	0·57 (38%) 0·66	0·51 from β + 1·34

TABLE 5.04—*Continued*

Element	Isotope	Production process	Physical half-life	Mode of decay	Electron energies (Max. in MeV)	γ-ray energies (MeV)
Copper	Cu^{67}	$Ni^{64}(\alpha, p)$	61 h.	β —	0·40 (45%) 0·48 (35%) 0·58	0·090, 0·092 0·182
Gold	Au^{198}	$Au^{197}(n, \gamma)$	2·70 d.	β —	0·96 (99%) 0·29, 1·37	0·412 (96·5%) 0·68, 1·09
	Au^{199}	$Pt^{198}(n, \gamma) Pt^{199}$ $Pt^{199} \xrightarrow{\beta} Au^{199}$	3·15 d.	β —	0·30 (70%) 0·25 (24%) 0·46	0·159 (42%) 0·050, 0·209
Hydrogen (Tritium)	H^{3}	$Li^{6}(n, \alpha)$	12·26 y.	β —	0·018 (100%)	
Iodine	I^{125}	$Sb^{123}(\alpha, 2n)$	60 d.	E.C. (100%)		0·037 (7% + 93% I.C.) [0·027 Te-X-rays]
	I^{131}	$U(n, \text{fission}) Te^{131}$ $Te^{130}(n, \gamma) Te^{131}$ $Te^{131} \xrightarrow{\beta} I^{131}$	8·04 d.	β —	0·61 (87%) 0·25, 0·33, 0·81	0·36 (80%) 0·08, 0·28, 0·64, 0·72
	I^{132}	$U(n, \text{fission}) Te^{132}$ $Te^{132} \xrightarrow{\beta} I^{132}$	2·26 h.	β —	0·73, 0·90 1·16, 1·53 2·12	0·67 (100%) 0·78 (85%) 0·96 (21%) 0·53 (27%), 0·62 1·16, 1·40 1·96, 2·20

Iridium	Ir^{192}	Ir^{191} (n, γ)	74·4 d.	β − (96%) E.C. (4%)	0·67 (50%), 0·54 (40%), 0·24	0·316 (83%), 0·468 (53%), 0·296 (30%), 0·308 (29%), 0·588, 0·605, 0·613
Iron	Fe^{55}	Fe^{54} (n, γ)	2·7 y.	E.C. (100%)		[0·0059 MnX-rays]
	Fe^{59}	Fe^{58} (n, γ)	45 d.	β −	0·46 (53%), 0·27 (46%), 0·13, 1·56	1·10 (56%), 1·29 (44%), 0·14, 0·19, 0·34
Krypton	Kr^{85}	U (n, fission)	10·6 y.	β −	0·67 (99·6%), 0·15	0·51
Magnesium	Mg^{28} parent of	Cl^{37} (p, 6p, 4n)	21·4 h.	β −	0·42 (100%)	0·032 (96%), 1·35 (70%), 0·40 (30%) 0·95 (30%)
	Al^{28}		2·27 m.	β −	2·87 (100%)	1·78 (100%)
Mercury	Hg^{197}M	Hg^{196} (n, γ)	24 h.	I.T. (97%)		0·133 (31%), 0·164 (4·5% + 92·5 I.C.), [0·071 − Hg X-rays]
	Hg^{197}		65 h.	E.C. (3%) E.C. (100%)		0·13, 0·28, 0·41, 0·077 (20% + 80% I.C.), 0·19, [0·069 − AuX-rays]
	Hg^{203}	Hg^{202} (n, γ)	47 d.	β −	0·21 (100%)	0·279 (83%)
Phosphorus	P^{32}	P^{31} (n, γ) S^{32} (n, p)	14·2 d.	β −	1·71 (100%)	
Potassium	K^{40}	naturally occurring	1·3 × 10^{9} y.	β − (89%) E.C. (11%)	1·32 (89%)	1·46 (11%)
	K^{42}	K^{41} (n, γ)	12·45 h.	β −	3·6 (82%), 2·0	1·52, 0·32

TABLE 5.04—Continued

Element	Isotope	Production process	Physical half-life	Made of decay	Electron energies (Max. in MeV)	γ-ray energies (MeV)
Potassium	K^{43}	$A^{40}(\alpha, p)$	22 h.	β –	0·83 (87%) 0·47, 1·24, 1·81	0·37 (85%) 0·61 (81%) 0·22, 0·39, 0·59 1·01
Radium	Ra^{226}	Naturally occurring	1620 y.	α	See Chapter V,	Tables 5.01, 5.03.
Radon	Rn^{222}	Decay of Ra^{226}	3·825 d.	α	See Chapter V,	Tables 5.01, 5.03.
Rubidium	Ru^{86}	$Ru^{85}(n, \gamma)$	18·7 d.	β –	1·77 (91·5%) 0·68	1·08
Sodium	Na^{22}	$Mg^{24}(d, \alpha)$	2·6 y.	β + (89%) E.C. (11%)	0·54 (89%) 1·83	0·51 from β + 1·28 (100%)
	Na^{24}	$Na^{23}(n, \gamma)$	15·0 h.	β –	1·39 (100%)	1·37 (100%) 2·75 (100%)
Strontium	Sr^{85} parent of Rb^{85M}	$Sr^{84}(n, \gamma)$ $Rb^{85}(d, 2n)$	65 d. 0·9 μs.	E.C. (100%)		0·513 (100%)
	Sr^{89}	$Sr^{88}(n, \gamma)$ U $(n,$ fission$)$	51 d.	β –	1·46 (100%)	0·91

Strontium	Sr^{90} parent of Y^{90}	28 y.	β –	0·54 (100%)	
		64·2 h.	β –	2·25 (100%)	
Sulphur	S^{35} S^{34} (n, γ) Cl^{35} (n, p)	87·2 d.	β –	0·167 (100%)	
Tantalum	Ta^{182} Ta^{181} (n, γ)	115 d.	β –	0·18 (38%) 0·36 (20%) 0·44 (23%) 0·25, 0·33, 0·48 0·51	0·068 (31%) 1·12 (33%) 1·22 (28%) 0·100 (13% + 43% I.C.) 0·066, 0·085 0·114, 0·156, 0·179 0·198, 0·222, 0·229 0·264, 1·0, 1·19, 1·23, 1·25, 1·29 [0·059 – W-X-rays]
Technetium	Tc^{99}M U $(n,$ fission$)$ Mo^{99} Mo^{98} (n, γ) Mo^{99}	6·0 h.			0·14, (80%)
	Tc^{99} Mo$^{99} \xrightarrow{\beta} $Tc^{99}	2·12 × 10^5 y.	β –	0·29 (100%)	
Thorium X	Ra^{224} Decay of Th^{228}	3·64 d.	α	See Chapter V,	Table 5.02.
Xenon	Xe^{133}M U $(n,$ fission$)$ Xe^{132} (n, γ)	2·3 d.	β –		0·23 (15% + 85% I.C.)
	Xe^{133}	5·27 d.	β –	0·34 (100%)	0·081 (35% + 65% I.C.)
Yttrium	Y^{90} Y^{89} (n, γ) decay of Sr^{90}	64·2 h.	β –	2·25 (100%)	

states usually persist for only a few minutes, but occasionally a nucleus will remain in an excited state for much longer. In this case the metastable nucleus behaves almost as a separate isotope. A metastable isomer is denoted by the letter M after the mass number, e.g. Tc[99M]. When positrons are emitted by a radioactive nucleus, in addition to any γ-ray photons emitted by the product nucleus in attaining stability, there will be two γ-ray photons of 510 keV. (0·51 MeV.) each,

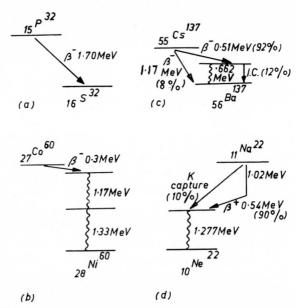

FIG. 5.16. Diagrammatic representation of radioactive disintegration schemes.

produced per disintegration. These photons result from the annihilation of the positron and an electron, a process which occurs whenever the positron is brought to rest (see Chapter VI). This is the radiation denoted by " 0·51 from β+ " in Table 5.04. When electron capture occurs and an orbital electron is absorbed into a nucleus, X-radiation characteristic of the product nucleus is of course produced, as electrons move in to fill the vacancy left by the captured electron.

Information about the modes of decay of an isotope is sometimes presented in the form of a disintegration diagram.

154

A few typical diagrams are shown in fig. 5.16. Fig. 5.16 (a) shows the particularly simple mode of decay of P^{32} and fig. 5·16 (b) shows the decay of Co^{60}, which have already been discussed. Fig. 5.16 (c) illustrates the decay of Cs^{137}, where two alternatives are possible, either a direct transition to the ground state of Ba^{137} or a transition to the isomeric state Ba^{137M}. Ba^{137M} also has two alternatives and may return to the ground state either by the emission of a γ-ray photon or by internal conversion. Fig. 5.16 (d) illustrates the decay of a proton-rich nucleus, Na^{22}. Either positron emission or electron capture may occur to produce an excited state of Ne^{22}. The neon nucleus emits a γ-ray photon to attain the ground state. (The 1·02 MeV. in this figure represents the energy equivalent of twice the electronic mass. It can be regarded as the energy dissipated when the positron is annihilated.)

5.14. Medical uses of artificial radioactive isotopes

Clinically, artificial radioactive isotopes may be used in two quite different ways. (1) the radiations they emit can be used as indicators of the position and/or the concentration of the isotope in some part of the body (i.e. as diagnostic tracers), (2) the biological action of the radiations can be used therapeutically. When used as tracers, the patient is given as small an amount of the isotope concerned as is practicable, so that the biological effect is minimal.

The use of isotopes as diagnostic tracers is discussed in Chapter XIII. In the remainder of this chapter we shall consider only those artifical radioactive isotopes which are used in therapy.

The therapeutic use of artificial radioactive isotopes also falls into two distinct categories:

(1) Discrete sources are used in a manner which is similar to and has been developed from the earlier use of radium and radon.

(2) Internally administered isotopes are used to treat organs in which they are biologically concentrated either because of their chemical nature or physical state. The principal uses are summarised in Table 5.05.

Compared with radium sources, most artificial isotopes are short-lived and their biological effect decreases with time. In some circumstances, e.g. in teletherapy units, this is a disadvantage, whereas in other cases the possibility of obtaining an effective treatment time of a desired duration without removing the source is an advantage.[9] Another difference between the natural and artificial radioactive sources is that

TABLE 5.05

SUMMARY OF PRINCIPAL THERAPEUTIC USES OF ARTIFICIAL
RADIOACTIVE ISOTOPES

γ-teletherapy sources
  Co^{60}, Cs^{137},
γ-brachytherapy sources (for superficial, interstitial, and intracavitary treatments)
  Co^{60}, Cs^{137}, Ta^{182}, Ir^{192}, — replacing radium,
  Au^{198}, — replacing radon
β-teletherapy sources
  Sr^{90}.
β-brachytherapy sources
  Sr^{90}, P^{32}, Y^{90}.
Isotopes localised by metabolism
  I^{131}, P^{32}.
Isotopes localised by physical state
  Colloidal Au^{198}. Colloidal chromic phosphate P^{32}.
Isotopes used as liquids, localised in balloons
  Br^{82}, Na^{24}, P^{32}.

---

the radiation emitted by artificial isotopes frequently consists of only one or two energies instead of a complex spectrum of both β and γ-rays. This is usually an advantage and an isotope may be selected for a particular treatment in preference to radium or radon because it gives a desired type of radiation, e.g. β radiation only. An artificial isotope may also be chosen because it can be obtained in a more convenient form e.g. as a malleable wire or as a liquid.

5.15. γ-sources for teletherapy

As already explained in connection with tele-radium units, the purpose of teletherapy equipment is to provide a beam of high energy γ-radiation which is used in treatments in a similar manner to a high energy X-ray beam. The principal isotopes used in these units are Co^{60} and Cs^{137}.

Co^{60} has a half-life of 5·27 years and emits β-rays of maximum energy 310 keV. and two γ-rays of energy 1·17 and 1·33 MeV. per disintegration (see fig. 5.16 (b)). Thus the γ-radiation is nearly monochromatic. The energy of this radiation is comparable with the mean energy of the γ-rays from a radium source or with the mean energy of X-rays generated with an accelerating voltage of 2 to 3 MV. The maintenance of cobalt units is considerably simpler than that of X-ray sets producing radiation of comparable energy. Also the output of isotope units does not fluctuate so that frequent calibrations are not required, although it is necessary to allow for the decay of the isotope in dosage calculations and to replace the source and recalibrate the equipment every few years. The early cobalt units were somewhat restricted by the limited activity of the available sources, but it is now possible to obtain sources of the order of 5 kilocuries or more which permit typical treatments to be delivered (at 80 cm. or 100 cm. source-skin-distances) in 2 or 3 minutes. Higher dose-rates can be obtained using an X-ray generator such as a linear accelerator, but it is doubtful whether there is much advantage in further reduction of the treatment time, which is already often less than the time spent in positioning the patient under the machine and so on. A more important difference between tele-isotope units and X-ray units is in the size of the radiation source. As Co^{60} is prepared by an (n, γ) reaction, the specific activity attainable is limited by the presently available neutron fluxes to about 200 Ci./g. It is not economic to use source lengths greater than about 2·0 cm. because of the self absorption in the source, so to obtain kilocurie sources, diameters also of the order of 2·0 cm. are required. The apparent focal spot size in an X-ray unit is commonly 3 or 4 mm. This means that with isotope units, more complicated collimating devices are necessary to obtain a well defined beam than are required with X-ray units.

A typical Co^{60} teletherapy unit is illustrated in fig. 5.17. The cobalt in the form of small pellets or discs is sealed in a stainless steel capsule and this is surrounded by an outer stainless steel cylinder, also hermetically sealed, to ensure that no radioactive dust escapes from the source. The source is normally placed near the centre of the treatment head which consists mainly of steel encased lead. The lead surrounds the source in all directions except for a cone extending from

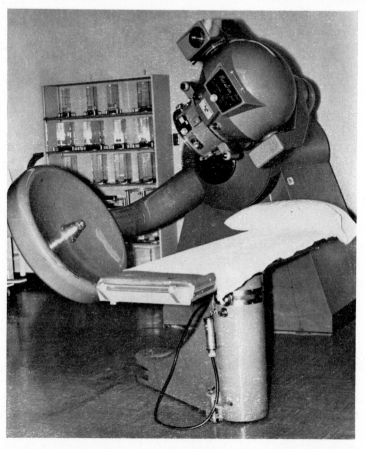

FIG. 5.17.   A Cobalt 60 unit for rotation therapy.   The lead disc opposite to the treatment head acts as a counter-weight and a radiation shield.

Courtesy British Columbia Cancer Institute, Vancouver, Canada.

the source to the edge of the shield in one direction which defines the treatment beam. Tungsten alloy or uranium which provide more shielding per unit volume than lead may replace lead in certain critical positions. In cobalt units the source usually remains permanently in the treatment head.

Therefore the shielding must be sufficient to reduce the dose-rate at the surface of the head to acceptable levels for occupational exposure (see Chapter XIV) and it is necessary to provide some means for turning the γ-ray beam "on" and "off". In some units the conical aperture in the treatment head is normally filled by mercury (which with a density

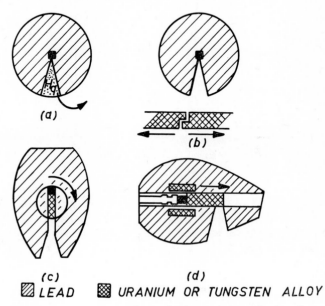

(a)

(b)

(c)   (d)

SOURCE   ▨ LEAD   ▨ URANIUM OR TUNGSTEN ALLOY

FIG. 5.18. Diagrammatic representation of alternative methods of turning isotope units "on" and "off". (a) mercury shutter; (b) metal jaws; (c) source on rotating wheel; (d) source in moving drawer.

of 13·6 g. per cc. is a rather better absorber per cc. than lead) which is driven out by compressed air when the set is turned "on". In other units, lead or tungsten jaws normally block the aperture and are moved apart by hydraulic pressure to start a treatment. In still other units, the source is moved from a position where it is screened to a position opposite the conical aperture in the shield, either by rotation of a wheel or by a lateral shift. (See figure 5.18.) In all sets the equipment is designed so that in the event of a power failure, the aperture is automatically closed or the source returned to its screened position.

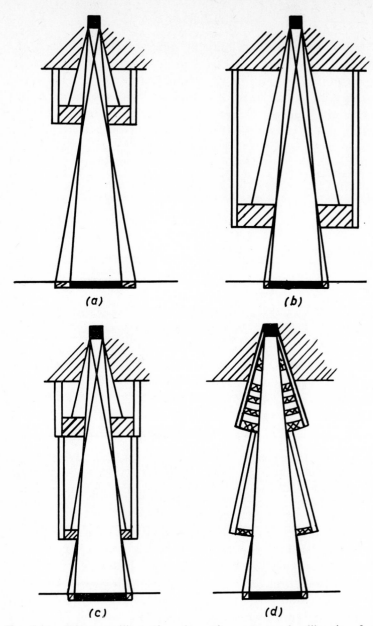

FIG. 5.19. Diagrams illustrating alternative systems of collimation for isotope units.

(a) A single plane collimator near the source keeps the head size small but there is a wide penumbra.

[*Continued opposite*

160

The dimensions of the treatment beam are adjusted by movable diaphragms of lead, tungsten alloy or uranium. In order to reduce the beam penumbra due to the finite size of the source, it is desirable that the collimating diaphragms be as close to the patient's skin and as far from the source as possible (fig. 5.19). However it is not desirable to place absorbing material within about 15 cm. of the patient's skin, since electrons ejected from the absorber by the radiation will then reach the skin surface. (One of the chief advantages of high energy X- or γ-radiation for therapy is that these radiations do not deliver a large dose to the most superficial layers of tissue. This advantage is lost if the beam is contaminated by electrons, see Chapter XI.) Furthermore if the main beam collimation is provided even as far from the source as (S-15) cm. (where S is the proposed source-skin distance), the amount of material required in the collimator (which has to cover a wider beam the more remote it is from the source) makes the treatment head bulky. If most of the collimation is achieved by diaphragms fairly close to the source and only the final beam defining diaphragms are carried remote from the source, a more convenient treatment head is produced. This is the reason for the use of multi-vane collimators and/or so called penumbra trimming diaphragms (see fig. 5.19 (c) and (d)).

Cs^{137} is a β-emitter with a half-life of 30 years but it decays to an isomer of Ba^{137} which emits 662 keV. γ-radiation (See fig. 5.16 (c).) Cs^{137} is a fission product of uranium and is now readily available. The earlier sources sometimes contained an appreciable proportion of Cs^{134} which emits a complex spectrum of γ-rays and has a half-life of only 2·3 years. The presence of Cs^{134} in a Cs^{137} source complicates dosage calculations, and (because about 40 per cent. of the γ-rays of Cs^{134} have an energy of 800 keV. and 3·5 per cent. have energy

---

(b) A single plane collimator remote from the source reduces the width of the penumbra but makes the head large.

(c) Single plane collimator with " penumbra trimmer ".

(d) Multivane collimator with " penumbra trimmer ".

Both (c) and (d) enable a narrow penumbra to be obtained without undue increase in the size of the head.

above 1 MeV.) means that additional shielding is required initially which becomes unnecessary after a few years. Modern sources are supplied with a Cs^{134} content of less than 1·5 per cent. The Cs^{137} as caesium chloride is compressed into pellets which are packed in double walled, sealed, stainless steel capsules. The capsule is normally mounted near the centre of a steel-encased lead treatment head, which is similar to those used for cobalt units, except that as the γ-radiation has a lower energy, the thickness of the shield required is considerably less. Arrangements for turning the beam " on " and " off " are generally similar to those used in cobalt units.

Caesium sources can only be obtained with a rather low specific activity (25 Ci./g., 3 g./cc.) and the γ-ray energy output per disintegration is also low compared with that from a cobalt source. This means that to obtain an adequate dose-rate without using an excessively large source it is necessary to use rather short source-skin distances (up to about 35 cm. say). It is therefore not possible in these units to keep the beam-defining diaphragms sufficiently far from the skin surface that no electrons from the diaphragms reach the skin and still produce a well-defined beam. At the shorter source-skin-distances, the beam defining system may have to be as close as 5 or 6 cm. to the skin. The electron contamination is reduced as much as possible by placing a copper or tin filter on the patient side of the diaphragm. Caesium units operating at 30 or 35 cm. S.S.D. can be used in a manner very similar to 200 to 400 kVp. X-ray therapy sets.

For treating head and neck tumours, caesium units operating at 15 or 20 cm. S.S.D. have been found convenient, since by using tungsten alloy in the treatment head a very compact unit can be obtained. In these units the beam is usually defined by interchangeable cones rather than by a diaphragm system.

5.16. γ-sources for brachy-therapy

Both Co^{60} and Cs^{137} sources can be used for superficial, interstitial and intracavitary treatments in essentially the same way as radium. Neither isotope has gaseous daughter products and neither emits a complex spectrum of γ-radiation which are

both advantages compared with radium. Co^{60} tubes and
needles consist of rods or wires of cobalt sheathed in platinum,
which is normally 0·3 mm. in thickness. This platinum
prevents radioactive material being rubbed off the sources and
also absorbs the β-radiation. For special purposes, cobalt
sources have the advantage that high activity sources can
be made of smaller dimensions than radium sources. The
rate of decay of cobalt sources (approximately 1 per cent.

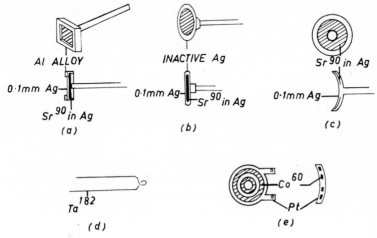

FIG. 5.20. Diagrammatic representation of some artificial radioactive
isotope sources used in therapy.

(a) and (b) Sr^{90} β-ray applicators.
(c) Sr^{90} β-ray ophthalmic applicator.
(d) Ta^{182} " hairpin ".
(e) Co^{60} ophthalmic applicator.

per month) is not small enough to be neglected, however,
and the changing activity complicates the planning of treatments,
particularly interstitial implants. For the treatment of certain
ocular tumours, ophthalmic applicators consisting of rings
or part rings of cobalt wire in a platinum container designed
to fit the eye, have proved convenient (see fig. 5.20).

Cs^{137} needles and tubes contain a caesium-silver alloy or
a caesium ceramic in a platinum-iridium cell. The cells
are enclosed in an outer platinum-iridium sheath similar to

those used for radium tubes and needles. This removes the β-radiation. The longer half-life of Cs^{137} gives it an advantage compared with Co^{60} as a substitute for radium.

Instead of specifying the activity of cobalt and caesium sources in millicuries, some centres find it more convenient to describe the sources by the number of milligrams of radium which would produce the same dose-rate at a specified position. The energy of the γ-rays from a Cs^{137} source (662 keV.) is somewhat less and the mean energy of the γ-rays from a Co^{60} source (1·25 MeV.) is somewhat greater than the mean energy of the γ-rays from a radium source, but the absorption in soft tissue of γ-rays of energy about 1 MeV. is not a rapidly varying function of the energy and it has been shown that the distribution of dose in soft tissue in the equatorial plane around a caesium or cobalt tube or needle is almost in-distinguishable from that around an " equivalent " radium source. However in directions where an appreciable amount of radiation travels obliquely through the wall of the source, the distributions may differ appreciably. (See Chapter XII for details of dose distributions.)

The radioactive isotope of tantalum, Ta^{182}, emits a spectrum of both β- and γ-rays, the latter having energies in the range 70 keV. to 1·29 MeV. It has a half-life of 115 days. For therapeutic use, a thin wire (0·2 mm. diameter) is sheathed with 0·1 mm. platinum. The platinum removes most of the β-radiation but the sheathed wire is still flexible. This flexibility is the great advantage conferred by the use of tantalum sources. " Hair-pins " of tantalum wire (see fig. 5.20) are now commonly used in the treatment of certain tumours of the bladder. By fastening the loops of the hair-pins to a urethral catheter, it is possible to withdraw the sources down the urethra when the treatment is completed, thus avoiding a second operation for removal.

In situations where a very flexible source is required, or an after-loading technique is desirable, it is often convenient to use hollow plastic tubes which contain small radioactive sources spaced at regular intervals. For these techniques, the tumour is usually implanted with hollow needles and the radioactive sources are introduced only after all the needles are correctly positioned. In addition to the isotopes already mentioned, an isotope of iridium, Ir^{192}, is also used. Nylon " ribbon " containing Ir^{192} sources, 3 mm. long and 0·5 mm. diameter, spaced 1 cm. apart, is available commercially. The iridium is sheathed in stainless steel to absorb the β-radiation. Ir^{192} emits a spectrum of γ-rays with energies between 296 and 613 keV., the mean energy being about 378 keV. The half-life is 74·4 days. The mean energy of the γ-radiation, while being high enough to give reasonable penetration in soft tissue, is low enough that the absorption in materials of high atomic number is high. This means iridium sources can be more easily shielded (in an operating room for example) than can radium, cobalt, or tantalum sources.

Cs^{137}, Co^{60}, Ta^{182} and Ir^{192} all have half-lives which although short compared with that of radium, are long in comparison with conventional treatment times and the sources therefore have to be removed when the treatment is completed. Radioactive gold (Au^{198}) has a half-life of 2·70 days and sources of this material can therefore be left permanently implanted in treated tissue. Gold grains are now frequently used in place of radon seeds, although some clinicians prefer the longer effective treatment time which is obtained with radon. (The average life of Au^{198} nuclei is 93·5 hours compared with 132·4 hours for radon.) The gold sources are 2·5 mm. long and 0·8 mm. in diameter including a platinum sheath 0·15 mm. in thickness which absorbs most of the β-radiation. Au^{198} emits mainly 960 keV. β-rays and 412 keV. γ-rays. Gold grains therefore require less shielding than do radon seeds.

5.17. β-ray sources

For the treatment of superficial lesions, isotopes which emit β-rays only, have the advantage that only a negligible amount of radiation reaches the underlying tissues. Surface applicators containing Sr^{90}, Y^{90} or P^{32} have therefore largely superseded radium β-applicators for the treatment of such lesions.

The isotope of strontium, Sr^{90}, has a half-life of 28 years and can therefore be used as a " permanent " β-ray source. It emits β-rays of maximum energy 0·54 MeV. and its radioactive daughter Y^{90} (half-life 64·2 hours) emits β-rays of maximum energy 2·25 MeV. Typical Sr^{90} applicators consist of plates of silver 1 mm. thick upon which the radioactive material is deposited, covered with 0·1 mm. of silver. They may also be protected against corrosion by a rolled gold coating and are usually mounted in an aluminium alloy case. Square and circular applicators are available commercially in various sizes from 2 cm.^{2} to 4 cm.^{2} in active area. Specially shaped applicators are also made for ophthalmic treatments (fig. 5.20). To treat large areas, multi-curie sources can be mounted in a treatment head, resembling the head of a teletherapy unit, and by suitable choice of treating distance and collimating devices, any area up to about 20 cm. $\times$ 40 cm. can be treated. (With multicurie sources, there is appreciably Bremsstrahlung production in the primary β-shield and the treatment head has to be designed to reduce this radiation to an acceptable level.)

The Sr^{90} applicators described above are rigid. Flexible β-ray applicators are obtained by incorporating either red phosphorus (containing the isotope P^{32}) or yttrium oxide (containing Y^{90}) in polyethylene sheet. The surfaces of the sheet are coated with a thin layer of inactive plastic. P^{32} emits β-rays with a maximum energy of 1·71 MeV and has a half-life of 14·2 days. As already mentioned Y^{90} emits β-rays with a maximum energy of 2·2 MeV. and has a half-life of 64·2 hours.

Small sintered rods of ytterbium oxide containing Y^{90} are used for the radiological obliteration of the pituitary gland.

5.18. Internally administered isotopes

A few organs have the power of concentrating particular elements. If a radioactive isotope of the appropriate element is ingested or injected, the organ in which the element is concentrated receives a greater dose of radiation than other tissue. The less the penetrating power of the radiations emitted, the less will be the dose received by tissues outside the organ in which the isotope is concentrated, so that for this type of treatment isotopes emitting mainly β-radiation or soft γ-radiation are preferred.[10, 11]

The outstanding example of an isotope which is used therapeutically because it is concentrated in a particular organ is I^{131} which is concentrated in the thyroid. Almost all the β-radiation and an appreciable fraction of the γ-radiation is absorbed in the gland. Small doses of I^{131} are used to treat thyrotoxicosis. Massive doses (sufficient to destroy malignant cells) are used to treat cases of thyroid cancer in which the gland retains its ability to take up iodine [12, 13] (unfortunately patients with thyroid cancer often suffer impairment of iodine uptake). Thyroid metastases are also sometimes treated similarly after removal of the gland itself.

Another example of the selective absorption of a radioactive isotope which is utilised therapeutically is the uptake of phosphorus by bone and by rapidly dividing cells. Thus P^{32}, which emits β-radiation only, can be used to treat blood dyscrasias such as polycythemia rubra vera and leukaemia.[14, 15]

Radioactive colloidal gold is an example of a material which is used because of its physical state. It has been widely employed for the treatment of malignant pleural or peritoneal effusions.[16] In these cases, a suspension of the colloid in saline is injected into the cavity after paracentesis. Its colloidal state prevents the gold diffusing through the cavity walls. The volume of liquid used is chosen so that when spread over the estimated area of wall it forms a layer of thickness rather less than the maximum range of the β-particles. A limited use has been made of radioactive colloidal particles of various kinds to treat organs which trap particles of a particular size, e.g. the liver, spleen, bronchial and lymphatic systems.[17, 18].

A few centres have used radioactive solutions to treat carcinoma of the bladder.[19] The solution is introduced into a balloon after the latter has been inserted in the bladder. This causes less discomfort than the introduction of a solid source. Br^{82}, Na^{24} or P^{32} may be used depending upon the depth of tissue to be treated.

Apart from the colloids, the internally administered isotopes discussed above are used as simple inorganic salts, e.g. I^{131} is administered as sodium iodide, P^{32} as sodium phosphate, etc. A number of organic compounds which have been " labelled " with radioactive isotopes are now used for diagnostic purposes (see Chapter XIII) and the possibility of using some of these compounds for therapy is now being investigated. For example, the ethyl ester of the fatty acid of poppy-seed oil which is commonly used as a radiopaque contrast medium (trade name "ethiodol") remains in the lymph nodes for long periods after instillation into the lymphatics. The use of this compound labelled with I^{131} to treat metastatic disease in the lymph nodes has been suggested.[20]

REFERENCES

1. REINES, F. and COWAN, C. L. (1953). *Phys. Rev.* **92**, 830.
2. GUENTHER, P. (1939). *Z. physik. Chem. A.*, **185**, 367.
3. KOHMAR, T. P., AMES. D. P. and SEDLET, J. (1947). MDDC-852 (U.S. Atomic Energy Commission Report.)
4. KAYE, G. W. C., ASTON, G. H. and PERRY, W. E. T. (1934). *Brit. J. Radiol.* **7**, 540.
5. NEARY, G. J. (1942). *Brit. J. Radiol.* **15**, 104.
6. ODDIE, T. H. (1937). *Brit. J. Radiol.* **10**, 348.
7. STROINGER, D., HOLLANDER, J. M. and SEABORG, G. T. (1958). *Rev. Mod. Phys.* **30**, 585.
8. *The Radiochemical Manual.* (1962). (Compiled by the Radiochemical Centre, Amersham, Bucks.).
9. COHEN, L. (1958). *Phys. Med. Biol.* **2**, 229.
10. BERMAN, M., RALL, J. E. and HESLIN, J. (1957). *Phys. Med. Biol.* **1**, 243.
11. HAYBITTLE, J. L. and PHILLIPS, A. F. (1957). *Phys. Med. Biol.* **1**, 383.
12. PATERSON, R., WARRINGTON, H. C. and GILBERT, C. W. (1952). *Brit. Med. Bull.* **8**, 154.
13. WAYNE, E. J., McGREGOR, A. G. and BLOMFIELD, G. W. (1952). *Brit. Med. Bull.* **8**, 148.
14. LAWRENCE, J. H. (1948). *Brit. J. Radiol.* **21**, 531.
15. EASSON, E. C., JONES, B. E. and MACKENZIE, L. A. (1954). *Proc. Radioisotope Conference*, Oxford, 42.
16. WALTON, R. J. and SINCLAIR, W. K. (1952). *Brit. Med. Bull.* **8**, 165.
17. SHEPPARD, C. W. and WELLS, E. B. *et al.* (1047). *J. Lab. Clin. Med.* **32**, 274.
18. POCHIN, E. E. and COOK, G. B., *et al.* (1954). *Proc. Radioisotope Conference*, Oxford, 30.
19. WALTON, R. J. and SINCLAIR, W. K. (1952). *Brit. Med. Bull.* **8**, 158.
20. SIEGEL, P. and LIEBNER, E. J. (1965). *Amer. J. Obst. Gyn.* **91**, 122.
21. *The International Commission on Radiological Units and Measurements.* (1962). Report 10a (reprinted with corrections 1964). U.S. National Bureau of Standards Handbook No. 85.

GENERAL REFERENCES

RUTHERFORD, E., CHADWICK, J. and ELLIS, C. D. (1930). *Radiations from Radioactive Substances.* New York, MacMillan.

CHADWICK, J. (1931). *Radioactivity and Radioactive Substances.* London, Pitman.

WILSON, C. W. (1956). *Radium Therapy, its Physical Aspects.* 2nd edn. London, Chapman & Hall.

EVANS, R. D. (1955). *The Atomic Nucleus.* New York, McGraw-Hill.

The Radiochemical Manual (Part I) (1962). Compiled and published by the Radiochemical Centre, Amersham, Bucks.

EXAMINATION QUESTIONS

1. (*a*) Describe the construction of a radium needle.
   (*b*) What kinds of needle are in common use?
   (*c*) Give an account of tests which must be applied to ensure that a radium needle is in good condition.

   M.S.R. (T.), 1964.

2. "The radioactive isotope iodine 131 has a half-life of eight days and emits β particles and γ-rays".
   Explain this statement, paying particular attention to the meaning of the terms radioactive, isotope, 131, half-life, β particle and γ-ray.
   If a particular sample of iodine 131 is known to have an activity of 4 millicuries at 3 p.m. on 2nd November, what will be its activity at 3 p.m. on 18th November in the same year?

   M.S.R. (R. & T.), 1962.

3. Give an account of the properties of β particles.
   Describe briefly a method of production of a β emitting radioactive isotope, suitable for use as an applicator for superficial therapy.

   M.S.R. (T.), 1965.

4. What advantages and disadvantages are there in using a radioactive source of γ rays rather than a megavoltage X-ray machine for producing high energy beams for radiotherapy?

   M.S.R. (T.), 1965.

5. Give a brief account of radioactivity and explain why nuclear radiations differ markedly in their penetration into matter. State the order of magnitude of the ranges of 4 MeV α particles and 2 MeV β particles in soft tissue. How is the penetration of γ rays usually specified?

   F.S.R., 1963.

6. Define and explain the following terms:
   isotope, nuclide, electron-volt, tenth-life-period, specific activity.
   If the half-life period of radioactive gold is $2\frac{2}{3}$ days, how long does it take for a source of 200 mc. activity to decay to 20 microcuries?

   F.S.R., 1962.

7. Give an account of the construction of a cobalt 60 beam unit. Discuss the problem of penumbra in this type of unit, and the limitation set by electron contamination in the design of the beam defining system.

F.S.R., 1963.

8. For any two " man-made " γ ray emitters commonly used in radio-therapy, give an account of the following, (a) method of production, (b) mode of decay, (c) half-life, (d) radiation output and quality, (e) the types of source in use.

F.S.R. (T.), 1965.

9. Discuss the characteristic features of exponential change, giving examples of importance in radiological physics. A radioactive source is known to contain two radionuclides of equal activity at a certain time. It they have half-life periods of 30 minutes and one hour respectively, show graphically or in a table, how the total activity of the source will change with time.

D.M.R., 1962.

10. Describe the phenomena of radioactive disintegration.

The half-lives of ^{222}Rn and ^{198}Au are very approximately 4 and 2·5 days respectively. A radon source is found to have an activity of 10 mc. About $1\frac{1}{2}$ days later, the activity of a gold source is also observed to be 10 mc. After what further period will the activities of the two sources be equal and what will be the value?

D.M.R., 1963.

11. Give a brief account of the simpler phenomena of radioactivity. Explain the meaning of the terms atomic number, mass number, half-life period of a radioactive substance.

What is the minimum quantity of a radioactive isotope of half-life 8 days which must be ordered if a dose of 500 millicuries is to be given to a patient 24 hours after it is despatched from the source of supply?

D.M.R., 1963.

12. What is meant by radioactivity? Describe the nature of the radiations from radioactive substances.

Give an account of the preparation and use of ONE radioactive isotope employed *EITHER* for diagnostic (tracer) investigations *OR* as a source of radiation for therapeutic purposes.

D.M.R., 1964.

CHAPTER VI

THE INTERACTION OF X- AND γ-RADIATION WITH MATTER

6.01. The exponential attenuation of X- and γ-radiation

WHEN a beam of X- or γ-radiation passes through matter, some of the radiation is scattered and some is absorbed. The number of photons (and hence also the energy carried by the photons), travelling in the original direction of the beam therefore decreases. The absorption of radiation is normally accompanied by the simultaneous production in the absorber of lower energy radiation (e.g. characteristic radiation, modified scatter or annihilation radiation). Also radiation scattered out of the beam may be subsequently scattered back in again. Therefore the total radiation intensity at any point in the path of the beam contains two components, the primary radiation and secondary radiation originating in the absorber. In this section we consider the attenuation of the primary radiation only.

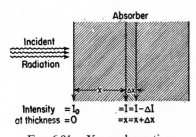

FIG. 6.01.   X-ray absorption.

By permission from *Nuclear Radiation Physics* by R. E. Lapp and H. L. Andrews.   (Prentice-Hall, Inc., New York.)

For simplicity consider initially a unidirectional beam of monoenergetic photons. The " *photon flux density* " for such a beam is measured by the number of photons incident per unit time per unit area of a plane normal to the direction of propagation. The *intensity* is measured by the amount of energy incident per unit time per unit area of such a plane. Again for simplicity we shall assume in the first instance that the photon flux density is constant from point to point across the plane normal to the direction of propagation and is unchanging in time. For monochromatic radiation, it is found experimentally

171

that equal thicknesses of the same absorbing material remove equal fractions of the radiation incident upon them, and the fraction removed is proportional to the thickness of the absorber. Let — ΔI_x denote the reduction in the intensity of the primary radiation by a thin slab of thickness Δx at a depth x in an absorber (fig. 6.01).

Then $\qquad - \Delta I_x / I_x = \mu \Delta x$ where μ is a constant.

or $\qquad\qquad \dfrac{\Delta I_x}{\Delta x} = - \mu . I_x .$

Provided that there are a large number of photons interacting with a large number of atoms in the absorber, as Δx is decreased the quotient $\Delta I_x / \Delta x$ tends to a limiting value which is not appreciably altered by further reduction in Δx. In these circumstances

As $x \rightarrow 0$, $\qquad \dfrac{\Delta I_x}{\Delta x} \rightarrow \dfrac{dI_x}{dx}$

$\therefore \qquad\qquad \dfrac{dI_x}{dx} = - \mu I_x .$

Integrating $\therefore \left[\log_e I_x \right]_{I_0}^{I_x} = \left[- \mu x \right]_0^x$

or $\qquad\qquad I_x = I_0 e^{-\mu x}$ where $I_x = I_0$ when $x = 0$.

Thus the intensity of the primary radiation decreases exponentially with the distance traversed, the rate of change of intensity being determined by the value of μ.

The relation $I_x = I_0 e^{-\mu x}$ is of the same form as that between the number of radioactive atoms and the time, and those not familiar with the calculus may obtain the relation by a method similar to that described in Chapter V, section 5. The relation between I_x and x for a hypothetical case in which the intensity is reduced by one-third by unit thickness of absorber is shown graphically in Fig. 6.02. If $\log I_x$ is plotted against thickness, a straight line graph is obtained as already explained in connection with radioactive decay.

μ is called the total linear attenuation coefficient of the material of the absorber for the particular radiation considered. (It was formerly customary to call μ the total linear apparent absorption coefficient, the word apparent being used because the reduction in intensity is brought about by scattering as well as by real absorption. However the use of the term attenuation when both scattering and absorption occurs, is now preferred.) The word total is used because different processes contribute to the intensity reduction and these are not distinguished.

For monochromatic radiation, the coefficient μ is a constant which depends upon the number of atoms per cc., the nature of the atoms and the wavelength of the incident radiation. If the absorber is compressed so that a given thickness contains more atoms, then μ will be increased. However, μ/ρ (where ρ denotes the density of the material) is unchanged. μ/ρ is

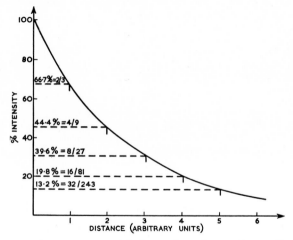

FIG. 6.02.   Exponential absorption of monochromatic radiation.

called the total mass attenuation coefficient (formerly the total apparent mass absorption coefficient) and has a characteristic value for a given substance, which is independent of the physical state of the absorber. Other coefficients which are sometimes employed are the attenuation coefficients per atom (μ_{at}) and per electron (μ_e). These are calculated by dividing the mass attenuation coefficient by the number of atoms per gram (n_{at}) or the number of electrons per gram (n_e) respectively. ($n_{at} = N/A$ and $n_e = NZ/A$ where N denotes Avogadro's number, A atomic mass and Z atomic number.) The relations between the coefficients is summarised below.

173

Name	Symbol	Unit
Total linear attenuation coefficient .	μ	per cm.
Total mass attenuation coefficient .	μ/ρ	cm.^{2} per g.
Total atomic attenuation coefficient .	μ_{at} $= \mu A/\rho N$	cm.^{2} per atom
Total electronic attenuation coefficient	μ_e $= \mu A/\rho NZ$	cm.^{2} per electron

The term cross-section is sometimes used instead of attenuation coefficient when the atomic or electronic coefficients are discussed. For if the incident radiation is visualised as striking a plane in the absorber, each atom or each electron in that plane can be regarded as presenting to the radiation an effective area (cross-section) equal to μ_{at} or μ_e respectively, such that the radiation falling upon that area is completely absorbed.

Illustrative Problem

Assuming that the γ-rays from a cobalt source are attenuated exponentially in lead, with a linear attenuation coefficient (μ) of 0·6 cm.$^{-1}$, calculate the thickness of lead which is needed to reduce the intensity of this radiation to 1 per cent. of its original value.

Let I_x denote the intensity of the radiation transmitted through x cm. of lead.

Then
$$I_x = I_0 e^{-\mu x},$$
or
$$\log_e (I_x/I_0) = - \mu x.$$

In this case, $\mu = 0·6$ cm.$^{-1}$ and we require $I_x/I_0 = 1/100$.

$$\therefore \log_e (1/100) = - 0·6x,$$

but
$$\log_e (1/100) = 2·3 \log_{10} (1/100) = 2·3(- 2) = - 4·6.$$

$$\therefore - 0·6x = - 4·6,$$

$$\therefore x = 7·7,$$

i.e. 7·7 cm. of lead are required.

Since the attenuation coefficient μ is a function of the wavelength or energy of the radiation, in a beam containing a range of wavelengths, each energy or wavelength is attenuated to a different extent. The intensity (I) of the beam as a whole after passage through a thickness x of absorber is given by

$$I = I_1 e^{-\mu_1 x} + I_2 e^{-\mu_2 x} + I_3 e^{-\mu_3 x} \ldots$$

where I_1 is the initial intensity of the wavelength for which the attenuation coefficient is μ_1, I_2 is the initial intensity for that with attenuation coefficient μ_2 and so on. It is sometimes convenient to write

$$I = I_0 e^{-\bar{\mu}x}$$

where $I_0 = I_1 + I_2 + I_3 \ldots \ldots$ and $\bar{\mu}$ is an effective attenuation coefficient for the beam as a whole, but if this is done $\bar{\mu}$ is *not* a constant, but a function of the absorber thickness. For example the effective attenuation coefficient of the γ-radiation from a radium source in a platinum container is somewhat less for a wall thickness of 1 mm. of platinum than for a thickness of 0·5 mm.

6.02. Summary of absorption and scattering processes

In this section, we outline the various absorption and scattering processes which may reduce the intensity of a beam of X- or γ-radiation as it passes through matter. Each process is discussed in more detail later.

The amounts of absorption and scattering and the particular mechanisms operating depend upon the photon energy. At low energies, the processes also depend upon whether the photon energy of the radiation is less than, comparable with, or greater than, the binding energy of the electrons in the atoms of the material of the absorber. At long wavelengths, and particularly when the photon energy is small in comparison with the energy with which electrons are bound in the atoms of the absorbing material, elastic scattering may take place. The incident photons can be regarded as rebounding from fixed electrons and the photons are thus changed in direction but do not lose energy. The classical electromagnetic theory of this process is a good approximation and can be used to predict the intensity of the radiation scattered through different angles. (Strictly the interaction of X- and γ-radiation with matter should be discussed in terms of wave mechanics, but at the lowest energies, the classical treatment, and at higher energies the older quantum theory, which are mathematically simpler, enable the experimental observations to be predicted fairly closely.) When the photon energy is

175

comparable with the binding energy of the electrons in any shell of the atoms of the absorber, the energy of a photon may be entirely absorbed by an atom and result in the liberation of an electron. This is known as photo-electric absorption. At these energies also, elastic scattering begins to be superseded by a modified form of scattering known as Compton scattering (after the American physicist who first developed the quantum theory of the process). In this process, the photons are deflected by the electrons in the absorber, but the photons also cause the electrons with which they collide to recoil and hence the photons give up some of their energy to the electrons. At energies greater than 1 MeV., another absorption process, pair production, becomes possible. The energy of a photon may be converted into matter in the form of an electron and a positron. Finally, when the energy of the incident radiation exceeds the binding energy of the components of the atomic nuclei, absorption of radiant energy by the nucleus may result in its disintegration. In most absorbers the ranges of energy for which these various processes can take place overlap, so that several processes occur simultaneously. A more detailed discussion of each type of process is given in the following sections.

6.03. Classical scattering

According to classical electromagnetic theory, electric charges in the path of an electromagnetic wave will be set into vibration by the wave. The charges will vibrate with the same frequency as the wave and in the direction of the electrical vector. The vibrating charges will then themselves radiate electromagnetic waves of the same frequency. These waves form the scattered radiation. By a calculation which is summarised below, it was shown by J. J. Thomson that at a distance r from an electron of charge e and mass m, the intensity of the radiation which is scattered at an angle θ to the direction of the incident radiation is given by

$$\frac{I}{2} \frac{e^4}{r^2 m^2 c^2} (1 + \cos^2 \theta)$$

where I denotes the incident intensity and c the velocity of light.

176

Thus the scatter from a single electron is least when $\theta = 90°$. (See fig. 6.09.) The resultant scatter *per atom* varies as the atomic number Z if the electrons scatter independently but as Z^2 if the electrons act together as a unit. In the latter case, the scatter per atom is coherent and is usually called Rayleigh scatter. The probability of Rayleigh scattering increases as the electron binding energy increases and the scattering angle decreases.

The photon energy of the radiations usually used in therapy is generally greater than the binding energy of the electrons in

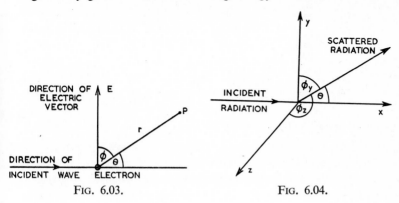

FIG. 6.03.   FIG. 6.04.

the absorbing material, and for such radiation the amount of energy which is elastically scattered is a small fraction only of the total energy lost by the beam. A comparison of the relative energy loss by Rayleigh and Compton scattering under different conditions is given in table 6.02 (p. 185).

Derivation of Classical Equation for X-ray Scattering.

Let E denote the electrical intensity of the incident wave. Then an unconstrained electron will be given an acceleration $a = Ee/m$ in the direction of the incident intensity. It will then emit electromagnetic radiation which will have an intensity E_ϕ at a point distance r from the electron such that

$$E_\phi = \frac{ea \sin \phi}{rc^2}$$

where ϕ is the angle between the direction of E and r as shown in Fig. 6·03. Hence, substituting for a

$$E_\phi = \frac{Ee^2}{mrc^2} \sin \phi$$

177

The intensity I of electromagnetic waves is proportional to the square of the electrical vector, hence

$$I_\phi = I \frac{e^4}{m^2 r^2 c^4} \sin^2 \phi$$

If the incident radiation is not polarised, i.e. if E may lie in any direction in the yz plane (Fig. 6.04), then

$$E^2 = E_y{}^2 + E_z{}^2 \quad \text{and} \quad E_y = E_z.$$

Thus $\qquad I = I_y + I_z \qquad$ and $I_y = I_z = I/2.$

The scattered intensity due to E_y

$$= \frac{I_y e^4 \sin^2 \phi_y}{r^2 m^2 c^4} = \frac{I e^4 \cos^2 \theta}{2 r^2 m^2 c^4} \quad \text{since } \phi_y + \theta = 90°.$$

The scattered intensity due to E_z

$$= \frac{I_z e^4 \sin^2 \phi_z}{r^2 m^2 c^4} = \frac{I e^4 \sin^2 90°}{2 r^2 m^2 c^4} \quad \text{since } \phi_z = 90°.$$

Thus the total intensity of the radiation scattered in the direction θ

$$= \frac{I}{2} \frac{e^4}{r^2 m^2 c^4} (1 + \cos^2 \theta)$$

6.04. Photo-electric absorption

When the energy of the incident radiation equals or just exceeds the energy required to remove an electron from some particular shell of the atoms of the absorber, the energy given up by the incident radiation shows a marked increase. The energy lost by the radiation is absorbed by the atoms and enables electrons to be set free. This is accompanied by the production of secondary X-rays characteristic of the absorbing material as outer electrons move in to fill the gaps in the inner orbits produced by the radiation. This process is called photo-electric absorption. The electrons ejected by the radiation are called photo-electrons and are emitted with a velocity v determined by the equation

$$h v = W + m v^2 / 2$$

where W is the energy required to remove the electron from its position in the atom and m is the electronic mass.

This equation implies that all the energy of the incident photon is dissipated in removing the photo-electron from its orbit and imparting to it the velocity v. Photo-electric absorption is most likely to occur when the photon energy equals or just exceeds the energy required to remove an electron from its position in the parent atom. The photo-electric attenuation coefficient τ is defined by the equation $I_x = I_0 e^{-\tau x}$ where the attenuation occurs by the photoelectric process. For a particular material, a graph of τ against wavelength or photon

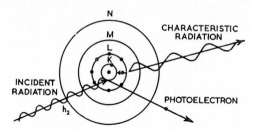

FIG. 6.05. The photoelectric effect.

energy has the form shown in fig. 6.06, the peaks occurring as the energy of the incident radiation equals the energies of the electrons in different shells or sub-shells of the atoms of the

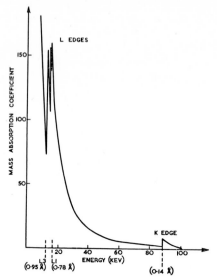

FIG. 6.06. Photoelectric absorption in lead.

absorber. When the incident radiation has sufficient energy to remove an electron from the innermost or K shell of the atom, the K absorption limit is reached. As the energy of the radiation increases above this, the probability of photo-electric

179

absorption decreases. The energy of the K shell increases with the atomic number of the absorber and hence the K absorption limit occurs at much lower energies (longer wavelengths) for light elements such as occur in tissue, than in the heavier elements that are used in screens and filters. (See table 6.01.)

At energies slightly greater than the K limit, the photo-electric attenuation coefficient varies approximately as λ^3 (where λ denotes wavelength). However, the exponent of λ depends upon the absorber and the radiation energy, varying between about 3·05 for light elements and 2·85 for heavy elements in the usual X-ray therapy range and tending to 1 for very high energy radiation. If the attenuation of radiation of a particular energy in one element is compared with that in another (the energy considered being above the K limit in each case), the photo-electric attenuation coefficient *per atom* varies

TABLE 6.01

K Critical Absorption Limit for Some Common Elements

Element	Atomic number	K limit wave-length (A°)	Photon energy (keV.)
Carbon .	6	43·5	0·285
Aluminium .	13	7·94	1·56
Copper .	29	1·38	9·00
Tin . .	50	0·425	29·3
Lead . .	82	0·140	88·3

approximately as Z^4 near the K absorption limit, tending to Z^5 for high energy radiation. In the usual X-ray range, the mass attenuation coefficient (τ/ρ) therefore varies as Z^4/A, where A is the atomic weight of the element considered, and the linear attenuation coefficient (τ) varies as $\rho Z^4/A$. (Since the ratio Z/A is nearly constant (it decreases slowly as Z increases), the mass attenuation coefficient for photoelectric absorption is sometimes said to vary as Z^3.)

Energy and distribution of photo-electrons

As already mentioned, the energy with which the photo-electron is emitted is determined by the equation

$$h\nu = W + m v^2/2$$

where W is the energy required to remove the electron from the atom. W is of the order of 0·5 keV. in light elements such as occur in tissue and increases with atomic number being about 88 keV. for lead. If the energy of the incident photon is fairly high, then the photo-electron is emitted with considerable energy (e.g. for a 200 keV. photon, the emission energy is 199·5 keV. in tissue and 112 keV. in lead).

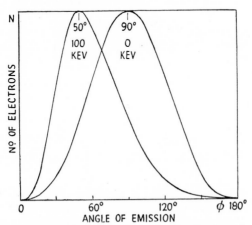

FIG. 6.07. Theoretical angular distribution of 0 and 100 keV. K-shell photo-electrons (wave-mechanical theory).

By permission from *Photons and Electrons* by K. H. Spring. (Methuen and Co. Ltd., London.)

With low energy radiation the photo-electrons are emitted in the direction of the electrical vector of the primary radiation, i.e. at right angles to the path of the incident beam. As the energy of the incident radiation increases, the electrons acquire a certain momentum in the direction of the incident radiation and are emitted in a progressively more forward direction. This is illustrated in fig. 6.07.

6.05. The Compton effect

For short wavelength, high energy radiation, where the energy of the incident quanta is much greater than the binding energy of the electrons in the material of the absorber, the quanta may be regarded as interacting with free electrons.

Part of the energy of the incident quantum is given up to the electron causing it to recoil, the remainder appears as a quantum of lower energy (i.e. lower frequency and longer wavelength radiation) which is scattered at such an angle that momentum is conserved. This is Compton scattering.

The change in wavelength of the radiation scattered through an angle θ may be calculated using the principles of conservation of energy and momentum. The result obtained is

$$\lambda - \lambda_0 = (1 - \cos \theta)h/mc$$

(where m denotes the rest mass of the electron, c the velocity of light, h Planck's constant).

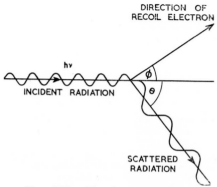

FIG. 6.08. The Compton effect.

It is necessary to use relativistic expressions for the energy and the momentum of the recoil electron since its velocity may approach that of light. The conservation of energy gives

$$h\nu_0 - h\nu = mc^2(K - 1) \qquad . \qquad . \qquad . \qquad (1)$$

i.e. $$h/\lambda_0 - h/\lambda = mc(K - 1) \qquad . \qquad . \qquad . \qquad (2)$$

where $K = 1/\sqrt{\{1 - (v/c)^2\}}$

The conservation of momentum gives

$$h/\lambda_0 - h\cos \theta/\lambda = Kmv \cos \phi \qquad . \qquad . \qquad (3)$$

and $$h \sin \theta/\lambda = Kmv \sin \phi \qquad . \qquad . \qquad (4)$$

Squaring and adding (3) and (4)

$$(h/\lambda_0)^2 + (h/\lambda)^2 - 2h^2 \cos \theta/\lambda\lambda_0 = K^2m^2v^2$$

Squaring (2)

$$(h/\lambda_0)^2 + (h/\lambda)^2 - 2h^2/\lambda\lambda_0 = m^2c^2(K - 1)^2$$

182

Subtracting

$$\frac{2h^2}{\lambda\lambda_0}(1 - \cos\theta) = m^2\{K^2v^2 - (K - 1)^2c^2\}$$

Now,

$$K^2v^2 = \frac{c^2v^2}{c^2 - v^2} \text{ and } (K - 1)^2c^2 = c^2\left\{\frac{c^2}{c^2 - v^2} - \frac{2}{\sqrt{\{1-(v/c)^2\}}} + 1\right\}$$

$$\therefore \frac{2h^2}{\lambda\lambda_0}(1 - \cos\theta) = m^2c^2\left\{\frac{2}{\sqrt{\{1-(v/c)^2\}}} - 2\right\}$$

$$= 2m^2c^2(K - 1)$$

$$= 2mc\left(\frac{h}{\lambda_0} - \frac{h}{\lambda}\right) \quad \text{from (2)}$$

$$\therefore \lambda - \lambda_0 = \frac{h}{mc}(1 - \cos\theta)$$

It follows from this formula, that the energy ($h\nu$) of the scattered photon is given by

$$h\nu = h\nu_0\bigg/\left[1 + \frac{h\nu_0}{mc^2}(1 - \cos\theta)\right].$$

If it is assumed that the number of photons scattered in a given direction is given by the classical equation, then the total energy scattered in a direction θ becomes,

$$I_\theta = I_{\theta \text{ classical}}\bigg/\left[1 + \frac{h\nu_0}{mc^2}(1 - \cos\theta)\right].$$

Thus the change in wavelength is zero when the radiation is scattered in the forward direction ($\theta = 0$) and increases to a maximum as θ approaches 180°, while the scattered intensity is that predicted by the classical equation in the forward direction but for other angles is reduced by an amount that increases with increasing energy of the incident radiation.

An analysis of the process using the methods of wave mechanics confirms the shift in wavelength and the reduction of scattering through large angles although the formula obtained for the scattered intensity is

$$I_\theta = I_{\theta \text{ classical}} \times [1 + \alpha(1 - \cos\theta)]^{-3}[1 + f(\alpha)]$$

where $\alpha = h\nu/mc^2$ and $f(\alpha)$ is a function of α which is extremely small unless $\alpha > 1$, i.e. unless the radiation has photon energy greater than 500 keV. This is known as the *Klein-Nishina* formula and is derived using Dirac's relativistic wave equations.

183

Fig. 6.09 shows the angular distribution of scattered radiation predicted by this equation.

The transition from elastic scattering to Compton scattering takes place gradually as the energy of the primary radiation increases. A full description can only be given in terms of wave mechanics but the general picture is as follows.

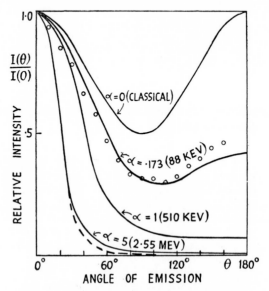

FIG. 6.09. Angular distribution of scattered radiation, full curve Klein-Nishina, dotted curve Dirac-Gordon, formulae, experimental points, Friederich and Goldhaber.

By permission from *Photons and Electrons* by K. H. Spring. (Methuen and Co. Ltd., London.)

At low energies the electrons are bound and unable to recoil and coherent Rayleigh scattering occurs. As the energy of the incident radiation increases, the outer electrons can be regarded as free while the inner electrons are still bound. Hence both Compton and Rayleigh scattering occur, so that some of the scattered radiation is changed in wavelength (the so-called "modified" radiation) and some is unchanged (unmodified). The ratio of the intensity of the modified to the unmodified scattered radiation, therefore, increases with

184

increase in energy of the incident radiation. It also increases with the angle of scattering. Some information on the ratio in a low atomic number material, in various directions and for different wavelengths is given in table 6.02. At energies considerably greater than that of the K shell of the absorber considered, the probability of Rayleigh scattering is negligible and only Compton scattering occurs. For these energies, the Compton attenuation coefficient *per electron* is independent of the atomic structure of the absorber. The mass attenuation coefficient (σ/ρ) for different elements therefore varies as the number of electrons per gram, i.e. as Z/A (where Z denotes

TABLE 6.02

RATIO OF MODIFIED TO UNMODIFIED SCATTER IN MATERIAL
OF LOW ATOMIC NUMBER $(Z = 8)$

Wavelength (Å)	Photon energy (keV.)	Angles for which ratio is		
		less than 1	10	*greater than* 100
0·2	62·0	< 29°	45°	> 71°
0·1	124	< 14°	22°	> 34°
0·01	1240	< 1·4°	2·2°	> 3·4°

atomic number and A atomic weight), and the linear attenuation coefficient (σ) varies as $\rho Z/A$. As already mentioned Z/A is approximately constant but decreases slowly as Z increases.

Although the Compton process is important at energies at which no other absorption process takes place, it must be emphasised that scattering (whether classical or Compton) never leads to as great a loss in energy as does photoelectrical absorption or pair production in the ranges where the latter processes are most effective.

Energy and distribution of recoil electrons

In the Compton process the energy of the incident quantum is shared between the secondary radiation and the recoil electron, and the energy received by the recoil electron is not usually a large fraction of the incident energy. For any particular element in the range of wavelength where both

185

photo-electric and Compton absorption may occur, the Compton recoil electrons are less energetic than the photo-electrons. This is illustrated in the case of water by table 6.06.

From the equations for conservation of momentum and energy given on page 114, it can be shown that

$$\tan \phi = \frac{1}{1 + \dfrac{h\nu_0}{mc^2}} \tan \frac{\theta}{2}$$

Since θ cannot exceed 180°, ϕ cannot exceed 90°, i.e. all the recoil electrons are emitted in a forward direction. Moreover, the greater the energy of the incident radiation, the smaller is ϕ. These general conclusions are confirmed when the more exact Klein-Nishina formula is used to determine the spatial distribution. This is illustrated in fig. 6.10.

6.06. Pair production

At energies above 1 MeV. interaction between the incident radiation and the nuclear field of an atom leads to yet another absorption process which is called pair production, since it is characterised by the simultaneous creation of a positive and negative electron. This process is not possible below 1 MeV., for the rest mass of an electron is $9 \cdot 11 \times 10^{-28}$ g. and using Einstein's relation $E = mc^2$, $9 \cdot 11 \times 10^{-28}$ g. is equivalent to $9 \cdot 11 \times 10^{-28} (3 \times 10^{10})^2$ ergs $= 82 \times 10^{-8}$ ergs $= 0 \cdot 511$ MeV. Since in order to conserve electrical charge, two particles (a positron and an electron) of this mass must be created simultaneously, a quantum of at least $1 \cdot 02$ MeV. in energy must disappear if a pair are to be produced. If the quantum which is absorbed has a higher energy, the excess above $1 \cdot 02$ MeV. appears as the kinetic energy of the electron and positron. The theoretical analysis of the process of production and annihilation of pairs requires the use of Dirac's relativistic wave equation. The analysis shows that the attenuation coefficient for pair production *per atom*, (1) increases rapidly with increase in the energy of the incident quantum, and (2) varies as the square of the atomic number of the absorber. Thus the mass attenuation coefficient for pair production (π/ρ) in different elements varies as Z^2/A, and the linear attenuation coefficient (π) varies as

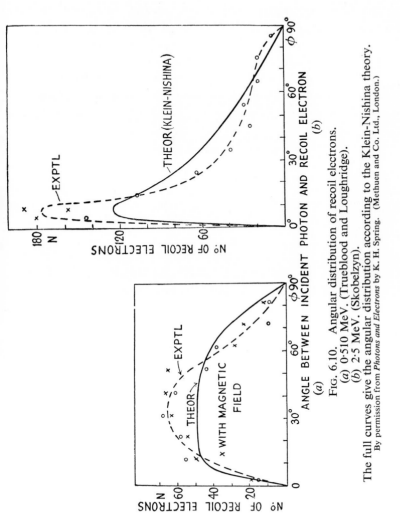

FIG. 6.10. Angular distribution of recoil electrons.
(a) 0·510 MeV. (Trueblood and Loughridge).
(b) 2·5 MeV. (Skobelzyn).

The full curves give the angular distribution according to the Klein–Nishina theory.
By permission from *Photons and Electrons* by K. H. Spring. (Methuen and Co. Ltd., London.)

$\rho Z^2/A$. (Again, since Z/A is approximately constant, π/ρ is sometimes said to be proportional to Z.) The electron and positron are usually each emitted at a fairly small angle ψ to the direction of the incident photon (fig. 6.12) and on the average are symmetrically distributed with respect to it.

The converse process, the combination of a positron and an electron to produce radiation is also possible and in an absorber irradiated by very high energy photons, the combination of the positrons with electrons of the absorber is a source of secondary

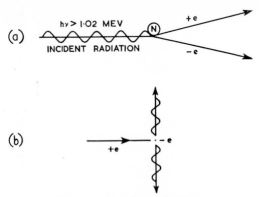

FIG. 6.11. (a) Pair production.
(b) Positron annihilation.

annihilation radiation. The probability of this process decreases with increase in energy of the positrons and is a maximum when the positron is nearly at rest, so the total energy which reappears as annihilation radiation is usually very nearly 1·02 MeV. This is usually in the form of two quanta of energy 0·51 MeV. which are emitted in opposite directions to one another, although a single quantum only may be emitted if the negative electron is strongly bound to a nucleus.

At energies above 2·04 MeV. (four times the electron rest mass), the pair production process can occur in the field of an electron as well as in the field of a nucleus. In this case, the original electron is set in motion (as well as the created pair) and the process is therefore usually referred to as triplet production. At high energies the probability of pair production in an electron field is approximately one-half that of pair production in the nuclear field.

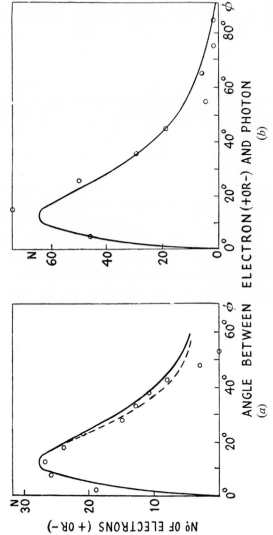

FIG. 6.12. Angular distribution of pair electrons, without regard to sign. The experimental points are determined (a) for argon (Zuber), (b) for nitrogen (Grosev), using thorium-C" γ-rays (2·62 MeV.). By permission from *Photons and Electrons* by K. H. Spring. (Methuen and Co. Ltd., London.)

6.07. Nuclear disintegration

Except in certain elements of very low atomic number ($Z < 5$), photo-nuclear disintegrations are not possible below about 7 MeV. Above this energy, however, it is possible for a photon to remove a neutron or proton from the nucleus of an atom. For each element, the probability of this process passes through a maximum at a particular energy and is relatively small except at energies within 3 or 4 MeV. of the peak. For the elements which occur in tissue, the maxima lie in the region of 20 to 25 MeV. and at the peak energy, the photonuclear absorption can amount to 10 to 15 per cent. of the total attenuation. Because the photonuclear process occurs over such a limited energy range, however, it normally represents a negligible fraction of the total energy absorbed from a beam of radiation with a continuous wavelength distribution.

6.08. The variation of total attenuation coefficients with wavelength

The characteristics of the different attenuation processes are summarised in table 6.03 and the values of the total mass attenuation coefficients for water, aluminium, copper, tin and lead are plotted against photon energy in fig. 6.13. In fig. 6.14 the photo-electric, Compton and pair production coefficients for water and lead are shown separately. (These graphs refer to the attenuation of monochromatic radiation. For X-ray beams such as are used in therapy, an approximate estimate of the attenuation processes which take place may be made by considering monochromatic radiation of photon energy numerically equal to about one-half of the accelerating voltage.) It will be noted that for all materials the total mass attenuation coefficient is high at long wavelengths, where it is mainly due to photo-electric absorption. It is low in the region where the Compton process predominates and increases again at short wavelengths due to the pair production process. For water, there is quite a wide range of wavelength (corresponding to photon energies of approximately 200 keV. to 2 MeV.) where energy loss is due almost entirely to the Compton process. (See fig. 6.14 and tables 6.05 and 6.06.)

Process	Absorption coefficient	Ionisation	Secondary radiation	Photon energy for which process makes significant contribution to total absorption (approx 10 %)
Classical scattering	—	None	Scattered radiation of same wavelength as primary distributed symmetrically in backward and forward direction about minimum intensity at 90° with primary radiation but increasing rapidly at very small angles.	May exceed 10 per cent. of total *scatter* in light elements at small angles up to about 50 keV, but is usually negligible fraction of total energy absorbed.
Photo-electric absorption	τ	Photo-electrons ejected with energies which (in light elements) may approach that of incident radiation and mainly at 90° to direction of primary radiation but in more forward direction at high energies. (See fig. 6.07)	Secondary radiation characteristic of the material of the absorber emitted mainly at right angles to photo-electrons, i.e. in backward and forward direction.	Below 70 keV. for light elements. Below 3 MeV. for lead.
Compton effect	σ	Recoil electrons ejected with energies usually fairly small fraction of that of incident radiation. Velocity has a forward component at all energies which becomes more marked as the energy increases. (See fig. 6.10)	Scattered radiation of wavelength greater than the primary radiation, distributed symmetrically backwards and forwards at low energies becoming more predominant in forward direction as energy of incident radiation increases. (See fig. 6.09)	15 keV. to 100 MeV. for light elements. 200 keV. to 20 MeV. in lead.
Pair Production	π	Positrons and negatrons emitted with increasing velocity as energy of incident radiation increases and nearly symmetrically at fairly small angles in forward direction. (See fig. 6.11)	Secondary annihilation radiation, usually two quanta of 0·5 MeV. energy emitted in opposite directions, at right angles to direction of primary radiation.	Above 8 MeV. in light elements. Above 2 MeV. in lead.

191

The energy range where the Compton process predominates decreases with increase in atomic number. Since both photoelectric absorption and the pair production process are greater

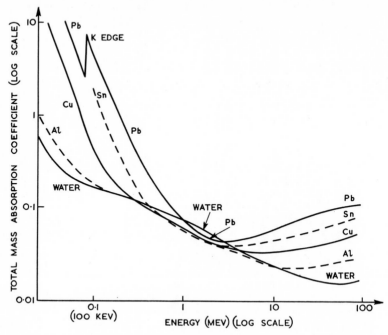

FIG. 6.13. Graph showing the variation with photon energy of the total mass attenuation coefficients (formerly called absorption coefficients) for water, aluminium, copper, tin and lead.

TABLE 6.04

	Aluminium	Copper	Lead
Photon Energy at which photoelectric and Compton attenuation co-efficients are equal .	50 keV.	150 keV.	500 keV.
Photon Energy at which Compton and pair production coefficients are equal	15 MeV.	9 MeV.	5 MeV.

in elements of high atomic number, the total mass attenuation coefficient is greater in elements of high atomic number at both low and at very high energies, but in the range where

192

attenuation is mainly due to the Compton process, the mass attenuation coefficient of elements with high atomic number may be less than that of light elements since Z/A (which determines the number of electrons per gram) decreases as Z increases. Thus at 1·0 MeV., for example, the mass attenuation coefficient of bone is somewhat less than that of soft tissue whereas at

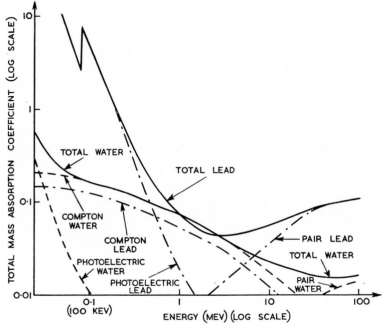

FIG. 6.14.   Graph showing the variation with photon energy of the total mass attenuation coefficient (formerly called absorption coefficient) for water and lead.   The contributions made by the photo-electric, Compton and pair production processes are shown separately.

50 MeV. the mass attenuation coefficient of bone is greater than that of soft tissue and at 50 keV. it is several times that of soft tissue. Thus in diagnostic radiography where definite differences in attenuation between bone and soft tissue are desirable, photon energies of the order of 50 keV. or less are used, whereas in radiotherapy where it is desirable to keep differences in absorption between bone and soft tissue a minimum, megavoltage radiation is preferred. (See Chapters IX and XI.)

193

The linear attenuation coefficient (μ) of any material varies with energy in the same way as the mass coefficient. In a comparison of the linear attenuation coefficients of different materials, however, because density does not vary systematically (regularly) with atomic number, the ratio of the densities of the materials as well as their atomic numbers must be considered. For example, in comparing lead with concrete as a protective barrier to attenuate radiation, the thickness of the barrier as well as the weight of material required may be of interest. At low energies, lead provides a thinner, less massive (and cheaper) barrier than concrete. The mass attenuation coefficient of lead will be of the order of twenty times that of concrete (the exact figure depending on the energy,) the density of lead is approximately five times that of concrete, so $\mu_{Pb} / \mu_{concrete}$ is approximately 100. At 1·5 MeV. the mass attenuation coefficient of lead is slightly less than that of concrete, so the concrete provides the less massive (and cheaper) barrier, but because of the greater density of lead, the linear attenuation coefficient of lead is still nearly five times that of concrete so lead provides a thinner barrier. In discussing, the shielding required around X- or γ-ray sources, the term " lead equivalent " of a material, denotes the thickness of lead affording the same attenuation under specified conditions, as the material in question.

6.09. Real absorption

So far, we have been considering the removal of energy from the incident radiation, whether by scattering or by absorption. When the biological effects of the radiation in the absorber are to be considered, however, it is important to know what fraction of the incident radiation gives up energy to the absorber (i.e. undergoes " real " absorption). For this purpose it is necessary to distinguish between the energy which is transferred from the beam to secondary electrons (i.e. is converted from electro-magnetic to kinetic energy) and that which is scattered or re-radiated as electro-magnetic energy. It is therefore usual to separate the various attenuation co-efficients into two parts, one part corresponding to the transfer of energy to electrons only. For example, for Compton attenuation, σ may be written as $\sigma_a + \sigma_s$ where σ_a is determined by the fraction of the energy removed from the primary beam which is given to the recoil electrons and σ_s by the fraction scattered as secondary radiation. Similarly for pair production, $\pi = \pi_a + \pi_s$ where π_a is determined by the fraction of the energy removed from the primary beam which reappears as

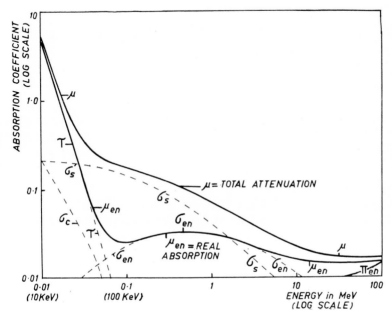

FIG. 6.15. Graph showing the variation with photon energy of the total mass attenuation coefficient (μ) and the real mass absorption coefficient (μ_{en}) for water.

the kinetic energy of the positron and the electron, π_s by the fraction which reappears as annihilation radiation. In photo-electric absorption a similar distinction may be made, τ_a depending upon the fraction of the energy appearing as kinetic energy of the photo-electrons, τ_s upon the fraction reradiated as characteristic radiation by the absorber. In elements of low atomic number, however, the secondary radiation is so soft that it is immediately reabsorbed and in this case therefore the total photo-electric attenuation coefficient τ represents

195

TABLE 6.05

ATTENUATION COEFFICIENTS OF WATER (cm.⁻¹)

Energy (MeV)	Photo-electric τ^*	Coherent scatter σ_c^*	Pair production				Compton Process					Total $(\mu-\sigma_c)$	μ^*
			π_k	π_{en}	π_s	π	σ_k	$\sigma_{en}\dagger$	σ_s	$\sigma\dagger$	$\mu_{en}\dagger$		
0·01	4·75	0·214					0·004		0·210	0·214	4·75	4·96	5·18
0·015	1·28	0·109					0·006		0·205	0·211	1·29	1·49	1·60
0·02	0·498	0·067					0·008		0·200	0·207	0·506	0·705	0·772
0·03	0·135	0·033					0·010		0·190	0·200	0·145	0·335	0·368
0·04	0·0495	0·019					0·0129		0·181	0·194	0·0624	0·243	0·262
0·05	0·0234	0·010					0·0152		0·173	0·188	0·0386	0·211	0·221
0·06	0·0130	0·008					0·0172		0·166	0·183	0·0302	0·196	0·204
0·08	0·0050	0·005					0·0200		0·153	0·173	0·0252	0·178	0·183
0·1	0·0023	0·004					0·0227		0·142	0·165	0·0250	0·167	0·171
0·15	0·0007	0·002					0·0269		0·122	0·149	0·0276	0·149	0·151
0·2	0·0003	0·001					0·0294		0·1066	0·1360	0·0297	0·136	0·137
0·3		0·0003					0·0318		0·0865	0·1183	0·0318	0·118	0·119
0·4							0·0328		0·0732	0·1060	0·0328	0·106	0·106
0·5			0·000	0·0000	0·0001	0·0001	0·0332	0·0328	0·0635	0·0967	0·0332	0·0967	0·0967
0·6			0·0002	0·0002	0·0002	0·0004	0·0328	0·0320	0·0567	0·0895	0·0328		0·0895
0·8			0·0007	0·0007	0·0004	0·0011	0·0321	0·0310	0·0466	0·0787	0·0320		0·0787
1·0			0·0014	0·0014	0·0004	0·0018	0·0311		0·0395	0·0706	0·0310		0·0706
1·5			0·0019	0·0019	0·0005	0·0024	0·0284	0·0283	0·0290	0·0574	0·0283		0·0575
2·0			0·0025	0·0025	0·0005	0·0030	0·0259	0·0258	0·0230	0·0489	0·0260		0·0493
3·0			0·0034	0·0034	0·0005	0·0040	0·0221	0·0220	0·0164	0·0385	0·0227		0·0396
4·0			0·0043	0·0042	0·0005	0·0048	0·0194	0·0192	0·0127	0·0321	0·0205		0·0339
5·0			0·0019	0·0019	0·0005	0·0024	0·0173	0·0171	0·0104	0·0277	0·0190		0·0301
6·0			0·0025	0·0025	0·0005	0·0030	0·0157	0·0154	0·0088	0·0245	0·0179		0·0275
8·0			0·0034	0·0034	0·0005	0·0040	0·0133	0·0130	0·0067	0·0200	0·0164		0·0240
10·0			0·0043	0·0042	0·0005	0·0048	0·0116	0·0112	0·0055	0·0171	0·0154		0·0219

energy transferred to electrons. The sum $\tau_a + \sigma_a + \pi_a$ (or $\tau + \sigma_a + \pi_a$ in low atomic number materials) is denoted by

TABLE 6.06 (a)

THE RELATIVE IMPORTANCE OF DIFFERENT ATTENUATION PROCESSES IN WATER

Quantum energy (MeV)	% of Quanta removed by			% of Secondary Electrons which are		
	Photo-electric absorption	Coherent scatter + Compton effect	Pair production	Photo-electrons	Compton electrons	Pair-electrons
0·01	91·7	8·3		95·8	4·2	
0·02	64·1	35·9		70·6	29·4	
0·05	10·4	89·6		11·1	88·9	
0·10	1·2	98·8		1·4	98·6	
0·20	0·2	99·8		0·2	99·8	
0·50		100·0			100·0	
1·0		100·0			100·0	
2·0		99·2	0·8		98·5	1·5
5·0		92·0	8·0		84·9	15·1
10·0		78·1	21·9		63·4	36·6
20·0		57·0	43·0		39·2	60·8
50·0		30·1	69·9		17·3	82·7

TABLE 6.06 (b)

THE ENERGY DISTRIBUTION AMONGST SECONDARY ELECTRONS IN WATER

Quantum energy (MeV)	% of Energy carried by			Electron Energy (MeV)				
	Photo-electrons	Compton electrons	Pair electrons	Photo-electrons	Compton electrons		Pair electrons	
					(max.)	(mean.)	(max.)	(mean)
0·01	99·9	0·1		0·0095	0·00038	0·00014		
0·02	98·4	1·6		0·0195	0·00145	0·00068		
0·05	60·6	39·4		0·0495	0·00818	0·00386		
0·10	9·2	90·8		0·0995	0·0281	0·0137		
0·20	1·0	99·0		0·1995	0·0878	0·0428		
0·50		100·0			0·331	0·170		
1·0		100·0			0·796	0·438		
2·0		99·2	0·8		1·774	1·056	0·98	0·49
5·0		90·1	9·9		4·76	3·12	3·98	1·98
10·0		73·0	27·0		9·75	6·79	8·98	4·44
20·0		50·3	49·7		19·8	14·5	19·0	9·2
50·0		25·3	74·7		49·8	38·5	49·0	23·6

μ_k and called the energy transfer coefficient. For moderate photon energies, all the energy transferred to secondary electrons is dissipated in collision processes and is deposited in the absorber, i.e. this energy undergoes " real absorption ". If the energy of the secondary electrons is sufficiently high for an appreciable fraction of their energy to be dissipated in Bremsstrahlung, however, then the energy so dissipated should not be included in that which is really absorbed. The total real absorption coefficient μ_{en} is therefore equal to μ_k at low energies but in general is given by $\mu_{en} = \mu_k (1 - G)$ where G denotes the fraction of the energy of secondary electrons which is converted to Bremsstrahlung. G is of course an average over the secondary electron energy spectrum. The magnitude of G increases with increasing atomic number of the absorber but it is usually negligible below about 1 MeV. Table 6.05 and fig. 6.15 show how the contributions made by the different processes to both the real absorption coefficient and the total attenuation coefficient vary with energy for water, and Table 6.06 shows how the energy which is really absorbed is distributed amongst the secondary electrons in water.

6.10. The use of filters to modify the quality of X-radiation

The spectral distribution of radiation from an X-ray therapy set was described in Chapter III. It will be recalled that the minimum wavelength is determined by the accelerating voltage, but that there is a continuous distribution of wavelengths above the minimum and that there are also lines characteristic of the material of the target (fig. 3.31, 3.32). In therapy except in the treatment of skin ailments, the presence of the longer wavelengths in the X-ray beam is undesirable, since such radiation is absorbed in the surface layers of the skin and increases the skin dose but does not penetrate to the lower tissues which it is desired to treat. It is usual therefore to insert filters in the X-ray beam to reduce the intensity of the longer wavelengths. It is possible to do this without simultaneously reducing the intensity of the shorter waves equally because of the variation in the photo-electric absorption with wavelength.

For most (but not all) energies it is possible to select a material of such atomic number that, in the range required, the attenuation coefficient, while not too large at the short wavelengths, is increasing rapidly with increase in wavelength so that the longer wavelengths are attenuated much more than the shorter waves. For X-rays generated at voltages below 120 kVp. aluminium is a suitable material. Above this it is necessary to use composite filters (see below) but the primary material used between 120 and 200 kVp. is copper, between 200 and 400 kVp. tin, and from 800 kVp. to a few MeV. lead. Above 2 MeV. the onset of pair production means that the attenuation coefficient of the heavier elements increases with decrease in wavelength and lead for instance begins to attenuate the very short as well as very long waves more than those of intermediate length. The advantages gained by the use of filters are much less in this region than at lower energies, although up to 30 MeV. materials with low atomic number reduce the long wavelength radiation slightly more than the shorter waves.

For X-rays generated between 120 kVp. and 2 MV., the primary filters of copper, tin and lead must be supplemented by filters of lower atomic number. These secondary filters are required because the longest wavelengths generated by the set are usually beyond the K absorption edge of the primary filter. Since there is a sharp decrease in attenuation coefficient at the K edge the primary filter would allow a band of low energy radiation to pass at this wavelength. Furthermore the primary filter itself produces secondary X-radiation of this wavelength so that secondary filters are necessary to reduce the intensity of the characteristic radiation from the primary filter. Filters of copper are usually supplemented by aluminium, those of tin by copper plus aluminium, and those of lead by tin plus copper plus aluminium. The effects of a tin, copper, aluminium combination (known as a Thoraeus filter) are illustrated in fig. 3.32 of Chapter III.

It is of course essential that compound filters be correctly inserted in the X-ray beam, i.e. with the element of highest atomic number nearest the X-ray tube, if the secondary filters are to absorb the characteristic radiation from the primary filter.

In practice, the thickness of filter used in conjunction with any particular X-ray set under given operating conditions depends upon the output of the tube and the time which is available, or which it is considered desirable to spend, in treating a patient. As explained above, the attenuation of the longer wavelengths is accompanied by simultaneous attenuation of the shorter waves (although to a lesser extent) and if a beam is heavily filtered although the homogeneity is increased, the intensity is reduced. This sets a limit to the thickness of filter which is practicable.

6.11. Specification of quality of X-ray beam by half-value layer

The nature of any particular X-ray beam can be specified completely only by stating the fraction of the energy which is associated with each particular (small) range of wavelength, but this is difficult to measure, so in radiology a statement of the penetrating properties of the radiation (which depends upon the energy distribution) is used instead. Thus it is the custom to specify the quality of an X-ray beam in terms of the thickness of some particular absorber which is required to reduce the radiation by one-half. This is known as the half-value layer (H.V.L.) or half-value thickness (H.V.T.) of the beam and is usually expressed in mm. of aluminium for X-rays generated below about 120 kVp., in mm. of copper for 120 to 400 kVp. and in mm. of lead for higher voltages.

To define half-value layer precisely, it is necessary to state how the reduction of the radiation "by one-half" is to be measured. The measure used, the exposure-rate, will be discussed in detail in the next chapter, but may be regarded as an experimentally measured quantity from which the radiation intensity may be calculated. (For monochromatic radiation, it makes no difference if the half-value layer is defined in terms of intensity instead of exposure-rate.) Thus the International Commission on Radiological Units and Measurements define half-value layer as "the thickness, or the surface density, of a specified material which attenuates the beam to such an extent that the exposure-rate is reduced to one-half, under narrow beam conditions".[3]

When carrying out an experimental determination of half-value layer, it is necessary to use a small well defined beam to reduce the amount of scattered radiation. It is also necessary to place the measuring instrument at a sufficient distance beyond the absorber to avoid any effects due to secondary radiation from the latter.

TABLE 6.07

Accelerating voltage (kVp.)	Filtration		Approximate half value layer
	Inherent	External	
6	1 mm. Be	None	0·01 mm. Al
15	„	„	0·04 mm. Al
30	„	0·01 mm. Al	0·1 mm. Al
50	„	1·0 mm. Al	1·0 mm. Al
100	Glass	None	1·0 mm. Al
100	window	1·0 mm. Al	2·0 mm. Al
120	„	3·0 mm. Al	4·0 mm. Al
140	„	0·25 mm. Cu + 1·0 mm. Al	8·0 mm. Al
200	„	1·0 mm. Cu + 1·0 mm. Al	1·5 mm. Cu
200	„	2·0 mm. Cu + 1·0 mm. Al	2·0 mm. Cu
250	„	1·0 mm. Cu + 1·0 mm. Al	1·75 mm. Cu
250	„	2·0 mm. Cu + 1·0 mm. Al	2·3 mm. Cu
250	„	0·4 mm. Sn + 0·25 mm. Cu + 1·0 mm. Al	2·3 mm. Cu
250	„	0·8 mm. Sn + 0·5 mm. Cu + 1·0 mm. Al	3·0 mm. Cu
400	„	2·0 mm. Cu + 1·0 mm. Al	3·5 mm. Cu
400	„	1·6 mm. Sn + 0·8 mm. Cu + 1·0 mm. Al	5·0 mm. Cu
1000	About 3 mm. Pb	None	8·0 mm. Cu 3·0 mm. Pb
2000	About 5·0 mm. Pb	None	6·0 mm. Pb
2000	„	4·0 mm. Pb	7·0 mm. Pb

The description of an X-ray beam in terms of half-value layer has the disadvantage that it is possible to produce two X-ray beams of the same half-value layer which are not absorbed in an identical manner at other depths. For example, a lightly filtered beam produced at a high kilovoltage may have the same half-value layer as a more heavily filtered beam produced at a lower kilovoltage, but will be more penetrating

201

at great depths. The kilovoltage and filtration are therefore usually stated in addition to the half-value layer.

Occasionally the second half-value layer (the thickness of absorber which reduces the radiation from 50 to 25 per cent. of its initial value) or the homogeneity coefficient (the ratio of the half-value layer to the second half-value layer) may be specified.

Table 6.07 gives typical half-value layers for some common operating conditions. It must be emphasised, however, that the half-value layer of any radiation used therapeutically should always be determined under the operating conditions used in any particular establishment.

6.12. Equivalent wavelength and equivalent photon energy

The quality of an X-ray beam may also be described by specifying the wavelength or the photon energy of mono-chromatic radiation which has the same half-value layer as the radiation considered. This is known as the "equivalent wavelength" or the "equivalent photon energy" of the beam.

TABLE 6.08

Half-value layer (mm. Cu)	Equivalent wavelength (Å)	Equivalent photon energy (keV.)
1·0	0·155	80
2·0	0·108	115
5·0	0·062	200
10·0	0·022	570

Now for monochromatic radiation, the half-value layer $(x_{\frac{1}{2}})$ is related to the linear attenuation coefficient (μ) by the equation

$$x_{\frac{1}{2}} = \frac{0 \cdot 693}{\mu}$$

This equation is obtained by substituting $I = \frac{1}{2} I_0$ when $x = x_{\frac{1}{2}}$ in the equation $I = I_0 e^{-\mu x}$.

202

The equation is analogous to that relating the half-life of a radioactive isotope to the decay constant.

For a monochromatic beam of specified H.V.L. in a particular absorbing material, the above equation can be used to calculate the linear attenuation coefficient and from tables relating the linear attenuation coefficient to photon energy, the latter can therefore be obtained.

The equivalent energy of a typical X-ray therapy beam is usually numerically of the order of one-half of the accelerating voltage. See tables 6.07 and 6.08. This fact should be borne in mind when reading Chapters VII and XI.

6.13. Change of Radiation quality with depth in tissue

A statement of the quality of a radiation beam such as half-value layer, normally refers to the energy distribution of the radiation measured in air. When the radiation enters an absorbing material, absorption and scattering change the energy distribution. The effective energy of an initially monochromatic beam of radiation is always reduced as it penetrates an absorber, since some of the primary radiation is removed and replaced by lower energy scattered radiation. In a heterogeneous beam, however, the *primary* radiation is hardened as it traverses an absorber, due to the preferential absorption of the less penetrating components. At energies up to a few MeV. in high atomic number materials and up to about 50 MeV. in tissue, this means the effective energy of the primary radiation is increased (since low energy radiation is more readily absorbed than higher energy radiation except at energies so high that absorption is mainly by the pair production process). At fairly low energies, where absorption is mainly by the photoelectric process, this effect may remove more low energy photons from the beam than are contributed by the scattered radiation, so that the effective energy of the beam increases as it enters an absorber. Thus at a depth of 2 or 3 cm. in tissue, the half-value layer of diagnostic or superficial therapy beams may be greater than that measured in air. With deep therapy radiation, however, where absorption is mainly by the Compton process, scattering is relatively much more important compared with absorption than at lower energies and the effective energy and half-value layer of such beams is invariably less at a depth in tissue than in air. The change in radiation quality depends upon the depth and area of the field considered, since this determines the amount of the scattered radiation. The change in quality is sometimes of importance in radiotherapy (see Chapter XI).

REFERENCES

1. GRODSTEIN, G. W. (1959).   National Bureau of Standards Circular 583 and supplement.
2. BERGER, R. (1961). *Radiation Research*, **15**, 8.
3. International Commission on Radiological Units and Measurements (1962). Report 10d.
   U.S. National Bureau of Standards Handbook. No. 87.

OTHER REFERENCES

COMPTON, A. H. and ALLISON, S. K. (1935). *X-rays in Theory and Experiment*. London, MacMillan.
HEITLER, W. (1944). *The Quantum Theory of Radiation*. Oxford, University Press.
SPRING, K. H. (1950). *Photons and Electrons*. London, Methuen.

EXAMINATION QUESTIONS

1. The attenuation (absorption) of monochromatic X-radiation is stated to be exponential. Explain the meaning of the terms " monochromatic " and " exponential ". Describe very briefly how the attenuation of a beam of X-rays by various thicknesses of aluminium may be used to determine the half-value thickness (layer) of the radiation.

M.S.R. (R. & T.), 1963.

2. Describe how the absorption of X-radiation depends upon the atomic number of the absorbing material.
Why is it usual (*a*) to filter the beam of X-rays coming from an X-ray tube, and (*b*) to incorporate a filter in a film badge holder? State materials which would be used for these purposes.

M.S.R. (R. & T.), 1962.

3. Name the two main processes by which a beam of X-rays (30 kV-250 kV) is attenuated (absorbed) by a thin slab of material and state how the magnitude of each depends upon: (*a*) the nature of the material, and (*b*) the quality of the radiation. Discuss briefly one important aspect of each of these processes in radiology.

M.S.R. (R. & T.), 1964.

4. What is meant by the lead equivalent of a brick wall? Upon what factors does the lead equivalent of an object depend, and in particular, how and why does it vary with radiation quality? Hence explain under what circumstances you would prefer concrete to lead for protection purposes.

M.S.R. (R. & T.), 1963.

5. The lead equivalent of a particular lead-rubber apron is 0·25 mm. lead. (a) What is meant by this statement? (b) How could the truth of this statement be checked? (c) What other tests would be necessary to pass the apron as fit for use? (d) What are the reasons that make lead a useful material for protection purposes, particularly in the diagnostic range of X-rays?

M.S.R. (R. & T.), 1965.

6. (a) State very briefly what is meant by the " Quality " of a beam of X-rays.
(b) State (in order of importance) the factors which control the Quality of an X-ray beam.
(c) A certain beam of X-radiation is said to have a Half Value Thickness of 1·5 mm. copper. Explain briefly the meaning of the statement.
(d) If the observed exposure rate (dose rate) at a point in the above beam is 60 r./min. what would you expect it to be after a 3 mm. thick sheet of copper has been placed between the tube and the point in question?
(e) The actual exposure rate measured in (d) might be more than that calculated. Explain why, very briefly.

M.S.R. (R. & T.), 1965.

7. Compare and contrast the Compton process and the photoelectric process in the X-ray attenuation by matter. Show how both of these processes are relevant to the variation of contrast in a radiograph with kilovoltage, both when a grid is used and when it is not.

F.S.R. (R. & T.), 1961.

8. Describe how the X- and γ-ray absorbing properties of materials depend on their composition and on the radiation quality. Illustrate your answer by reference to the tissues of the human body.

F.S.R. (T.), 1964.

9. What is meant by the quality of an X-ray beam? Explain how the quality may be specified (a) as fully as possible; (b) in a way suitable for practical purposes.
For the shortest wavelength in an X-ray beam the H.V.T. in soft tissue is 4 cm. whilst for the effective wavelength it is 2 cm. Calculate the percentage transmission at each of these wavelengths through 16 cm. of soft tissue.

F.S.R. (R.), 1964.

10. Describe the processes which contribute to the attenuation of a beam of X-rays as it passes through matter.

Explain the advantages gained by the use of filters in *either* diagnostic radiology or therapeutic radiology.

D.M.R., 1963.

11. Describe and discuss the physical factors which influence the transmission of X-rays through a patient.

For the shortest wavelength of an X-ray beam the half-value thickness of soft tissues is 4 cm., while for the effective wavelength of the beam it is 2 cm. By a graphical or any other method determine the percentage of radiation at each of these wavelengths transmitted by 14 cm. of soft tissue.

D.M.R., 1963.

12. Describe the physical processes involved in the *scattering* of X-ray or γ-ray beams, and show how these processes depend on the wavelength of the radiations.

Explain either (*a*) how the deleterious effects of scattering can be minimised in diagnostic radiology, or (*b*) how scattering affects the distribution of dose in a therapeutic treatment.

D.M.R., 1963.

13. Describe (*a*) the photo-electric effect, (*b*) the Compton effect, in relation to X-rays. Discuss the importance of the photo-electric effect for diagnostic radiology and of the Compton effect for radiotherapy.

Discuss the significance of classical scattering and of pair-production in normal radiological practice.

D.M.R., 1964.

CHAPTER VII

THE MEASUREMENT OF IONISING RADIATIONS

7.01. General discussion of the measurement of X- and γ-radiation in radiology

A UNIDIRECTIONAL beam of monoenergetic X- or γ-radiation (such as was considered in Chapter VI), can be described by stating the wavelength or photon energy of the radiation and either the intensity or the photon flux density. However, in the X- and γ-ray beams used in medicine, the energy of the photons is often spread over a wide range, the photons may travel in diverse directions and the photon flux density may vary from point to point and possibly also from one instant of time to another. Such radiation is completely specified only if the number of photons of each energy travelling in a given direction at each point in the beam and at each instant of time is known. In practice, it is difficult to obtain such complete information and fortunately in radiology such a complete description is not essential. The aim of measuring the radiation is to be able to assess the biological effects which will be produced. For this purpose, a measure of quality, such as half-value layer, together with a measure of quantity which can be easily and accurately determined and which is uniquely related to the biological effects, is sufficient.

The biological effect of any ionising radiation upon cells of a given type in a given environment, is believed to depend upon (1) the energy absorbed per unit mass of the irradiated material, and (2) the spatial distribution of the ions. For *electromagnetic* radiation, the distribution of ions is a fairly slowly varying function of the energy (except at very low energies), i.e. the biological effects vary only slowly with radiation quality. Thus for X- and γ-radiation the biological effects should be closely correlated with the energy absorbed by the material at the place of interest. One method of describing the quantity of radiation with which a region has been treated is therefore to specify the energy imparted to the region considered per unit mass of irradiated material. This is called the " *absorbed dose* ".

However, the energy absorbed by any material from a beam of radiation depends upon the nature of the absorbing material as well as upon the intensity and quality of the incident radiation. For some purposes it is desirable to be able to describe the quantity of radiation to which a region has been exposed without reference to the nature of the particular material in which the radiation is absorbed. For this purpose a measure of the radiation determined by the ionisation produced per unit mass of a standard absorbing material (namely air) has been introduced. This is called " *exposure* ". (Notice that exposure is measured by the ionisation produced in air not by the energy absorbed. This means it is directly related to what is usually recorded by the measuring instrument. However, except when Bremsstrahlung production is important, the ionisation is proportional to the energy removed from the beam in air (see section 7.03).) Historically the concept of exposure (although not given this name) is much older than that of absorbed dose, which was only formally recognised in 1953. In certain circumstances (which happen to be commonly met with in practice) the absorbed dose may be calculated if the exposure is known. For radiations of moderate energy, exposure is relatively easily measured and is the quantity usually determined experimentally but as the radiation energy increases above a few MeV., exposure becomes progressively more difficult to measure and the absorbed dose is the quantity determined by experiment.

The relationship between exposure and absorbed dose may be made clearer by considering their values at two points such as P and Q in fig. 7.01. P is situated in soft tissue but Q is situated in bone. If we consider for simplicity that all the radiation reaching P and Q is travelling in the forward direction (i.e. back-scattered radiation is neglected) then if P and Q are at the same distance from the radiation source and the same depth below the tissue surface, the exposure at Q will be equal to the exposure at P. The absorbed dose and the biological effects at Q, however, will in general differ from the absorbed dose and biological effects at P because the absorbing medium at Q is bone, whereas the medium at P is soft tissue.

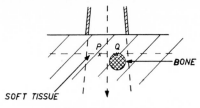

SOFT TISSUE

BONE

FIG. 7.01.

There are thus two methods commonly used in radiology for describing how a region has been treated by radiation (1) by specifying the absorbed dose, (2) by specifying the exposure. These two quantities, whose general meaning have been indicated above, have been defined by the International Commission on Radiological Units and Measurements[1] in terms which are given below.

7.02. Definitions of absorbed dose and exposure

The definition of absorbed dose given by the I.C.R.U. in 1962 is as follows :

" The absorbed dose (D) is the quotient of ΔE_D by Δm, where ΔE_D is the energy imparted by ionising radiation to the matter in a volume element, and Δm is the mass of the matter in that volume element."

Thus $$D = \Delta E_D / \Delta m$$

The symbol Δ is used, to indicate that the volume element considered should be small, since in most situations encountered in radiology the absorbing material is not uniformly irradiated. Strictly the quotient $\Delta E_D / \Delta m$ represents an average value over the volume element considered. The absorbed dose at a point in a non-uniform radiation field is the limiting value of $\Delta E_D / \Delta m$ as the volume considered is reduced in size until a further decrease makes no appreciable change in the value of the quotient. It is assumed (unless the contrary is explicitly stated), that this limit can be reached while the volume element considered is large enough for a considerable number of interactions between photons and atoms to take place within it.

209

The absorbed dose may be measured in any units of energy per unit mass, but is usually measured in special units called rads. 1 rad represents an energy absorption of 100 ergs per gram.

The definition of exposure given by the I.C.R.U. in 1962 is as follows:

" The exposure (X) is the quotient of $\varDelta Q$ by $\varDelta m$, where $\varDelta Q$ is the sum of the electrical charges on all the ions of any one sign produced in air when all the electrons (negatrons and positrons), liberated by photons in a volume element of air whose mass is $\varDelta m$, are completely stopped in air."

Thus $$X = \varDelta Q / \varDelta m.$$

The symbol $\varDelta$ is used with the connotation already discussed. Exposure may be measured in any units of charge per unit mass but is usually measured in special units called roentgens.

1 roentgen $(R) = 2 \cdot 58 \times 10^{-4}$ coulomb per kilogram.

The roentgen unit was first formally defined in 1928. From 1928 until 1962 slight changes in the wording of the definition were made from time to time, but the definition prior to 1962 was essentially as follows: "The roentgen is that quantity of X- or γ-radiation such that the associated corpuscular emission per 0·001293 g. of air, produces, in air, ions carrying one electrostatic unit of quantity of electricity of either sign." This statement actually describes what is now called exposure, as well as specifying the size of the unit in which it is to be measured. This was necessary at a time when the concept of exposure had not been precisely formulated, but the roentgen is now precisely defined by stating that it represents an exposure of $2 \cdot 54 \times 10^{-4}$ C./kg. This value is numerically equal to 1 e.s.u. per 0·001293 g. so the size of the roentgen unit has not been changed.* (0·001293 g. is the mass of 1 cc. of dry air at 0°C and 760 mm. pressure.) Before 1962, the abbreviation r. was used for roentgen, but R. is now preferred.

---

* It should be noted that prior to 1956, the exposure measured in roentgens was usually called the radiation " dose ". In 1956, the term " exposure dose " was introduced to emphasise the difference between the measure of the radiation in roentgens and the absorbed dose in rads, then in 1962 the word " dose " was dropped from " exposure dose ". However neither the quantity which is measured in roentgens, nor the size of the unit has been changed. It is only the name given to the quantity which has been altered.

7.03. The relation between the intensity of a beam of X- or γ-radiation and the exposure rate

Consider for simplicity a unidirectional, mono-energetic beam of X or γ-radiation and a volume element throughout which the intensity (I) in ergs per cm.^{2} per sec. can be considered constant. Then the energy really absorbed (i.e. converted to kinetic energy of secondary electrons and not re-radiated) in air is given by $(\mu_{en}/\rho)_{air}$. I ergs per gram per second, where $(\mu_{en}/\rho)_{air}$ denotes the (real) mass energy-absorption coefficient of air for radiation of the particular energy considered.

The kinetic energy of the secondary electrons which is not re-radiated, is dissipated in producing excitation and ionisation. The energy lost on the average by the secondary electrons per ion pair produced is a constant regardless of the initial energy of the electrons (at least above 20 keV). Electrons of greater initial energy merely produce proportionately more ions before they are stopped. (This fact has been established experimentally in various ways, (1) by measuring the ionisation produced by β-rays of known energy, (2) by measuring the ionisation produced by electrons accelerated to a known energy, (3) by observing in a Wilson cloud-chamber the ionisation along the tracks of photo-electrons generated by X-rays of known wavelength, (4) by comparing the ionisation produced by an X-ray beam with its heating effect.) In air, recent experiments indicate that the average energy expended by electrons per ion pair produced, is 33·7 eV.[2] (The average energy per ion pair is greater than the ionisation energy, i.e. the minimum energy required to remove an electron from an atom, which is about 16 eV., because some energy is used up in other processes such as excitation.) But if a constant amount of energy is required per ion pair produced, it follows that the total number of ions formed can be used as a measure of the energy really absorbed from the radiation.

Consider a mass of air exposed to X roentgens of radiation. Then from the definition of the roentgen, the charge produced
$$= 2\cdot58 \cdot 10^{-4} \cdot X \cdot C/kg.$$
Since the electronic charge is $1\cdot602 \cdot 10^{-19}C.,$

∴ the number of ion pairs produced

$$= 2 \cdot 58 \cdot 10^{-7} \cdot X/1 \cdot 602 \cdot 10^{-19} \text{ per g.}$$
$$= 1 \cdot 610 \cdot 10^{12} \cdot X \cdot \text{ per g.}$$

If the production of an ion pair requires on the average 33·7 eV., the energy required to produce the above number of ions

$$= 33 \cdot 7 \cdot 2.58 \cdot X \cdot / 1 \cdot 602 \times 10^{12} \text{ eV. per g.}$$
$$= 33 \cdot 7 \cdot 2 \cdot 58 \cdot X \cdot \text{ergs per g.}$$
$$(1 \text{ eV.} = 1 \cdot 602 \cdot 10^{-12} \text{ ergs})$$
$$= 86 \cdot 9 \, X \cdot \text{ergs per g.}$$

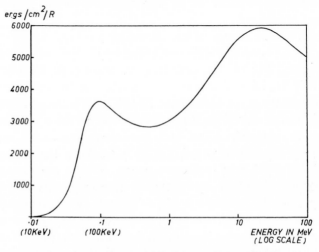

FIG. 7.02.   Graph showing variation of energy fluence per roentgen with photon energy.

If the X roentgens are delivered in t seconds so that the exposure-rate is X/t roentgens per second then the rate at which energy is required to produce the observed ionisation

$$= 86 \cdot 9 \, X/t \text{ ergs per g per sec.}$$

Equating this to the energy really absorbed from the radiation, gives

$$X/t = \frac{1}{86 \cdot 9} \left(\frac{\mu_{en}}{\rho} \right)_{air} \cdot I$$

or

$$X = \frac{1}{86 \cdot 9} \left(\frac{\mu_{en}}{\rho} \right)_{air} \cdot F$$

where F denotes a quantity called the energy fluence. The energy fluence is the time integral of the intensity. For a beam of constant intensity, the energy fluence is measured by the product intensity×time, i.e. $F = I \cdot t$.

Thus for a particular beam of radiation, the exposure-rate, measured in roentgens per unit time is directly proportional to the intensity. It is important to notice, however, that the intensity which will produce a particular exposure-rate depends upon the value of the (real) energy-absorption coefficient of air for the radiation considered and that this coefficient varies with wave-length. Hence the energy fluence per roentgen varies with the wavelength or photon energy of the radiation. (See fig. 7.02).

7.04. The relation between exposure and absorbed dose

A measurement of exposure enables the amount of energy which is transferred from the radiation beam in air to secondary-electrons (and not re-radiated) at any particular point to be determined. The ratio of the energy transferred to secondary-electrons and not re-radiated in a medium other than air (tissue say) to the energy transferred and not re-radiated in air, is given by the equation

$$\frac{\text{Energy transfer per gram of tissue}}{\text{Energy transfer per gram of air}} = \frac{\left(\dfrac{\mu_{en}}{\rho}\right)_{tissue}}{\left(\dfrac{\mu_{en}}{\rho}\right)_{air}} .$$

where $\left(\dfrac{\mu_{en}}{\rho}\right)$ denotes the (real) mass energy-absorption co-efficient for the radiation considered. The ratio $\left(\dfrac{\mu_{en}}{\rho}\right)_{tissue} \Big/ \left(\dfrac{\mu_{en}}{\rho}\right)_{air}$ varies with the wavelength of the radiation, but in muscle the variation does not exceed ±10 per cent for radiation with photon energy between 10 keV. and 50 MeV. and between 200 keV. and 2 MeV. where energy absorption takes place mainly by the Compton process, the ratio is constant to within 1 per cent. Thus in muscle (but not in bone or fat) the energy lost by the radiation is in a nearly constant ratio to the energy which would be lost in air, and therefore to the exposure, whatever the radiation quality.

However, the energy loss by radiation at a particular place is not necessarily equal to the energy absorbed by the medium at that place. This is because the secondary electrons produced by the radiation travel a certain distance from the point at which they are produced before they give up all their energy. The absorbed dose in a particular volume element depends upon the energy given up by the secondary electrons in that element and therefore depends upon the exposure and the nature of the medium throughout the region from which secondary electrons can reach the volume element considered. If there is no significant change in the exposure-rate in this region and the absorbing medium is homogeneous, then on the average for every electron leaving the volume element, another electron of equal energy will enter. This condition is known as electronic equilibrium. If this condition is satisfied then the energy dissipated within the volume is equal to that which would be dissipated if all the electrons generated in the volume completed their tracks in the volume considered and no other electrons entered the volume, i.e. the absorbed dose in the volume element is equal to the energy really absorbed from the radiation in that volume. In this case, the absorbed dose can be calculated from the exposure as indicated below.

However, if the radiation intensity changes over a distance comparable with the range of the secondary electrons, or if the element considered is near an interface between different media (within the range of secondary electrons from the interface), then the ionisation at the point considered is due in part to electrons originating in a region of different intensity or of different composition. In this case the absorbed dose in the volume element will not be equal to the energy removed from the radiation beam in that volume.

Table 7.01 shows the maximum range in water of secondary-electrons produced by photons of given energy and also the thickness of water which attenuates the incident radiation by 1 per cent. It will be observed that below 500 keV., the maximum secondary-electron range is less than 1 mm. in water and is also less than the 1 per cent. attenuation thickness. For these radiations (which were formerly those most commonly used in radiotherapy), for practical purposes electronic equilibrium can be regarded as attained in most situations of interest in therapy.

When there is electronic equilibrium as defined above (sometimes called strict, true or absolute electronic equilibrium), the total kinetic energy of electrons leaving the volume considered is equal to the total kinetic energy of electrons entering the volume (and the spectral distribution of electrons entering and leaving

TABLE 7.01

X-RAY ATTENUATION AND SECONDARY-ELECTRON RANGES IN WATER

Quantum energy MeV.	μ cm.$^{-1}$	Distance for 1% attenuation cm.	Max. sec. electron energy MeV.	Max. sec. electron range cm.
0·010	5·18	0·002	0·0095	0·0002
0·020	0·772	0·014	0·0195	0·0008
0·050	0·221	0·047	0·0495	0·0042
0·10	0·171	0·0601	0·0995	0·014
0·20	0·137	0·0735	0·1995	0·044
0·50	0·0967	0·104	0·331	0·097
1·0	0·0706	0·142	0·796	0·33
2·0	0·0493	0·203	1·774	0·84
5·0	0·0301	0·382	4·76	2·3
10·0	0·0219	0·457	9·75	4·7
20·0	0·0177	0·565	19·75	10·0

the volume is the same). Where a beam of megavoltage radiation traverses a homogeneous absorber, because there is attenuation of the radiation in a distance equal to the secondary-electron range and because the secondary electrons are emitted mainly in the forward direction, the electrons entering a given volume element carry more energy than those leaving the element. The energy deposited in the volume element therefore exceeds that removed from the beam in the element considered. However if the attenuation of the radiation is exponential and there is no appreciable change in the quality, the two quantities are proportional (and approach equality as the secondary electron range decreases.) This condition is called relative or transient electronic equilibrium.

215

When absolute electronic equilibrium exists, the absorbed dose in any volume element can be equated to the energy transferred from the radiation to secondary electrons and not re-radiated, in the same element. Hence the absorbed dose E_{med} in any medium is given by

$$E_{med} = \left(\frac{\mu_{en}}{\rho}\right)_{med} . F$$

where F is the energy fluence at the element considered.

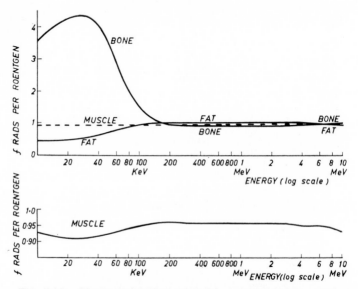

FIG. 7.03. The variation of f, the rad per roentgen factor with energy in biological materials. The variation of f_{muscle} is shown on an expanded scale in the lower figure.

But the exposure X (in roentgens) is related to the energy fluence F (in ergs/cm.²) by the relation

$$X = \frac{1}{86 \cdot 9} \left(\frac{\mu_{en}}{\rho}\right)_{air} . F \qquad \text{(section 7.03)}$$

Hence $\qquad E_{med} = 86 \cdot 9 . X . \left(\frac{\mu_{en}}{\rho}\right)_{med} \bigg/ \left(\frac{\mu_{en}}{\rho}\right)_{air}$ ergs/g.

or the dose $\quad D$ (in rads) $= 0 \cdot 869 . X . \left(\frac{\mu_{en}}{\rho}\right)_{med} \bigg/ \left(\frac{\mu_{en}}{\rho}\right)_{air}.$

This is frequently written $D = fX$ where f is the rad per roentgen conversion factor for the particular medium and radiation energy considered. (When the radiation is not monochromatic, then an effective value, $\bar{f}$, is obtained by averaging $\left(\dfrac{\mu_{en}}{\rho}\right)_{med} \bigg/ \left(\dfrac{\mu_{en}}{\rho}\right)_{air}$ over the appropriate energy spectrum.)

For soft tissue, the value of f is approximately constant from about 200 keV. to 2 MeV. Muscle which is exposed under conditions of electronic equilibrium to 1 roentgen of X- or γ-radiation with photon energy between 200 keV. and 2 MeV. absorbs a dose of about 96 ergs per gram or 0·96 rad. For this range of photon energy the energy absorption per roentgen in other biological materials (e.g. bone and fat) does not differ greatly from the absorption in muscle. However, for both lower and higher photon energies, bone absorbs more and fat less than muscle (see fig. 7.03). These differences are of importance in radiotherapy and will be discussed further in Chapter XI.

7.05. Experimental methods for the measurement of exposure: the inverse square law

The variation of exposure-rate in air with distance from the radiation source

Consider a source of radiation which is small enough to be regarded as a point and suppose that both absorption and scattering of the radiation in the medium considered is negligible. Then the intensity measured at different distances from the source will vary inversely as the square of the distance from the source.

This result may be derived by considering the radiation leaving a source S in a particular direction as shown in fig. 7·04.

In a given time, the same number of photons (n say) will fall on area a at a distance d from the source S as will fall on the larger area A at a greater distance D. But the intensity is proportional to the number of photons per unit area which is n/a at distance d and n/A at D.

i.e. $\dfrac{\text{intensity at distance } d}{\text{intensity at distance } D} = \dfrac{n/a}{n/A} = \dfrac{A}{a} = \dfrac{D^2}{d^2}.$

Thus the intensity and therefore also the exposure-rate for a particular beam of radiation, varies inversely as the square of the distance from the source, provided, as assumed above, that the source is small and that scattering and absorption can be neglected.

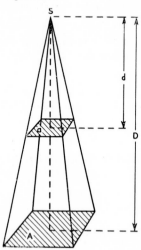

FIG. 7.04. Diagram illustrating the inverse square law.

These conditions are usually satisfied when the output of an X-ray or γ tele-therapy machine is being measured. Thus for the calculation of exposure-rates in air at different distances from the target of an X-ray tube, the inverse square law is usually applicable. However the long wavelength radiations obtained from superficial therapy tubes having beryllium windows are appreciably absorbed in air, and for such radiations the inverse square law must be corrected to allow for absorption. γ-ray brachy-therapy sources usually approximate to a line or plane rather than to a point. In this case there are mathematical methods of calculating the variation of exposure-rate with distance which are equivalent to dividing the source into a great many small sources, applying the inverse square law to each elementary source and then adding the various contributions. These are discussed in Chapter XII.

7.06. The free air chamber

In order to satisfy the definition of exposure, an absolute measurement of the radiation at a particular place in roentgens requires the collection of all the ions of any one sign generated at that place in a known mass of free air. An ionisation chamber constructed as indicated in fig. 7.05. is used.

The incident radiation is collimated by lead so that it passes between the electrode system. The latter consists of one plate

A maintained at a high potential and a collecting plate *C* surrounded by an earthed guard ring *G*. The latter is necessary to ensure that the lines of electrical intensity run normally

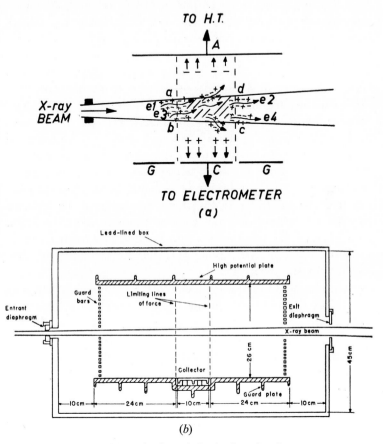

FIG. 7.05.   The free air ionisation chamber.

(*a*) schematic diagram
(*b*) horizontal section of Canadian standard chamber (after Henry and Garrett[7]).

between *A* and *C*.   Guard bars or wires maintained at graded potentials and spaced uniformly between the edges of the electrodes prevent lateral field distortion.   Consider the ionisation resulting from the absorption of radiation in the volume *abcd* (fig. 7.05*a*).   In order that all secondary electrons

219

generated in *abcd* shall complete their tracks in air, *abcd* should be surrounded by a thickness of air greater than the range of the most energetic secondary electrons. Usually for 200 kVp. X-rays, the distance between the electrodes is about 20 cm. at atmospheric pressure, while for 1 MeV. radiation several metres separation is required unless the air pressure is increased. All the positive or all the negative ions formed between A and C are collected by C. Some of these ions are due to electrons such as e_1 generated outside (mainly in front of) *abcd*, but provided the ions are formed in air, on the average they just balance ions which are lost because electrons such as e_2 generated in *abcd* leave the space between A and C. The potential difference between the electrodes must be sufficiently great to ensure that all the ions are collected before they have time to recombine. The value required depends upon the exposure-rate and the size of the chamber but is usually of the order of 100-200 V. per cm. for exposure-rates not exceeding 50 R./min. If, however, very intense ionisation is produced in intervals of short duration, special precautions are necessary to ensure that all the ions are collected.

A direct determination of the volume *abcd* from which ions are collected, would be difficult, because with a source of X- or γ-rays of finite size the edges of the beam are necessarily diffuse. It is customary to measure the aperture of the limiting diaphragm (A say) and the length (L) of the collecting plate. The cross-section of the radiation beam at P within the volume *abcd* and at a distance f_p from any point in the source is $(f_p/f)^2 A$ where f is the distance of the diaphragm from the source. According to the inverse square law, the exposure-rate at the front surface of the limiting diaphragm due to radiation from the particular point considered, is related to that at P by the same ratio $(f_p/f)^2$, provided that the attenuation of the radiation within the chamber is so small that it can be neglected. This is usually the case for radiation generated between 50 kVp. and 500 kVp. Therefore the collecting volume is taken as AL and the measured current gives the exposure-rate at the front surface of the diaphragm.

Ionisation chambers of the free-air type are used in the principal standardising laboratories of each country.[2, 3, 4, 5, 6, 7]

220

Most of these chambers are used in the 50 kVp. to 500 kVp. range and have plate separations of the order of 20 cm. to 30 cm. Below 50 kVp. considerably smaller chambers are used and the electrode system can be placed at different distances from the diaphragm so that air attenuation (which may be appreciable below 50 kVp.) can be measured. Above 500 kVp. the long range of the secondary electrons makes free air chambers operated at atmospheric pressure impractical. A few national standardising laboratories maintain pressurised free air chambers but in most cases, a different method of measurement, the use of thimble or cavity ionisation chambers is adopted.

Even at moderate energies, the size of free air chambers makes it impractical to use such chambers for day to day measurements in hospitals and for these measurements also thimble chambers are used.

The theory of thimble chambers will therefore now be discussed.

7.07. Thimble chambers

In thimble chambers, the ionisation which is measured is that produced in a small gaseous cavity surrounded by solid walls. The theory of such chambers has been developed by Bragg[8] and by Gray[9] and is as follows:

Consider a small cavity in a large mass of an absorbing medium which is uniformly irradiated. If the cavity is small enough, its introduction does not alter appreciably either the number or the distribution of the secondary electrons in the medium. Hence the number of secondary electrons crossing the cavity is determined by the energy absorption in the medium. The secondary electrons lose energy as they traverse either the medium or the gas. The energy loss per cm. of electron path is determined primarily by the number of electrons per cc. in the material traversed, but it depends also upon the chemical composition (see below). Let s_{gas}^{med} denote the ratio of the rates at which an electron loses energy in the medium and in the gas of the cavity. (s_{gas}^{med} is called the linear stopping power ratio of the medium with respect to the gas). Then if E denotes the energy transferred to secondary electrons (and not re-radiated)

221

per cc. of the medium, the number of ion pairs produced per cc. of the gas in the cavity (J) is given by

$$J = E/s_{gas}^{med} . W \qquad (1)$$

where W is the average energy expended by electrons in producing an ion pair in the gas. Thus if W and s_{gas}^{med} can be evaluated, a measurement of the ionisation produced in the cavity enables the energy absorption in the medium to be determined.

This theory can be applied to an ionisation chamber in which a small gas cavity is surrounded by solid walls provided (1) the wall thickness exceeds the range of secondary electrons in the wall material (for radiations up to a few MeV. in energy a wall thickness of a few millimetres is sufficient) and (2) the dimensions of the cavity are small compared with the range of secondary electrons in the gas. If these conditions are satisfied, the chamber is referred to as a thimble chamber. If the wall material can be made to resemble air in absorbing properties and the chamber is used in conditions of electronic equilibrium, then a thimble chamber may be used to determine exposure. Alternatively if the wall material resembles some biological material of interest (e.g. bone or muscle) in absorbing properties, a thimble chamber may be used for the measurement of absorbed dose in the biological material.

Before discussing these uses of thimble chambers in detail however (see the following sections 7.08 and 7.09) it is useful to develop an alternative expression of the Bragg-Gray relation and to consider the evaluation of W and s_{gas}^{med}.

Let E_m denote the energy absorption per unit mass of the medium and J_m the ionisation produced per unit mass of the gas. (E and J in equation (1) referred to unit volumes.) Also let $(s_m)_{med}$ and $(s_m)_{gas}$ denote the rate of energy loss of secondary electrons per unit mass per cm^2 of the wall and of the gas respectively.

Then $\qquad\qquad E = E_m \, \rho_{med} \qquad\qquad$ where ρ denotes density

$$J = J_m \, \rho_{gas}$$

and $\qquad\qquad s_{gas}^{med} = (s_m)_{med} . \rho_{med}/(s_m)_{gas} . \rho_{gas}$

i.e. $\qquad\qquad s_{gas}^{med} = (s_m)_{gas}^{med} . \rho_{med}/\rho_{gas}$

where $\qquad\qquad (s_m)_{gas}^{med} = (s_m)_{med}/(s_m)_{gas}$

222

$(s_m)_{gas}^{med}$ is called the mass stopping power ratio of the medium relative to the gas.

Substituting in the equation $J = E/s_{gas}^{med} \cdot W$

$$\therefore \qquad J_m = E_m/(s_m)_{gas}^{med} \cdot W \qquad (2)$$

The gas used in thimble chambers is usually air. Applying equation (2) to a thimble chamber with a solid wall containing an air cavity, we can write

$$J_m = (E_m)_{wall}/(s_m)_{air}^{wall} \cdot W_{air} \qquad (3)$$

The measurement of W_{air}, the average energy dissipated by electrons per ion pair produced, in air, has already been discussed in section 7.03. For electrons exceeding 20 keV. in energy, $W_{air} = 33 \cdot 7$ eV.,[2, 10, 11] with an uncertainty probably less than 1 per cent. The mass stopping power ratio $(s_m)_{air}^{wall}$ is a slowly varying function of the atomic number of the wall material and depends also upon the secondary electron energy spectrum. For wall materials which do not differ greatly from air in atomic number, $(s_m)_{air}^{wall}$ can usually be calculated as described below, with an uncertainty of the order of 1 or 2 per cent. Useful tabulations of $(s_m)_{air}^{wall}$, are given in reports of the International Commission on Radiological Units and Measurements[2] and of the United States Study Group on Radiation Protection.[12]

The rate at which an electron loses energy, per electron of the medium transversed, can be calculated for an electron of given initial energy, using a formula due to Bethe.[13] The rate of energy loss is a slowly varying function of the atomic number of the absorbing medium because Bethe's formula includes a term in log I where I is the mean excitation potential of the atoms of the absorber. Bethe's original formula did not allow for the fact that the medium surrounding an electron is polarised by the electric field of the electron. This polarisation reduces the effect of the electron field at a distance, by an amount which depends upon the density of the medium. Since distant interactions are relatively more important at high energies, this polarisation or density effect increases with increasing electron energy (Whyte[14]). Modern tabulations of mass stopping power ratios relative to air, normally include a correction for this effect in solid and liquid materials (the effect is negligible in gases). Since the rate of energy loss per electron is a function of electron energy, the value of the stopping power ratio required in connection with thimble chambers is a mean averaged over the spectrum of all the electrons crossing the cavity. This spectrum is usually assumed to be that corresponding to electronic equilibrium, which implies that the electrons lose energy continuously both in the walls and in the cavity. This is an approximation and attempts have been made to develop a more rigorous analysis which allows for discrete energy transfers (Spencer and Attix,[15] Burch,[16]). It then becomes necessary to consider the actual size of the gas cavity.

7.08. Thimble chambers for the measurement of exposure

Consider a small volume of air from which ions can be collected, situated in an extensive, uniform, radiation field. Suppose the collecting volume is surrounded by air on all sides to a distance which exceeds the range of secondary electrons (as in the free air ionisation chamber). Now suppose that the air surrounding the collecting volume could be compressed into a solid wall. It can be shown that the secondary electron flux in the collecting volume and hence the ionisation would be almost unchanged [17, 18] but the collecting volume and its " air wall " now form a thimble ionisation chamber. If the ionisation produced in the cavity, $(J_m)_{air}$ is measured in electrostatic units of charge per gram, then the ionisation in such a chamber is related to the exposure (X) in roentgens by the equation

$$(J_m)_{air} = X/0\cdot001293 \text{ e.s.u./g.}$$

or if $(J_m)_{air}$ is measured in e.s.u. per $0\cdot001293$ g., then

$$(J_m)_{air} = X$$

In practice, of course, it is not possible to obtain an " air wall " as described above. However the idea may be found helpful in obtaining a qualitative understanding of how thimble chambers may be used to measure exposure if wall materials can be obtained which resemble " solid air ". We now consider the choice of actual wall materials and the conditions in which thimble chambers with different kinds of wall may be used to measure exposure.

Consider first a thimble chamber which is exposed to radiation of energy less than 500 keV. Then at the inner surface of the chamber walls there is absolute electronic equilibrium (since it has already been stipulated that the walls of a thimble chamber must exceed the secondary electron range and that the cavity must not alter the number or distribution of secondary electrons). The ionisation $(J_m)_{thimble}$ produced per unit mass of

224

gas (air) in the cavity is related to the energy absorbed per unit mass of the wall $(E_m)_{\text{wall}}$ by the Bragg-Gray equation

$$(J_m)_{\text{thimble}} = (E_m)_{\text{wall}}/(s_m)_{\text{air}}^{\text{wall}} \cdot W_{\text{air}}$$

In a free air chamber, the corresponding ionisation $(J_m)_{\text{air}}$ and energy absorption $(E_m)_{\text{air}}$ are related by the equation

$$(J_m)_{\text{air}} = (E_m)_{\text{air}}/W_{\text{air}}$$

$$\therefore \qquad (J_m)_{\text{thimble}} = (J_m)_{\text{air}} \cdot (E_m)_{\text{wall}}/(E_m)_{\text{air}} \cdot (s_m)_{\text{air}}^{\text{wall}}$$

But if there is absolute electronic equilibrium

$$(E_m)_{\text{air}} = \left(\frac{\mu_{\text{en}}}{\rho}\right)_{\text{air}} \cdot F$$

and
$$(E_m)_{\text{wall}} = \left(\frac{\mu_{\text{en}}}{\rho}\right)_{\text{wall}} \cdot A \cdot B \cdot F$$

where F is the energy fluence of the radiation at the point considered in the absence of the thimble chamber and $A \cdot B \cdot F$ denotes the energy fluence at the same point when the thimble chamber is present. (The energy fluence will be altered slightly by the introduction of the chamber if there is either appreciable attenuation of the radiation in the walls of the chamber or if the chamber introduces an appreciable amount of scattering material into the radiation beam. The modifying factors A and B are introduced to allow for these two effects. Both A and B should be close to $1 \cdot 0$ for well designed chambers.)

Thus
$$(J_m)_{\text{thimble}} = (J_m)_{\text{air}} \cdot \left(\frac{\mu_{\text{en}}}{\rho}\right)_{\text{wall}} \cdot A \cdot B \Big/ (s_m)_{\text{air}}^{\text{wall}} \cdot \left(\frac{\mu_{\text{en}}}{\rho}\right)_{\text{air}}$$

If J_m is measured in e.s.u. per $0 \cdot 001293$ g.

then
$$(J_m)_{\text{air}} = X$$

where X denotes the exposure in roentgens

$$\therefore \qquad (J_m)_{\text{thimble}} = X \cdot \left(\frac{\mu_{\text{en}}}{\rho}\right)_{\text{wall}} \cdot A \cdot B \Big/ (s_m)_{\text{air}}^{\text{wall}} \cdot \left(\frac{\mu_{\text{eu}}}{\rho}\right)_{\text{air}} \qquad (3)$$

$$\text{e.s.u. per } 0 \cdot 001293 \text{ g.}$$

or
$$(J_v)_{\text{thimble}} = X \cdot \frac{p}{760} \cdot \frac{(273)}{(273+T)} \cdot A \cdot B \cdot \left(\frac{\mu_{\text{en}}}{\rho}\right)_{\text{wall}} \Big/$$

$$(s_m)_{\text{air}}^{\text{wall}} \cdot \left(\frac{\mu_{\text{en}}}{\rho}\right)_{\text{air}} \text{ e.s.u. per cc.}$$

where p denotes pressure in millimetres of mercury and T denotes temperature in degrees Centigrade.

225

If the radiation energy exceeds about 500 keV., so that there is transient but not absolute electronic equilibrium at the inner surface of the chamber walls, equation (3) is still valid, provided the attenuation factor A is calculated for the mean photon path in the wall, not the total wall thickness. (This is discussed further below.)

The exposure X can therefore be determined from the ionisation produced in any thimble chamber under equilibrium conditions provided the stopping power ratio $(s_m)_{air}^{wall}$, the ratio of the (real) mass energy absorption coefficient of the wall material relative to air $\left(\dfrac{\mu_{en}}{\rho}\right)_{wall} \bigg/ \left(\dfrac{\mu_{en}}{\rho}\right)_{air}$ and the modifying factors A and B are accurately known for the particular radiation considered. In a national standardising laboratory, a thimble chamber is used with only one or two standard sources and these quantities can be evaluated for the radiation spectra of the particular sources.[19] The thimble chambers that are used in day-to-day measurements in radiological departments, however, are normally used to measure a wide variety of X- and γ-ray beams, and the precise spectral distribution of the radiation is frequently unknown. In these circumstances, it is desirable that the ionisation produced in the cavity per roentgen exposure shall be independent of radiation quality. Now for materials of low atomic number, the ratio of the mass stopping power of the wall relative to air $(s_m)_{air}^{wall}$ and the correction factors A and B vary only slowly with energy (e.g. $(s_m)_{air}^{wall}$ changes about 2 per cent. for graphite and 3 per cent. for aluminium between 100 keV. and 1 MeV.; the change in A might be 2 or 3 per cent. over the same range). In the energy range where Compton absorption is the only process occurring $\left(\dfrac{\mu_{en}}{\rho}\right)_{wall} \bigg/ \left(\dfrac{\mu_{en}}{\rho}\right)_{air}$ is independent of energy but if photo-electric absorption or pair production are appreciable, the ratio $\left(\dfrac{\mu_{en}}{\rho}\right)_{wall} \bigg/ \left(\dfrac{\mu_{en}}{\rho}\right)_{air}$ varies rapidly with energy and the variation depends upon the atomic number of the wall material. Only if the effective atomic number of the wall is equal to that of air does $(\mu_{en}/\rho)_{wall}$ vary with energy in the same way as $(\mu_{en}/\rho)_{air}$. To obtain thimble chambers which can be used to measure exposure for a wide range of radiations it is therefore necessary for the wall material to have the same effective atomic number as air.

The effective atomic number of a compound in this context is determined as follows. For photo-electric absorption, at X-ray wavelengths the absorption coefficient per atom of an element of atomic number Z, can be considered to be approximately proportional to Z^4. (See Chapter VI.) The absorption coefficient per electron is therefore proportional to Z^3, since the number of electrons per atom is Z. Hence the photo-electric absorption coefficient for a compound may be calculated in terms of the number of electrons per cc. of the compound (n) from the formula

$$\tau = kn(a_1Z_1{}^3 + a_2Z_2{}^3 + a_3Z_3{}^3 + \ldots)$$

where k is a constant, and a_1, a_2, a_3, . . . are the fractional contents of electrons belonging to atoms of atomic number Z_1, Z_2, Z_3, . . .

Thus $\qquad \tau = kn\overline{Z}^3.$

where $\qquad \overline{Z} = {}^3\sqrt{(a_1Z_1{}^3 + a_2Z_2{}^3 + a_3Z_3{}^3 \ldots)}$

$\overline{Z}$ is called the effective atomic number of the compound for photo-electric absorption. For pair production, the absorption coefficient per atom is proportional to Z^2. The electronic absorption coefficient is therefore proportional to Z and the effective atomic number of a compound for pair production is $\overline{Z}$ where $\overline{Z} = a_1Z_1 + a_2Z_2 + a_3Z_3$. . . . For air, $\overline{Z}$ is numerically equal to 7·64 for photo-electric absorption and 7·36 for pair production. Thus to obtain thimble ionisation chambers in which the ionisation current per cc. is equal to that which would be produced in a free air chamber, it is necessary to use wall materials with effective atomic number close to 7·64 for low energy radiation, and close to 7·36 for high energy radiation.

At one time, graphite ($Z = 6$) was widely used as wall material. A bakelite-graphite mixture is now more commonly employed. It is sometimes convenient to use a metal in the construction of thimble chambers. There is no metal or alloy which has an atomic number close to air but when a metal is necessary, aluminium ($Z = 13$) is used. A wall material in which the energy absorption per gram is the same as that of air is commonly referred to as an " air-wall ". The use of an " air-wall " with an air-filled chamber has the additional advantage that the volume of the cavity can be considerably increased without violating the condition that it shall not disturb the secondary electron flux.

The thickness of the wall which is required to produce electronic equilibrium in the chamber, depends of course upon

227

the quality of the radiation which is to be measured (since the wall thickness must exceed the range of the secondary electrons). Fig. 7.06 shows the variation with wall thickness of the ionisation current from a thimble chamber exposed to 2 MV. X-rays.[2] The current increases with wall thickness initially, as the number of secondary electrons from the walls increases.

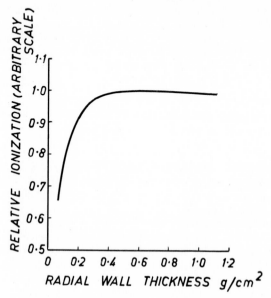

FIG. 7.06. Graph showing the variation of ionisation within an air-wall chamber exposed to 2MV X-radiation with increase in wall thickness. (After Barnard, Axton and Marsh.) [19]

Further increase in wall thickness then causes a slight reduction in the current because the radiation reaching the inner layers of the walls (where most of the secondary electrons which cross the cavity originate) is attenuated by the outer layers. When thimble chambers are used for absolute measurements, allowance must be made for the attenuation of the radiation in the chamber walls. If a single chamber is used to measure radiations differing widely in quality, the wall will absorb a large fraction of the incident radiation when this is soft, but may not be sufficiently thick to produce electronic equilibrium when the radiation is penetrating. It is now customary to add an extra cap or sleeve to increase the wall thickness when measuring the more energetic radiations, in order to obtain (relative) electronic equilibrium at the higher energies without excessive wall attenuation at the lower energies. To allow for effects due to either the thickness or the atomic composition of the wall or the chamber size, the chambers used for routine measurements in radiotherapy are usually calibrated against a standard chamber for a series of radiations covering the range of qualities which the chamber will be used to measure. (This method also has the advantage that the chamber need not be designed so that the volume can be accurately determined.)

The standard chamber is usually a free air chamber for radiation generated below 400 kVp. and a standard thimble chamber for radiation from 400 keV. to a few MeV. in energy. When a thimble chamber has been calibrated by a standardising laboratory, the calibration factor given is usually such that, after correcting for the ambient temperature and pressure, the instrument reading multiplied by the calibration factor gives the exposure which would have been received at the position of the centre of the chamber in free air, i.e. any corrections required for wall attenuation or lack of electronic equilibrium are included in the calibration factor.

When megavoltage radiation first began to be widely used, there was considerable discussion as to the position at which the exposure was measured by a thimble chamber. At low energies, the electrons which cross the cavity originate very close to the inner surface of the chamber walls. In this case there is no doubt that the photon flux producing the electrons has been attenuated by essentially the total thickness (t say) of the chamber walls. To calculate the exposure at the position of the chamber centre in the absence of the chamber, a correction for the photon attenuation in the thickness t is required. At high energies, some of the electrons which produce ionisation in the cavity originate an appreciable distance from the inner surface. The photons producing these electrons have been attenuated by traversing a wall thickness t' (say) which is less than the total thickness t. To determine the exposure in the absence of the chamber in this case, it is necessary to calculate

229

a correction for the average attenuation of the photons (which is less than the attenuation produced by the total wall thickness). For Co^{60} γ-rays, the difference between the mean thickness t' and the total thickness t makes a difference of the order of

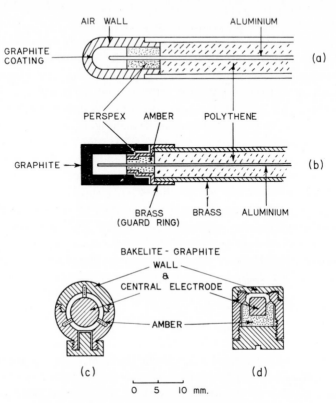

FIG. 7.07.   Typical thimble ionisation chambers.
(*a*) and (*b*) current measuring type.
(*c*) Sievert condenser chamber,[21]
(*d*) Medical Research Council BD2 condenser chamber.

0·5 per cent. in the attenuation correction.[2]   The difference between t and t' increases with increasing energy and the uncertainty in the attenuation correction also increases.   This places an upper limit upon the energies for which thimble chambers can be used for the absolute measurement of exposure.

The design of some typical thimble chambers is illustrated in fig. 7.07.   The commonest form of chamber consists of a central electrode, projecting into an air cavity, which is surrounded by an outer cylindrical electrode which forms the chamber wall. The central electrode is usually supported by the insulator which separates it from the outer electrode. If the electrodes are not made of conducting materials, the electrode surfaces are made conducting by a graphite coating. In use, one electrode is charged positively, the other negatively, and the ions attracted to one electrode, the collecting electrode (usually the central electrode), are measured. Since the ionisation produced in a thimble chamber is small, it is essential that the collecting electrode be well insulated. Amber or polystyrene is usually employed. Furthermore, irradiation of the insulator must not contribute any ions to those collected from the cavity. This can be prevented by the introduction of a guard ring between the high voltage and collecting electrode as shown in fig. 7.07(b). The guard ring is maintained at the same potential as the collecting electrode so that the insulation around the collecting electrode is in a field-free space. Alternatively the insulator may be shielded from radiation, but this is difficult at high energies and in any case introduces undesirable scattering material into the X-ray field.

7.09 The use of thimble chambers for the measurement of absorbed dose

There are three principal methods of using thimble chambers to determine absorbed dose in tissue-like phantoms. Two of these may be regarded as direct methods, in which the ionisation produced in the cavity provides direct information about the energy absorbed in the phantom material. In the third method, a chamber calibrated for exposure is used and the absorbed dose is calculated from what is essentially an exposure measurement, although the exposure is not necessarily explicitly evaluated.

The two direct methods are as follows:

(1) Extremely thin-walled chambers are used so that the electron flux crossing the cavity is that produced in the phantom, i.e. electrons from the walls make a negligible contribution to the ionisation. This method can be used whether electronic

equilibrium does or does not exist and it can be used to measure the absorbed dose delivered by a fast electron beam as well as that due to X- or γ-radiation. If the absorbed dose in the medium is denoted by E_{med} and the observed ionisation in the gas (air) in the cavity is J_m then

$$J_m = (E_m)_{\text{med}}/(s_m)^{\text{med}}_{\text{air}} \cdot W_{\text{air}}$$

or $\qquad (E)_{\text{med}} = J_m \cdot (s_m)^{\text{med}}_{\text{air}} \cdot W_{\text{air}}.$

If J_m is measured in e.s.u. per 0·001293 g. of air, then the absorbed dose in rads is given by

$$D = 0 \cdot 869 \cdot (s_m)^{\text{med}}_{\text{air}} \cdot J_m.$$

(2) A thimble chamber, with walls of known composition, resembling the phantom material as closely as possible in atomic number is used. The thickness of the walls exceeds the range of the secondary electrons produced by the radiation so that the electrons crossing the cavity are those produced in the chamber walls.

The energy absorption per unit mass of the chamber walls is related to the ionisation per unit mass of the gas (air) in the cavity by the equation

$$J_m = (E_m)_{\text{wall}}/(s_m)^{\text{wall}}_{\text{air}} \cdot W_{\text{air}}.$$

For conditions of electronic equilibrium, the energy absorption in the medium is related to the energy absorption in the cavity walls by the equation

$$(E_m)_{\text{med}}\Big/(E_m)_{\text{wall}} = \left(\frac{\mu_{\text{en}}}{\rho}\right)_{\text{med}}\Big/\left(\frac{\mu_{\text{en}}}{\rho}\right)_{\text{wall}} \cdot A^1 \cdot B^1.$$

The correction factor A^1 is introduced to allow for the difference between the attenuation (A_{wall} say) in the chamber itself and the attenuation (A_{med} say) in the medium displaced by the chamber. $A^1 = A_{\text{wall}}/A_{\text{med}}$. B^1 is an additional factor to allow for changes in the energy fluence such as might be produced by back-scatter from the stem, but B^1 should normally be close to 1·0.

Thus $\qquad (E_m)_{\text{med}} = \left(\dfrac{\mu_{\text{en}}}{\rho}\right)_{\text{med}} \cdot A_{\text{med}} \cdot (E_m)_{\text{wall}}\Big/$

$$\left(\frac{\mu_{\text{en}}}{\rho}\right)_{\text{wall}} \cdot A_{\text{wall}} \cdot B^1.$$

232

If J_m is measured in e.s.u. per 0·001293 g. of air then the absorbed dose D in rads is given by

$$D = 0.869 \left(\frac{\mu_{en}}{\rho}\right)_{med} . A_{med} . (S_m)_{air}^{wall} . J_m \bigg/ \left(\frac{\mu_{en}}{\rho}\right)_{wall} . A_{wall} . B^1 \quad (4)$$

If the wall material has an effective atomic number close to that of the medium in which the absorbed dose is required, then $(\mu_{en}/\rho)_{wall} A_{wall}$ will vary with energy in the same way as $(\mu_{en}/\rho)_{med} A_{med}$. The ratio $\left(\frac{\mu_{en}}{\rho}\right)_{med} . A_{med} \bigg/ \left(\frac{\mu_{en}}{\rho}\right)_{wall} . A_{wall}$ will then be independent of energy and the instrument can be calibrated to read absorbed dose over a wide range of qualities.

It should be noted that in the calculation of the attenuation factors, the thickness of wall or medium actually traversed by the radiation is required. For cylindrical chambers used with the axis at right angles to a unidirectional beam, the wall thickness parallel to the beam is greater than the radial thickness by an amount which depends upon the size of the cavity (see fig. 7.08). Also, on account of the finite size of the air cavity, the chamber always displaces a greater volume of the medium than the volume occupied by the chamber walls. Therefore if the latter are somewhat denser than the medium, the correction factor for attenuation $A^1 = A_{wall}/A_{med}$ can be made very close to 1·0.

(3) A thimble chamber already calibrated to read exposure is used. Suppose first that the calibration has been carried out for the particular radiation quality which is being measured. In this case the observed ionisation enables the exposure at the centre of the chamber to be determined. Provided there is absolute electronic equilibrium, the absorbed dose in the medium can then be calculated using the appropriate rad per roentgen conversion factor for the medium considered. Thus suppose the chamber reads X roentgens. Then the exposure at the centre of an air-filled cavity in the medium, equal in size to the chamber, will be $\beta . X$ (say) where β is a correction factor for any differences between effects such as scattering by the chamber stem, when the latter is in the medium instead of in air. The

233

exposure at the same point when medium fills the cavity, is reduced by the attenuation (A_{med}) in the medium displaced by the chamber, so the exposure in the homogeneous medium is $A_{med} . \beta . X$.

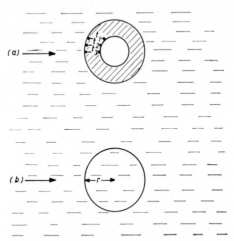

FIG. 7.08. Comparison of the attenuation of radiation in the walls of a thimble chamber and in the medium displaced by the chamber. The attenuation of radiation in the wall of a thimble chamber depends upon the weighted mean of path lengths such as t_1, t_2, t_3, and depends on cavity size as well as wall thickness.

The absorbed dose in rads is then given by

$$D = f . A_{med} . \beta . X$$

where $\qquad f = 0.869 . \left(\dfrac{\mu_{en}}{\rho}\right)_{med} \Big/ \left(\dfrac{\mu_{en}}{\rho}\right)_{air}$

as already discussed in section 7.04.

For megavoltage radiation, two problems arise with this method. Firstly, there is transient but not absolute electronic equilibrium and the absorbed dose at the position of the centre of the chamber is determined by electrons which originate at points superficial to the centre. The attenuation correction A_{med} must therefore be calculated for an effective thickness t' which is less than the radius of the cavity (see the discussion in section 7.08). Secondly, a chamber may be available which has been calibrated to read exposure at one energy, but has not been

234

calibrated for the particular radiation quality which it is desired to measure. (In Great Britain, exposure meters can be calibrated at 2 MV. only, in the megavoltage range.)

Referring to equation (4), the absorbed dose in rads is related to the ionisation current J_m (in e.s.u. per 0·001293 g. of air) by

$$D = 0\cdot869 \cdot J_m \cdot \left[\left(\frac{\mu_{en}}{\rho} \right)_{med} \cdot A_{med} \cdot (s_m)_{air}^{wall} \middle/ \left(\frac{\mu_{en}}{\rho} \right)_{wall} \cdot A_{wall} \, B^1 \right]$$

where the expression in brackets is evaluated for the particular radiation quality considered. When the chamber is calibrated the ionisation current J_m (in e.s.u. per 0·001293 g. of air) is related to the exposure X (equation (3)) by

$$J_m = X \cdot \left[\left(\frac{\mu_{en}}{\rho} \right)_{wall} \cdot A \cdot B \middle/ (s_m)_{air}^{wall} \cdot \left(\frac{\mu_{en}}{\rho} \right)_{air} \right]$$

where the expression in brackets is evaluated at the calibration energy (2 MV. say).

Thus

$$\frac{D}{X} = 0\cdot869 \frac{\left[\left(\frac{\mu_{en}}{\rho} \right)_{med} \cdot A_{med} \cdot (s_m)_{air}^{wall} \middle/ \left(\frac{\mu_{en}}{\rho} \right)_{wall} \cdot A_{wall} \cdot B^1 \right] \quad \text{Energy E}}{\left[\left(\frac{\mu_{en}}{\rho} \right)_{air} \cdot (s_m)_{air}^{wall} \middle/ \left(\frac{\mu_{en}}{\rho} \right)_{wall} \cdot A \cdot B \right] \quad \text{Calibration energy}}$$

The quotient of the two expressions in brackets multiplied by 0·869 has been evaluated for some commercial thimble chambers and a range of megavoltage energies.[20, 22] It is usually referred to as the " overall dose conversion factor ". For these chambers, an instrument reading corrected for temperature and pressure and multiplied by the national standardising laboratory's calibration factor, may be converted directly into an absorbed dose by multiplication by the appropriate overall conversion factor.

7.10. Other types of ionisation chambers

Extrapolation Chambers

For the measurement of very soft radiation which is rapidly absorbed in air, or for the measurement of absorbed dose close

235

to the interface between different media where the dose-rate is changing very rapidly, extrapolation chambers may be used. These are very thin-walled chambers in which one electrode is movable so that the effective volume may be varied. By taking

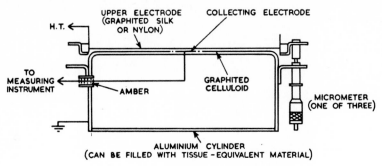

FIG. 7.09. Diagrammatic illustration of extrapolation chamber.
(After Failla.[23])

a series of measurements with different electrode separations the ionisation which would be produced in a very thin layer of air at a particular position can be obtained by extrapolation. The use of such a chamber to measure the ionisation at the surface of a phantom is illustrated in fig. 7.09.

X-ray output monitoring chambers

Ionisation chambers are now frequently included in the heads of therapeutic X-ray sets to act as indicators of the constancy of the X-ray output. In these chambers the electrodes are usually mounted parallel and close to the tube window, so that the X-ray beam passes through them.

The electrodes are sometimes made of graphited plastic (such as perspex) which is approximately air equivalent but they are also frequently made of metal. When metal is used, the ionisation current from the monitor at different qualities is not proportional to the exposure-rate. The monitors should be regarded merely as indicators of the constancy of the tube output under given conditions. Monitor chambers should be sealed so that variations in temperature and pressure do not change the mass of gas in the chamber.

236

Ionisation chambers for the Measurement of Radioisotope Activity

The activity of radio-active isotopes is usually measured by counting methods (using Geiger-Müller or scintillation counters) which are described in the next chapter. However, the magnitude of the current produced by a radioactive isotope in

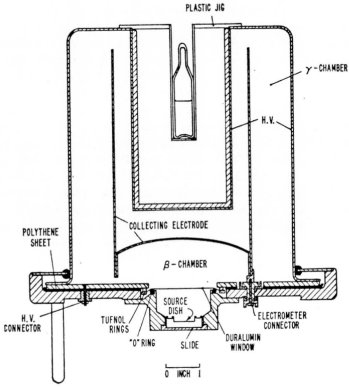

PLASTIC JIG

γ-CHAMBER

H.V.

COLLECTING ELECTRODE

POLYTHENE SHEET

β-CHAMBER

H.V. CONNECTOR

TUFNOL RINGS

SOURCE DISH

"O"RING SLIDE

ELECTROMETER CONNECTOR

DURALUMIN WINDOW

0 INCH 1

FIG. 7.10. Ionisation chamber for the measurement of isotopes emitting either β or γ radiation. (After Dale, Perry and Pulfer.[24])

a particular ionisation chamber, provides a convenient method of checking the activity of bulk shipments of isotopes and of therapy sources. The particular chamber employed is normally calibrated with sources of known activity. Fig. 7.10 shows an ionisation chamber of fairly large volume which is typical of the type of chamber found convenient for measuring the

237

strength of either β- or γ-emitting radioactive isotopes of high activity. β-emitters may be introduced below a thin window at the base of the chamber whereas γ-emitters are placed in the re-entrant cylinder at the top of the chamber.

7.11 The measurement of ionisation currents[25, 26, 27]

Some ionisation chambers have a volume of a few cubic centimetres. Thimble chambers usually have a volume of a fraction of a cubic centimetre because they are used primarily for measurements in positions where the exposure-rate or dose-rate varies rapidly from point to point. An exposure-rate of 1 R./min. produces an ionisation current of about 5×10^{-12} A. per cubic centimetre of chamber volume, so the currents obtained range from about 10^{-14} to 10^{-10} A. These small currents may be measured in one of three ways: (1) the ionisation chamber is connected in series with a sensitive current measuring device and the current is measured while the chamber is exposed to the radiation; (2) the ionisation chamber is connected to a charge measuring device during the exposure and the charge accumulated during any convenient interval of time is measured; (3) the chamber forms an air condenser; it is given a measured charge before exposure, then isolated from the measuring instrument while it is exposed to radiation, and the loss in charge due to the ionisation current measured after the exposure is completed. (See fig. 7.11.) The current measuring method gives the instantaneous value of the exposure-rate and has the advantage that the exposure-rate can be observed continuously, but has the disadvantage that leads are required from the chamber to the measuring instrument. Leads are both cumbersome and a possible source of error. For example, charge may leak across the insulation and this effect is frequently enhanced if the leads are exposed to stray radiation. When a series of measurements is to be made, the current measuring method is quick and convenient and is usually adopted. When only one or two measurements are required, the condenser method may be preferred. The charge measuring methods (2) and (3) above, give the total exposure in a given time, but in most situations in radio-therapy, the exposure-rate is constant over the time required for the measurement. The charging and measuring devices that are commonly used with thimble chambers used as

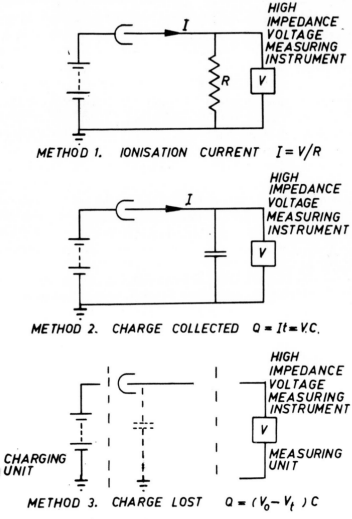

METHOD 1. IONISATION CURRENT $I = V/R$

METHOD 2. CHARGE COLLECTED $Q = It = V.C.$

METHOD 3. CHARGE LOST $Q = (V_0 - V_t)C$

FIG. 7.11. Diagrammatic illustration of three methods of measuring ionisation currents.

condensers are discussed in section 7.12 while other charge measuring and current measuring instruments are described in section 7.13 and 7.14 respectively.

239

7.12 Condenser exposure meters

A condenser exposure meter usually includes one or more thimble ionisation chambers, a charging device and a measuring instrument. The measuring instrument may be a string electrometer (one type is described below), a Lindemann electrometer or a vacuum tube electrometer (or " valve voltmeter ") of high impedance. The charging and measuring systems are sometimes combined in one unit. The chamber is charged before exposure to the radiation. Usually the chamber is charged until a pre-selected potential difference (V_0 say) is obtained between the chamber electrodes. After exposure for a known time (t), the potential difference between the electrodes (V_t say) is again measured. The loss of charge by the chamber is then $C \cdot (V_0 - V_t)$ where $C (= C_1 + C_2)$ is the effective capacity of the chamber (C_1) and the measuring instrument (C_2). Since an exposure of 1 roentgen produces 1 e.s.u. of charge per 0·001293 g. of dry air (i.e. per cubic centimentre of dry air at N.T.P.), if the chamber has a true " air wall " the exposure X in roentgens is given by

$$X = \frac{C}{v} \cdot (V_0 - V_t) \cdot \frac{T + 273}{273} \cdot \frac{760}{p} \qquad (5)$$

where C, V_0 and V_t are in e.s.u. and v denotes the chamber volume in cubic centimetres (1 e.s.u. of potential = 300 volts). In general

$$X = \frac{C}{v} \cdot (V_0 - V_t) \cdot \frac{T + 273}{273} \cdot \frac{760}{p} \cdot k$$

where k is a correction factor to allow for differences between the ionisation produced in the actual chamber and in an " airwall " chamber.

The exposure-rate is given by

$$\frac{X}{t} = \frac{C}{v} \cdot \frac{(V_0 - V_t)}{t} \cdot \frac{T + 273}{T} \cdot \frac{760}{p} \cdot k.$$

The sensitivity of the condenser chamber is usually measured by the change in potential per roentgen exposure. Since from equation (5), $(V_t - V_0)/X$ is proportional to v/C, the sensitivity is increased by increasing the chamber volume or by decreasing the capacity. In order to avoid having to measure the capacities of the chamber and of the measuring system (the latter is required since the charge on the condenser is shared with the measuring system during the process of measurement), the volume of the chamber and the correction factor k, it is customary to calibrate the chambers in terms of the deflections obtained on a particular measuring instrument when the chambers are exposed to a known amount of radiation.

Small condenser chambers such as those shown in fig. 7.07(c) and fig. 7.07(d) are particularly useful for measurements on irregular surfaces or in small cavities. Instruments suitable for charging and measuring such chambers have been designed by Farmer and others.[27, 28]

The Victoreen company roentgen-meter

A very widely used " roentgen meter " consisting of a set of condenser ionisation chambers and a charging and measuring system is made by the Victoreen Instrument Co. of Ohio. The ionisation chambers are available with different air volumes, so that a wide range of exposures can be measured. A cross-section of an ionisation chamber and its supporting stem is shown in fig. 7.12(a). Ions produced by the radiation in the cavity of the thimble chamber are collected and measured. It will be noticed that there is also an air cavity in the stem of the instrument, but ions produced here are not collected since there is no potential difference across this air space. The stem of the chamber forms a condenser which is in parallel with the thimble chamber itself (the metal shield serves as the outer electrode and the graphite lining of the air space in the stem as the inner electrode) so the effective capacity of the chamber is the sum of the thimble chamber capacity and the stem capacity. The stem capacity increases the range of exposures that can be measured.

The charging and measuring system is illustrated in fig. 7.12 (b). In order to charge the ionisation chamber it is inserted into the side tube where the central electrode I makes contact with a platinum wire E connected to a quartz loop H. An electrostatic charge can be generated by friction by rotating a wheel F against a brush and this charge is transferred to the wire E. E is observed through a microscope and it is usual to

charge the electrode system until the wire, which is deflected by
the electrostatic forces between a deflection electrode and the
quartz loop, takes up a predetermined position opposite the

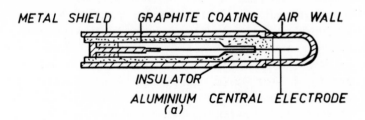

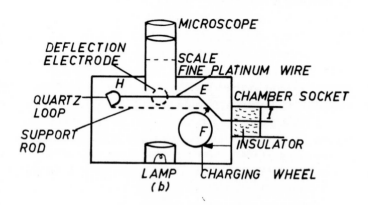

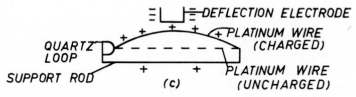

FIG. 7.12. The Victoreen Co. roentgen meter.

(*a*) Thimble chamber unit.

(*b*) Charging and measuring unit.

zero on a scale in the microscope eye-piece. The ionisation
chamber is then removed, exposed separately to the radiation
for a known time and returned to the side-tube. The new
position of the wire is observed. The eye-piece scale is calibrated so that the reading is obtained directly in roentgens.

The lamp illuminating the microscope scale can be run from a battery, and when the friction charging system is used, this equipment does not require any other electrical supplies. An alternative model is available, which is run from ordinary A.C. mains. In this model a transformer and rectifier replace the rotating wheel, and provide a voltage supply to charge the chamber.

The Victoreen instrument is widely used for measuring the output of X-ray sets. The detachable portion of the instrument is fairly large, however, and is not convenient for measurements on irregular surfaces or in small cavities. In some situations, scatter from the metal stem, or stem leakage, may also make the instrument unsuitable.

Pocket meters

In order to ascertain the amount of radiation to which radiographers and others may be exposed during their work, it is convenient to have exposure meters which can be readily

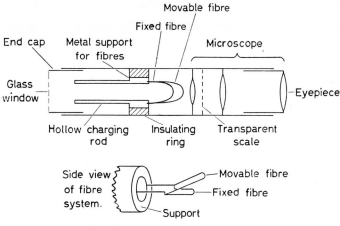

FIG. 7.13. A pocket dosemeter.

worn or carried in a pocket. Some instruments of this type are used in conjunction with a charging and measuring unit similar to that used with the Victoreen chambers discussed above. This has the disadvantage that the chamber must be returned to the measuring instrument before the exposure can be determined. In another type of pocket meter, the measuring system is included in the unit carried in the pocket, so that the exposure can be observed at any time. Such a direct-reading pocket exposure meter is shown in fig. 7.13. The instrument is prepared for use by removing an end cap and charging a hollow insulated rod to a predetermined voltage from an appropriate charging device. The rod carries a fixed wire and a light movable metal-coated fibre. Electrostatic repulsion causes the movable fibre to move away from the fixed wire as shown. On exposure to radiation, the charge leaks away from wire and fibre and the latter therefore gradually returns to its uncharged position. The moving fibre is observed through a microscope system with a built-in scale, which is calibrated to give readings directly in roentgen or milliroentgen. The entire instrument is about the size of a fountain pen.

(*Note.* The use of small photographic films for recording the exposure of staff to radiation is discussed in Chapter XIV.)

7.13 The Townsend Balance Method

If the collecting electrode of a thimble ionisation chamber is connected to one plate of a condenser and also to a sensitive, high impedance, voltage measuring device as shown in fig. 7.11(*b*), the ionisation current will charge up the condenser. The total charge Q collected after an interval of time t can be determined from the voltage V read at the end of the exposure. ($Q = V . C = V(C_1 + C_2 + C_3)$ where C is the effective capacity of the thimble chamber (C_1) the condenser (C_2) and the measuring instrument (C_3).) A more accurate but more tedious procedure consists in using the high impedance voltage measuring device merely as a null indicator. This is done in the Townsend balance method. As the ionisation current charges up one plate of the condenser, the potential of the other plate is increased by means of a potentiometer (see fig. 7.14(*a*),) so that the potential difference between the two plates remains zero. When the exposure is terminated, the potential applied to the condenser plate by the potentiometer is noted. This system has the advantage that the potential of the collecting electrode of the thimble chamber and of the lead connecting

244

the chamber to the condenser and high impedance voltage measuring system need never differ appreciably from earth potential. Consequently loss of charge across the insulation is reduced to a minimum.

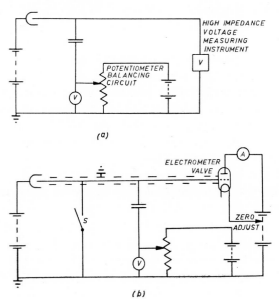

FIG. 7.14. The Townsend balance method.
(a) Simplified diagram illustrating the method
(b) Simplified circuit diagram of Farmer-Baldwin exposure meter.

The high impedance voltage measuring system is usually either a quadrant type electrometer such as the Lindemann or a vacuum tube electrometer. The Lindemann electrometer has the advantage of stable operating characteristics and mechanical robustness but the disadvantage that the deflection must be observed by means of a microscope or by a lamp and scale system. Electrometer valves are usually more sensitive but less stable than the Lindemann electrometer.

A simplified diagram of the circuit of the Farmer-Baldwin exposure meter[29] which uses the Townsend balance principle with a vacuum tube electrometer is shown in fig. 7.14(b). This instrument is widely used as a secondary standard for the calibration of tele-therapy equipment (see Chapter XI). One

9   245

advantage of the Townsend balance method in this application is that the therapy set can be adjusted and the shutter opened while the collecting electrode of the thimble chamber is earthed (switch S in fig. 7.14(b) is closed). When the operator is ready, the switch S is opened, a stop-watch is started simultaneously and the condenser begins to charge up. The stop-watch can be stopped at any instant when the potentiometer is correctly adjusted (i.e. when the electrometer indicates there is no potential difference across the condenser) and the voltmeter reading noted. For a given thimble chamber and condenser, the voltmeter V is usually calibrated to read directly in roentgens. The voltmeter reading then gives the exposure in the time indicated by the stop-watch and no corrections are necessary for shutter opening and closing times.

7.14. Direct reading ionisation current meters using electronic amplifiers

The Townsend balance method is frequently used for calibration measurements because it has the advantage of being a null method and gives very accurate results. For the measurement of the larger ionisation currents or when a high degree of accuracy is not essential, it is usually more convenient to use a method of measurement in which a steady deflection of the measuring instrument is obtained. Also to observe rapid changes in the ionisation current, an instrument which indicates the instantaneous value of the current is required. For these purposes, the ionisation current is passed through a high resistance (10^{10} to 10^{12} ohms) as shown in fig. 7.11(a). The potential difference across the resistance is then measured using a high impedance measuring system. This normally consists of either (1) an electrometer valve used either alone or in conjunction with further stages of direct current amplification or (2) a vibrating reed and alternating current amplifier. We consider first the direct current system.

The essential elements of a single valve circuit are shown in fig. 7.15. The high resistance is connected between the grid and cathode of an electrometer valve. It is essential that the grid current in the valve shall be small in comparison with the ionisation current to be measured, and that any voltage drifts which occur shall be small in comparison with the potential difference across the resistance. Thus in order to measure a current of 10^{-11} A., the valve should have a grid current less than 10^{-13} A. and voltage fluctuations should not exceed 10 mV. (For 10^{-11} A. the input voltage will usually be a few volts, as the highest stable resistances which can be obtained are of the order of 10^{12} ohm.) For such currents, a meter can be included in the anode circuit and calibrated to give the potential difference across the input resistance directly. To measure a current of 10^{-14} A., an electrometer valve with a

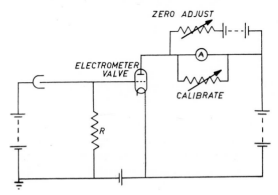

FIG. 7.15. Essentials of a single valve direct reading exposure-rate or dose-rate meter.

grid current of 10^{-16} A. is desirable, and it is necessary to follow the first electrometer valve with one or more stages of amplification, and to use special techniques (in particular negative feedback, see below) to increase stability.

The connection from the thimble chamber to the high resistance and the electrometer grid must be highly insulated and it is convenient to make this connection as short as is compatible with keeping the electrometer tube and resistance out of the main radiation fields. It is common practice to mount these components at the base of the thimble chamber " stem ". Cable connections can then be made to the meter, batteries and further stages of amplification if these are used.

The principle of negative feedback is as follows. Suppose that the ionisation current produces a voltage V_i across the input resistance or condenser, and that this is applied to the

247

grid of an electrometer valve which is followed by an amplifier. Let the total amplification produced be M, and let the output voltage from the amplifier be V_0. Suppose this produces a current I_0 in the output circuit which includes a micro-ammeter, a large resistance R and a small resistance r, the ratio R/r being known precisely. (See fig. 7.16.) If the voltage developed

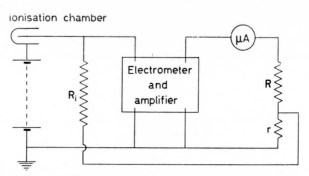

FIG. 7.16. Valve electrometer circuit with negative feed-back.

across the small resistance r is " fed back " into the amplifier so that it opposes the voltage V_i, then the input to the amplifier becomes

$$V_i - \frac{r}{r + R}V_0$$

but the output $\quad V_0 = M \times \text{input} = M\left(V_i - \frac{r}{r + R}V_0\right)$

$$\therefore \quad V_0 = MV_i \Big/ \left(1 + \frac{rM}{r + R}\right)$$

If the amplifier gain is large, so that $\dfrac{rM}{r + R} \gg 1$

$$V_0 = \frac{r + R}{r}V_i \text{ and } I_0 = V_i/r.$$

Thus if the gain M is large, its exact value does not alter the current through the milliammeter in the output circuit, which will be proportional to the value of the " ionisation " voltage V_1. In this way it is possible to obtain a direct reading instrument for the measurement of small currents which is reasonably stable.

In the vibrating reed electrometer,[30, 31] the voltage from the high resistance is connected across a condenser, one plate of which is a vibrating metal strip, the " reed ". The reed is maintained in vibration by an electro-magnet, energised by alternating current. The capacity of the condenser increases and decreases as the reed vibrates (usually at about 500 c./sec.) and when the ionisation current charges up the condenser, a potential difference which rises and falls with the same frequency is produced. This potential difference is amplified by an alternating current amplifier tuned to the same frequency as the electromagnet. A.C. amplifiers can be made much more stable than d.c. amplifiers and voltage drifts in a.c. amplifiers may be as little as $10 \, \mu V$. compared with $1 \, mV$. in a d.c. amplifier. In this respect the vibrating reed system is superior to an electrometer valve. However the reed is not small and cannot be mounted in the stem of a thimble chamber, so spurious charges originating in the cable connecting the chamber and the reed are more troublesome than with the electrometer valve system.

Although the above circuits are used primarily as current measuring systems (i.e. to determine exposure-*rates* or dose-*rates*), if the high resistance R is replaced by a condenser, then the same voltage measuring circuits can be used to determine the total exposure or total dose received in a given time. When used in this way, the meter shows a continually increasing reading while the chamber is exposed to radiation and it is the final steady reading, when the exposure is completed, which is required. The instruments are usually calibrated so that for any particular combination of ionisation chamber and condenser the meter indicates exposure (or dose) directly.

7.15. Integrating monitor circuits

In therapy equipment in which the output is fairly constant, an ammeter on the control panel is commonly used to indicate the magnitude of the (amplified) ionisation current from the output monitoring chamber. In some equipment, however, and particularly in units where the ouput is expected to fluctuate, a recording device which indicates the *total* ionisation produced in the monitor may replace the ammeter. In this type of device, the ionisation current is usually fed into a condenser connected between the grid and cathode of a gas-filled triode. When the potential of the condenser rises to the appropriate value, the valve " fires " and the anode current operates a relay connected to the recording device. At the same time the condenser is discharged. The potential of the condenser then begins to rise again and the cycle is repeated. At the end of the treatment, the reading of the recording device indicates the total ionisation which has been produced in the monitor chamber. This may be related to the total exposure or total dose delivered if the equipment has been suitably calibrated. Alternatively, the recording device may be arranged so that the exposure is automatically terminated when a preset reading is reached.

7.16. Solid state radiation meters[32]

For some medical applications, particularly intracavitary measurements, small and mechanically robust measuring instruments are desirable. Solid state radiation detectors can be made very small in comparison with ionisation chambers, since most solids contain 1,000 or more times as many atoms per unit volume as air and the energy required to produce an ion pair may be considerably less. Most of the solid state systems have the disadvantage that the response depends upon the radiation quality (lithium fluoride is the only material used with atomic number at all close to that of air or soft tissue) and many materials have other drawbacks such as a response which varies non-linearly with exposure-rate or total exposure, or is dependent upon the previous irradiation history of the specimen. Nevertheless provided the limitations of the particular system used are recognised, and the system is suitably calibrated, these devices can be very useful in particular applications. The devices fall into two main groups (*a*) those used as exposure-rate (or dose-rate) meters and (*b*) those used for the measurement of total exposure or total dose. The first group includes *p-n* junction detectors as well as the cadmium crystal detectors, while the second group consists primarily of photoluminescent and thermoluminescent dosimeters.

Junction detectors and cadmium sulphide crystal detectors

When a *p-n* junction (see Chapter II) is irradiated, electron-hole pairs are produced by the radiation. Those within the depletion region (or within diffusion distance of the depletion region) change the potential across the junction. Either this voltage, or the current obtained when the junction is short-circuited, may be used as a measure of the exposure-rate at the junction. The latter method is usually more convenient for dosimetry since the current varies more nearly linearly with exposure-rate than the open circuit voltage and is more nearly independent of temperature.[33] The junctions have a very fast response time, and are very useful for measuring charged particles, but are less suitable for the measurement of X- and γ-radiation because relatively little energy is absorbed in the depletion layer, even when this is deliberately increased in thickness. The currents obtained are of the order of 10^{-9} ampere per roentgen per minute, which although high compared with that from a gas filled ionisation chamber, is still several orders of magnitude less than the currents which can be obtained from cadmium sulphide probes (see Table 7.02). The latter are therefore preferable for most clinical applications except for a few situations where their slow response (see below) is a serious handicap.

If an electric field is maintained across a crystal of cadmium sulphide or cadmium selenide, exposed to radiation, the current due to electron-hole pairs produced by the radiation, is amplified by a factor of 10^3 to 10^4. According to Bube,[34] this is due to the presence in these crystals of negatively charged sensitising centres, which have a larger cross-section for photo-excited holes than for the subsequent capture of photo-excited electrons. So long as there are " trapped " holes in the crystal, electrons will pass through the crystal from one electrode to the other. On the average, 10^3 to 10^4 electrons cross an average crystal at room temperature before recombination occurs. Currents of the order of 10^{-6} A. per R./min., can be readily obtained.

The variation of current with exposure-rate is fairly close to linear for cadmium sulphide (which is better in this respect than cadmium selenide) although the relationship appears to

251

vary somewhat from one crystal to another (values of the current exposure-rate exponent from 0·85 to 1·0 have been reported). This variation is a disadvantage. Other drawbacks are (1) the response per roentgen is very quality dependent on account of the high atomic number of cadmium (although the quality dependence can be reduced by the use of filters) and (2) the response is slow. The current may take 1 to 100 seconds to build up to its steady value (and to die away) depending

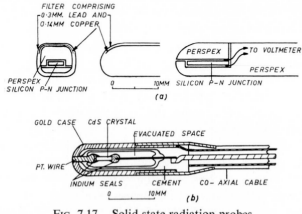

FIG. 7.17.   Solid state radiation probes.
(a) Si p-n junction probe.
(b) CdS crystal probe.
((a) After D. Whelpton and B. W. Watson [33] (b) after D. E. A. Jones.[36])

upon the exposure-rate and previous radiation history of the specimen. The response time can be reduced by special techniques known as " priming " and " biassing ", i.e. by irradiating the crystal at a known exposure-rate either before, or during, the exposure which is being measured.[35]   For many therapy applications, the slow response is not a serious problem and the crystals can be calibrated at the radiation qualities and exposure-rates likely to be used.   A very simple clinical probe can then be constructed, consisting merely of a cadmium sulphide crystal in series with a battery and micro-ammeter, with none of the problems associated with the measurement of the very small ionisation currents obtained from a thimble cavity chamber probe of comparable size.[36]

TABLE 7.02

COMPARISON OF PROBE TYPE EXPOSURE-RATE MEASURING DEVICES

Device	Sensitivity to Co^{60} γ-rays. Current for $1R./min.$	Sensitivity at $50\ keV.$ compared with $1\ MeV.$
Thimble ionisation chamber	10^{-12} A.	1
Si p-n junction	10^{-9} A.	6
CdS single crystal	10^{-6} A.	50

Colour changes in glasses and plastics and luminescent dosimeters [32, 37]

In some solids, electrons freed within the material by irradiation, may enter traps where they can remain for very long periods of time. The new centres formed by the combination of electrons and traps may have properties which can be used to measure the number of centres produced and hence to determine the total radiation dose received. For example, many such centres absorb visible light and the coloration of clear glasses and plastics after irradiation is a well-known phenomenon. However, measurable changes in the optical and ultra-violet absorbing properties of glasses, plastics and dye stuffs are usually produced only by exposures in the kiloroentgen to mega-roentgen range, so these materials are of limited use in most clinical situations.

In silver-activated glass, in addition to the colour centres which absorb visible light, a second type of centre is also produced by ionising radiation which has the property of absorbing ultra-violet light and simultaneously producing an orange fluorescence. The intensity of the fluorescent light, (measured by a photomultiplier) can be used as a measure of the exposure. This system can be used to measure exposures in the range of 10 to 10^4 R. Miniature glass rods, called " fluorods " are available commercially and have been used clinically. The response per roentgen is, of course, quality dependent although special " low-Z " glass rods have been produced. Metal filters can be used to reduce the quality dependence. However the most serious drawback to fluorods, is that in the specimens presently (1965) available the response is not sufficiently reproducible (from rod to rod). By giving a small standard radiation dose to a number of rods and rejecting those whose readings do not fall within (say) 5 per cent. of the mean, the spread of readings can be reduced or alternatively if 3 or 4 rods can be used for each measurement, a more reliable estimate can be obtained. There are obvious drawbacks to either of these procedures, however, and until the reproducibility of readings can be improved, this defect seriously limits the use of this system.

In the materials so far discussed, the measurement procedure does not destroy the " dose " centres. In thermo-luminescent materials, the trapped electrons are released by heating and the dose centres are therefore destroyed. The recombination of the released electrons is accompanied by the emission of fluorescent light and the total quantity of light emitted can be used as a measure of the absorbed dose. The principal thermo-luminescent materials are calcium fluoride and lithium fluoride to which suitable activators have been added. For the maximum sensitivity calcium fluoride is used and exposures from a few milli-roentgen to 10^5 roentgen can be measured. Lithium fluoride is somewhat less sensitive but has the great advantage of an effective atomic number quite close to that of air and a response per roentgen (or per rad in soft tissue) which is therefore relatively independent of the radiation quality.

The usual measurement or " read-out " procedure is to raise the temperature of the thermo-luminescent material at a standard rate until the temperature reaches about 400°C. The light emitted is measured by a photomultiplier (separated by a heat shield and infra-red filter from the fluoride). A graph plotted between the light emitted and the temperature is known as a " glow curve ", and shows one or more characteristic peaks at temperatures depending upon the traps in the phosphor. Lithium fluoride is often used as a loose powder. About 20–30 mg. (accurately weighed or dispensed volumetrically with suitable precision) is required for measurement. The use of loose powder is convenient in some situations but if small doses are to be measured, it is necessary to guard against spurious thermo-luminescence which is produced by mechanical agitation of the powder. This " tribo-thermo-luminescence " is small enough to be neglected if doses of 10 rad or more are being measured. It can be eliminated by heating the powder in nitrogen or by fixing the powder to a suitable base with enamel or by incorporating the powder in a plastic such as polytetrafluorethylene (teflon). The latter method reduces the sensitivity but makes it possible to fabricate dosimeters in the

TABLE 7.03

COMPARISON OF SMALL VOLUME, TOTAL DOSE MEASURING SYSTEMS

	Dose range (rads)	Sensitivity at 50 keV. compared to 1 MeV.
Ionisation chamber	$10-10^2$	1
Photo-luminescence in silver-phosphate glass	$10-10^5$	20 (high Z) 7 (low Z)
Thermo-luminescence in lithium fluoride	$10^{-2}-10^5$	1·3

form of thin discs or rods. (Rods of 2 mm. diameter or discs 1 cm.^{2} in area and 2 mm. deep are available commercially.) The principal advantages of lithium fluoride dosimeters are good reproducibility, and a response per roentgen (or per rad in soft tissue) which is (1) nearly independent of radiation quality,* (2) is independent of dose-rate, and (3) varies linearly with total dose up to about 1,000 rads (slight deviations from linearity occur at higher doses). It is sometimes stated that the dose received may be read at any time after the exposure over a period up to several months. However some fading of the light output occurs if the dose reading is delayed and the extent of the fading depends upon the storage conditions and may vary from one batch of phosphor to another. It is

* A fairly small, but unexpected, reduction in sensitivity at high energies has recently been reported. [38]

therefore desirable to standardise the storage conditions and the storage time, if the read-out process is to be delayed. It is of interest that lithium fluoride dosimeters sent by post from one centre to another have already been used in intercomparisons of radiation sources. The lithium fluoride can be re-used after " annealing " but must be recalibrated.

REFERENCES

1. International Commission on Radiological Units and Measurements (1962). Report 10a. *U.S. National Bureau of Standards Handbook* 84.
2. International Commission on Radiological Units and Measurements (1962). Report 10b. *U.S. National Bureau of Standards Handbook* No. 85.
3. WYCKOFF, H. O., ASTON, G. H. and SMITH, E. E. (1954). *Brit. J. Radiol.* **27**, 325.
4. SMITH, E. E. (1955). *Brit. J. Radiol.* **28**, 662.
5. KEMP, L. A. W. and HALL, S. M. (1954). *Brit. J. Radiol.* **27**, 219.
6. WYCKOFF, H. O. and ATTIX, F. H. (1957). *U.S. National Bureau of Standards Handbook*, No. 64.
7. HENRY, W. H. and GARRETT, C. (1960). *Can. J. Phys.* **38**, 1680.
8. BRAGG, W. H. (1912). *Studies in Radioactivity.* MacMillan, New York.
9. GRAY, L. H. (1936). *Proc. Roy-Soc. A.* **156**, 578. (1937). *Brit. J. Radiol.* **10**, 600 and 721.
10. WEISS, J. and BERNSTEIN, W. (1957). *Radiation Res.* **6**, 603.
11. CURRAN, S. C. and VALENTINE, J. M. (1958). *Reports on Progress in Physics*, **21**, 1.
12. U.S. National Committee on Radiological Protection (1961). *U.S. National Bureau of Standards Handbook*, No. 79.
13. BETHE, H. A. (1933). *Handbuch der Physik*, **24**, 273.
14. WHYTE, G. N. (1954). *Nucleonics.* **12**, No. 2, 18.
15. SPENCER, L. V. and ATTIX, F. H. (1955). *Radiation Res.* **3**, 239.
16. BURCH, P. R. J. (1955). *Radiation Res.* **3**, 361.
17. FANO, U. (1954). *Radiation Res.* **1**, 237.
18. FAILLA, G. (1956). *Radiation Res.* **4**, 102.
19. BARNARD, G. P., AXTON, E. J. and MARSH, A. R. S. (1959). *Phys. in Med. and Bio.* **3**, 366. (1962). *Phys. in Med. and Bio.* **7**, 229.
20. BARNARD, G. P. (1964). *Phys. in Med. and Bio.*, **9**, 287, 321.
21. SIEVERT, R. M. (1932). *Acta Radiol.* Sup. XIV.
22. Hospital Physicists' Association (1964). *Phys. in Med. and Bio.* **9**, 451.
23. FAILLA, G. (1937). *Amer. J. Roentgenol.* **29**, 202.

24. PERRY, W. E., DALE, J. W. G. and PULFER, R. F. (1961). *Int. J. Appl. Radiat. and Isotopes*, **10**, 65.
25. KORFF, S. A. (1946). *Electron and Nuclear Counters.* New York, Van Nostrand.
26. ROSSI, B. B. and STAUB, H. H. (1949). *Ion Chambers and Counters.* New York, McGraw-Hill.
27. WILSON, C. W. (1945). *Radium Therapy. Its Physical Aspects.* London, Chapman & Hall.
28. FARMER, F. T. (1942). *Proc. Phys. Soc.* **54**, 435.
29. FARMER, F. T. (1955). *Brit. J. Radiol.* **28**, 304.
30. LAFFERTY, J. M. and KINGDOM, H. H. (1946). *J. Appl. Phys.* **17**, 894.
31. REESE, H. (1950). *Nucleonics*, **6**, No. 3, 40.
32. FOWLER, J. F. (1959). *Phys. in Med. and Bio.* **3**, 395. (1963). *Phys. in Med. and Bio.* **8**, 1.
33. WHELPTON, D. and WATSON, B. W. (1963). *Phys. in Med. and Bio.* **8**, 33.
34. BUBE, R. H. (1961). *J. Applied Phys.* **32**, 1707.
35. TURNER, B. A., MASH, D. H. and FOWLER, J. F. (1963). *Phys. in Med. and Bio.* **8**, 439.
36. JONES, D. E. A. (1960). *Phys. in Med. and Bio.*, **4**, 370.
37. KARZMARK, C. J., WHITE, J. and FOWLER, J. F. (1964). *Phys. in Med. and Bio.* **9**, 273.
38. CROSBY, E. H., ALMOND, P. R. and SHALEK, R. J. (1966). *Phys. in Med. and Bio.* **11**, 131.

GENERAL REFERENCES

WHYTE, G. N. (1959). *Principles of Radiation Dosimetry*, New York, John Wiley & Sons.
HINE, G. J. and BROWNELL, G. L. (ed.), (1956). *Radiation Dosimetry.* New York, Academic Press.

EXAMINATION QUESTIONS

1. Name and define the units used for the expression of (*a*) *exposure* (dose) of radiation, (*b*) *absorbed dose* of radiation. In what circumstances may the absorbed dose be different although the exposure is the same? How does this difference depend upon the wavelength (energy) of the radiation?

M.S.R. (R. & T.), 1964.

2. Define the roentgen.
   Describe with the aid of a simple diagram the construction of a thimble ionisation chamber pointing out the necessary properties of its components. State what additional equipment and information is needed to determine an exposure (dose) in roentgens.

M.S.R. (R. & T.), 1963.

3. What quantities are measured by (*a*) the roentgen, (*b*) the rad? Define these units. Why do both of these units appear in various aspects of radiotherapy?

M.S.R. (T.), 1964.

4. Describe three methods other than the Geiger-Müller counter, of measuring X-radiation, noting whether they are useful for small or large amounts of radiation. Describe *one* X-radiation measuring instrument based on one of these methods.

M.S.R. (T.), 1964.

5. Explain and distinguish between the terms *intensity, exposure* (dose), *absorbed dose* as applied to radiation, and state the units in which each is measured. How would the skin dose be measured on a patient during a diagnostic procedure?

F.S.R. (R.), 1965.

6. Explain the meaning of the terms *dose* and *exposure* in relation to X- and gamma-ray measurements.
Define the units of these radiation quantities. Explain how the dose at a point in an irradiated material can be calculated from a measurement of the exposure at that point. Discuss this conversion in relation to the tissues of the human body.

F.S.R. (T.), 1965.

7. Describe the construction of an ionisation chamber with special reference to (*a*) " build-up ", (*b*) its calibration to measure in Röntgens.

F.S.R. (T.), 1964.

8. Define the röntgen and the rad and discuss their relationship at radiation energies of (*a*) 50 keV.—150 keV., (*b*) 200 keV.−400 keV., (*c*) 1 MeV. −5 MeV.

D.M.R., 1964.

CHAPTER VIII

THE MEASUREMENT OF IONISING
RADIATIONS (cont'd)

8.01. Geiger-Müller counters

IN ionisation chambers, the charge or current which is measured is due solely to ion pairs produced either by the radiation itself or by secondary electrons produced by the radiation. Each ion pair carries a charge of $4·8 \times 10^{-10}$ e.s.u. or $1·6 \times 10^{-19}$ coulomb, so that to produce the minimum charge that can be fairly readily measured, say 10^{-14} coulomb, approximately 60,000 ion pairs must be produced in the chamber. As it completes its path in the chamber, a single α-particle will usually produce sufficient ion pairs to be detected, but a single fast electron, whether a β-particle or a secondary electron produced by X- or γ-radiation, will produce only about 10^3 ion pairs or less. (Fast electrons produce between 50 and a few hundred ion pairs per cm. in air depending upon their energy.) For β-, X- and γ-radiation, therefore, ionisation chambers can only be used to measure the mean intensity of a beam of radiation over a certain interval of time (they cannot detect individual electrons or photons) and the intensity must be such that about 60 electrons or more cross the chamber each second. (This will produce a minimum current of 10^{-14} ampere in a typical chamber.) When the radiation intensity is less than this, ionisation chambers are not suitable for the measurement of β-, X- or γ-radiation and either Geiger-Müller counters, proportional counters or scintillation counters are generally employed.

Geiger-Müller counters differ from ionisation chambers in that the gas is usually under reduced pressure and a much higher potential gradient is maintained between the electrodes. In these circumstances, ions and more especially free electrons are accelerated by the intense field and acquire sufficient velocity between collisions to ionise the gas molecules. The secondary ions so produced may likewise acquire sufficient energy to produce ionisation on collision. Thus a considerable increase in the total number of ions is obtained. The primary ionisation produced by the radiation is multiplied to such an extent that each electron or each photon generates sufficient ions to produce a measurable pulse of charge at the collecting electrode. These pulses are then counted by electronic counters.

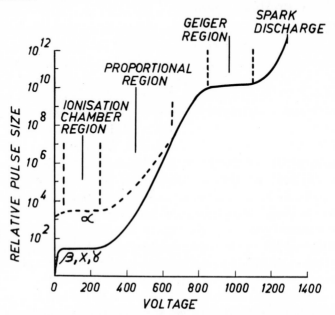

FIG. 8.01. The variation of pulse size with chamber-counter voltage.

The ratio of the number of ion pairs collected to the number produced by the radiation is called the gas amplification factor and increases as the electric field between the electrodes is increased. (See fig. 8.01.) The amplification factor varies from 1 in ionisation chambers through about 10^3 in proportional counters to about 10^8 in Geiger-Müller counters. Proportional counters are operated with voltages such that secondary ionisation only occurs near the primary ions and hence the total current is proportional to the number of primary ions. Geiger-Müller counters are operated with higher voltages and the ionisation produced is independent of the initial number of ions.

This means that the pulse from a proportional counter depends upon the nature of the ionising particle (being greater for the more densely ionising radiations) whereas Geiger-Müller tubes do not discriminate between different types of radiation. Since

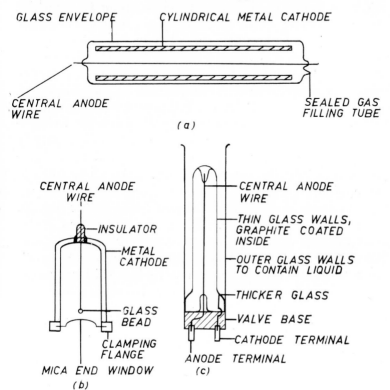

FIG. 8.02. Geiger-Müller counters.
(a) Cylindrical γ counter.
(b) End-window β counter.
(c) Cylindrical β counter for liquids.

proportional counters are not widely used in medical practice they will not be considered further here. The mechanism and use of the Geiger-Müller counter is discussed in more detail below.

The most usual form of counter consists of a cylindrical cathode a few centimetres in diameter with an axial tungsten wire as anode. (See fig. 8.02.) For β-counters, the cathode is usually a thin film of graphite, copper, or silver deposited on the glass walls but may be a separate cylinder of thin metal foil or gauze. For γ-counters a fairly thick metal tube is used as cathode. This is most frequently of copper, but since the ionisation produced in the chamber is mainly due to secondary electrons from the cathode, to obtain the maximum sensitivity, lead cathodes are sometimes used. Argon, with a high specific ionisation, is the usual filling gas. For the measurement of low energy β-radiation, the counter must be provided with a window thin enough to absorb only a small fraction of the radiation. Windows of mica which form one end of the counter are commonly used (fig. 8.02(b)). For very soft β-radiation, the sample may be placed inside the counter (which then has to be refilled with the counting gas each time a sample is introduced). H^3 and C^{14} are sometimes converted into gases before being introduced into the counter to reduce the effects of self-absorption.

The anode is normally maintained 200 to 1500 V. positive with respect to the cathode. The electric field is most intense near the central wire and it is here that avalanche ionisation takes place. Electrons formed in this process are rapidly attracted to the central wire, the positive ions which are heavier move towards the cathode more slowly and hence a short time after an ionising event has occurred, when the free electrons have already reached the central wire, a cloud of positive ions remains near the wire and these reduce the field intensity and stop further ionisation. When the positive ions reach the cathode and are discharged, however, they may form excited molecules, returning to the ground state with the emission of radiation. Some of this radiation may be of such a frequency as to cause photo-electric emission from the cathode and if this takes place a second discharge is initiated. If the tube is to be used as a detector of ionising radiation these secondary discharges must be prevented. This may be achieved either by the use of electronic quenching circuits or by the use of a quenching gas in the Geiger-Müller tube.

Although some details of their mode of action are not yet satisfactorily understood, the general nature of the part played by quenching gases is fairly clear. Consider a gas with the following properties :

(1) an ionisation potential (V_Q) lower than that of the main gas (V_M) ;

(2) broad and intense ultra-violet absorption ;

(3) a tendency to dissociate rather than radiate when excited.

If a small amount of such a gas is mixed with the main gas (say 1 part in 10) ions of both gases will be produced in the avalanche. By the time the positive cloud reaches the cathode however, it will consist almost entirely of ions of the quenching gas, since in collisions between main gas ions and neutral quenching molecules, the latter will lose an electron to the former, because the quenching gas has a lower ionisation potential than the main gas.   In this process the main gas atoms may be left with sufficient energy to radiate and for most gases the excitation energy will exceed the photo-electric threshold ϕ of the cathode and thus be able to cause the emission of photo-electrons.   However, if the quenching gas absorbs strongly wavelengths corresponding to $V_Q - \phi$, any radiation emitted will be absorbed by the quenching gas before reaching the cathode.   We have postulated that excited molecules of the quenching gas tend to lose excess energy by dissociation rather than by radiation which might cause photo-electric emission from the cathode.   Thus the probability of initiating a second discharge is very considerably reduced.

The first materials to be successfully employed as quenching gases were polyatomic organic vapours such as alcohol and xylene.   These substances are gradually dissociated and therefore used up as the counter is employed.   Most counters with organic quenching gases have a useful life of about 10^8 counts. Subsequently the use of halogens as quenching gases was introduced since they have suitable ionisation potentials and absorption characteristics.   Since the dissociated halogen molecules recombine after the discharge, the halogen quenched counters have the advantage of a longer life than the organic vapour quenched counters.   Larger pulses can also be obtained from halogen counters and they can be operated with about 400 V. on the anode instead of the 1,000 V. which is usually required for the organic vapour counters. Temperature effects are also reduced.

Halogen counters have two disadvantages however. (1) The " plateau " region (see fig. 8.01) is shorter and steeper with halogen quenching than with organic vapour quenching and (2) the electrodes must either be constructed of materials which are resistant to attack by the halogens or be coated with an inert material to prevent attack by these very reactive gases. Stainless steel electrodes are commonly employed.

8.02. Associated electrical circuits for Geiger-Müller counters

Geiger-Müller counters are normally operated as shown in fig. 8.03 with a resistance R_1 in series with the high voltage supply.

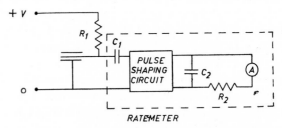

FIG. 8.03. Schematic diagram of Geiger-Müller counter and rate-meter.

When an ionising event occurs, a current pulse flows through the resistance, the potential difference across the tube is reduced and this assists in quenching the discharge. The early Geiger-Müller tubes relied on this effect alone to quench the discharge, but this is not done now, because the high value of the resistance which is required slows the discharge and increases the counter resolving time (i.e. the minimum time which must elapse after an ionising event before the counter is again in a condition to record another ionisation). Self-quenching tubes, i.e. tubes containing a quenching gas, can be connected to counting circuits through a small condenser C_1 (50 to 100 $\mu\mu f.$) but with tubes which do not contain a quenching gas, a quenching circuit is inserted between tube and coupling condenser. There are a variety of possible quenching circuits, which are fully described in books on counter circuits. (See references at end of chapter.) The advantage of an external quenching circuit is that the time during which the counter will not respond to an ionising event may be fixed by the circuit, otherwise it is a function of both the Geiger-Müller tube and the counting rate.

The pulses from the coupling condenser are normally fed either to a rate-meter or to a scaler. In a *rate-meter* a meter on the output side indicates the mean rate at which pulses are received over some convenient time interval (e.g. 1 sec., 10 sec., 100 sec.). This is achieved by feeding the pulses from the counting tube first through a " shaping " circuit which ensures that they are all of equal height and duration (this circuit may be combined with the quenching circuit) and then into a condenser C_2. Each pulse charges the condenser but between pulses the charge leaks away through the resistance R_2 and microammeter A. The potential difference across the condenser depends upon the rate at which pulses are received and it is this potential difference which determines the current recorded by the meter. The values of the capacity C_2 and the resistance R_2 determine the time constant, i.e. the period of time for which the rate is averaged.

At low counting rates it is preferable to record the total number of pulses received in a certain time and not an automatically averaged rate of arrival of pulses. The ratemeter is then replaced by a scaler. The older type of scaler consists of a series of circuits each of which produces a single pulse for each two pulses it receives. Thus a two-stage scaler will produce an output pulse for every four (2×2) input pulses, a three-stage scaler will produce an output pulse after 8 $(2 \times 2 \times 2)$ input pulses and so on. The purpose of these circuits is to reduce the number of pulses so that they can be recorded on a mechanical register, which cannot operate sufficiently rapidly to record every pulse from the Geiger tube. Neon lamps in the scaling circuits enable the operation of the circuits to be checked and record pulses which have not operated the mechanical register. The newer types of scaler employ decade counting tubes. Amplified pulses from the Geiger-Müller tube are fed to the decade tubes which provide a direct visual indication of the number of pulses which have

265

been received. Two types of decade counting tube are described below.

A decade counting tube known as a dekatron[1] is illustrated diagrammatically in fig. 8.04. The glass envelope contains gas at low pressure. A central anode is surrounded by thirty wires or metal strips which are connected to form three sets as shown. These are referred to as the cathode, the first guide and the second guide systems. The cathode system is normally at a lower potential than the guides so that a discharge normally

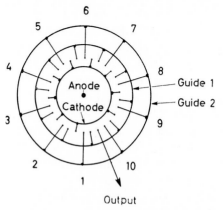

FIG. 8.04. A cold cathode decade counter or " dekatron ".

takes place between the anode and one of the wires of the cathode system. Pulses from the counting tube are fed directly to the first guide system and through a delay line to the second guide system. The arrival of a pulse causes the potential of the first guide system to fall sufficiently below that of the cathode to cause the discharge to move from the cathode wire to the nearest guide wire, i.e. to move in a clockwise direction (fig. 8.04). An instant later, the arrival of the pulse at the second guide system reduces the potential of that system and the discharge transfers to the adjacent second guide wire, again moving clockwise. When the second guide system returns to its normal potential, the discharge moves to the nearest cathode wire which is once again in the clockwise direction. Thus the inclusion of the

266

guide systems ensures that the discharge will always move from one cathode wire to the next cathode wire in the clockwise direction. After ten pulses the discharge takes place between the anode and an output wire and can operate another dekatron and so on. The dekatrons cannot operate at very high counting rates (the minimum time required between pulses depends upon the nature of the gas filling but is usually of the order of 50 μ sec.) but are sufficiently fast for most measurements made with Geiger-Müller tubes.

For higher counting rates, a decade counting tube has been produced which is essentially a small cathode-ray tube. An

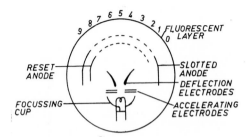

FIG. 8.05. A fast decade counter.

electron beam from a heated filament is focused and accelerated across the tube to a slotted anode (see fig. 8.05). The beam passes between two deflection electrodes and is initially deflected to (say) the extreme right. Most of the electrons are collected by the anode, but in this position of the beam, some electrons pass through the extreme right hand slot and produce a bright spot on the fluorescent screen behind the anode (in position 0 say). When a pulse is received from the Geiger-Müller counter, the potential of the deflecting electrodes is changed in such a manner that the electron beam falls on the second slot and the bright spot on the fluorescent screen moves into position 1. Further pulses move the beam successively across the tube until position 9 is reached, the next pulse resets the beam to zero and passes a pulse to the next decade tube. This type of tube is now widely used in " fast " scalers. Other designs of decade counter are produced but the above examples illustrate the kinds of system that are used.

8.03. Scintillation counters

Scintillation counters depend upon the fact that when certain solid or liquid materials, called phosphors, are exposed to ionising radiations, some molecules are raised to excited states from which they return to the ground state by radiating photons of visible or ultra-violet light. Although the flashes

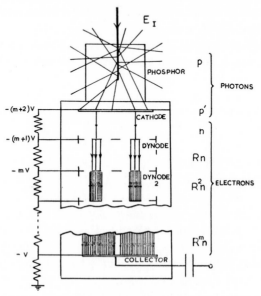

FIG. 8.06. Diagrammatic representation of a scintillation counter.

By permission from *Scintillation Counters*, by J. D. Birks. (Pergamon Press, Ltd., London.)

of light produced are of very short duration and low intensity and are therefore difficult to observe visually, Rutherford and his co-workers counted α-particles by the scintillations which they produce in zinc sulphide. Nowadays, in scintillation counters the phosphor is mounted above the window of a photo-multiplier tube. The scintillations are thus converted into pulses of electrical charge which are then amplified and counted.

Compared with a Geiger-Müller counter where the ions produced in the gas are used directly, a scintillation counter might be expected to be rather inefficient on account of the additional conversion processes that take place. In the phosphor, the incident particles or the secondary electrons produced by the incident photons, ionise and excite the phosphor molecules. The energy given up to the phosphor is then converted to photons of visible or ultra-violet light as the phosphor molecules return to the ground state. (The mechanisms of photon emission are somewhat different in the organic phosphors and in impurity activated inorganic phosphors such as thallium activated sodium iodide but the details of these processes will not be considered here.) This is followed by a second conversion process when the photons of light are absorbed by the photo-cathode of the photo-multiplier and electrons are emitted. In fact, the efficiency of both these conversion processes is relatively high, but even so, the release of one photoelectron from the cathode of the photomultiplier requires the dissipation of about 500 eV. of energy in the phosphor. This should be compared with 25 to 40 eV. per ion, for the production of an ion pair in most gases. Furthermore the amplification which is obtained in commercially available photomultiplier tubes is usually about 10^6 to 10^7 compared with 10^8 to 10^9 obtained in the Geiger-Müller discharge. Thus there are appreciably fewer electrons per pulse from a scintillation counter. Despite this disadvantage, for the measurement of penetrating radiations, a scintillation counter is preferable to a Geiger-Müller counter because a much higher counting rate can be obtained. This is because a larger fraction of the incident radiation can be utilised. In the case of penetrating radiation, Geiger-Müller discharges are mainly initiated by secondary electrons from the electrodes or walls (a small fraction only are initiated by electrons formed in the gas). The range of electrons in the wall materials is only a few microns so that only the radiation absorbed in this distance is effective in initiating discharges. Phosphors are available which are relatively transparent to the light which they emit when excited, even when several centimetres thick. Thus the thickness of material in which radiation can be absorbed and still be effective in producing counts is much greater in the phosphor than in the Geiger-Müller tube.

The energy which is absorbed from the incident radiation in the phosphor determines the number of light photons produced and hence the size of the electron pulse obtained from the photomultiplier. Ionising particles of a given energy produce pulses all approximately equal in size, but variation in the length of the light path in the phosphor and statistical fluctuations in the number of electrons produced per photon in the photomultiplier result in a detectable spread in pulse size. Monoenergetic X- or γ-ray photons normally produce an appreciable background of low energy pulses in addition to the pulses corresponding to the total absorption of the photon energy. This is because photons are usually being absorbed by the Compton process in addition to photo-electric absorption (or at high energies pair production). Photo-electrons of a given energy produce pulses of approximately one size, but the recoil electrons produced in the Compton process are spread over a wide range of energy and the pulses they initiate have a corresponding spread. Furthermore some of the scattered electromagnetic radiation produced in the crystal is also absorbed and this likewise contributes pulses of lower energy. Thus when a mono-energetic γ-ray (such as that from Cs^{137}, for example), is incident upon a phosphor there are a large number of pulses of nearly equal size corresponding closely to the energy of the incident radiation (these pulses are produced by photo-electrons and are usually spoken of as the " photo-peak ") accompanied by a continuous distribution of pulses of lower energy. (See fig. 8.07(a)). When the incident photons are of sufficiently high energy for pair production to take place, the absorption of the annihilation radiation also contributes to the background continuum (fig. 8.07(b)).

Some materials commonly used as phosphors are listed in table 8.01. It will be noted that zinc sulphide has the highest light conversion efficiency of any known phosphor but because it cannot be obtained in single crystals and must be used as a powder, the transmission of light through the phosphor is low and it is only practical to use a thin layer. Hence it is used predominantly for counting α-particles. The decay time is also rather long. Thallium activated sodium iodide combines a high light conversion efficiency with a relatively short decay time and can be obtained in single crystals which are very transparent to the emitted radiation. Unfortunately it is deliquescent and must therefore be sealed from the atmosphere. The protective coating necessary makes it unsuitable for the detection of α-radiation but it is widely used for the measurement of β- and γ-radiation. Potassium iodide is not deliquescent but is otherwise inferior to sodium iodide. Calcium tungstate has a high density and high atomic number with a

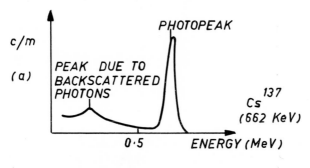

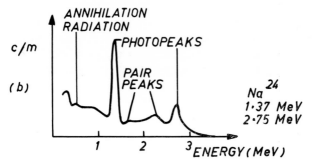

FIG. 8.07. Energy distribution of pulses from a sodium-iodide scintillation counter, exposed to (a) Cs[137] γ rays; (b) Na[24] γ rays.

reasonably high conversion efficiency so that for limited thicknesses it is the most efficient detector of γ-radiation. Unfortunately it has a rather long after-glow. Also some of the frequencies of the emitted radiation are readily absorbed. For this reason large crystals of tungstate are inferior to large crystals of sodium iodide.

The organic phosphors such as anthracene and naphthalene do not respond to heavy particles to the same degree as they respond to electrons. For β- and γ-radiation, their conversion efficiency is reasonably high and very large single crystals which

TABLE 8.01

Substance	Efficiency of photon production	Form available and transparency to emitted radiation	Decay time μ sec.	Effective atomic no.	Density	Type of radiation for which most suited	Comments
Zinc sulphide (activated with copper, silver or nickel)	25%	Multicrystalline powder, therefore not very transparent	3·0	30	4·09	α	
Sodium iodide (thallium activated)	8%	Single crystals Transparent	0·25	53	3·67	β, γ	Deliquescent
Potassium iodide (thallium activated)	2%	Single crystals Transparent	> 1·0	53	3·13	α, β, γ	Some K^{40} is present (naturally radio active)
Scheelite (calcium tungstate)	5%	Single crystals. Absorbs some frequencies which are emitted, therefore not very transparent.	0·5 Phosphorescence 2·0	74	6·06	γ	
Anthracene	4%	Large crystalline blocks. Transparent.	0·02	6	1·25	β, γ	
Naphthalene	1%	Large crystalline blocks. Transparent.	0·06	6	1·14	β, γ	
Anthracene in polystyrene	0·5%	Plastic. Large volumes transparent.	0·02	6	1·06	β, γ	
p-terphenyl in xylene	2%	Liquid. Large volumes transparent.	0·002 −0·004	6	0·87	β, γ	

272

are transparent to the emitted radiation can be obtained. The low atomic number and density mean the absorption of γ-radiation is not very high, but on the other hand the materials are approximately air-equivalent. Mixtures of organic phosphors in plastics or solutions of organic phosphors although

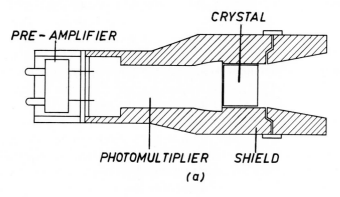

PRE - AMPLIFIER

CRYSTAL

PHOTOMULTIPLIER   SHIELD

(a)

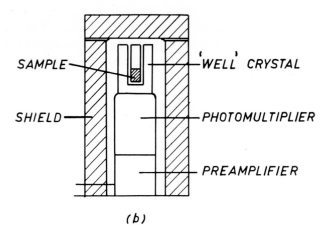

SAMPLE

'WELL' CRYSTAL

SHIELD

PHOTOMULTIPLIER

PREAMPLIFIER

(b)

FIG. 8.08.   Scintillation counters (a) probe type; (b) well type.

of lesser efficiency than the crystals can readily be obtained in large volumes and are useful in particular applications.

The phosphor in a scintillation counter is usually mounted directly above the photo-multiplier, but sometimes, in order to keep the dimensions of the detector itself small, the photo-multiplier is some distance away and a light guide is interposed between the crystal and the photo-cathode. If a long light-guide is used, the size of the pulses generated in the photo-multiplier may not be appreciably larger than random impulses which are due to statistical variations in the thermionic emission of electrons from the electrodes of the photo-multiplier ("noise"). To reduce this random emission, the photo-multiplier is sometimes cooled by liquid nitrogen. Typical scintillation counters are shown diagrammatically in fig. 8.08.

In medical applications, the chief advantages of scintillation counters are (1) the high sensitivity to γ-radiation, (2) the fact that the size of the electron pulse is proportional to the energy given up by the incident radiation in the phosphor, (3) the short response time, (4) the mechanical robustness of the detecting element. The variation of pulse size with the energy absorbed in the phosphor means that with suitable counting equipment (discussed below), by counting pulses in a selected size range only, it may be possible to measure the activity of one isotope in the presence of another or to measure primary radiation in the presence of scattered radiation. Calibrated scintillation counters can be used to identify the energy of the radiation incident upon the crystal and thus to establish the identity of a radioactive material or for the analysis of the spectrum of radiation from (say) an X-ray tube.

Liquid scintillation counters are particularly valuable for counting low energy β-emitting isotopes such as tritium (H^3) or C^{14} or isotopes such as Fe^{55} which emit soft X-radiation. The radioactive material is distributed throughout a liquid phosphor and introduced into a suitable container in front of the photomultiplier. Good optical contact is necessary between the vial and photomultiplier and in some designs, the vial remains in position and is used repeatedly. Since it is difficult to remove all activity after a measurement, this technique tends to result in a slowly rising background and removable vials are usually preferred, despite some loss in the efficiency of light collection. Since the pulses obtained are of low energy and frequently also few in number, it is essential that the background current in the photomultiplier be as small as possible and (as mentioned earlier) refrigeration is sometimes used to reduce this current. Alternatively the phosphor may be placed between two photomultipliers and only those pulses produced simultaneously in the two photomultipliers (and therefore due to light pulses in the phosphor not to random events in the multiplier tubes) are counted.

Instead of counting individual pulses, if a radiation beam of sufficient intensity is to be measured, the total current from the photomultiplier may be recorded. This gives a measure of the mean rate of absorption of energy in the phosphor. Scintillation counters with organic phosphors, which have an effective atomic number not very different from that of air, can be used in this way in place of thimble ionisation chambers in the energy range 150 keV. to 3 MeV. (See end of section 8.08.)

8.04. Associated electrical circuits for scintillation counters

As already explained, the pulses from scintillation counters are not usually as large as those obtained from Geiger-Müller tubes and therefore require more amplification before they can be counted. A pre-amplifier is customarily connected directly to the photomultiplier, and the crystal, photomultiplier and pre-amplifier are mounted together in a single unit. The pre-amplifier may then be connected by cables to a rate-meter or scaler as already described in section 8.02. It is more usual, however, to include a discriminator or pulse height analyser between the pre-amplifier and the counting circuits. This is because the size of each pulse obtained from the photo-multiplier depends (as already explained) upon the corresponding energy absorbed in the crystal and it is often desirable to be able to count pulses of a selected size only.

A *discriminator* is an electronic circuit which permits only pulses which exceed some selected size to pass on to the counting circuits. The number of counts due to photomultiplier " noise " can be considerably reduced by use of a discriminator. Also since scattered radiation is of lower energy than primary radiation, a discriminator may be used, for example, to exclude counts due to scattered photons. A *single channel pulse-height analyser* contains electronic circuits which permit only pulses lying within a selected size range (commonly called the " window ") to pass to the counting circuits. This enables high energy as well as low energy pulses to be excluded from

275

" background " measurements and sometimes permits one isotope to be counted in the presence of a second isotope. A multichannel pulse-height analyser enables the number of pulses of each of a number of selected sizes to be counted simultaneously.

8.05. Counting techniques

In this section we shall give a brief account of the technique of measurement of radioactive sources using Geiger-Müller tubes or scintillation counters.

Certain preliminary tests of the equipment are necessary before any measurements can be made. The first of these is the determination of the optimum operating conditions for the particular Geiger-Müller tube or scintillator which is to be used. For a Geiger-Müller tube this consists in the determination of the best operating voltage for the anode. For a scintillation counter it includes the selection of suitable pre-amplifier gain and the determination of that particular combination of high-voltage (applied to the photo-multiplier electrodes) and discriminator or pulse-height analyser setting which gives the optimum counting conditions for the particular type of radiation which is being measured. Geiger-Müller tubes produce approximately the same size pulse for any ionising event within the active volume so that the optimum operating conditions are independent of the quality of the radiation. With scintillation counters, the energy given up to the phosphor and hence the pulse size depends upon the quality of the incident radiation so that the optimum operating conditions must be determined separately for each type of radiation which is to be measured.

Determination of optimum operating voltage for a Geiger-Müller counter

The counter is exposed to a source of radiation of long half-life and either the number of counts recorded in a definite interval of time or the count-rate (R) is noted at each of a series of gradually increasing operating voltages. A graph of count-rate against voltage will normally take the form shown in fig. 8.09. In the region AB, called the plateau, a change in operating voltage produces only a small change in the number of

276

counts recorded and therefore the operating voltage is chosen in this region so that any drifts which may occur in the voltage during measurement will not introduce serious errors. If the background counting rate (R_b) in the absence of the source is

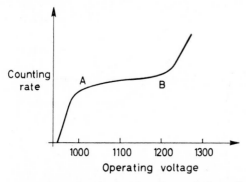

Counting rate

A

B

1000   1100   1200   1300

Operating voltage

Fig. 8.09. Graph showing the variation of counting rate with anode voltage in a Geiger-Müller tube.

determined similarly at various voltages, the graph of background count against voltage usually takes a similar form to that with the source present so that, if R_s denotes the counting rate due to the source only, i.e. $R_s = R - R_b$, the ratio R_s/R_b is constant in the plateau region.

Selection of operating voltage and discriminator bias for scintillation counters

The counter is exposed to the source of radiation to be measured and for a given setting of the amplifier gain and high voltage on the photo-multiplier electrodes, the number of counts recorded in a definite interval of time (or the count-rate) is noted at each of a series of values of the discriminator bias. The observations are sometimes repeated for each of a series of values for the high voltage. The forms of the graphs obtained when the counts are plotted against the discriminator bias for various values of the high voltage depend upon the quality of the radiation but usually resemble the form shown in fig. 8.10. The complete series of observations must now be repeated in the absence of the source, and curves can then be drawn

10   277

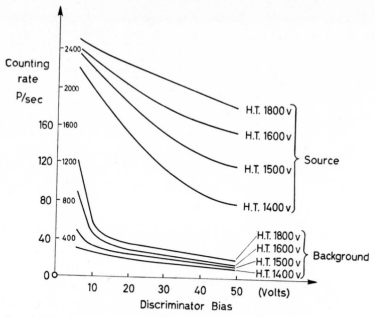

FIG. 8.10. Graph showing the variation of counting rate with dynode voltage and discriminator bias in a scintillation counter.

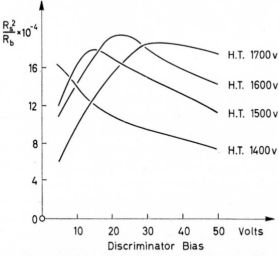

FIG. 8.11. Graph showing the variation of the function R_s^2/R_b with dynode voltage and discriminator bias for a particular scintillation counter exposed to radiation from I^{131}.

278

showing the variation of the background rate with discriminator bias and high voltage.

The ratio R_s/R_b usually increases with increase in the discriminator bias (although this depends upon the particular quality of the radiation being measured and upon the factors contributing to the background count-rate) but to determine the optimum operating conditions it is desirable to plot R_s^2/R_b. (See fig. 8.11.) It may be shown [2,3] that when R_s^2/R_b is a maximum, the total time required to obtain a reading of a given accuracy (including the time required to measure the background) is a minimum and the choice of operating conditions making R_s^2/R_b a maximum therefore gives the most efficient use of the equipment.

When a pulse height analyser replaces a discriminator, assuming a single isotope is being counted, the procedure is usually as follows. A fairly narrow " window " is selected and the window width is kept constant. The position of the window is then varied continuously, with the selected source present, until the count-rate is a maximum. This usually means the window is centred on the photo-peak. The window may then be widened and for each setting the ratio of the count-rate with the source present (R) to the background count-rate (R_b) determined. As before the settings giving the maximum value of $(R_s)^2/R_b$ represent the most efficient use of the equipment.

8.06. Evaluation of resolving time

Any type of counting equipment is insensitive for a certain minimum time after recording one ionising event before it will respond to another ionising event. This is known as the resolving time of the equipment. Thus time is required to quench the discharge in a Geiger-Müller tube or for light to die away in a phosphor. Time is also required to operate other parts of the counting equipment such as dekatrons, scale-of-two circuits and so on. In a Geiger-Müller tube the insensitive time depends upon the count-rate, i.e. the insensitive time after a given event depends upon how much time has elapsed since the previous count. Hence some writers restrict the term " resolving time " to the limiting value of the insensitive time as the count-rate approaches zero, but this convention is not always observed. In practice, most modern counting equipment is provided with electronic circuits which paralyse the equipment after each recorded event for a constant time which is greater than the insensitive time of the detecting element (i.e. the Geiger-Müller tube or phosphor), and is independent of the count-rate. The resolving time of most Geiger-Müller tubes is of the order of 100 μ sec. whereas the resolving time of scintillation counters may be less than 1 μ sec.

When the resolving time of the equipment is known, it becomes possible to correct an observed count-rate for " lost " counts. We shall consider here only the usual case, in which the counter is rendered insensitive by an external circuit, after recorded counts only, and for a time (τ) which is independent of the count-rate. Then if the observed count-rate is n_0, the counter will be inoperative for $n_0\tau$ sec. per sec. so that the number of counts lost per sec. is $n_t n_0 \tau$ where n_t denotes the true count-rate.

$$\therefore\ n_t = n_0 + n_t n_0 \tau$$

or
$$n_t = n_0/(1 - n_0\tau).$$

The resolving time in this case may be determined experimentally by counting two sources of approximately equal intensity, first separately (giving counts n_1/min. and n_2/min. above background say), and then together (giving a count n_{12}/min. above background). Equating the true count-rate due to the combined source to the sum of the true count-rates due to the separate sources gives

$$n_1/(1 - n_1\tau) + n_2/(1 - n_2\tau) = n_{12}/(1 - n_{12}\tau)$$

and hence
$$\tau = (n_1 + n_2 - n_{12})/2n_1 n_2.$$

Terms in τ^2 have been neglected since τ is small.

8.07. Source geometry

It is usually desirable that as much as possible of the radiation emitted by the source enters the counter. For a point source the fraction of the emitted radiation travelling in the direction of the counter window is $\theta/4\pi$, where θ is the solid angle subtended by the source at the window. The efficiency

280

of collection therefore increases as the source is brought nearer the window. Geometry is particularly important when sources of low activity are to be measured. The well-type of crystal counter which has nearly 4π geometry (fig. 8.08b) is very useful for low intensity γ-emitters but the volume of a source which is to be measured in this way must be small.

For any absolute measurement of activity, the fraction of the radiation which enters the counter and the intrinsic efficiency of the counter for the particular radiation must both be known accurately. The number of counts recorded also depends upon the absorption of the radiation (1) in the air between the source and the counter, and (2) in the window of the counter. These factors are more important for specimens emitting α- or low energy β-rays than for those emitting harder radiation. Corrections may also be required for self absorption of the radiation within the source. On the other hand, backscatter from the source mounting and from lead shielding will increase the observed counting rate. The correction for this effect is more important the more penetrating the radiation. Because of the difficulty of determining all these factors with sufficient accuracy, absolute measurements of activity are not normally attempted in hospitals ; sources are measured by comparison with standard sources (supplied by the national standardising laboratories).

8.08. Accuracy of measurements with counters

The accuracy of any measurement made with counting equipment is ultimately limited by the random nature of the ionising events. Thus if $A_1 A_2 \ldots A_n$ are the number of counts recorded in equal intervals of time with some particular source, $A_1 A_2 \ldots A_n$ will not be all equal although all will approximate to a mean value $\overline{A}$. To indicate the amount of scatter of the individual measurements $A_1 A_2 \ldots A_n$ about $\overline{A}$, it is usual to give either the standard deviation σ defined by

$$\sigma = [(A_1 - \overline{A})^2 + (A_2 - \overline{A})^2 \ldots (A_n - \overline{A})^2]^{\frac{1}{2}}/[n-1]^{\frac{1}{2}} \quad (1)$$

or the standard deviation of the *mean*, ∂ (which is sometimes called the standard error of the mean) defined by

$$\partial = [(A_1 - \overline{A})^2 + (A_2 - \overline{A})^2 \ldots (A_n - \overline{A})^2]^{\frac{1}{2}}/[n(n-1)]^{\frac{1}{2}} \quad (2)$$

281

The nature of radioactive disintegrations is such that the probability of any particular value A_K being observed is so related to the deviation $A_K - \overline{A}$ that the expression for the standard deviation of individual observations given in equation (1) reduces to

$$\sigma = (A_1 + A_2 + \ldots A_n)^{\frac{1}{2}} = \sqrt{N}$$

where N is the total number of counts observed in the complete series. (It follows that the standard deviation of the *mean* of the series ∂ in this case reduces to $\sqrt{(N/n)}$.)

The percentage deviation, i.e. the standard deviation expressed as a percentage of the observed count, can be reduced to any desired value by increasing the number of counts recorded. This is illustrated in table 8.02.

TABLE 8.02

No. of counts (N)	Deviation $\sqrt{N}$	Percentage deviation $(\sqrt{N}/N) \times 100$
100	10	10
1000	32	3·2
10,000	100	1·0
100,000	316	0·32

It should be noted that in a rate-meter, the indicated count-rate is an average over a period of time determined by the time constant. By increasing the time constant, the total number of counts from which the count-rate is determined is increased and the percentage deviation of the count-rate is therefore decreased, but the response of the instrument to a change in count-rate is slower (see figure 8.12). Since the count-rate indicated by a rate-meter is usually averaged over only a few seconds, a rate-meter is not suitable for measuring low counting rates.

If $\sqrt{N}$ is the standard deviation for a total count N, the deviation of the counting rate $R = \sqrt{N}/t = \sqrt{R/t}$.

The standard deviation (σ_s) of the net counting rate $R_s (= R - R_b)$ is given by $\sqrt{\sigma^2 + \sigma_b^2}$ where σ denotes the standard deviation of the total counting rate R and σ_b denotes the standard deviation of the background counting rate R_b.

$$\sigma_s = \sqrt{R/t + R_b/t_b}$$

282

It can be shown[2] that the optimum division of the total counting time between counting with the source present and background counting is given by $t/t_b = \sqrt{R/R_b}$. If a preliminary approximate estimate of the ratio R/R_b is made, the total

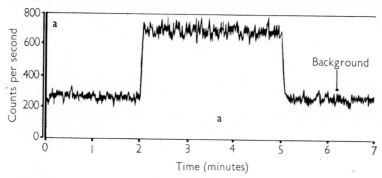

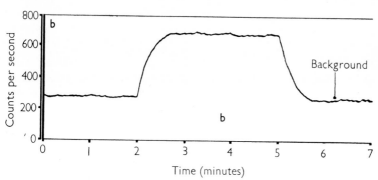

FIG. 8.12.   Ratemeter records, showing statistical fluctuations:
(a) Integrating time, 1 second.
(b) Integrating time, 20 seconds.
The responses are shown to a sudden burst of radiation lasting for three minutes.
By permission from *Isotopes*, by J. L. Putnam. (Penguin Books, Harmondsworth.)

number of counts required with the source present (and also the total number of background counts) required to obtain a selected percentage deviation can be read off from a graph such as that in fig. 8.13.   The graph assumes $t/t_b = \sqrt{R/R_b}$.

It will be appreciated that when very weak sources are to be measured, it is necessary to continue counting for a considerable time to obtain a reasonable accuracy.   If a count is

283

to last for an hour or more, instrument fluctuations may not be negligible. Furthermore very long counts are an uneconomic use of the counting equipment. The minimum time required to obtain a given percentage deviation can be used

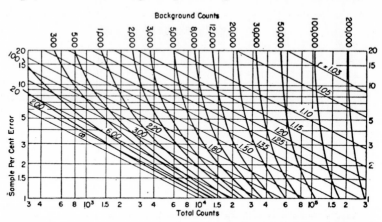

Fig. 8.13. The optimum number of counts for minimising combined counting time when per cent. error is assigned and total-to-background ratio (r) is known. (After Loevinger and Berman.[2])

as a criterion of counting efficiency, both in comparing different types of counter and in selecting operating conditions for any one counter. Corresponding figures for the measurement of I^{131} using a particular Geiger-Müller counter (measuring mainly β-radiation) and a scintillation counter (measuring mainly γ-radiation) which illustrate this point are given in table 8.03.

TABLE 8.03

	G.M. counter	Scintillation counter	Ratio S. counter G.M. counter
Sample volume .	10 cc.	10 cc.	—
Background . .	0·17 p./s.	0·46 p./s.	2·7
Count due to 10^{-4}			
μc./cc. . . .	0·26 p./s.	2·26 p./s.	8·7
Rs/Rb . . .	1·53	4·90	3·2
Minimum combined counting time for relative deviation of			
10 per cent. . .	2000 sec.	100 sec.	0·05

TABLE 8.04

DATA ON PREFERRED METHODS OF MEASUREMENT OF RADIONUCLIDES FOR CLINICAL AND BIOLOGICAL USE.[4]

Purpose	Detector	Background equivalent activity (μc)					
		Beta-gamma		Pure beta			Brehms-strahlung P^{32}
		I^{131}	Co^{60}	H^3	C^{14}	P^{32}	
Calibration of bulk shipments and therapy quantities	Calibrated well-type ion chamber	1	0·2	—	—	0·04	100
Checking of aliquot for administration	Simple, fixed-geometry GM counter	4	1	—	—	—	200
	Simple, fixed-geometry scintillation counter	0·1	0·2	—	—	—	10
Dose-rate measurement on sealed sources	Fixed-geometry ion chamber	100	100	—	—	—	*
	Extrapolation ion chamber	—	—	—	100	100	—
Relative surface activity in vivo	Small, hand-held scintillation counter	0·01	0·02	—	—	—	0·6
	Small, end-window GM counter	*	*	—	—	*	—

285

TABLE 8.04—*Continued*

| Purpose | Detector | Background equivalent activity (μc) | | | | | |
| | | Beta-gamma | | Pure beta | | | Brehms-strah-lung P^{32} |
		I^{131}	Co^{60}	H^3	C^{14}	P^{32}	
Uptake in tissue in vivo	Fixed geometry scintillation counter	0·2	0·3	—	—	—	20
Distribution in vivo	Scintillation counter and mechanical scan	0·04	—	—	—	—	—
Relative activity within tissue in vivo	Needle-probe GM counter	10	*	—	—	$3 \times 10^{-4}\ \mu c/ml$	—
	Needle-probe scintillation counter	*	*	—	—	*	—
Unprocessed excreta and other large samples	Scintillation counter	0·07	0·05	—	—	—	30
	Ring of large GM tubes	0·1	0·1	—	—	—	20
	Well-type ion chamber	3	1	—	—	—	300

TABLE 8.04—Continued

| Purpose | Detector | Background equivalent activity (μc) | | | | | |
| | | Beta-gamma | | Pure beta | | | Brehms-strahlung P^{32} |
		I^{131}	Co^{60}	H^3	C^{14}	P^{32}	
Blood and other small samples	Well-type γ scintillation counter	2×10^{-4}	2×10^{-4}	—	—	—	9×10^{-3}
	Well-type β scintillation counter	—	—	—	—	4×10^{-5}	—
	Liquid scintillator	—	—	1×10^{-3}	4×10^{-5}	—	—
	Thin-wall liquid GM counter	5×10^{-4}	8×10^{-4}	—	—	4×10^{-5}	—
Dry samples	End-window GM counter	5×10^{-5}	5×10^{-5}	—	8×10^{-4}	5×10^{-5}	—
	Gas-flow GM counter	1×10^{-5}	1×10^{-5}	1×10^{-4}	1×10^{-4}	1×10^{-5}	—
Chromatographic and auto-radiographic samples	End-window GM counter	5×10^{-5}	5×10^{-5}	—	8×10^{-4}	5×10^{-5}	—
	Gas-flow GM counter	1×10^{-5}	1×10^{-5}	*	1×10^{-4}	1×10^{-5}	—

287

TABLE 8.04—Continued

| Purpose | Detector | Background equivalent activity (μc) | | | | | |
| | | Beta-gamma | | Pure beta | | | Brems-strahlung P^{32} |
		I^{131}	Co^{60}	H^3	C^{14}	P^{32}	
Routine laboratory monitoring	End-window GM counter	1×10^{-4}	1×10^{-4}	—	2×10^{-5}	1×10^{-4}	—
	Scintillation counter	0·02	0·03	—	—	—	2
Disposal	Simple fixed-geometry GM counter	4	1	—	—	—	200
	Simple fixed-geometry scintillation counter	0·1	0·2	—	—	—	10
	Calibrated ion chamber	3	1	—	—	—	300

* No suitable data available.

Another method of comparing radiation detectors is in terms of the " background equivalent activity ". This quantity for any given instrument, given geometry and radioactive nuclide is defined as the activity of the nuclide which produces a reading of the instrument equal to its background reading. The International Commission on Radiological Units and Measurements [4] have prepared a table which shows the background equivalent activity for the principal methods of measurement of isotopes commonly employed in hospitals. Table 8.04 is based upon the I.C.R.U. table. The " minimum detectable activity " of a particular nuclide with a particular counting system is defined as that activity of the radionuclide concerned, which, in a given counting time, increases the reading of the instrument by an amount equal to three times the standard deviation of the background recorded in that time (I.C.R.U. 1962).

8.09. The use of counters as exposure meters of X or γ radiation

In most measurements with counters, a determination of the counting rate produced under standard conditions is all that is necessary, but if a counter is to be used as an exposure meter for X or γ radiation, it must be calibrated against a standard meter for the particular quality radiation which is to be measured. Counters are normally only used in this way in the energy range where their response per roentgen is fairly constant. Owing to the effect of photoelectric absorption in the cathode, this means that lead cathode Geiger-Müller counters are restricted to energies above 1 MeV. and copper cathode Geiger counters to energies above 300 KeV. At these energies an exposure-rate of 1 mR./hr. will produce approximately 30 pulses per second in a typical counter. To avoid a marked quality dependence when scintillation detectors are used for dosimetry, the total current must be measured (this is proportional to the rate of energy absorption in the phosphor), not the number of pulses of a particular size. Used in this way, the response per roentgen of most organic scintillators is approximately constant between 150 keV. and 3 MeV. (The limits are determined by the onset of photoelectric absorption and pair production in the phosphor.) It is possible to obtain a constant response over a greater energy range by using a mixture of phosphors, but the sensitivity is reduced. Between 150 keV. and 3 MeV. an exposure-rate of 1 mR./hr. will produce a current of about 10^{-9} amp. in a scintillation detector with a 20 gm. (1" cube) anthracene crystal.

REFERENCES

1. LAMB, J. L. and BRUSTMAN, J. A. (1949). *Electronics*, **22**, No. 11, 92.
2. LOEVINGER, R. and BERMAN, M. (1951). *Nucleonics*, **9**, No. 1, 26.
3. HAIGH, C. P. (1954). *Nucleonics*, **12**, No. 1, 34.
4. International Commission on Radiological Units and Measurements (1962). Report 10c. *National Bureau of Standards Handbook*, No. 86.

GENERAL REFERENCES

KORFF, S. A. (1946). *Electron and Nuclear Counters*. New York, Van Nostrand.

ROSSI, B. B. and STAUB, H. H. (1949). *Ionisation Chambers and Counters*. New York, McGraw-Hill.

CURRAN, S. C. and CRAGGS, J. D. (1949). *Counting Tubes*. London, Butterworth.

BIRKS, J. D. (1953). *Scintillation Counters*. London, Pergamon.

HINE, G. J. and BROWNELL, G. L. (ed.) (1956). *Radiation Dosimetry*. New York, Academic Press.

PRICE, W. J. (1964). *Nuclear Radiation Detection*. New York, McGraw-Hill.

SHARPE, J. (1964). *Nuclear Radiation Detectors*. London, Methuen.

EXAMINATION QUESTIONS

1. Describe the construction of (*a*) a beta-ray Geiger-Müller counter.

Part question. F.S.R. (T.), 1965.

2. Describe the construction and explain the action of a Geiger counter suitable for gamma ray detection.

Discuss the use of Geiger counters in determining the activities of radioactive materials.

D.M.R., 1961.

3. Give an account of the phenomenon of fluorescence with particular reference to . . . (*c*) scintillation counters.

Part question. D.M.R., 1962.

CHAPTER IX

PHYSICAL PRINCIPLES OF DIAGNOSTIC RADIOGRAPHY

9.01. Density, correct exposure, contrast, γ, latitude, speed of films

X-RAYS resemble visible light in their ability to affect a photographic plate or film. When they fall upon silver halide crystals they initiate the reduction of the halide to silver, forming a latent image. Development is carried out by chemical reducing agents as in ordinary photography. After development, unchanged silver halide is removed from the film (" fixation "). Details of the chemical processing of X-ray films or plates will not be discussed here. We shall consider only the physical factors which determine the nature of the radiographic image.

After development and fixation, a radiograph placed before a uniformly illuminated surface (a viewing screen), appears to be whitish in the " shadowed " regions where the X-ray intensity was low and dark in the regions where the X-ray intensity was high. The appearance of such films is usually described by certain technical terms used in photography. These will be defined before we consider the properties of the X-radiation, etc., which contribute to the nature of the radiographic image.

The degree of blackening of a photographic film is described in terms of the optical density D which is defined by the equation

$$D = \log_{10} (F_0/F_1)$$

where F_0 and F_1 denote the luminous flux incident upon and transmitted through the area considered respectively. Thus when $F_0 = 10F_1$, the density is 1. The average density of most radiographs is about 1.

Instruments for measuring optical densities are called densitometers. Older models depend upon the visual judgement by an observer of equal brightness in two areas viewed simultaneously, one area being illuminated by light passing through the film to be measured, the other illuminated by light from the same source passing through an adjustable light attenuator whose properties are known. More modern instruments use the response of photo-electric cells to the light beams. Densitometers are used to measure the blackening of personnel monitoring films.

To obtain a satisfactory radiographic image, the X-ray film must be " correctly exposed ". The term " correctly

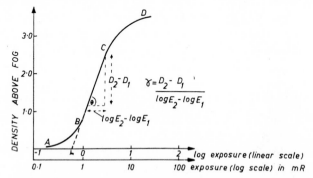

FIG. 9.01. Graph showing variation of film density with logarithm of exposure.

exposed " has the following technical significance. Suppose different areas of the same piece of film are exposed to the same beam of radiation under identical conditions, but for different periods of time. If the density of each area of the processed film is plotted against the logarithm of the exposure (E) (in this case E is proportional to the time), then a curve of the form shown in fig. 9.01 is obtained. This is called a characteristic curve. The section from B to C is approximately a straight line and is the region of correct exposure. Sections AB and CD correspond to under-exposure and over-exposure respectively. In medical radiography the lower portion only of the straight line section of the characteristic curve is normally used with densities in the range 0·4 to 2·0. This provides a sufficient range of density and keeps the patient exposure to a minimum.

The contrast between two areas of a film is determined by the difference in density of the two areas. In the region of correct exposure

$$D_2 - D_1 = \gamma(\log_{10}E_2 - \log_{10}E_1)$$
$$= \gamma \log_{10}(E_2/E_1)$$

where γ is a constant which depends upon the nature of the film (or film-screen combination) used and the method of processing, γ is measured by the gradient of the linear portion of the characteristic curve ($\gamma = \tan \theta$, fig. 9.01). Clearly the greater the value of γ, the greater is the contrast produced by

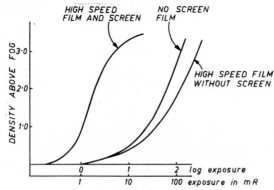

FIG. 9.02. Graph showing variation of film density with logarithm of exposure for different types of film and a film-screen combination.

a given difference in exposures. Fig. 9.02 shows characteristic curves for different types of X-ray film. For the films used without screens, γ is greater for the no-screen than for the high speed film. γ is usually between 2 and 3.

Film *latitude* is usually defined as either the range of exposures corresponding to the region of correct exposure, or alternatively, as the range of exposures corresponding to the useful density range. The latter definition may be employed when the characteristic curve continues as a straight line to densities higher than would be acceptable for normal viewing. The film latitude decreases with increase in gamma, i.e. films which produce high contrast have a reduced exposure range.

If the line CB (fig. 9.01) is extended to cut the density axis at L, the value of the exposure at L is called the inertia. If the

293

inertia is small, then the exposure required to produce a given density is small and the film is described as being of high speed. The speed of X-ray films used in medicine is usually compared by determining the reciprocal of the exposures required to produce a density of 1.

9.02. The nature of X-ray films and the use of intensifying screens

The films used in radiography differ from ordinary photographic films in that the photographic emulsion is used in a much thicker layer on the X-ray films and is applied to both sides of the supporting base. (See fig. 9.03.) This is because X-rays are very much more penetrating than visible light and only a small fraction of the radiation incident upon the film is absorbed in the emulsion. Increasing the emulsion thickness increases the amount of X-radiation which is absorbed and hence increases the sensitivity of the film. Even so, much of the radiation passes through the film and is wasted. A very important device which considerably reduces the exposure required to produce a satisfactory radiograph, is the intensifying screen. This consists of a layer of a material which emits visible or ultra-violet light when irradiated (i.e. a phosphor) supported on a cardboard or plastic base. The X-ray film may be sandwiched between two such intensifying screens. Upon irradiation, the light emitted by the fluorescent screens is absorbed by the X-ray film and considerably enhances the direct effect of the radiation on the film. In fact, when screens are used, most of the film blackening is due to the light from the screens. Since the light is totally absorbed in a relatively thin layer of photographic emulsion, films designed to be used with screens have a thinner coating of emulsion than films intended for use without screens.

The *intensification factor* or *speed* of a pair of screens is defined as the ratio of the exposure time required under given operating conditions to produce a certain density without screens to the time required under the same conditions to produce the same density with screens. This depends mainly upon the chemical nature of the phosphor used, the thickness of the phosphor layer and the size of the phosphor grains. The intensification factor is typically about 10 for so-called " detail " or high definition screens, and in the range 30 to 60 for high speed screens (see below). The precise value depends upon the kVp., and the density considered. In fig. 9.02 the characteristic curves obtained with a particular high-speed film used both

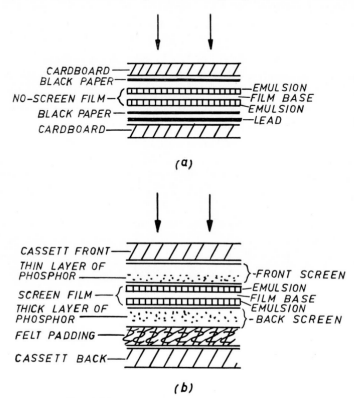

(a)

(b)

Fig. 9.03. Diagrammatic representation of:
(a) a " no-screen " film in a cardboard holder;
(b) a film used with fast intensifying screens.

with and without " par-speed " intensifying screens are illustrated. The exposure required to produce a density of 1·0 is reduced from 37 mR. to 1 mR. by the use of screens, i.e. the speed of the screens in this particular case = 37.

The fluorescent material most widely used in intensifying screens is calcium tungstate. Upon irradiation this substance emits both violet and ultra-violet light to which the photographic film is very sensitive. In high definition screens, both

295

members of the pair are usually coated with a fairly thin layer of calcium tungstate of small grain size. In the faster screens, the grain size is larger and the back screen is usually coated with a thicker layer of the phosphor than the front screen.

At high energies (of the order of 100 kVp. or more say), barium-lead sulphate which emits mainly ultra-violet light upon irradiation, may be used as the fluorescent material in fast screens. Barium-lead sulphate screens are comparable with calcium tungstate screens in speed at low energies but absorb more of the incident radiation and are therefore more effective at the higher energies. Below 30 kVp. zinc sulphide screens are sometimes used.

The chief disadvantage of intensifying screens is that they decrease the sharpness of the radiographic image, since each phosphor grain acts as a separate light source. This is discussed in section 9.05.

9.03. The factors determining the contrast and mean density of radiographs

The intensity of the radiation reaching an X-ray film and hence the blackening of the film, varies from point to point in a manner determined by the absorbing and scattering properties of the various parts of the object. Diagnostic X-ray tubes are normally operated at voltages such that the radiation generated is absorbed mainly by the photo-electric process. The linear photo-electric attenuation coefficient for different elements is proportional to $\rho Z^4 / A$ where ρ denotes density, Z atomic number and A atomic weight. Hence elements of high atomic number absorb the radiation very much more strongly than elements of low atomic number and dense elements absorb more than less dense. The difference between the absorption occurring in different elements on account of the difference in atomic number decreases with increasing tube voltage, since photo-electric absorption becomes a smaller part of the total attenuation as the photon energy of the radiation increases, and the linear Compton attenuation coefficient varies as $\rho Z / A$. Thus the contrast between different regions on the radiograph decreases as the kilovoltage is increased. It is usual to select for each body section, the kilovoltage which will produce the optimum contrast. This depends upon the thickness and nature of the parts being radiographed. If too low a kilovoltage is used, very small differences in absorption will result in either over-exposure or under-exposure, i.e. there will be too small a range of contrast. If too high a kilovoltage is used there will be insufficient difference in density to enable different structures to be differentiated. If even with the optimum kilovoltage, a particular anatomical structure which it is desired to study still does not differ sufficiently from adjacent tissues in absorbing properties to produce a clear image on the radiograph, it is sometimes possible to introduce into the structure concerned a medium of either greater or less radio-opacity than the surrounding tissues. The radio-lucent substances commonly employed are gases (so that their density is low), e.g. air, oxygen or carbon dioxide. The radio-opaque substances are compounds of elements having atomic numbers high in comparison with those found in tissue, e.g. barium, bismuth or iodine.

The mean density of a radiograph depends upon both the quality and the quantity of the radiation reaching the film. The quality of the radiation is determined primarily by the kilovoltage and to a lesser extent by the filtration. The quantity of the radiation or the exposure depends upon (1) the kilovoltage and filtration, (2) the tube current, (3) the exposure time, (4) the focus-film distance, and (5) the nature of absorbing and scattering media in the path of the X-ray beam (this includes the part to be irradiated and auxiliary equipment such as grids, etc.).

The exposure due to primary radiation varies directly as the tube current (I), and the exposure time (t) and inversely as the square of the focus-film distance (d). A change in any of these factors usually changes the scattered radiation in the same ratio as the primary radiation, so the total exposure and the film density also vary as It/d^2. The variation of film density with a change in kilovoltage (V) is more complicated. Firstly, the exposure due to the primary radiation, varies as V^n where n is always greater than 2, but may take any value from about 3 to about 5·5 depending upon the particular X-ray tube and voltage range considered. Secondly, the ratio of scattered radiation to primary radiation is not constant when the kilovoltage is

297

changed. Thirdly, for a given exposure the blackening of the X-ray film and the intensification factor of screens (if these are used) are both changed by a change in kilovoltage. Blackening per roentgen exposure in X-ray film itself is a maximum about 40 kVp., because at this voltage the photo-electric absorption in the silver halide is a maximum, but when screens are used (particularly fast screens) the blackening per roentgen exposure of the film-screen combination usually increases slowly with increasing kVp. to a shallow maximum in the 100 kVp. region, where the photo-electric absorption in the screens is a maximum. (The K absorption edge occurs at 69·6 keV. in tungsten and at 88 keV. in lead, the maximum absorption takes place when the *effective* energy of the X-ray beam is close to these values, see Chapter VI.) Thus the relationship between film blackening and kilovoltage is complex. However the most important factor is the change in exposure rate and in the 50-100 kVp. range when screens are used, film density may be regarded as varying approximately as V^5. This means that an increase of kilovoltage of 15 per cent. will produce about the same change in density as doubling the exposure time ($1·15^5 = 2·0$).

9.04. Magnification and distortion in radiographs

Since the radiation diverges from the X-ray tube focus, the shadow of any particular structure will be magnified. Consider first an object which is large in comparison with the size of the focal spot so that the latter can be regarded as a point and let the object lie in a plane parallel to the X-ray film. Then the linear magnification (i.e. the ratio of any length in the image to the length of the corresponding structure in the object), is determined by the ratio of the focus-film distance to the focus-object distance. See fig. 9.04. Structures on the tube side of a patient are therefore magnified more than those closer to the film. If measurements are to be made upon the radiograph, the magnification must be known. It may be made approximately unity by using a long focus-film distance, so that the difference between the focus-film and focus-object distances becomes small in comparison with either.

Because it is analogous to the projection on a plane of a solid structure, the shape of an image on an X-ray film depends

298

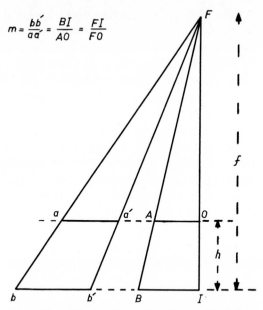

$$m = \frac{bb'}{aa'} = \frac{BI}{AO} = \frac{FI}{FO}$$

FIG. 9.04. Production of radiographic image. The linear magnification of the image $(m) = BI/AO = FI/FO$ since triangles FIB, FOA, are similar. Likewise $bb'/aa' = Fb/Fa$ since triangles Fbb', Faa' are similar and $Fb/Fa = FI/FO$ since triangles FbI, FaO are similar. Hence $bb'/aa' = FI/FO$ also.

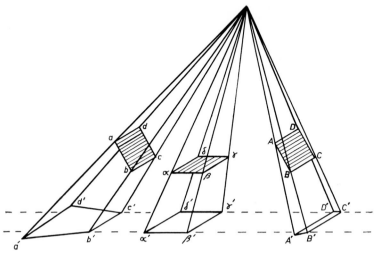

FIG. 9.05. Distortion of a radiographic image.

299

upon (1) the angle at which the X-rays pass through the object and (2) the angle at which the X-ray beam strikes the film. If it is desired to produce an image of structures in any particular plane in an object without distortion, then the object must be placed so that that particular plane is parallel to the film. For example, in fig. 9.05, $abcd$, $\alpha\beta\gamma\delta$, $ABCD$, represent squares of equal size. $\alpha\beta\gamma\delta$ is parallel to the X-ray film and the image $\alpha'\beta'\gamma'\delta'$, although magnified, is still a square, i.e. there is no distortion; whereas the images $a'b'c'd'$ and $A'B'C'D'$ are no longer squares. The sides $a'd'$ and $A'D'$ are magnified to a greater extent than the sides $b'c'$ and $B'C'$ since ad and AD are further from the film than bc and BC. Furthermore the sides $a'b'$ and $c'd'$ are elongated while the sides $A'B'$ and $C'D'$ are fore-shortened.

9.05. Resolving power and the sharpness of radiographic images

In practice the focal spot on the X-ray tube target is of finite size and the X-rays cannot be regarded as originating from a point. In consequence radiographic images are not sharply defined but surrounded by a penumbra where the film receives radiation from a part but not the whole of the focal spot. The width of the penumbra depends upon

(1) the size of the focal spot ;
(2) the focus-film distance ;
(3) the object-film distance.

For the production of sharp images, it is desirable that the focal spot shall be small, the focal-film distance long and the object-film distance short. This is illustrated in figures 9·06, 9·07, 9.08. On account of the inclination of the X-ray tube target, the penumbra is actually slightly larger at the cathode than at the anode side of a film.

It may be shown geometrically that when the focal spot size is not negligible, the total extent of the radiographic image is given by

$$\text{Length of image} = \text{length of object} \times \frac{\text{focus-film distance}}{\text{focus-object distance}}$$

$$+ \text{effective length of focal spot} \times \frac{\text{object-film distance}}{\text{target-object distance}}$$

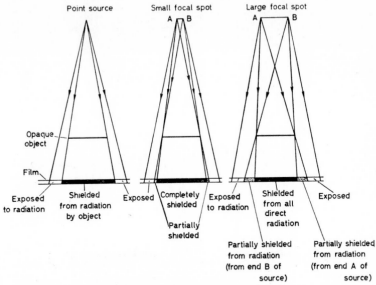

FIG. 9.06. Diagrams illustrating the effect of the size of the focal spot upon the sharpness of the radiographic image.

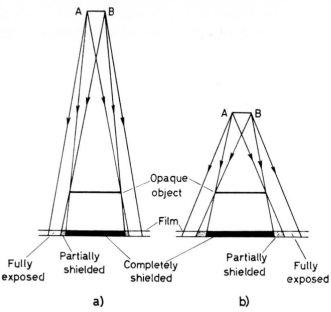

FIG. 9.07. Diagrams illustrating the effect of focus-film distance upon the sharpness of the radiographic image.

301

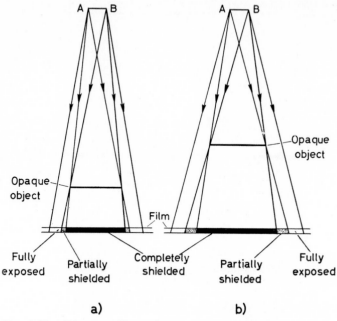

FIG. 9.08. Diagrams illustrating the effect of object-film distance upon the sharpness of the radiographic image.

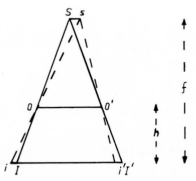

FIG. 9.09. Diagram illustrating the geometrical factors determining the size of an X-ray image. OO' = object. II' = Image projected from point source S. $II' = OO' \times f/(f-h)$. The total image iI' projected from the finite source Ss exceeds II' by iI where $iI = Ss \times h/(f-h)$.

302

The first term of this equation is the magnified shadow of a finite object as projected from a point source (already discussed in section 9.04) and the second term is the increase in the shadow due to the finite size of the source. See fig. 9.09. If the object is much smaller than the focal spot, the size of the total shadow is determined primarily by the second term of the equation, i.e. by the size of the focal spot rather than by the size of the object. In the limiting case when the object is

(A)   (B)   (C)

Fig. 9.10. Diagram to illustrate meaning of resolving power.
(*a*) Poorly defined shadows of points are resolved if the separation of the points is large.
(*b*) With smaller separation of the points, the shadows are not resolved.
(*c*) With the same separation as in (*b*), shadows are resolved if more sharply defined.

reduced to a geometrical point, the shadow still has a finite size, determined by the second term of the equation. The fact that the shadow of a point object is of finite size limits the *resolving power* attainable in a radiograph. Resolving power may be defined qualitatively as a measure of the ability to form distinguishable shadows of adjacent point objects. The higher the resolving power, the closer together two objects may be situated without their shadows being confused. Clearly the smaller the shadows, the closer together they may be formed and still be recognised as separate. (See fig. 9.10.) Resolving power is increased by the same factors which increase the sharpness of the shadow of finite objects, i.e. by use of a small focal spot, a long focus-film distance and a short object-film distance.

In addition to these geometrical factors, sharpness and resolving power also depend upon (1) the grain size of the photographic emulsion, and (2) the grain size and position of

303

intensifying screens when these are used. The sharpness and resolving power are increased by the use of small grains and by

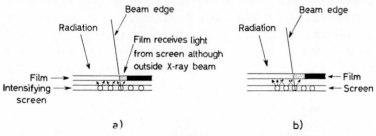

FIG. 9.11. Diagrams illustrating the effect of film-screen distance upon the sharpness of the radiographic image.

as close contact as possible between screen and film. (See fig. 9.11.) In high-speed intensifying screens, a thick layer of phosphor is used so some phosphor grains are inevitably remote from the film and hence resolving power and sharpness

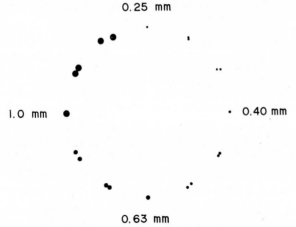

FIG. 9.12. Test object to demonstrate resolving power.

are reduced. However with present-day films and screens the principal factor limiting resolution is the size of the focal spot and not the grain size of films and screens. Fig. 9.12 shows the construction of an object designed for tests of resolving power. Fine wires of the diameters indicated were embedded in a plastic square which in turn was mounted in a tissue equivalent phantom. Fig. 9.13(*a*) to (*d*) show radiographs of this object.[1]

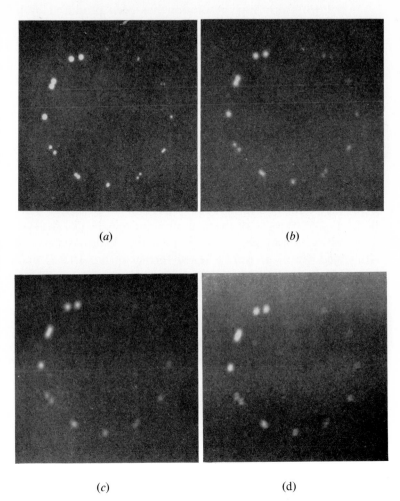

(a)   (b)

(c)   (d)

FIG. 9.13. Radiographs of the object shown in fig. 9.12 taken with the following exposure factors.

(a) Object-film distance 2·5 in., small focal spot, target film distance 30 in., 70 kVp., " Blue brand " film " Hi-speed " screens

(b) *Object film distance* 10·5 in. small focal spot target film distance 30 in., 70 kVp., " Blue-brand " film and " Hi-speed " screens

(c) Object film distance 10·5 in., *large focal spot* target film distance 30 in., 70 kVp., " Blue-brand " film and " Hi-speed " screens

(d) Object film distance 10·5 in., large focal spot *target film distance* 24 in. 70 kVp., " Blue-brand " film and " Hi-speed " screens.

305

In 9.13(*a*), fairly high resolution has been produced by a choice of favourable exposure factors. One factor only has been changed between each successive radiograph, and the factor which has been changed is under-lined in the caption. Thus the only difference between 9·13(*a*) and 9·13(*b*) is that in (*a*) the object-film distance was 2·5 inches and in (*b*) 10·5 inches. The difference between 9·13(*b*) and 9·13(*c*) is due to a change in the focal spot size, from small to large, and the difference between 9·13(*c*) and 9.13(*d*) is due to a decrease in the target film distance. Comparing fig. 9.13(*a*) directly with 9.13(*d*) shows the marked deterioration in resolving power when all factors are unfavourable. It will be noted in fig. 9.13(*d*), that as already pointed out, where the object is small compared with the focal spot, the size of the shadow is independent of the size of the object (although the contrast of the shadows increases with object size.) It will be noted further in fig. 9.13(*d*) that many of the shadows show a characteristic doubling. These shadows can be regarded as reversed pin-hole images of the target and the doubling is due to the fact that the electrons striking the target are not uniformly distributed but are concentrated in strips on either side. (This is a deliberate design feature already mentioned in Chapter III.)

In order that fine detail of anatomical structures can be adequately reproduced on a radiograph, it is necessary that the exposure factors be selected so that there is

(1) adequate resolving power;
(2) adequate contrast;
(3) no motion.

If these conditions are satisfied the shadows on the radiograph will be sharply defined. (Such radiographs are sometimes described as showing good (or high) definition.)

Adequate contrast implies a correct choice of kilovoltage, the use of grids, cones, etc., where necessary to reduce scattered radiation (see section 9.06) and a film which is neither under-exposed nor over-exposed. The absence of motion usually means that a short exposure time is desirable. For a short exposure time, the radiation intensity at the film must be high. This limits the extent to which the focal spot can be reduced in size (since the size of the focus determines the maximum power which may be dissipated), and the extent to which the focus-film distance can be increased (since the intensity of the primary radiation at the film varies approximately inversely as the square of the focus-film distance). It is therefore necessary to compromise upon conditions which enable an image with adequate resolving power to be obtained in a reasonably short time.

9.06. The effects of scattered radiation and the use of grids

So far we have considered only the direct radiation which reaches the X-ray film. However, when radiation passes through matter an appreciable proportion of the radiation is scattered, i.e. changed in direction, with or without an accompanying change in wavelength. Consequently unless steps are taken to prevent it, scattered radiation can reach the film, not only from the object itself but also from any nearby irradiated object (including objects beyond the film since some radiation is scattered backwards as well as forwards). If an appreciable amount of scattered radiation reaches the film it reduces the contrast. This effect is particularly serious when thick objects are radiographed.

The amount of scattered radiation reaching the film can be reduced (1) by the use of diaphragms and cones to limit the X-ray beam and prevent scattering from regions other than that being examined (this is also an important factor in reducing the integral radiation dose received by the patient), (2) by placing an absorbing material (usually lead) beyond the film to reduce backscatter, (3) by the use of a grid between the object and the film which permits radiation travelling in the direction of the primary beam to reach the film, but intercepts radiation travelling in other directions. The principle of such grids is illustrated in fig. 9.14.

The grid normally consists of long narrow strips of lead deeper than they are wide, arranged parallel to one another. In an " unfocused " grid the strips are at right angles to the table top. In a " focused " grid they are slightly inclined so that they point towards the focal spot. Focused grids are each designed for use at a particular focus-grid distance. As can be seen from fig. 9.14 the grid permits only radiation travelling approximately in the direction of the primary beam to reach

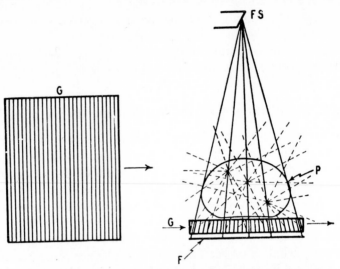

FIG. 9.14. Diagram illustrating the use of a grid to reduce the amount of scattered radiation reaching the film.

By permission from *Radiologic Physics*, by C. Weyl and S. R. Warren. (Charles C. Thomas, Springfield.)

the film, and intercepts most of the scattered radiation which is travelling in other directions. The grid ratio is defined as the ratio of the length of the lead strips in the direction of the primary beam to the distance between them (fig. 9.15). The greater the grid ratio, the more efficient is the grid in intercepting the scattered radiation. Grid ratios are usually between 5 and 16, a higher ratio being used the higher the kilovoltage.

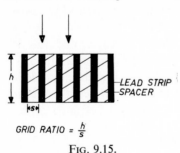

GRID RATIO = $\frac{h}{s}$

FIG. 9.15.

Two grids placed so that the lead strips are at right angles are sometimes used. These "crossed grids" are more efficient than a single grid of double the ratio, since a single grid cannot stop scatter parallel to the strips. If a non-focused grid is used, or a focused grid is employed at some other focus-grid distance than that for which it was designed, the intensity of the radiation at the edges of the film is reduced. (See fig. 9.16.) In the Lysholm grid, which is unfocused, the grid ratio is reduced at the edges of the grid so that the loss of primary radiation is reduced, but so also is the efficiency of the grid.

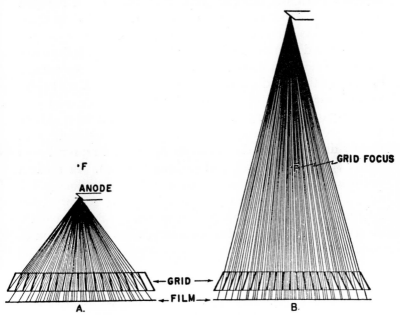

FIG. 9.16. Diagram illustrating the effect of using a focused grid at the wrong focus-film distance.

By permission from *Fundamentals of X-Ray and Radium Physics*, by J. Selman. (Charles C. Thomas, Springfield.)

In order to prevent shadows of the grid interfering with the shadows of the structure being radiographed, grids which remain stationary during an exposure must consist of very thin strips of lead. In a typical Lysholm grid, for example, there are from about 60 to 100 strips per inch. The grid shadows are so numerous and so close together, that the eye does not normally distinguish them. An alternative method of preventing the formation of grid shadows, which permits the use of fewer, wider, lead strips, is to move the grid at right angles to the strips during the exposure. A moving grid was designed and first used by Potter and Bucky and is usually referred to as

11   309

a Potter-Bucky grid or " Bucky ". The older type of Potter-Bucky grid was moved by a spring, the speed being controlled by the movement of a piston rigidly connected to the grid, which forced oil through a small adjustable aperture. The size of the aperture and hence the grid speed was automatically adjusted when the exposure time was set, so that the grid travelled a distance of about two inches during the exposure. (The grid was set in motion just before the X-ray tube was energised and continued to move until just after the exposure was complete.) In units in which the exposure is terminated by a photo-timer and is therefore not predetermined, a " single-stroke " mechanism of this type is not practicable, and it is necessary to move the grid to and fro across the film for as long as the exposure continues. Early reciprocating grids were usually driven in one direction electrically and returned at a slower speed by a spring and hydraulic system. In modern equipment, the grid is usually driven in both directions at the same speed by an auxiliary electrical motor. Reciprocating systems have the disadvantage that it is impossible to avoid a short period when the grid is stationary, when the direction of travel is reversed.

9.07. Fluoroscopy and fluorography

In *fluoroscopy* or " screening " a single fluorescent screen is substituted for the X-ray film and viewed by the physician. In *fluorography*, the image formed on a fluorescent screen is photographed using a camera. We consider first conventional fluoroscopy in which the fluorescent screen is viewed directly. This technique enables the radiologist to observe continuously the progress of particular physiological processes and also to observe the results of manipulations as he performs them. The phosphor used on screens for fluoroscopy is usually zinc cadmium sulphide since this material emits a yellow-green light to which the human eye is very sensitive. The screen is normally backed by lead glass which is transparent to visible light but opaque to most of the X-rays, and thus reduces the X-radiation received by the observer.

Since it is frequently necessary to observe for several minutes (i.e. for a time long compared with that required to obtain a single X-ray photograph), limitation of the total dose to be given to the patient in an examination means limitation of the X-ray intensity, and, consequently, of the brightness of the fluorescent image. At low brightness levels, visual acuity, i.e. the ability to distinguish between adjacent parts of the image, is considerably reduced and the physician may find it difficult to observe detail in the image, even when he has spent 10 minutes or more in a dark room to become adapted to the low brightness level. The difficulty is enhanced because for a

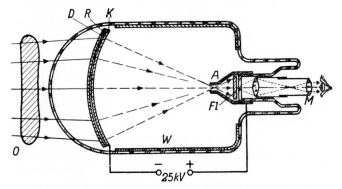

FIG. 9.17. Diagrammatic cross-section of image intensifier. R = fluoroscopic screen; D = support for screen and for photocathode K; A = perforated anode; Fl = viewing screen; M = microscope.

Courtesy of *Philips Industries Ltd.*

given exposure difference, the contrast obtained on a fluoroscopic screen is less than that obtained on a radiograph. To increase the brightness of the fluorescent image it is now customary to use fluorescent image amplifiers or intensifiers. (The name " image amplifier " has been widely used but " image intensifier " is a more accurate description.) The principle of one type of image intensifier[2, 3, 4] is illustrated in fig. 9.17.

The fluorescent screen R is mounted within an evacuated tube and supported beside a photocathode. The electrons released from the cathode by the light from the screen are accelerated and focused on to a smaller screen Fl which is viewed by a microscope. Fl is typically either $\frac{1}{2}$ or 1 inch in diameter and the image is 1,000 to 3,000 times as bright as the original screen F. The total gain in brightness at Fl is due both to the higher energy of the impinging electrons and to their concentration upon a smaller area. The fluorescent screens used are of fine grain and can be made thinner than those normally used for screening to give an increase in definition at the expense of some loss in brightness. There is some loss in contrast because of a uniform low light intensity over the whole viewing screen due to stray radiation, light, thermionic electrons, etc. At first, the usefulness of this type of intensifier was limited by the fact that only regions less than 5 inches in diameter could be covered, but 9-inch and some 11-inch diameter intensifiers are now generally available.[4, 5, 6]. The microscope M shown in fig. 9.17 is also now frequently replaced by a magnifying system which permits binocular viewing in a mirror. (See fig. 9.20.) This gives more freedom of movement to the radiologist. The development of image intensifiers has made possible both cine-fluorography (described below) and television fluoroscopy.

In *television fluoroscopy*, the output phosphor of the image intensifier is observed by a television camera. There are two types of camera commonly employed, the image orthicon and the vidicon camera. The image orthicon is more sensitive but also considerably larger and more cumbersome and also more expensive than the vidicon camera.[7] Users appear to be divided in opinion as to whether the increased brightness that can be obtained with the orthicon camera at low radiation levels outweighs the disadvantage of bulky equipment.

A vidicon television camera is illustrated diagrammatically in fig. 9.18. A well focused electron beam is produced by the " electron gun " and passes through a deflecting system as shown. The latter makes the electron beam scan back and forth across the distal end of the tube. At this end of the tube a transparent conducting layer forms the " signal electrode ". Upon this a photoconductive layer is deposited. When light falls upon the photo-conductor its resistance at each point is reduced in proportion to the light intensity at the point. A voltage applied to the signal electrode therefore produces a charge pattern on the inner surface of the photo-conductor, which mirrors the light pattern. This surface of the photo-conductor is scanned by the electron beam. It is arranged that the electrons arrive at the photo-conductor with very low velocity and are either deposited on the photo-conductor or reflected, depending upon the charge on the conductor at the position considered. As the beam scans from point to point, the deposited electrons produce a varying current to the

312

signal electrode. This current is used to modulate the electron beam in the monitor or television receiving tube. In the latter, a well-focused electron beam scans back and forth across a fluorescent screen. The brightness of the spot produced at each point is determined by the signal from the camera tube.

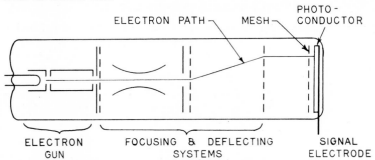

FIG. 9.18. Diagrammatic representation of vidicon television camera.

In the image orthicon camera, an electron beam is again used to scan a charge pattern. In this tube, however, the charge pattern is produced on a target within the tube by electrons which are accelerated from a photocathode to the target. The output signal is obtained from the electrons from the scanning beam which are reflected from the target. These are returned to an electron multiplier and the amplified current so obtained provides the output signal for the television receiving tube. The acceleration of the photo-electrons and the use of an electron multiplier make the orthicon camera more sensitive than the vidicon but, as already explained, also make it about three times as large.

The chief advantages of television fluoroscopy are:

(1) The image brightness may be increased electronically. This usually means that the patient's exposure is reduced.

(2) The image contrast may be modified electronically to enhance the image quality. Enhanced contrast often enables detail to be observed on the television monitor, which would not be seen with direct viewing, although there may be some loss of resolving power with the television system. (The resolving power is limited by the size of the spot on the fluorescent screen.)

(3) The image is large and the radiologist's movements are not restricted while viewing.

(4) Simultaneous viewing is possible by large numbers of people.

(5) The current from the television camera may be recorded on magnetic tape. The latter then provides the signal to the television receiving tube and may be " replayed " at any time and repeatedly if desired, for example, with differing contrast enhancement.

In *fluorography, or mass miniature radiography* a full-sized fluorescent screen is photographed. A reduced picture is

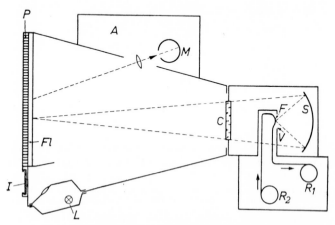

Fig. 9.19. Fluorography or mass miniature radiography
using a mirror camera.

Fl = fluorescent screen; P = grid; S = spherical mirror; C = correction plate; F = film strip pressed out against film gate V; R_1 and R_2 = rewinding and unwinding reels; A = automatic timer with photo-multiplier M; I = identification card; L = lamp for illuminating this card.

Courtesy of *Philips Industries Ltd.*

produced with a consequent reduction in the cost of film and processing materials compared with the production of a full-size radiograph by the normal method. The process is used mainly in surveys where a large number of persons are to be examined, hence the name *mass miniature radiography*. Since only a fraction of the light emitted from the fluorescent screen reaches the photographic film, exposures 10 to 20 times greater than those used in normal radiography (where the fluorescent screen is in contact with the photographic film) are required. It is customary to use mirror cameras (see fig. 9.19) which have a higher light-gathering power than lens systems.[8, 9]

Cinefluorography

Early attempts to obtain photographic records of fluoroscopic images at successive intervals of time, by use of cine or motion picture cameras, were hampered by the low brightness level of the conventional fluorescent screen. However, as already mentioned, the development of fluorescent image

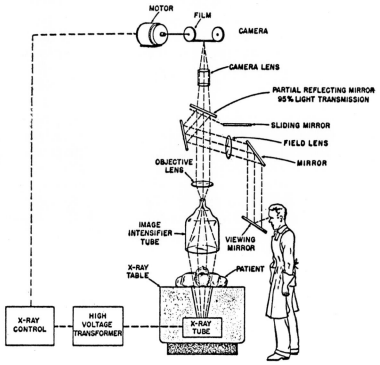

FIG. 9.20. Schematic diagram illustrating the principal components of an image intensifier cinefluorographic unit. (After Euler.[10])
By permission from *Cinefluoroscopy* by G. H. S. Ramsey et al. (Charles C. Thomas, Springfield.)

intensifiers, has now made cine-fluorography possible. The cine camera photographs the output phosphor of the image intensifier. The essential components of the camera and viewing system of a cine-fluorographic unit are illustrated diagrammatically in fig. 9.20.[10]

Since the radiologist normally wishes to observe the fluorescent screen at the same time as the cine pictures are being taken, a partial reflecting mirror is introduced between the objective

315

lens of the image intensifier and the cine camera. This mirror permits 95 per cent. of the light to reach the camera but 5 per cent. is reflected to the direct viewing system. A sliding full-reflecting mirror may be moved into position to reflect all the light to the direct viewing system when the cine camera is not in use.

In a cine camera, the photographic film is stationary while the camera shutter is open and is moved forward (one " frame ") when the camera shutter is closed. If X-rays are incident upon the patient while the shutter is closed, the X-ray tube is producing radiation (and heat) and the patient receiving a radiation dose which serves no useful purpose. It is therefore desirable that the X-rays shall be interrupted in synchronisation with the motion of the cine film, so that X-rays are produced only when the camera shutter is open and the film stationary. This is achieved either by interrupting the high voltage supply to the X-ray tube, or alternatively by interrupting the electron stream crossing the X-ray tube (by using a grid-controlled X-ray tube) in synchronism with the cine camera. A signal is normally obtained from a commutator and brush arrangement connected to the motor that drives the cine film in the camera. This signal may be fed to the grid of thyratrons in the primary circuit of the high tension transformer (fig. 9.21(a)) to the grid of specially designed triode switching tubes in the secondary circuit of the high tension transformer (fig. 9.21(b)), or to the cathode cup or " grid " of the X-ray tube. (fig. 9.21(c).) When the synchronising signal interrupts the high voltage supply the X-ray pulse is not as sharply defined as when the synchronising signal is applied to the X-ray tube itself (the capacity of the high voltage cables to the X-ray tube slows the build-up of voltage and the cables continue to discharge through the X-ray tube after the voltage is cut off), hence synchronisation by means of grid-controlled X-ray tubes is now generally preferred. Some manufacturers use a half-wave rectified voltage supply and permit one or more complete half-wave pulses of X-rays per frame. Other manufacturers use a full-wave rectified or a constant voltage supply and limit the duration of each pulse electronically. The latter method has the advantage that a somewhat shorter exposure time is possible

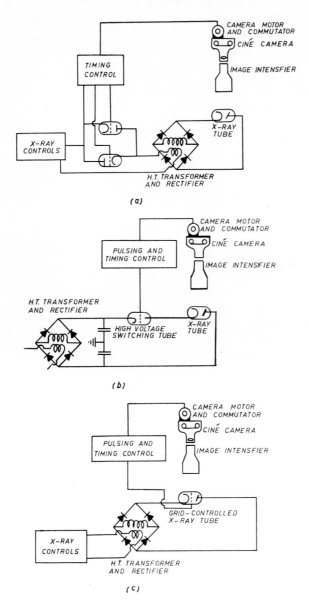

FIG. 9.21. Alternative methods of synchronising X-ray output with cine-camera.
(a) Switching tubes in the primary circuit of the H.T. transformer.
(b) Switching tube in the secondary circuit of the H.T. transformer.
(c) Grid-controlled X-ray tube.

317

(typically 1/250 sec.) and the number of pulses per frame is not necessarily increased at the lower frame speeds. (See fig. 9.22.)

Cine-fluorography can be carried out simultaneously with television fluoroscopy by one of two methods. Either light from the image intensifier is " shared " between the cine camera and the television camera by a system of mirrors, or the cine camera records the image produced on a separate (small) television monitor. The latter method has the advantage that a

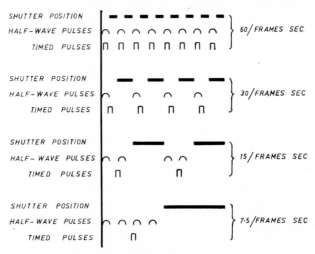

FIG. 9.22. Diagrammatic illustration of relation between X-ray pulses and frame speeds. (This figure assumes the mains frequency is 60 cycles/sec. For 50 cycles/sec., the corresponding frame speeds are 50, 25, $12\frac{1}{2}$ and $6\frac{1}{4}$ frames per second).

brighter picture (with enhanced contrast if desired) can be obtained from the television monitor and this usually permits the radiation dose to the patient to be reduced. However, when photographing the television monitor the cine camera must be synchronised with the monitor and is therefore restricted to the slower frame speeds, since the electron beam in the monitor takes 1/50 or 1/60 second (depending on the mains frequency) to scan the face of the monitor and either two or three interlaced scans are required to present a complete picture.[11] Where higher recording rates are considered essential, the cine camera must view the image intensifier.

To obtain "spot films" during the course of cine-fluorography or television fluoroscopy, light from the image intensifier or the television monitor may be diverted (by mirrors) to a still camera. Cameras taking 4×5 inches polaroid film, or 120 mm., 70 mm., or 35 mm. films are commonly used, so the spot films are reduced in size compared with a direct radio-graph.

9.08. Special procedures: stereoscopy, location of foreign body, tomography

A single radiograph gives no information as to the relative depth of the structures producing the observed shadows. In general, this information is supplied by prior knowledge of the anatomical relations of the structures, but it may sometimes be necessary to locate a structure radiographically. The simplest method is to obtain two radiographs at right angles which both show the structures. If this is not possible or is insufficient to enable the solid structure to be visualised, either stereoscopy or tomography may be used.

In stereoscopy, two films are exposed, the X-ray tube being displaced between the two exposures by a small distance. The two films are then viewed in inclined mirrors or prisms in such a way that simultaneously the left eye sees the film taken when the X-ray tube was displaced to the left and the right eye sees the film taken with the tube displaced to the right. As in normal vision the two images are correlated by the brain giving the impression of a solid structure. To obtain a proper three-dimensional effect, the ratio of the tube shift to the focus-film distance should equal the ratio of the interpupillary distance (about 6 cm. in a normal adult) to the viewing distance.

A double exposure with tube shift similar to that used in stereoscopy is also used in the location of foreign objects. Suppose first that the position of the object in a horizontal plane is known or has been determined by fluoroscopy. Then the simplest method of determining the depth of the object below the surface is as follows : The patient is carefully immobilised and the X-ray tube centred vertically over the object. One exposure is made, the X-ray tube shifted

319

transversely a small distance t and a second exposure made on the same film.

If the distance between the two images of the object on the film is x, the focus-film distance is f, the film table-top distance y_1 and the distance of the object from the table-top y_2, then from the similar triangles T_1T_2F, S_1S_2F (fig. 9.23).

$$\frac{S_1S_2}{T_1T_2} = \frac{S_1F}{T_1F}$$

i.e.
$$\frac{x}{t} = \frac{y_1 + y_2}{f - (y_1 + y_2)}$$

$$\therefore \quad \frac{x}{x + t} = \frac{y_1 + y_2}{f}$$

$$\therefore \quad y_2 = \frac{fx}{x + t} - y_1$$

Various modifications of this method are used in practice, e.g. the tube may be displaced first to one and then to the other side of the vertical over F. Some radiologists prefer to use markers on the skin surface and compare the shift of the image of the foreign object with the shift of the image of the marker rather than rely on a measurement of the film-table-top distance.

If the position of the object is known approximately and it is desired to avoid preliminary localisation by fluoroscopy, the foreign object can be simply localised in the horizontal plane if two wires intersecting at right angles are stretched across the casette holding the film used in the depth determination. In this case, however, the casette must be placed directly under the patient so that the film-patient distance is very small. It is convenient if the two wires are parallel and perpendicular respectively to the long axis of the body. It is

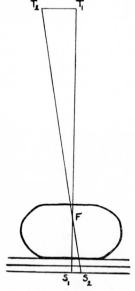

FIG. 9.23. Foreign body localisation.

320

also convenient to touch the wires with ink so that they mark themselves on the patient's skin.

If the tube is centred over the intersection of the cross-wires and then moved 3 cm. along one wire for the first exposure and an equal distance in the opposite direction for the second exposure, the position of the foreign body in the horizontal plane is given by the intersection (P) of lines drawn from the two images of the object (S_1 and S_2) to the projected positions of the tube target T_1 and T_2. (See fig. 9.24.)

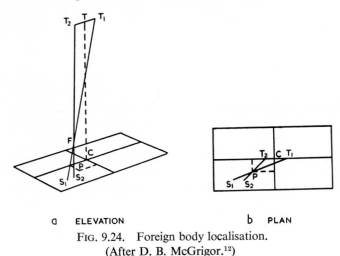

a   ELEVATION   b   PLAN

FIG. 9.24.   Foreign body localisation.
(After D. B. McGrigor.[12])

Tomography or *Layer Radiography* enables a sharply defined image of structures in a plane at a particular depth to be obtained, unobscured by the shadows of intervening objects. This is achieved by connecting the X-ray tube and film by a rigid bar pivoted so that the tube and film can be moved in opposite directions during an exposure.   Objects in the plane of the pivot then produce clear images on the film, since the images of these objects remain in the same position on the film. All other structures are blurred since their images move relative to the film during the exposure.   (See fig. 9.25.)   The image of the object P for example (fig. 9.25(a)) remains near the centre of the film throughout the exposure, while the image of the object Q moves from one end of the film to the opposite end. The thickness of the section in which detail can be observed,

321

depends upon the focus-film distance and the extent of the tube travel. The shorter the focus-film distance for a given tube travel or the longer the tube travel for a given focus-distance, the thinner is the section.

To obtain multi-layer or multi-plane tomographs with a single exposure, the usual cassette holding a single film may be replaced by a cassette which holds several films simultaneously.

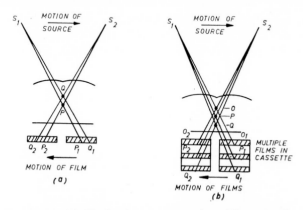

FIG. 9.25. (*a*) Single-plane tomography. The point *P* is in the plane of the pivot and the images P_1 and P_2 remain in a constant position relative to the X-ray film. The images of the point *Q* move relative to the film.
(*b*) Multi-plane tomography.

Each film is mounted between a pair of screens, with the screen speed increasing from top to bottom to counteract the effects of the decreasing X-ray intensity. On each film, objects in one particular plane only are in focus, but on successive films, successive object planes are in focus. The separation of the object planes (*h*) is related to the separation of the films (*y*) by the equation

$$\frac{h}{y} = \frac{f-d}{f}$$

where *f* is the focus film distance and *d* the pivot film distance. (See fig. 9.25(*b*).

The older type of tomographic equipment provided only linear movement of the tube and film. This movement can be obtained by a relatively simple attachment to an ordinary

322

diagnostic X-ray set but has two disadvantages. Firstly, it cannot be used to obtain tomographs in a plane at right angles to the long axis of the body and secondly, objects parallel to the plane of the section cast a streaking shadow on the film. To avoid the latter effect, many tomographic units now execute non-linear movements such as circles, ellipses or more complex evolutions.

To obtain tomographs at right angles to the long axis of the body, the so-called "axial transverse" tomographic units[13] include a rotating seat for the patient and a rotating film carrier, (see fig. 9.26). The film is carried horizontally and the X-ray

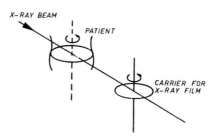

FIG. 9.26. Diagrammatic illustration of relative positions of X-ray tube, patient and film for trans-axial tomography.

beam is directed obliquely so that the central ray intersects the axis of rotation of the patient in the plane of interest and the axis of rotation of the film in the film. Both patient and film are usually carried through one complete revolution in about 3 to 5 seconds. (Faster rotation is disturbing to the patient.) Clear images of all structures in the selected horizontal plane are obtained because as the patient moves, the film moves so that the image of any structure in this plane remains at the same position on the film. The images of structures above the plane are displaced a greater distance and the images of structures below the plane a lesser distance and are consequently blurred.

9.09. Techniques to minimise the patient dose in diagnostic radiology

Any exposure of tissue to X-radiation may result in chemical and biological effects which are harmful (see Chapters X and XIV). In diagnostic radiology, it is therefore desirable to reduce the radiation dose to the patient to the minimum which is compatible with obtaining a radiograph of satisfactory diagnostic value. Hence it is very important that the fastest films and screens which will produce a radiograph with adequate detail be used and that the radiation beam be restricted in area to the minimum that will cover the region under investigation.

The second condition means that the X-ray tube should be adequately shielded in all directions except that in which the direct beam emerges (although this should be carried out by the manufacturers, new equipment should always be tested for radiation " leaks "); and readily adjustable cones and diaphragms should be provided so that the beam can be easily altered from case to case. If diaphragms are used a " visual localiser " (i.e. a lamp and mirror system which produces a light beam of the same dimensions as the X-ray beam) is essential.

It is particularly important that the X-ray dose to certain critical organs, principally the gonads and, in pregnant women, the foetus, be kept as low as possible. Therefore the gonads should never be included in the X-ray beam if this can be avoided and if it is necessary to include the gonads in the direct beam, they should be shielded if possible. For example, in examinations of the lumbar spine in males, a lead screen can be placed over the testes, without impairing the diagnostic value of the radiograph. In women of child bearing age, the International Commission on Radiological Protection have recommended that all radiological examinations of the lower abdomen and pelvis, that are not of importance in connection with the immediate illness of the patient, be limited in time to the ten-day interval following the onset of menstruation when it is virtually certain that no pregnancy exists. (I.C.R.P. report dated 1962, published 1964.)[17]

The effect of changes in kilovoltage and filtration upon the radiation dose received by a patient has been the subject of considerable investigation. The subject is complicated by the changes in film and screen speed with radiation quality, the changes in grid ratio necessary to remove scatter as the kilovoltage is increased and subjective appraisement of what constitutes a satisfactory radiograph. There is fairly general agreement that in the direct beam, the skin dose decreases as the kilovoltage and filtration increase. Most of the experimental data also suggests that *in the direct beam*, the gonad dose also decreases with increasing kV. and filter, although for radiation of half-value layer about 3 to 4 mm. Al. the change in gonad dose with quality is small. If the gonads are outside the direct beam, then the situation is more complicated, because as the half-value layer is increased, the scattered radiation becomes more penetrating and the effect of radiation quality depends upon the distance of the beam from the gonads. For a gonad-beam edge distance of 5 inches, the gonad dose decreases with increasing quality for very soft radiation, but then increases again at the higher kilovoltages. Different investigators are not agreed about the quality of radiation at which the dose is a minimum. This may well vary from one set to another since scattered radiation includes not only scatter produced in the patient, but also scattered radiation from the collimating devices and any leakage radiation that escapes from the tube housing. Table 9.01(a) illustrates the order of magnitude of these effects. The total dose received by active bone marrow (which is also of considerable interest since irradiation of the marrow is believed to increase the incidence of leukemia (see Chapter XIV)) probably increases in general with increase in radiation quality. Very soft radiation which penetrates only a few millimetres in tissue certainly plays no part in producing the radiographic image but does contribute to the skin dose and should always be removed. The International Commission on Radiological Protection [18] recommend a total filter equivalent to 1·5 mm. Al. for sets operating below 70 kVp. and a filter equivalent to 2 mm. Al. for sets with an operating potential above 70 kVp.

Table 9.01(b) illustrates the effect upon the patient dose of changes in other operating conditions, such as focus-film distance. Decrease in focus-film distance increases the skin dose so exceptionally short distances should be avoided. This consideration is of more importance in fluoroscopy than in radiography. The doses delivered during fluoroscopy are normally very much greater than during radiography so fluoroscopy should be avoided unless it is essential. For direct viewing of the fluorescent screen, it is important that the radiologist be fully dark adapted and the use of image intensifiers whenever possible is highly desirable. The use of

TABLE 9.01

THE EFFECT OF CHANGES IN TECHNIQUE UPON THE SKIN AND GONAD DOSES
RECEIVED BY A FEMALE PATIENT DURING A PELVIC EXAMINATION

(a) *Effect of change in radiation quality*

F.S.D. = 72 inches and screens used in each case.   Grid ratio adjusted so that
secondary radiation reaching film does not exceed 20 per cent. of primary.

Tube voltage	75 kVp.	75 kVp.	85 kVp.	130 kVp.
Added filter	None	1 mm. Al	2 mm. Al	2 mm. Al
H.V.L.	1 mm. Al	2 mm. Al	3 mm. Al	4 mm. Al.
Grid ratio	5 : 1	5 : 1	8 : 1	15 : 1
Skin dose	875 mrad	274 mrad	175 mrad	109 mrad
Gonad dose in primary beam	86 mrad (9·8%)	58 mrad (21%)	48 mrad (27·5%)	44 mrad (40%)
Gonad dose 5 inches away from primary	0·65 mrad	0·45 mrad	0·41 mrad	0·50 mrad
Exposure at cassette	1·75 mR. (0·2%)	1·5 mR. (0·6%)	1·5 mR. (0·9%)	1·75 mR. (1·6%)

(b) *Effect of distance and screens*

Tube voltage 85 kVp., added filter 2 mm. Al, H.V.L. 3 mm. Al in each case

F.S.D.	72 in. = 183 cm.	26½ in. = 67 cm.	72 in. = 183 cm.
Grid ratio	8 : 1	8 : 1	8 : 1
Technique	Screen	Screen	Non-screen
Skin dose	175 mrad	240 mrad	3,500 mrad
Gonad dose in primary bream	48 mrad (27·5%)	58 mrad (25·2%)	960 mrad (27·5%)
Gonad dose 5 in. away from primary	0·41 mrad	0·50 mrad	8·1 mrad
Exposure at cassette	1·5 mR. (0·9%)	1·5 mR. (0·7%)	30 mR. (0·9%)

television techniques usually results in a decreased dose. Some radiologists find it helpful to use automatic timers, which give an audible signal at pre-set intervals as well as terminating the exposure. Cine-fluorography particularly at the higher frame speeds, always requires a high dose-rate.

TABLE 9.02

RADIATION EXPOSURES TO SKIN AND GONADS IN DIAGNOSTIC PROCEDURES

Examination	Average values† (mR.)			Values obtainable with techniques chosen to minimise exposures‡ (mR.)		
	Skin	Male Gonads	Female Gonads	Skin	Male Gonads	Female Gonads
Chest, heart and lungs	120	2·8	5·4	8	0·01	0·02
Abdomen	1,500	105·0	183·0	360	0·5*	75·0
Lumbar spine A.P.				480	0·5*	95·0
Lumbar spine lat	2,200	370·0	392·0	2,000	2·25	270·0
Lumbar-sacral joint				3,000	2·0	350·0
Pelvis A.P.				480	20·0*	80·0
Barium meal (Fluoroscopy 5 mins.)	50,000	44·0	333·0	1,500	5·0	5·0

* Gonad shield used
† Skin exposures based on I.C.R.P. report (1955)[14], gonad exposures based on 2nd report of Committee on Radiological Hazards to Patients (1960)[15]
‡ Values reported by Ardran and Crookes[16]

Table 9.02 shows typical values[14, 15] of the exposures delivered to the skin and to the gonads in a number of diagnostic examinations. For comparison, the much lower exposures which Ardran and Crookes [16] have been able to achieve by careful choice of operating conditions are also tabulated. (The corresponding doses in mrad can be assumed to be numerically equal to the exposures in mR., since we are concerned, here, only with the order of magnitude of the doses.)

9.10. Xeroradiography [19, 20]

In conventional radiography, a certain time is required to develop the film after the X-ray exposure before the film can be viewed. In some situations, particularly during operations, this delay is undesirable. By the use of " polaroid " film, however, the processing time can be so reduced that this is no longer a serious consideration. Before polaroid film was available, another process known as xeroradiography (from the Greek " xeros " meaning dry) was developed as a possible means of obtaining developed " radiographs " very rapidly. In this process the X-ray " plate " consists essentially of a thin layer of a material such as selenium which is normally a good insulator but which becomes conducting when irradiated by X-rays. The selenium is mounted upon a conducting backing plate. Before an exposure is made, the surface of the selenium is charged by passing the plate beneath a fine wire maintained at a high potential (several kilovolts) with respect to earth. Since light will discharge the selenium, the plate must be kept in a light-tight container after charging. X-ray exposures are made in the same manner as in ordinary radiography. Under the action of radiation, the resistance of the selenium decreases to an extent which depends upon the local intensity of the radiation, so that the charge on the selenium surface leaks away from different parts to an extent which is determined by the amount of radiation to which each part has been exposed. The distribution of charge on the selenium after exposure thus forms a " latent image " which is " developed " by depositing a pigmented powder on the charged areas, the amount of powder deposited in any local region being determined primarily by the amount of charge in that region. " Development " takes only a few seconds. The plate may then be viewed directly, or if a permanent record is required, the image may be transferred to paper by electrostatic or adhesive transfer methods, or photographed. The xeroradiographic plate may then be wiped clean and used again.

The main disadvantage of xeroradiography is that the exposures required are about ten times as great as when films are used in conjunction with intensifying screens. This means that the process is not acceptable as a general diagnostic method, because of the increased radiation dose to the patient. However the method has been used in radiotherapy centres to verify the positioning of the patient during therapy treatments.

REFERENCES

1. YUEN, K. and BATHO, H. F. (1964). *J. Can. Ass. Radiol.* **15**, 202.
2. TEVES, M. C. and TOL, T. (1952). *Philip's Technical Review*, **14**, 33.
3. TEVES, M. C. (1955). *Brit. J. Radiol.* **28**, 216.
4. COLTMAN, J. W. (1948). *Radiology*, **51**, 359.
5. FEDDEMA, J. (1960). *Cinefluorography*, ed. by G. H. S. Ramsey, T. A. Tristan, J. S. Watson, S. Weinberg and W. S. Cornwell. Illinois, Thomas.
6. WEGENER, A. S. (1962). *Cathode Press*, **19**, 16.
7. STAUFFER, H. M. and HENNY, G. C. (1961). *Radiology*, **76**, 269.
8. MARK, G. S. (1948). *Amer. J. Roentgenol.* **59**, 282.
9. BOLDINGH, W. H. (1952). *Philip's Technical Review*, **13**, 269.
10. EULER, F. J. (1960). *Cinefluorography*, ed. by G. H. S. Ramsey, T. A. Tristan, J. S. Watson, S. Weinberg and W. S. Cornwell. Illinois, Thomas.
11. GARTHWAITE, G. W. (1961). *Brit. J. Radiol.* **34**, 741.
12. McGRIGOR, D. B. (1939). *Brit. J. Radiol.* **12**, 622.
13. AMASONO, P. (1955). *Amer. J. Roentgenol.* **74**, 777.
14. International Commission on Radiological Protection (1955). *Brit. J. Radiol.* Suppl. 6.
15. Ministry of Health, Dept. of Health for Scotland (1960). Second Report of the Committee on Radiological Hazards to Patients. London, H.M.S.O.
16. ARDRAN, G. M. and CROOKS, H. E. (1964). *Recent Advances in Radiology*, ed. by T. Lodge. London, Churchill.
17. International Commission on Radiological Protection (1964). Publication No. 6, 1962 Amendments to the 1959 Recommendations. London, Pergamon.
18. International Commission on Radiological Protection, (1960). Report of Committee III. London, Pergamon.
19. McMASTER, R. C. (1951). *Non-destructive Testing*, **10**, 1.
20. OLIPHANT, D. B. (1956). *Brit. J. Radiol.* **28**, 543.

GENERAL REFERENCES

FILES, G. W. (1951). *Medical Radiographic Technic*. Illinois, Thomas. 3rd edn. (1965), edited by W. L. Bloom, J. L. Hollenbach and J. A. Morgan.
FARR, R. F., SCOTT, A. C. H., OLLERENSHAW, R. and EVERARD, G. J. H. (1964). *Transverse Axial Tomography*. Oxford, Blackwell.

EXAMINATION QUESTIONS

1. What is meant by the following photographic terms:
   - (*a*) intensification factor;
   - (*b*) gamma;
   - (*c*) latitude;
   - (*d*) density;
   - (*e*) definition.

M.S.R. (R.), 1964.

2. Why are X-ray films coated with emulsion on both sides of the film base? How would it affect your work if X-ray films were coated with emulsion on one side only?

M.S.R. (R.), 1964.

3. Discuss the reasons for the use of intensifying screens in radiography, and describe the effects, advantageous and disadvantageous, that their use may have on the radiograph.

M.S.R. (R.), 1963.

4. State and explain the inverse square law as applied to X-radiation. Point out any limitations to its applicability. A chest X-ray is taken at 66 kV., 6 mAs. at 36 inches focus film distance and results in an acceptable radiograph. If it is required to change the distance to 6 feet, what exposure (in mAs.) would be expected to give a radiograph of similar density at the same kV.? Calculate also the dimensions of the opening of a rectangular diaphragm placed at 18 inches from the target which will enable a 17×14 inches film at 6 feet to be just covered.

M.S.R. (R. & T.), 1963.

5. Explain the relationship between focal spot size and detail (sharpness) in the radiographic image. Discuss fully the advantages of the broad focus and fine focus. In what circumstances might it be preferable to employ the broad focus?

M.S.R. (R.), 1964

6. A radiograph has been taken *without* the use of intensifying screens. Discuss the factors which control

(a) the size of the image on the film of a stationary object placed between the film and the X-ray tube;

(b) the sharpness of the image.

Illustrate your answer with suitable diagrams.

What will be the length of the image of an object 6 inches long, placed 4 inches from the film and parallel to it? The F.F.D. used is 36 inches.

Part question. M.S.R. (R. & T.), 1964.

7. Explain the purpose and function of a secondary radiation grid. What advantages and disadvantages result from arranging for it to move during the exposure? What types of grid movement do you know?

M.S.R. (R.), 1964.

8. Describe one type of image intensifier, illustrating with a simple diagram its main features. What are the advantages of such equipment over a conventional fluoroscopic unit?

M.S.R. (R.), 1963.

330

9. Describe one type of equipment for tomography. How is the thickness of the recorded layer altered?
   What additional equipment is needed to convert single layer tomography to multi-section tomography?

   M.S.R. (R.), 1963.

10. Explain briefly what is meant by scattered X-radiation and how it arises. What are the deleterious effects of scattered X-rays in diagnostic radiology and how are they minimised?

    F.S.R. (R.), 1965.

11. Compare the output screen image of an image intensifier with that of a TV monitor with respect to

    (a) brightness gain;
    (b) gamma (contrast);
    (c) definition.

    How would the above factors influence your choice of cine recording material and its processing?

    F.S.R. (R.), 1965.

12. Explain the terms (a) density, (b) exposure, (c) characteristic curve, with reference to X-ray film. What is meant by the gamma of the film?
    Describe the use of intensifying screens in radiography, indicating the arrangement of the various components in the cassette. Discuss briefly the advantages and disadvantages of such screens.

    D.M.R., 1964.

13. Explain the necessity for the smallest possible focal spot in an X-ray tube. Describe how it is achieved. What factors put a limit to the smallness of the spot?
    Discuss the inter-relationship of focal spot size and focus-film distance in the production of a good radiograph.

    D.M.R., 1964.

14. Outline the principles of shadow formation by objects in a beam of X-rays.
    A radiograph of two implanted radioactive needles, parallel to each other and to the film, was taken with a focus film distance of 80 cm., and with the needle plane 18 cm. from the film. The centres of the needle shadows are 1·6 cm. apart. Calculate (a) the needle separation and (b) the geometrical penumbra if the effective focal size was 2×2 mm.

    D.M.R., 1963.

15. Describe and explain the principles of a displacement method for the radiographic localisation of a foreign body or radium needle.

In the localisation of a needle in a limb the following data was obtained:

Focus-film distance	= 50 cm.
Tube shift	= 6 cm.
Displacement of shadow	
one end	= 0·6 cm.
other end	= 1·0 cm.

Determine the position of the needle relative to the film.

D.M.R., 1962.

CHAPTER X

SOME CHEMICAL AND BIOLOGICAL EFFECTS OF IONISING RADIATIONS

THE primary results of the absorption of α-, β-, X- or γ-radiation by matter are the ionisation and excitation of the atoms of the absorber. In the ionisation process, an electron is ejected from a parent atom leaving a positive ion. The free electron is eventually either captured by another atom or molecule to produce a negative ion, or is recaptured by the same or another positive ion. The fate of the positive ions and the free electrons depends upon their spatial distribution and upon both the physical state and the chemical nature of the absorber. These primary changes initiate further processes leading to chemical changes in the irradiated material. Since tissue contains a large proportion of water, the chemical effects in pure water and in water containing simple solutes, make a logical starting point in the study of the effects of radiation on biological materials. These effects have been widely studied, but the nature of the reactions which occur are still not fully understood. The description which follows is therefore tentative and may require modification in the future.

10.01. Radiation chemistry of water

The main experimental observations which any theory must explain are as follows :

(1) In water *vapour*, the ions produced have been identified by using a mass spectrometer as H_2O^+ (the most abundant), HO^+, H^+ and HO_3^+ with very small quantities of O^+ and H_2^+.

(2) In pure air-free liquid water which is exposed to α-radiation, hydrogen peroxide (and sometimes some oxygen) is produced together with an equivalent amount of hydrogen. On the other hand, X- or γ-radiation produce very little if any of these substances.

(3) In aerated or oxygenated liquid water, exposure to X- or γ-radiation, as well as α-radiation, results in the production of hydrogen peroxide.

(4) If solutes are dissolved in air-free water which is exposed to radiation, the solutes may be either oxidised or reduced. Powerful reducing agents are oxidised and powerful oxidising agents are reduced but oxidative reactions preponderate. (Only systems having a redox potential greater than about 0·9 V. are reduced.)

In order to explain the above data it is necessary to consider the distribution of ions produced by different types of radiation. Let us consider first the primary processes which occur when fast electrons (either β particles or the secondary electrons produced by the absorption of electromagnetic radiation) of initial energy about 1 MeV. travel through water. Such electrons give up energy at a rate of about 100 eV. per 5,000 Å. About half this energy is given up in low energy reactions which produce clusters of ion pairs along the track. On the average there are 2·5 ion pairs per cluster. The remaining energy is given up in reactions which produce electrons with sufficient energy to travel a short distance from the main track. The tracks of these electrons are called δ-rays and clusters of ion pairs are produced along them also. The spacing of the ion pairs along δ-rays is considerably reduced compared with the spacing along the main track. About 7 per cent. of the total number of interactions result in δ-ray formation.

If the primary radiation is very much less energetic than 1 MeV., or consists of heavy particles, the separation of ion clusters along the main track is considerably reduced. For radiation of a given energy, the initial rate of transfer of energy to the medium per unit length of track (the linear energy transfer or L.E.T.) can be readily determined. However, the primary particles are slowed down as they traverse the medium and hence the energy transfer is greater and the separation of ion clusters is less towards the end of the track. For electromagnetic radiation there is a wide variation in L.E.T. along the track. Average L.E.T. values for various types of radiation have been calculated and some representative values are listed in Table 10.01. This table also shows the corresponding separation of ion clusters, assuming (as a convenient round number only), that the average energy required to produce an ion cluster is 100 eV.

TABLE 10.01

Radiation	L.E.T. in keV./μ		Cluster separation in Å.	
	Average over main track	Average along δ- ray tracks	Average over main track	Average along δ- ray tracks
Co⁶⁰ γ radiation	0·25	50	4,000	20
200 kVp. X-rays	2·0	60	500	16
5 MeV. neutrons	15·0	—	60	—
5 MeV. α particles	100·0	—	10	—

N.B.—The above figures are intended to illustrate the order of magnitude of the average L.E.T. and cluster separations only.

For the γ-rays from Co^{60}, the average separation of clusters and δ-rays along the main track is about 4,000 Å while for 200 kVp. X-rays it is about 500 Å. For the heavy particles, the average cluster separations are 10 to 100 times smaller and the clusters are formed so close together that there is essentially a continuous column of dense ionisation. The spacing of ion clusters in relation to the size of some biological structures is illustrated in fig. 10.04.

In pure water, the positive ion of each ion pair remains near the track of the ionising particle and on hydration produces hydrogen ions and hydroxyl radicals.

$$H_2O^+ + H_2O = H_{aq}^+ + OH\cdot$$

Hydrogen ions are normal stable constituents of liquid water but hydroxyl radicals contain one less electron than the usual hydroxyl ions. Stable atoms or groups of atoms usually contain an even number of electrons but atoms or groups of atoms, such as the hydroxyl radical, which contain an " unpaired " electron, are very reactive chemically. The hydroxyl radicals are strong oxidising agents.

The fate of the electron from the ion pair has been a matter of some argument. It was at one time assumed that the electron could travel about 150 Å from its point of origin and would then be captured by a neutral molecule.[1, 2] The latter upon dissociation would produce hydroxyl ions and hydrogen atoms

$$e^- + H_2O \rightarrow H_2O^- \rightarrow OH_{aq}^- + H\cdot$$

(Hydrogen atoms are very reactive chemically since they contain unpaired electrons and are strong reducing agents.) However some radiation chemists [3, 4, 5] maintained that the electron was unable to escape from the field of the positive ion with which it recombined to produce an excited molecule. This would then dissociate to produce hydroxyl radicals and hydrogen atoms

$$e^- + H_2O^+ \rightarrow H_2O^* \rightarrow H\cdot + OH\cdot$$

Subsequently, evidence accumulated suggesting that two reducing species are formed in irradiated water [6, 7, 8, 9, 10] and that one of these species is negatively charged. In 1962, hydrated electrons were detected experimentally in irradiated water by means of their absorption spectrum.[11, 12] Water molecules are slightly polarised and a ring of neutral molecules probably forms around the electron, the molecules being orientated by the electrical attraction. The water molecules " shield " the electron and reduce its reactivity.

The present (1965) view [13, 14] is therefore that most of the electrons probably escape from the field of the positive ion and become hydrated. A few escaping electrons probably react with neutral molecules to form hydrogen atoms [15] and a few electrons will be recaptured by the positive ion. H atoms and OH radicals are probably produced also by the dissociation of molecules excited directly by the ionising radiation, but these appear to be relatively unimportant. (Because they are formed close together, a large fraction of the H atoms and OH radicals produced from excited water molecules probably react together very rapidly to reform water.) Thus a short time (viz. 10^{-13} second) after the passage of an ionising particle through water there are hydroxyl radicals (OH·), hydrated positively charged hydrogen ions (H_{aq}^+), and some hydrogen atoms (H·) probably within 10 Å of the track of the ionising particle, and hydrated electrons (e_{aq}^-) out to perhaps 25-50 Å from the track (fig. 10.01). Along the main tracks of high energy electrons (including those produced by the absorption of X- or γ-radiation), the separation of successive ion clusters is much greater than the separation of radicals and electrons within a cluster. The predominant reaction is therefore recombination of radicals and electrons with one another

$$OH \cdot + e_{aq}^- = OH_{aq}^-$$

However in the tracks of densely ionising radiations such as protons and α-particles the ion clusters overlap, so that there will be a cylinder of hydroxyl radicals along the track surrounded by a more diffuse cylinder of hydrated electrons. In these

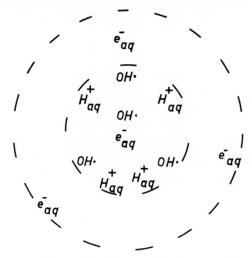

Fig. 10.01. Distribution of primary radiation products in water.

circumstances recombination is more likely to take place between similar radicals so that both hydrogen peroxide and molecular hydrogen can be formed

$$OH \cdot + OH \cdot \rightarrow H_2O_2$$
$$e_{aq}^- + e_{aq}^- \rightarrow H_2 + 2 OH_{aq}^-$$

In the presence of dissolved oxygen the formation of hydroxyl radicals is unaltered but the hydrated electrons (or hydrogen atoms) can react with the dissolved oxygen to form HO_2 radicals

$$e_{aq}^- + O_2 \rightarrow O_{2\,aq}^- \rightarrow HO_2^- + OH^-$$

or
$$H \cdot + O_2 \rightarrow HO_2^-$$

337

The formation of hydrogen peroxide by X- and γ-rays in water containing oxygen is probably due to secondary reactions of the HO_2' radical, e.g.

$$2HO_2' \rightarrow H_2O_2 + O_2$$

As the concentration of the primary products of any of these reactions increases, the products may react with newly formed radicals and a number of back reactions occur, which limit the quantity of primary product produced. For example, in air-free water exposed to α radiation, the following processes are all possible

$$(1) \quad OH \cdot + H_2 \rightarrow H_2O + H \cdot$$

$$(2) \quad OH \cdot + H_2O_2 \rightarrow HO_2' + H_2O$$

$$(3) \quad e_{aq}^- + H_2O_2 \rightarrow OH_{aq}^- + OH \cdot$$

or $\qquad (4) \quad H \cdot + H_2O_2 \rightarrow H_2O + OH \cdot$

$$(5) \quad HO_2 + H_2O_2 \rightarrow H_2O + OH \cdot + O_2$$

$$(6) \quad e_{aq}^- + O_2 \rightarrow O_{2aq}^- \rightarrow HO_2' + OH^-$$

or $\qquad (7) \quad H \cdot + O_2 \rightarrow HO_2'$

giving a net back reaction

$$H_2 + H_2O_2 \rightarrow 2H_2O$$

If dilute aqueous solutions are considered instead of pure water, then the species $OH \cdot$, e_{aq}^- and $H \cdot$ may also react with the solutes. For example, in ferrous solutions, $OH \cdot$ oxidises the ferrous ions (Fe^{2+}) to ferric ions (Fe^{3+})

$$Fe^{2+} + OH \cdot \rightarrow Fe^{3+} + OH^-$$

This reaction is used in the Fricke dosimeter (see below).

The efficiency of production of a particular species in a radio-chemical reaction is usually measured by stating the number of radicals, atoms or molecules produced per 100 eV. of energy absorbed. From the measured yields of final products obtained under carefully controlled conditions, it is possible to deduce the primary yields of species such as $OH \cdot$ radicals, hydrated electrons, etc., if the chemical reactions that take place can be determined. In dilute acid solutions, irradiated by ionising radiation of low L.E.T. (e.g. Co^{60} γ-rays), the following values for primary yields are fairly well established[14]

$$G_{OH\cdot} = 2\cdot95, \qquad G_{H_2O_2} = 0\cdot8$$
$$G_{H\cdot} = 3\cdot65 \qquad G_{H_2} = 0\cdot45$$

(In acid solutions, hydrated electrons are rapidly converted to hydrogen atoms

$$e_{aq}^- + H_{aq}^+ \rightarrow H\cdot + H_2O)$$

Notice that the total yield for oxidising species $G_{OH\cdot} + 2G_{H_2O_2}$ ($2\cdot95 + 1\cdot6$) is equal to the total yield for reducing species $G_{H\cdot} + 2G_{H_2}$ ($3\cdot65 + 0\cdot9$). (The factor 2 occurs in front of the molecular yields since two hydroxyl radicals are required to produce one molecule of hydrogen peroxide and two hydrogen atoms are required to produce one molecule of hydrogen.) This equality is to be expected since the oxidising species originate in reactions of the positive ions produced by the radiation and the reducing species originate from the electrons. Also the number of water molecules interacting per 100 eV. = 4·55. In neutral water, there is some uncertainty as to whether the total yield of oxidising and reducing species is the same as in acid solution (with hydrated electrons included amongst the reducing species) or is somewhat less. Because there is better agreement as to the primary yields in acid solutions these are normally used for dosimetry.

In the Fricke dosimeter,[16, 17] the yield of ferric ion in an air-saturated solution of 0·001 N. ferrous sulphate and 0·002 M. sodium chloride in 0·8 N. sulphuric acid is measured. The principle reactions which yield ferric ion are

$$OH\cdot + Fe^{2+} \rightarrow OH^- + Fe^{3+}$$
$$OH\cdot + OH\cdot \rightarrow H_2O_2 + Fe^{2+} \rightarrow OH^- + OH\cdot + Fe^{3+}$$
$$H\cdot + O_2 \rightarrow HO_2^\cdot + Fe^{2+} \rightarrow Fe^{3+} + HO_2^-$$

Also
$$HO_2^- + H_{aq}^+ \rightarrow H_2O_2 + HO_2^\cdot$$

Hence if $G(Fe^{3+})_{O_2}$ denotes the yield of ferric ion in the presence of oxygen, and if the above reactions fully describe the processes taking place

$$G(Fe^{3+})_{O_2} = G_{OH\cdot} + 2G_{H_2O_2} + 3G_{H\cdot}$$

The experimentally determined value for $G(Fe^{3+})_{O_2}$ for Co^{60} radiation is 15·67,[18] i.e. for each 100 eV. of energy absorbed,

15·67 ferric ions are produced. (Substitution of the primary yields in the above equation gives $G(Fe^{3+}) = 15·5$.) The chief disadvantage of the dosimeter is that the yield is a function of the L.E.T. of the ionising radiation. However provided the radiation quality is known the yield of ferric ion enables the energy dissipated in the solution, i.e. the absorbed dose, to be calculated. Details of the various precautions required when using ferrous sulphate solutions for dosimetry can be found in Report 10b of the International Commission on Radiological Units and Measurements (1962).[19]

10.02. Direct and indirect action

The preceding discussion will have made it clear that any material which is suspended in an aqueous medium exposed to the action of ionising radiation, even though itself unaffected by the radiation, will be liable to attack by the entities (free radicals, hydrogen peroxide, etc.), produced by the radiation in the water. If such a secondary reaction takes place, molecules of the organism or solute under study receive energy indirectly by transfer from the molecules of the suspending medium, and the action of the radiation is said to be *indirect*, whereas if the molecules under study are themselves ionised or excited by the radiation, the action is said to be *direct*. When a pure substance is irradiated dry, then only the direct action of the radiation is possible, but in biological material, which is irradiated *in vivo* or in aqueous solution both direct and indirect effects may occur.

The principal methods of distinguishing direct from indirect action consist in observing the effect of

   (1) freezing the material ;

   (2) diluting the solution ;

   (3) adding chemicals which will compete for free radicals.

In frozen material, the diffusion of radiation products is retarded and indirect action is greatly reduced. This test is not always possible with biological material however. If the number of molecules or organisms affected by the radiation is independent of their initial concentration, the reaction is probably indirect, for in this case the number of radiation products formed from the suspending medium remains constant and it is these which produce the observed effect. If the effect is direct, the number of molecules altered by the radiation will increase as the number present increases, i.e. as the concentration increases. (See fig. 10.02.) Finally, if the addition of chemicals which will compete for radiation products from the solute reduces the observed effect, then it is probable that the action is indirect.

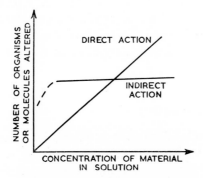

FIG. 10.02. Graph showing variation in effect of radiation with concentration of material in solution.

The results of direct and indirect action upon a particular chemical or biological system may be the same or they may be different. For example alcohols are oxidised in a similar manner either when irradiated directly or in aqueous solutions. In benzene, on the other hand, the direct action of radiation produces a number of products such as hydrogen, acetylene and a polymer, whereas the indirect effect in aqueous solution is mainly the production of phenol.

The number of cases where a direct comparison is possible of the relative importance of direct and indirect effects of radiation *in vivo* is limited. However, the possibility of providing protection against very diverse types of radiation damage by the same chemicals (which are known to react with the primary radiation products formed in water) suggests that, in many cases, the indirect effect of radiation is of major importance. Hutchinson and his co-workers have measured the inactivation by radiation of two enzymes and a co-enzyme in a living yeast cell, both before and after vacuum drying.[20] They found a loss of biological activity, 2, 20 and 60 times greater in the wet than the dry state, the relative importance of indirect action increasing as the molecular size decreased. They calculated that aqueous radiation products diffusing about 30 Å would produce the observed ratios. These workers also irradiated pneumococci both wet and dry and then measured the ability of DNA (desoxyribosenucleic acid, a constituent of chromosomes) extracted from the bacteria to genetically transform the cells of a related strain.[21] The dose required to destroy the transforming ability of a given fraction of the DNA was found to be approximately three times as great in the dry as in the wet state.

10.03. The oxygen effect

The magnitude of the effect produced by X- and γ-radiation upon a great variety of materials varies in a characteristic manner with the oxygen tension in the organism or solution during the irradiation.[22, 23, 24] In general, the dose of radiation required to produce a given effect is two to three times as great in the absence of oxygen as under normal oxygen tension, whereas an increase in ambient oxygen tension above normal levels has a relatively small effect (see fig. 10.03). The results of irradiation with densely ionising particles are usually much less dependent upon the oxygen concentration. Widely different cell types and widely different radiation effects are modified similarly by the presence of oxygen (e.g. oxidation of a variety of chemicals in aqueous solution, inactivation of phages and viruses, inhibition of mitosis and production of chromosome aberrations in a variety of organisms, lethal effects in bacteria, yeast, tumour cells, mice and rats, see Table 10.02). In some of the cases which respond in this way, the radiation effect may be indirect and the effect of oxygen due to the modification it causes in the nature of the primary radiation products in water, but oxygen also reacts readily with most organic radicals and hence can modify direct radiation effects also.

L. H. Gray [25, 26] was the first to point out that the oxygen effect might be of importance in radiotherapy since malignant tumours are frequently avascular and therefore under normal conditions are irradiated at a low oxygen tension. If the oxygen tension in the tumour could be increased, a considerable increase in the effect of the radiation on the tumour might be produced, while the damage to adjacent normal tissue (already well-oxygenated) should increase only slightly. One method

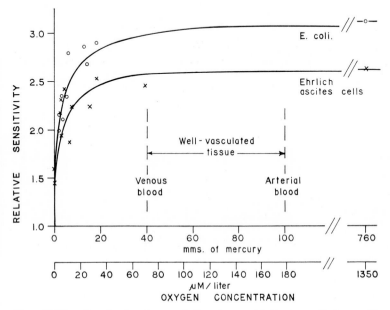

FIG. 10.03. Graph showing variation in sensitivity to radiation with oxygen concentration (data from Deschner and Gray[23], Howard-Flanders[24] and Churchill-Davidson et al.[25]).

of increasing the oxygen tension in avascular tissue, is for the patient to breathe oxygen at pressures two or three times greater than atmospheric. (Under normal conditions, almost all the oxygen carried in the blood is combined with haemoglobin, but when the patient breathes hyperbaric oxygen, additional oxygen is carried in solution in the plasma.) Clinical trials are now in progress in a number of radiotherapy centres to determine the effect of irradiating tumours when the patient breathes pure hyperbaric oxygen (usually at 3 atmospheres pressure), both immediately before, and during, the period of irradiation.

TABLE 10.02

RATIO OF AEROBIC TO ANAEROBIC SENSITIVITY TO X-RADIATION
(after Gray [22])

Category	Organism	Ratio (m)
Microorganisms	E. coli B/r	3
	E. coli B/r	$3 \cdot 11 \pm 0 \cdot 11$
	Shigella flexneri Y6R	$2 \cdot 92 \pm 0 \cdot 07$
	Saccharomyces cerevisae	2·4
Plant tissues	Vicia roots:	
	Growth	$2 \cdot 9 \pm 0 \cdot 25$
	Chromosome structural damage (all forms)	2·9
	Tradescantia microspores—chromosome structural damage	2·6
	Maize, endosperm mutants:	
	Entire	$3 \cdot 1 \pm 0 \cdot 3$
	Partial	$2 \cdot 2 \pm 0 \cdot 2$
Mammalian cells	Ehrlich ascites Tumor cells:	
	3° C.	$2 \cdot 2 \pm 0 \cdot 15$
	18° C.	$3 \cdot 1 \pm 0 \cdot 15$
	37° C.	$2 \cdot 9 \pm 0 \cdot 15$
Mammalian tissues	Tail bone growth in young mice	$2 \cdot 7 \pm 0 \cdot 15$
	Graying of hair:	
	Resting follicles	3·1
	Growing follicles	2·9
	Rat lymphocytes in lymph nodes	11·0

10.04. In vitro irradiation of biological materials * [27, 30]

A certain number of the compounds which occur in living organisms have been irradiated in the pure form, either dry or in aqueous solution. The results of some of these experiments are described below although it must be emphasised that the effect of radiation upon the same materials *in vivo* may be altered by the changed environment. For example, when pure unsaturated fatty acids are irradiated *in vitro*, the acids are oxidised to hydroperoxides. The yield is very high and greatly increased by the presence of oxygen. Fatty acids extracted from animals are much less sensitive to radiation, however, owing to the presence of α-tocopherol (vitamin E) which is a powerful anti-oxidant.

* The chemical formulae of the substances mentioned in this section are given in appendix II.

344

Similarly various enzymes which are very sensitive to radiation when irradiated alone in aqueous solution, appear very resistant when irradiated in the presence of their substrates. In a series of experiments carried out in the early 1940's Dale [28] demonstrated that this is due to competition by the substrates for the primary radiation products produced in the solution. Conversely some enzymes appear to be sensitised when absorbed on particular supporting materials. [29]

The effects of irradiation upon certain types of biological material have been investigated by the method known as " electron-spin resonance " (abbreviated e.s.r.). This technique sometimes makes it possible to determine at which atom in a complex molecule, an unpaired electron is produced. Substances examined in this way include acids, proteins, enzymes, and the nucleic acids. However electron-spin resonance studies are not normally attempted with wet specimens, so provide information only about the direct effects of radiation.

Upon irradiation of pure organic acids there is a general tendency for an atom or group on the α carbon atom (adjacent to the carboxyl group) to be broken off. In α amino acids both direct and indirect action usually result in the loss of the amino group. Cysteine is an exception and is not de-aminated by irradiation. Electron-spin resonance studies suggest that in this case the unpaired electron is in the vicinity of the sulphur atom. [31] Cysteine in aqueous solution is oxidised to cystine, probably by the action of the OH· radicals. [27, 32]

$$\underset{\underset{NH_2}{|}}{COOH-CH}-CH_2-SH+OH·\rightarrow \underset{\underset{NH_2}{|}}{COOH-CH}-CH_2-S·+H_2O$$

$$2\ \underset{\underset{NH_2}{|}}{COOH-CH}-CH_2-S·\rightarrow \underset{\underset{COOH-CH-CH-S}{\underset{|}{NH_2}}}{\overset{\overset{NH_2}{|}}{COOH-CH}-CH_2-S}$$

In proteins, the unpaired electron usually appears on glycine or cystine residues. Since the primary ionisation may occur anywhere along the protein molecule it appears that there must be a migration of charge to particular sites. As a result of a large number of observations, Gordy [30] has come to the conclusion that the unpaired electron is most likely to be found in the vicinity of (1) S, (2) —C = O bonds, (3) —C = C— bonds. These observations suggest that proteins containing cystine or cysteine units may be protected from radiation damage, by allowing the unpaired electron to migrate to the side group containing sulphur, where perhaps it is less important. It is interesting in this connection that silk fibres which do not have disulphide links are more readily weakened by radiation than wool fibres which contain sulphur. On the basis of experiments with synthetic polymers, Bacq and Alexander [27] suggest that aromatic rings can also protect the main chain in this way. The presence of oxygen during the irradiation of proteins has been shown to change the e.s.r. spectrum and it is believed

that a stable free radical of the type $-\overset{|}{\underset{|}{C}}-O-O\cdot$ is produced

(from the carbon atom in the polypeptide), which undergoes a chain reaction with oxygen to yield hydroperoxides.

The end-products of protein irradiation may be either smaller (degraded), due to breaking of the main chain, or larger, due to cross-linking of residues, than the parent material. When fairly large molecules, such as proteins, are irradiated in the liquid phase, the larger radiation products cannot escape from one another's influence whereas hydrogen atoms and other small groups of atoms can diffuse away. The large residues resulting from the loss of hydrogen then frequently combine with one another producing cross-linking.

It has already been mentioned that enzymes are very readily inactivated by irradiation, particularly in aqueous solution but are normally afforded a considerable degree of protection by their substrates.[28] Enzymes which contain SH groups have been extensively investigated. Barron[32] reported that these enzymes were particularly sensitive to radiation damage and suggested that this was because the SH groups were both the biologically active centres and the groups which were modified by the radiation. Later workers, however, have not been able fully to confirm Barron's observations and in some cases the loss of enzyme activity appears to be faster than the destruction of SH groups.[33]

The effects of radiation on the nucleic acids, DNA and RNA are of considerable interest in view of the genetic effects of radiation. A comparison of the effects of the radiation on the acids themselves and their constituent nucleosides by the e.s.r. method suggests that unpaired electrons tend to migrate to the vicinity of adenosine and cytosine rings.[30] No oxygen sensitisation was detected. In aqueous solution, viscosity measurements indicate that DNA is depolymerised.[34, 35] Scholes and Weiss[36] found that massive doses of radiation produced free ammonia, free inorganic phosphate and free purine bases. The yield of ammonia is increased in the presence of air compared with vacuum and is therefore attributed to attack on the bases by OH radicals, while the yield of phosphate is reduced and is therefore attributed to attack on the main chain by hydrated electrons or hydrogen atoms. Subsequent study[37] of the oxidation of the pyrimidine bases has established that OH· radicals attack the 5-6 bond in these compounds and that the reaction is relatively efficient. For example, the G values for the destruction of thymine, are 2·4 in the presence of oxygen and 0·8 in the absence of oxygen.

10.05. Effects of ionising radiations *in vivo*; the target theory[38]

When the effects of radiation on biological materials *in vivo* are considered, it is usually quite impossible to refer any gross change (death of cells or organisms, anatomical lesions, etc.) to a particular chemical reaction. Information of interest, however, may sometimes be obtained about the size of the entity which is changed or inactivated by the radiation.

Suppose that a particular biological effect is produced by direct action and that a single ionisation within a certain critical volume or " target " is sufficient to produce the effect. Then:

(1) The effect produced should be independent of the dose-rate.

347

(2) Sparsely ionising radiations should be more efficient than densely ionising radiations since the probability of producing more than one ionisation in each critical volume and therefore "wasting" ionisations is less. (See fig. 10.04.)

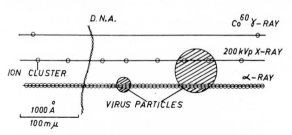

FIG. 10.04. Diagram illustrating the separation of ion clusters in relation to the size of some biological structures.

(3) The number of organisms surviving unchanged should decrease exponentially as the radiation dose increases. For let n denote the number of organisms surviving a dose D. The increment in the number of organisms damaged $(-dn)$ produced by an increment of dose dD is given by $-dn/n = dD/D_0$ where D_0 is the mean lethal dose, i.e. the dose required to produce an average of one "hit" per organism. Integrating

$$\log (n/n_0) = -D/D_0 \text{ or } n = n_0 e^{-D/D_0}$$

where n_0 is the initial number of organisms. D_0 is sometimes described as the 37 per cent. survival dose and designated by D_{37} since when $n/n_0 = 37$ per cent., $D = D_0$.

If the mean lethal dose is determined, then the dimensions of the "target" volume can be calculated if certain assumptions are made about the spatial distribution of ions produced by the radiation and about the energy required to produce an ion pair or ion cluster in the medium. For example, for megavoltage X- or γ-radiation, suppose it is assumed that the ion clusters are produced at random and we take 100 eV. (as a convenient round number) for the average energy required to produce a cluster in the medium considered. Then if D_0 is measured in rads, the energy absorbed per g. of the medium $= 100 D_0$ ergs

348

$$= \frac{100\,D_0}{1\cdot6\times10^{-12}}\ \text{eV. and the number of ion clusters per g.} =$$

$\dfrac{D_0}{1\cdot6\times10^{-12}}.$ If each ion cluster inactivates a " target ", the

target mass $= \dfrac{1\cdot6\times10^{-12}}{D_0}$ g. or if the target has density ρ, the

target volume $= \dfrac{1\cdot6}{\rho D_0}\times10^{-12}$ cc. $= \dfrac{1\cdot6}{\rho D_0}$ cubic microns.

This calculation is valid if the target size is small in comparison with the separation of ion clusters but large in comparison with the separation of ions within a cluster. In general, particularly when more densely ionising radiations are considered, it is necessary to take into account the different spatial distributions of ions produced by different types of radiation. The necessary mathematical methods were developed mainly by Lea,[38] who analysed a considerable number of experimental results in this way.

Lea found that for certain phages and other small viruses and some enzymes, the sparsely ionising radiations were more efficient than the densely ionising (see fig. 10.05). He also found that the number of surviving organisms decreased exponentially with dose (fig. 10.06), that the same value for the target size was obtained using different types of radiation, and that the calculated size corresponded quite closely with the physical dimensions of the organism. This suggested that in these small organisms the whole volume was sensitive to radiation. In some cases however Lea found the target size calculated from irradiation experiments was less than the physical size of the organism. It is now known that a large range of viruses consist of a nucleic acid " core " coated with protein, and later workers have established that the radiation sensitive volume agrees very closely with independent estimates of the volume occupied by nucleic acid.[39, 40]

It should be noted that it was stipulated above that the observed effect should be produced by direct action. This makes possible a simple quantitative treatment. If indirect action also takes place, then an organism may be affected if it is within the diffusion distance of some reaction product from an ionisation. From the life-times, reactivities and diffusion

349

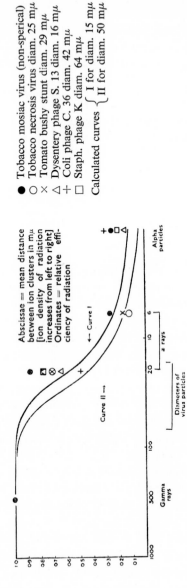

● Tobacco mosiac virus (non-sperical)
○ Tobacco necrosis virus diam. 25 mμ
× Tomato bushy stunt diam. 29 mμ
△ Dysentery phage S. 13 diam. 16 mμ
+ Coli phage C. 36 diam. 42 mμ
□ Staph. phage K diam. 64 mμ
Calculated curves { I for diam. 15 mμ
                II for diam. 50 mμ

Fig. 10.05. Relative efficiencies of ionising radiations for the inactivation of viruses. (After L. H. Gray.[41])

By permission from *Brit. med. Bull.* (1954), 4, 14.

rates of the various radiation products it may be possible to estimate the "sphere of influence" of an ionisation, but the required parameters are not usually known with any degree of precision. Nevertheless if a single reaction between the organism considered and a radiation product produces the observed effect, the general features will be qualitatively similar

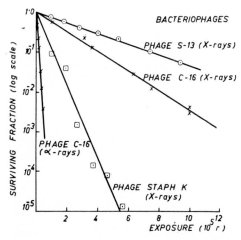

FIG. 10.06. Graphs showing the relation between the number of survivors and the radiation dose for bacteriophages (data from Lea[31]).

whether direct or indirect action takes place, i.e. the effects will be independent of dose-rate, the number of organisms surviving unchanged will decrease exponentially with dose and sparsely ionising radiations will be more efficient than densely ionising radiations.

In marked contrast with the results obtained with viruses, it is found that for the production of gross damage in larger biological structures, e.g. the production of chromosome breaks in tradescantia pollen-grains, inhibition of growth of vicia faba root-tips, wheat-seedlings, chick embryos, etc., the densely ionising radiations are more efficient than the less densely ionising. (See fig. 10.07.)

If several ionisations must occur within a given organism to produce the radiation effect there will be a critical ionisation

351

density depending upon the target size, when the required number of ionisations is produced in the target whenever an ionising particle passes through it. For radiations which are more densely ionising than this, the radiation efficiency will decrease, the response will be independent of dose-rate and the number of organisms surviving unchanged will decrease

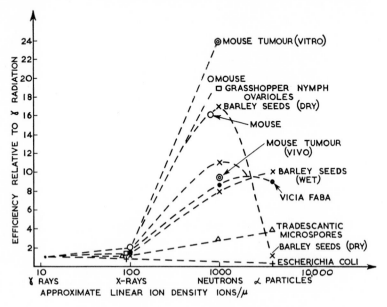

FIG. 10.07. Relative efficiencies of ionising radiations for the production of gross damage in biological material.

exponentially with the dose. For more sparsely ionising radiation, however, the response may depend upon the dose-rate and the survival curve will generally be of the sigmoid type, such as those shown in figs. 10.09 and 10.10. Two situations may be envisaged: (1) the biological system contains m targets, each of which must be inactivated before the system is affected, (2) there is a single target which must receive m " hits " before it is inactivated. These have been described as multi-target and multi-hit models respectively.[42] It may be shown that for the multi-target model the fraction n/n_0 of organisms surviving a dose D is given by

$$n/n_0 = 1—(1—e^{-D/D_0})^m \qquad (2)$$

whereas for the multi-hit model

$$n/n_0 = e^{-D/D_0} \sum_{i=0}^{m-1} \left\{ (D/D_0)^i / \underline{i} \right\} \tag{3}$$

If equation (2) is applicable the survival curve becomes exponential at high doses, i.e. if log (n/n_0) is plotted against D then a straight line is obtained at high doses. Equation (3) represents a curve which becomes continuously steeper at high doses on a semi-log plot.

Since the dose required to produce a given biological effect is not in general the same when delivered by different types of radiation, it is desirable to have a measure of the effectiveness of radiation of a given type in producing a given effect. For this purpose the quantity " relative biological effectiveness " or R.B.E. has been introduced. The R.B.E. of a " test " radiation compared to a standard radiation is equal to the ratio D_s/D_t, where D_s and D_t are the absorbed doses of the standard and test radiations, respectively, that produce the same effect in a particular biological system. If the nature of the standard radiation is not explicitly stated, it is assumed to be X-radiation generated at about 200 kVp. The value of the R.B.E. depends upon the particular effect being considered and usually varies with environmental factors such as the degree of oxygenation during the irradiation.

10.06. The effect of radiation on the reproductive ability of mammalian cells

One of the most important functions of a cell is the ability to reproduce. The impairment of reproductive ability by ionising radiation is probably the most important single biological effect of the radiation so far as radiotherapy is concerned. In 1956 Puck and Marcus [43] reported experiments upon the effects of radiation on tissue cultures in which the ability of individual cells to multiply and produce macroscopic colonies (called " clones ") was used as the criterion of " survival ". Many other workers have since used this criterion in reporting the effects of radiation upon cells of diverse types (studied both in tissue cultures and in vivo), and some typical " survival " curves of this kind are shown in figures 10.08, 10.09 and 10.10.

Fig. 10.08 illustrates some effects produced by changes in the radiation quality. These curves represent results obtained by Barendsen and his co-workers [44] using a strain of human cells, originating from the kidney and cultured *in vitro*. The number of clones produced after given doses of radiation expressed as a percentage of unirradiated controls is plotted on a logarithmic scale against dose. Curves (1) and (2) represent the results of irradiation with polonium α-particles in air and in nitrogen respectively and are straight lines, i.e. the percentage survival decreases exponentially with increase in dose for α-irradiation, and is influenced only slightly by the presence of oxygen.

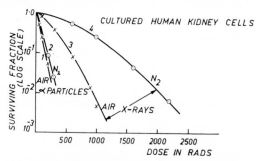

FIG. 10.08. Graphs showing the relation between the surviving fraction and dose for cell cultures (originating from human kidney) exposed to P_0 α-particles and 250 kVp. X-rays in air and nitrogen (after Barendsen *et al.*[44]).

Curves (3) and (4) represent irradiation with 250 kVp. X-rays in air and nitrogen respectively, and these curves become progressively steeper as the dose increases. The presence of oxygen now makes a much greater difference to the survival.

Fig. 10.09 shows survival curves, obtained by Berry and Andrews,[45] for lymphocytic leukemia cells proliferating *in vivo* in the host mouse, after irradiation with 3 MV. X-rays. These curves after an initial " shoulder " become straight lines on a semi-log plot, i.e. the survival varies exponentially with dose except at the lowest doses. Such curves are commonly described by the mean lethal dose (D_0) determined from the linear portion of the curve and the " extrapolation number (m) ", i.e. the intercept on the ordinate to which the linear portion extrapolates. For a considerable variety of mammalian cells,

354

examined both in cell culture and also *in vivo*, using the ability to reproduce as the index of radiation effect, this type of survival curve is obtained and the mean lethal dose lies in the range 100 to 200 rads. (See Table 10.03.) The extrapolation number varies more than the mean lethal dose with cell type but is frequently between 1 and 2. It is of interest that survival curves obtained *in vitro* which become continuously steeper at

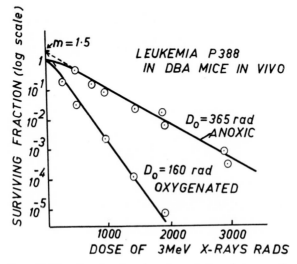

FIG. 10.09. Graphs showing the relation between the number of cells retaining reproductive integrity and dose for P 388 lymphocytic leukemia cells injected intraperitoneally into DBA/2JN mice (after Berry and Andrews[45]).

high doses (on a semilogarithmic plot) can sometimes be converted to curves which are linear at high doses by changes in the nutrient medium, made after the irradiation.[56]

The initial shoulder on cell survival curves of the sigmoid type and the fact that there is an increased survival with X- or γ-radiation when doses are fractionated, suggests that in these cases, radiation damage must be accumulated before the effect becomes manifest. Elkind and Sutton,[57] using Chinese hamster cells, conducted a series of experiments upon the recuperation of irradiated cells. Their results are illustrated in fig. 10.10. The reproductive ability of cells receiving a single dose of radiation was compared with that of cells receiving

355

the same dose given in two fractions. Elkind and Sutton found that when there was an interval of 12 hours or more between the fractionated doses, the survival curve had the shape and sensitivity which would be expected if the cells surviving the

TABLE 10.03.[46, 55]

Cell type	Mean lethal dose (rads of 200 KVp.) X-rays	Extra-polation no.	Reference
Human			
HeLa; liver, conjunctive, appendix (Chang), amnion AV2, leukemia (Osgood)	140	2	48
Spleen, ovary, skin	109	1–2	43, 48
Embryonic lung	241	2	47
HeLa S 3–2	85–204†	5·5–13	49
HeLa S 3–1	111–128†	2	49
Liver (Westwood)	119	1·6	50
Mouse			
Leukemia in CBA strain	134†	1·7	51
Leukemia in DBA strain	136†	1·5	45
Ascites carcinoma (Ehrlich)	114	15·4	53
Solid lymphosarcoma (6C 3HED)	110	1·2	54
Normal marrow	81†	1·5	52
Chinese Hamster			
Ovary, clone A	128*	4·5–5·2	57
Lung, clone V79–1	150*	8	57

* 55 KV. X-rays
† Assuming an R.B.E. of 0·85 for Co^{60} γ-rays, and 2–3 MV. X-rays.

initial irradiation had never been irradiated (see fig. 10.10), i.e. in twelve hours the cells appeared to recover completely at, least in respect of reproductive ability. If the time interval between fractions was less than 12 hours, the recovery was a function of the time interval.

The results of these experiments with cell cultures are of considerable interest to radiotherapists. Firstly there is the (perhaps disappointing) observation that the mean lethal dose for malignant cell types appears to be of the same order (or possibly rather greater) than the mean lethal dose for normal cells. (See Table 10.03.) Secondly, assuming representative values for the mean lethal dose and extrapolation number, from the equation $D = D_0 (\log_e n/n_0 - \log_e m)$ it is possible to calculate the total dose D (say) required to sterilise all cells in a

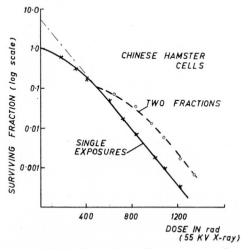

FIG. 10.10 Test for cell recovery after irradiation of chinese hamster cells with 55kV. X-rays.
Crosses—single exposures.
Circles—two fractions with 18-hour interval for recovery after first 505 rads (after Elkind and Sutton [56]).

tumour of given size (the criterion of " sterilisation " usually adopted is that there is only 1 chance in 10 of a single cell per tumour retaining reproductive integrity).[58]

Thus for $D_0 = 150$ rads and $m = 2$, for $n/n_0 = 10^{-10}$ (i.e. a tumour containing 10^9 cells and therefore about 1 cm. in diameter), $D = 3,600$ rads. For a tumour containing 10^{11} cells and therefore perhaps 5 cm. in diameter, for $n/n_0 = 10^{-12}$, $D = 4,250$ rads. These values assume the tumour is well oxygenated. If the cells are anoxic, however, the value of D_0 is increased by a factor of 2 to 3. Suppose D_0 is 2·5 times as great for anoxic compared with oxygenated cells. Then a dose of 3,600 rads will reduce the surviving fraction of anoxic

357

cells by about 10^{-4}, i.e. it will only sterilise a 1 cm. diameter tumour if less than 0·001 per cent. of the cells are anoxic. If an appreciable percentage of anoxic cells are present, the dose for sterilisation increases rapidly (see table 10.04).

TABLE 10.04

Percentage of Anoxic Cells	1 cm. diameter tumour (10^9 cells) Sterilising dose (rads)	5 cm. diameter tumour (10^{11} cells) Sterilising dose (rads)
10·0	7,100	8,800
1·0	6,250	7,950
0·1	5,400	7,100
0·01	4,550	6,250
0·001	3,700	5,400
0·0001	3,600	4,550
Zero	3,600	4,250

D_0 for oxygenated cells $= 150$ rads, extrapolation number $= 2$
D_0 for anoxic cells $= 2·5 \times 150$ rads

It has been assumed above that all the radiation is delivered in a single short exposure. A sigmoid type of survival curve implies that the total dose required to produce a given effect will be greater if the dose is given in fractions instead of in a single exposure (as Elkind and Sutton demonstrated). Assuming (1) that cell recovery is complete between fractions and (2) that no appreciable increase in cell numbers occurs during the treatment period, the total dose required to produce a given effect, when the dose is given in any specified number of fractions, may be calculated for a given survival curve. (The rate and manner of cell reproduction will clearly affect the number of cells surviving after a given period of time, but it is convenient to consider the effect of cell reproduction separately.) It is interesting to compare such calculated values with the doses given in typical fractionated therapy treatments.

Fowler and Stern[59] have reviewed published clinical data and fig. 10.11 (taken from their review) shows the ratio of the total dose in n equal fractions to the single equivalent dose, as a function of the number of fractions, as reported by a number of clinicians. Assuming 6,000 rads in 30 fractions as a typical therapy dose, Fowler [60] has also calculated the equivalent total

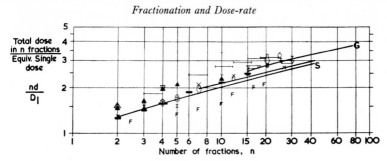

Fractionation and Dose-rate

FIG. 10.11 Dose-time data from clinical sources. The ratio of (total dose nd in *n* fractions) to (equivalent single dose D, required to produce the same reaction) is plotted against the number of " daily " fractions on a log-log scale. The two lines shown for Strandqvist's results are for five fractions per week and seven fractions respectively, to show that the difference is comparatively small.

DOSE-TIME DATA: HUMAN SKIN AND TUMOUR REACTIONS.

   ɪ   Ellis (1942). 6×8 low, 20×15 high. Normal recovery after MD small or DD large fields. (MD = moist desquamation. DD = dry desquamation).

├──┤ Jolles and Mitchell (1947). 3–4 f/week. MD and normal healing four weeks after end of treatment.

  ∇ Paterson (1952). Small field radical treatment. Data corrected by clinical experience.

  ◊ Mitchell (1960). Tumour response: squamous celled Ca. skin.

G—— Garcia (1955). Cure of Ca. cervix.

S══► Strandqvist (1944). 5 f/week and 3 f/week. Skin and squamous celled Ca. reactions. Also Allen and Freed (1956).

  □ Hale and Holmes (1947). Cure of skin Ca. at 85 per cent. and 96 per cent. cure levels.

  F Friedman and Pearlman (1955). Cure of metastatic breast Ca., doses lethal for 75 per cent. of secondaries (different treatments in same patient).

  ▲ Friedman and Pearlman (1956). Iso-effect mean lethal dose for mycosis fungoides.

  ■ De Moor *et al.* (1961). Optimal dose for treatment of breast Ca.

  o Quimby and MacComb (1937). Threshold erythema, in 80 per cent. cases. (Experiments).

  × Reisner (1933). Sharp erythema, assessed by erythema meter. (Experiments).

  △ Duffy *et al.* (1934). Threshold erythema. (Experiments).

doses for various numbers of fractions (*a*) using the clinical data, *(b)* assuming a survival curve with $D_0 = 140$ rads and

$m = 2 \cdot 8$. This comparison is shown in Table 10.05. The values of D_0 and m were chosen as being typical of mammalian cells. Better agreement with the clinical data would be obtained if it were assumed that m is greater (about 10 or more) or that the survival curve is not exponential at high doses, but resembles the curves obtained by Barendsen et al. (fig. 10.08) and becomes continuously steeper at high doses.

TABLE 10.05

(after Fowler [60])

EXAMPLES OF TOTAL DOSES (ASSUMING 6,000 RADS IN 30 FRACTIONS IN SIX WEEKS AS A BASIS)

Number of fractions	(A) Animal experiments and Modal clinical data	(B) Survival curve $n = 2 \cdot 8$, $D_0 = 140$ rads	Difference between estimates A and B (as percentage of A)
30	6,000	6,000	0
20	5,460 ± 50	5,040	− 8
15	5,070 ± 70	4,380	−13
12	4,810 ± 70	4,020	−17
10	4,560 ± 70	3,790	−17
8	4,300 ± 80	3,540	−18
6	4,010 ± 80	3,260	−18
4	3,490 ± 120	2,980	−15
2	2,730 ± 160	2,700	− 1
1	2,000 ± 250	2,560	+28

It is to be noted that the values given in the " survival curve " column of Table 10.05 result solely from the assumption that the effect of n dose fractions of size D/n is less than the effect of a single dose D; the time interval between fractions is immaterial provided cell recovery is complete. Now in practice, in radiotherapy, treatments are usually given in daily fractions and a large number of fractions therefore also implies an extended overall treatment time. If long term " repair " processes (i.e. processes requiring more than the interval between fractions for completion) also take place, then if the treatment time is increased, the effect of the earliest fractions will have been diminished by the repair processes by the time the latest fractions are given and hence a higher total dose is to be expected for this reason. However, experiments with animals have shown that the number of fractions is more important than the overall treatment time in determining the total dose (at least for dose fractions in the range 200 to 700 rads delivered at intervals of 1 to 6 days). Thus in pigs, to produce the same skin reaction, 5 fractions in 28 days require a dose 17 per cent. greater than 5 fractions in 5 days, while 21 fractions in 29 days required a dose 43 per cent. greater than 5 fractions in 29 days.[61]

Nevertheless, if the long-term repair processes postulated above consist principally of cellular repopulation, then the relation between the interval between fractions and the population doubling time is clearly of critical importance. Consider, for example, two populations A and B, and suppose the population doubling time is two days for A, but greater than two days for B. Then, neglecting all effects except those due to radiation, dose fractions sufficient to reduce the surviving number of cells to 50 per cent. given at two-day intervals, will maintain a stationary population in A but will continuously depopulate B. The effects of the manner of growth and re-population of different kinds of tissue upon the " efficiency " of dose fractionation schedules have been discussed in some detail by Lathja and Oliver,[62] Patt[63] and others. It is known that tumour cells divide no more rapidly than many types of normal cells even during the rapid initial exponential phase of growth, and during subsequent phases, the doubling time may be considerably longer (e.g. a minimum doubling time of 11 days has been reported for lung metastases).[64] In radiotherapy, the advantage of delivering the total dose in many fractions over an extended period of time has usually been attributed to the fact that tissue " repair " occurs more rapidly in the normal tissues which are irradiated (particularly the skin), than in the tumour. However, in therapy, as mentioned earlier, treatments have usually been given daily and hence the effects due to (1) the number and size of the dose fractions and (2) the overall treatment time have not been clearly distinguished. Some clinical trials are now in progress to attempt to determine optimum dose fractionation schedules for particular types of treatment.

10.07. Histologically observable radiation damage and radiation effects upon chromosomes

The most striking histologically observable effects of radiation are the suppression of mitosis and the production of chromosome aberrations.[65, 66] In general, irradiation of a cell population causes an immediate drop in the number of cells entering mitosis. For a period of several hours (depending on the species) no cells divide, then there is typically a rapid rise in the number of mitoses to a value which may approach or exceed that of unirradiated controls. A second drop and peak usually occur approximately one cell cycle later. After low doses of radiation, the cells entering delayed mitosis appear to divide normally but sometimes are only able to complete a few subsequent divisions. At higher doses an increasing proportion of the cells which enter delayed mitosis break down. It is of considerable interest that the interruption of mitosis occurs immediately after irradiation. For example it has been established that irradiation interferes with the synthesis of DNA[67] but this process is completed several hours before mitosis and therefore the interruption of DNA synthesis cannot be the cause of mitotic delay in cells irradiated just before division. A number of workers have studied the effects of irradiation at different times in the cell cycle and have established that the cell is particularly sensitive both during mitosis itself and also in the period immediately prior to DNA synthesis.[68] (In a normal cell population, cells are continually entering mitosis and cells at all stages of the cycle are present. The above studies have been considerably facilitated by the development of techniques for obtaining synchronised populations in which all cells enter mitosis at approximately the same time.)

There is a considerable body of experimental evidence that suggests that chromosomal damage of some kind is the principal reason for the loss of reproductive integrity.[22] Some of the experimental findings which support this view are as follows. Firstly, nuclear and in particular chromosomal damage is produced at doses which do not appear to impair other cell functions, e.g. honeybee spermatozoa irradiated with 5,000 R. can fertilise egg cells but the progeny do not survive due to

362

chromosome damage, while much greater doses (of over 30,000 R.) to the spermatozoa are required before the eggs develop parthogenetically.[69] Secondly, replacement of irradiated by unirradiated chromosomes can in certain circumstances restore normal cell development. Thus in the wasp, Hebracon, if the females are irradiated with a dose which destroys the chromosomes in the egg nucleus, then mated with unirradiated males, haploid male progeny are produced, a set of male chromosomes replacing the set normally contributed by the egg.[70] Similarly in bacterial-virus systems, heavily irradiated bacteria can still support an infecting (unirradiated) virus where the viral DNA " organises " the production of further virus, but a much smaller radiation dose to the virus prevents further development.[71] Thirdly, it is possible to modify the radiation sensitivity of certain cells grown in culture by feeding 5-bromo-uracil.[72] This material is incorporated into the DNA molecule but not into RNA or protein and this suggests therefore that the radiation acts upon the DNA molecule. Additional evidence is provided by the fact that the incorporation of 5 fluoro-uracil into RNA (in bacteria) does not modify the radio-sensitivity.[73]

The hypothesis that radiation damages the chromosomal DNA can explain the fact that some cells can complete one or two divisions after irradiation, if it is postulated that the cell is unable (due to the DNA damage) to produce fresh supplies of some critical material, but can divide until its store of this material is exhausted. However, although there have been a very large number of experiments with very diverse material, it has not been established that there is a regular increase in the mean lethal dose for loss of reproductive integrity with increased chromosome number, as might perhaps be expected, if chromosomal damage was the main reason for interference with mitosis. Observed chromosome aberrations can in the main be simply explained by postulating one or more breaks in the whole chromosome or the individual chromatids followed by rejoining of the broken ends in various new arrangements. If the broken ends restitute (i.e. rejoin in the original way) there may be no observable consequences and this must be born in mind in interpreting radiation experiments. For example, for the production of observable chromosome aberrations, the densely ionising radiations appear to be more efficient than X- or γ-radiation, and it was at one time suggested that 15 or 20 ionisations must occur within a chromosome to produce a break. However, when the frequency of point mutations is measured as a function of X-ray dose, the dose-response curve is of exponential form. This is usually regarded as implying that point mutations or single breaks in a chromosome can be produced by a single cluster of ionisations. The greater efficiency of the densely ionising radiations in producing observable aberrations is attributed to the greater probability of broken ends rejoining in new ways when many ends are formed in close proximity to one another. The recognition that mechanisms able to repair chromosomal damage exist within the cell is extremely important.[74, 75, 76] Several chemical agents are now known, which if present during or immediately after *ultra-violet* irradiation, appear to modify the repair processes and many investigations are presently in progress to elucidate some of the mechanisms involved.

Early experiments upon the induction of point mutations by irradiation suggested that point mutation frequency was virtually independent of any other factor than the total radiation dose.[77] For example when mature spermatozoa in the fruit fly drosophila were irradiated (by irradiating the males), the total number of mutations induced was found to be independent of dose-rate and fractionation so long as the total dose was constant. More recent experiments have indicated that this simple relation does not hold at all stages of development. The first evidence for a dependence of mutation frequency upon dose-rate and fractionation was observed by Russell [78, 79] who irradiated mice and then delayed mating so that the sperms at the time of mating had been in the spermatogonial stage at the time of irradiation. The frequency of point mutations then depended upon the dose-rate and fractionation. A marked dose-rate dependence was later observed also in irradiated oocytes. When mature sperm were irradiated, however, the results resembled those obtained with mature sperm irradiation in Drospholia in showing no effect of dose-rate.

Within a chromosome there appear to be regions which are more readily damaged than others. Observable breaks are not randomly distributed and the rate of production of point mutations varies from one site to another. It seems probable that the radiation energy (or electric charge) is transferred along the molecule to the particular sites which are vulnerable.

10.08. The radiation response of organised tissues in radiotherapy

Since (1) cells appear to be particularly sensitive to radiation damage when they enter mitosis and (2) radiation damage often becomes manifest only when cells enter mitosis, the response of a particular type of tissue to radiation will clearly be markedly influenced by the frequency with which the cells divide and the extent to which cell division is essential to the proper functioning of the organ or tissue considered. As early as 1906 Bergonie and Tribondeau[80] suggested that the higher the reproductive activity of the cells of a particular tissue and the less their differentiation, the greater would be the sensitivity to radiation damage. Thus in the human body some of the tissues showing effects of radiation most markedly are those which are continually producing blood cells (e.g. bone marrow and spleen) or (like intestinal epithelium) require cell proliferation in order to function.

Malignant tumours are frequently described as either radio-sensitive or radio-resistant according to the rate at which the tumour regresses after irradiation. Many authors[81] have pointed out that tumours which are radio-sensitive in this sense, are not necessarily radio-curable, in that they may recur at a later time, either at the same site or elsewhere. Some factors which influence *radio-curability* have been discussed by Lathja and Oliver,[62] Till[55] and others and are listed in Table 10.07.

The efficiency of ionising radiation from an external source in the treatment of malignant disease could be greatly increased if it were possible either (1) to render the malignant cells only more sensitive to the radiation, or (2) to protect the normal tissue without protecting the malignant tissue. Although *in vitro* and animal experiments have shown that there are some chemicals which appear to augment the effect of radiation and quite a large number which reduce these effects, the great

365

difficulty is to obtain *selective* sensitisation or protection of the appropriate tissues. If a tumour contains anoxic cells, an increase in the sensitivity of the tumour relative to well-oxygenated tissue may be obtained if the patient breathes hyperbaric oxygen, as already discussed in section 10.03.

TABLE 10.07

SOME FACTORS AFFECTING THE RADIOCURABILITY* OF TUMOURS (after Till [55])

Factor	High radio-curability	Low radio-curability
1. Colony-forming cells outside the radiation field	no	yes
2. Dose-survival curves for colony-forming ability of tumour and normal cells	similar	favour tumour cells
3. Proportion of anoxic cells	low	high
4. Dose-fractionation schedule favours normal cells	yes	no
5. Tumour site favourable; few proliferating normal cells in the radiation field	yes	no
6. Rate of removal of cells after irradiation†	fast	slow
7. Rate of cell growth after irradiation	slow	fast
8. Proportion of colony-forming cells initially present	low	high
9. Number of surviving cells required to overcome host resistance and regenerate the tumour	high	low

* Radiocurable tumour: a tumour that is not regenerated following irradiation.
†This factor is probably most important in determining whether or not a tumour appears " radiosensitive," i.e. rapidly decreases in size after irradiation.

However, if there are normal tissues which are not well-oxygenated (such as bone and cartilage) which are also in the radiation field, it must be remembered that these tissues also will be sensitised. A chemical which appears to be preferentially absorbed by neoplastic tissue, " synkavit " (the tetrasodium salt of 2-methyl-1-4-naphthohydroquinone) has been used by

Mitchell [82] and his collaborators at Cambridge as a sensitising agent (with external radiation), and radioactive forms of synkavit are presently being investigated.[83]

An alternative approach is to time the radiation doses so that successive fractions are given at the most sensitive stage in the cell cycle of the neoplastic tissue. Hale [84, 85] and his colleagues at Bristol, " monitor " the activity of accessible tumours. The patient is given an oral dose of P^{32} and the count-rate from Geiger-Müller counters implanted in the tumour is recorded continuously. About half the tumours investigated (mainly breast tumours) show rhythmic variations in count-rate. In others, rhythmic response can often be induced by cytotoxic drugs. It is stated that radiotherapy given at or near the times of peak count-rate is more effective than that given at other times.

Amongst the chemical protectors, cysteine and cysteinamine (β-mercapto ethylamine) have probably been most extensively investigated. *In vitro* and animal experiments have shown that these substances reduce the extent of radiation damage if administered prior to irradiation. It has been suggested that cysteinamine or cysteine could be used to reduce the danger to workers, who have to suffer exposure to radiation, but no protective agents are at present known which are absorbed by normal but not by malignant tissues.

It is to be noted that the ultimate results of irradiation of a particular region which forms part of a complex organism such as the human body, depend not only on the local damage produced in the cells within the radiation beam, but also upon reciprocal effects between the irradiated and unirradiated tissues. Thus cells which are not themselves irradiated may be affected either by the diffusion of toxins or breakdown products from the irradiated cells; or by being deprived of vital materials (for example, if blood vessels are damaged the tissues supplied by those vessels will suffer); or via the neuro-endocrine system. Conversely repair processes may be stimulated in damaged cells by substances produced in unirradiated tissues. Jolles[86] provided a striking example of the interplay between irradiated and unirradiated tissue when he showed that the degree of erythema produced in squares of skin irradiated simultaneously through lead grids depended upon the distance separating the squares. These are sometimes referred to as " abscopal " effects.

REFERENCES

1. WEISS, J. (1944). *Nature*, **153**, 748.
2. LEA, D. E. (1947). *Brit. J. Radiol.* Suppl. 1, 59.
3. PLATZMAN, R. L. (1953). *U.S. Nat. Res. Council Publ.* **305**, 34.
4. SAMUEL, A. M. and MAGEE, J. L. (1953). *J. Chem. Phys.* **21**, 1080.
5. STEIN, G. (1952). *Faraday Soc. Disc.* **12**, 227, 289.
6. HAYON, E. and WEISS, J. J. (1959). *Proc. of 2nd Int. Conf. Peaceful Uses of Atomic Energy*, **29**, 80.
7. BAXENDALE, J. H. and HUGHES, G. (1958). *Z. physik. Chem.* **14**, 306.
8. BARR, N. F. and ALLEN, A. O. (1959). *J. Physic. Chem.* **63**, 928.
9. COLLINSON, E., DAINTON, F. S., SMITH, D. R. and TAZUKÉ, S. (1962). *Proc. Chem. Soc.* 140.
10. CZAPSKI, G. and SCHWARZ, H. A. (1962). *J. Physic Chem.* **66**, 471.
11. HART, E. J. and BOAG, J. W. (1962). *J. Amer. Chem. Soc.* **84**, 4090.
12. BOAG, J. W. and HART, E. J. (1963). *Nature*, **197**, 5.
13. MATHESON, M. S. (1964). *Radiation Res.* Suppl. 4, 1.
14. ALLEN, A. O. (1964). *Radiation Res.* Suppl. 4, 54.
15. SCHOLES, G., SIMIC, M. and WEISS, J. (1963). *Faraday Society Discussions*, **36**, 214.
16. FRICKE, H. and MUNSE, S. (1929). *Phil. Mag.* **7**, 129.
17. ALLEN, A. O. and ROTHSCHILD, W. G. (1957). *Radiation Res.* **7**, 591, 603.
18. HOLM, N. W., BRYNJOLFSSON, A. and MAUL, J. E. (1961). *Selected Topics in Radiation Dosimetry.* Vienna, I.A.E.A.
19. Recommendations of the International Commission on Radiological Units and Measurements (1962). Report 10b. *U.S. Nat. Bureau Standards Handbook*, No. 85.
20. HUTCHINSON, F., PRESTON, A. and VOGEL, B. (1957). *Radiation Res.* **7**, 465.
21. HUTCHINSON, F. and ARENA, J. (1960). *Radiation Res.* **13**, 137.
22. GRAY, L. H. (1959). *Radiation Res.* Suppl. 1, 92. (1961). *Am. J. Roentgenol.* **85**, 803.
23. DESCHNER, E. E. and GRAY, L. H. (1959). *Radiation Res.* **11**, 115.
24. HOWARD-FLANDERS, P. and ALPER, T. (1957). *Radiation Res.* **7**, 518.
25. GRAY, L. H., CONGER, A. D., EBERT, M., HORNSEY, S. and SCOTT, O. C. (1953). *Brit. J. Radiol.* **26**, 638.
26. CHURCHILL-DAVIDSON, I., SANGER, C. and THOMLINSON, R. H. (1957). *Brit. J. Radiol.* **30**, 406.
27. BACQ, Z. M. and ALEXANDER, P. (1955). *Fundamentals of Radiobiology.* London, Butterworth (2nd edn. 1961).
28. DALE, W. M. (1942). *Biochem. J.* **36**, 80.

29. OKADA, S. and FLETCHER, S. L. (1960). *Radiation Res.* **13**, 92.
30. GORDY, W. (1959). *Radiation Res.* Suppl. 1, 491.
31. PATTEN, F. and GORDY, W. (1961). *Radiation Res.* **14**, 573.
32. BARRON, E. S. G. (1952). Symposium on Radiobiology. New York, Wiley. (1954). *Radiation Res.* **1**, 18.
33. LUSE, R. A. (1964). *Radiation Res.* Suppl. 4, 192.
34. SPARROW, A. H. and ROSENFELD, F. M. (1946). *Science*, **104**, 245.
35. BUTLER, G. C. (1949). *Canad. J. Res.* **B27**, 972.
36. SCHOLES, G. and WEISS, J. (1950). *Nature*, **166**, 640.
37. LATARJET, R., EKERT, B., DEMERSEMAN, P. (1963). *Radiation Res.* Suppl. 3, 247.
38. LEA, D. E. (1946). *Actions of Radiation on Living Cells.* Cambridge Univ. Press (2nd edn. 1955).
39. ALPER, T. *Mechanisms in Radiobiology* (1961). Vol. 1. Edited by M. Errera and A. Forssberg, New York, Academic Press.
40. GINOZA, W. and NORMAN, A. (1957). *Nature*, **179**, 520.
41. GRAY, L. H. (1954). *Brit. Med. Bull.* **4**, 14.
42. HUTCHINSON, F. and POLLARD, E. (1961). *Mechanisms in Radiobiology*. Vol. 1. Edited by M. Errera and A. Forssberg, New York, Academic Press.
43. PUCK, T. T. and MARCUS, P. I. (1956). *J. Exper. Med.* **103**, 653.
44. BARENDSEN, G. W. and WALTER, H. M. D. (1964). *Radiation Res.* **21**, 314.
45. BERRY, R. J. and ANDREWS, R. (1961). *Radiology*, **77**, 824.
46. MUNRO, T. R. and GILBERT, C. W. (1961). *Brit. J. Radiol.* **34**, 246.
47. PUCK, T., MORKOVIN, D., MARCUS, P. I. and CIECURA, S. J. (1957). *J. Exp. Med.* **106**, 485.
48. MORKOVIN, D. and FELDMAN, A. (1959). *Brit. J. Radiol.* **32**, 282. (1960). *Brit. J. Radiol.* **33**, 197.
49. BASES, R. E. (1959). *Cancer Res.* **19**, 1223.
50. DEWEY, D. L. (1960). *Nature*, **186**, 780.
51. HEWITT, H. B. and WILSON, C. W. (1959). *Brit. J. Cancer*, **13**, 69.
52. MCCULLOCH, E. A. and TILL, J. E. (1962). *Radiation Res.* **16**, 822.
53. HORNSEY, S. and SILINI, G. (1962). *Radiation Res.* **16**, 712.
54. POWERS, W. E. and TOLMACH (1963). *Nature*, **197**, 710.
55. TILL, J. E. (1963). *Amer. J. Roentgenol.* **90**, 917.
56. BERRY, R. J. (1964). *Brit. J. Radiol.* **37**, 948.
57. ELKIND, M. M. and SUTTON, H. (1959). *Nature*, **184**, 1293 (1960). *Radiation Res.* **13**, 557.
58. WILSON, C. W. (1961). *Radiology*, **77**, 940.
59. FOWLER, J. F. and STERN, B. E. (1963). *Brit. J. Radiol.* **36**, 163.
60. FOWLER, J. F. (1965). *Brit. J. Radiol.* **38**, 365.
61. FOWLER, J. F., MORGAN, R. L., SILVESTER, J. A., BEWLEY, D. K. and TURNER, B. A. (1963). *Brit. J. Radiol.* **36**, 188.
62. LATHJA, L. A. and OLIVER, R. (1962). *Brit. J. Radiol.* **35**, 131.
63. PATT, H. M. (1963). *Amer. J. Roentgenol.* **90**, 928.

64. COLLINS, V. P., LOEFFLEN, R. K. and TIVEY, H. (1956). *Amer. J. Roentgenol.* **76**, 988.
65. GLUCKSMANN, A. (1950). *Brit. J. Radiol.* **23**, 265.
66. KOLLER, P. C. (1953). *Progress in Biophysics*, **4**, 936.
67. FORSSBERG, A. and KLEIN, G. (1954). *Exp. Cell. Res.* **6**, 211.
68. TERASIMA, T. and TOLMACH, L. J. (1963). *Biophys. J.* **3**, 11.
69. LEE, W. R. (1958). *Genetics*, **43**, 480.
70. ROGERS, R. W. and VON BORSTEL, R. C. (1957). *Radiation Res.* **7**, 484. (1958). *Radiation Res.* **8**, 248.
71. ROUYER, M. and LATARJET, R. (1947). *Ann. Inst. Pasteur*, **72**, 89.
72. DJORDJEVIC, B. and SZYBALSKI, W. (1960). *J. Exper. Med.* **112**, 509.
73. TANOOKA, H. (1964). *Radiation Res.* **21**, 26.
74. CATCHESIDE, D. G. (1959). *Phys. in Med. and Biol.* **4**, 117.
75. WITKIN, E. M. (1958). *Proc. Xth Int. Cong. Genet.* 280.
76. RUPERT, C. S. (1960). *J. Gen. Physiol.* **43**, 573. (1961). *J. Cell. Comp. Physiol.* **58**, Suppl. 1, 57.
77. MULLER, H. J. (1954). *Radiation Biology*. Ed. by A. Hollaender New York, McGraw-Hill.
78. RUSSELL, W. L., RUSSELL, L. B. and KELLY, E. M. (1958). *Science*, **128**, 1546.
79. RUSSELL, W. L. (1962). *Proc. Nat. Acad. Sci.* **48**, 1724.
80. BERGONIE, J. and TRIBONDEAU, D. (1906). *Acad. Sci. Paris*, **143**, 983.
81. PATERSON, R. P. (1948). *The Treatment of Malignant Disease by Radiotherapy*. London, Arnold. (2nd edn. 1963).
82. MITCHELL, J. S. (1953). *Brit. J. Cancer*, **7**, 213.
83. MITCHELL, J. S., KING, E. A., MARRIAN, D. H. and CHIPPERFIELD, B. (1963). *Acta Radiologica*, **1**, 321.
84. HALE, B. T. (1961). *Lancet*, **2**, 345.
85. BULLEN, M. A., MARSHALL, D. H., FREUNDLICH, H. F., GODDEN, T. J., HALE, B. T., TODWAY, R. C. and SAXENA, V. S. (1964). *Brit. J. Radiol.* **37**, 563.
86. JOLLES, B. (1950). *Brit. J. Radiol.* **23**, 18.

GENERAL REFERENCES

LEA, D. E. (1955). *Actions of Radiations on Living Cells*. 2nd Edn. Cambridge, University Press.
BACQ, Z. M. and ALEXANDER, P. (1961). *Fundamentals of Radiobiology*. 2nd Edn. London, Butterworth.
Proceedings of the International Congress of Radiation Research (1959). *Radiation Research*, Suppl. 1.
Mechanisms in Radiobiology. Edited by M. Errera and A. Forssberg (1961). Vol. 1 and 2. New York, Academic Press.
Fundamental Processes in Radiation Chemistry (1963). *Discussions of the Faraday Society*, No. 36.
Basic Mechanisms in the Radiation Chemistry of Aqueous Media (1964). *Radiation Research*, Suppl. 4.

EXAMINATION QUESTIONS

1. Write a short essay on mitosis and the effects produced by X-radiation on human cells.

M.S.R. (T.), 1965.

2. Discuss the relationship of total dose to fractionation and overall treatment time.

F.S.R. (T.), 1964.

3. Discuss the use of high pressure oxygen in radiotherapy.

F.S.R. (T.), 1965.

4. What do you understand by the LET and R.B.E. of an ionising radiation?

Part question.   D.M.R. (T.), 1963.

5. Discuss the implications for radiotherapy of the results obtained from studies of the effects of radiation in single human and other mammalian cells grown in cultures.

D.M.R., (T.) 1963.

CHAPTER XI

THE THERAPEUTIC USE OF IONISING RADIATION

11.01. X- and γ-ray teletherapy. Classification of types of treatment

The following names are usually given to treatments delivered with the types of radiation indicated.

Treatment	Radiation	Generating voltage (X-rays) or photon energy (γ-rays)
Grenz ray therapy	X-rays	4-12 kVp.
Low voltage superficial therapy	X-rays	12-60 kVp.
Superficial therapy	X-rays	60-120 kVp.
Medium voltage therapy	X-rays	120-140 kVp.
Deep therapy or ortho-voltage therapy	X-rays	200-400 kVp.
Megavoltage therapy	X-rays or γ-rays of comparable energy	Above 1 MV.
Supervoltage therapy	X-rays	Above 20 MV.
γ-ray teletherapy	γ-rays from Cs^{137}	660 keV.
	γ-rays from Co^{60}	1·17, 1·33 MeV.

It should be noted that the X-ray generators produce continuous spectra (so the equivalent photon energy of the X-ray beams is numerically of the order of one half of the peak accelerating voltage), whereas the γ-ray sources emit either monoenergetic or nearly monoenergetic radiation. Cs^{37} γ-rays are comparable in quality with X-rays generated at a peak voltage between 1 and 2 MV. and Co^{60} γ-rays are comparable with X-rays generated between 2 and 3 MV.

The division of superficial therapy into a low-voltage and an " ordinary " range, is a result of the fact that before the development of beryllium windows for X-ray tubes, it was not practicable to operate tubes with ordinary glass windows below about 50 to 60 kVp. since at lower voltages most of the radiation was absorbed in the tube walls. Softer radiation (such as Grenz rays) could only be obtained by using very thin and therefore very fragile windows of a special type of glass, known as Lindemann glass.

The name " contact therapy " is given to superficial treatments carried out with the tube close to or in contact with the

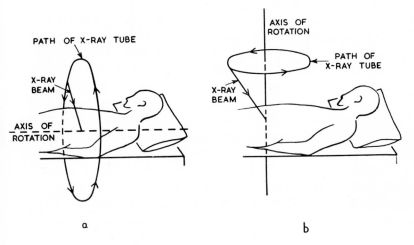

FIG. 11.01. Diagrammatic illustration of different methods of rotation therapy.
(*a*) Circum-axial or planar rotation.
(*b*) Paraxial or conical rotation.

skin. The use of a short focus-skin distance enables a rapid decrease of dose-rate with depth to be obtained even with radiation generated at 50 to 60 kVp.

In " fixed field " or " stationary field " therapy, the radiation beam remains in a constant position relative to the patient during any one treatment. In " rotation " or " moving field " therapy, there is relative motion between the beam and the patient during the course of treatment. There are two principal methods of using rotation. In the first method (fig. 11.01(*a*)), the radiation source describes a circular path around the patient (regardless of whether the source or the patient is actually in motion) and it has been suggested that this should be called circum-axial or planar rotation therapy. (If a full circle is not

13   373

completed, the names "arc" or "pendulum" therapy are sometimes used.) In the second method, which is much less common than circum-axial rotation, the source remains on the same side of the patient throughout the rotation (fig. 11.01(*b*)). This is called paraxial or conical rotation therapy. Some units have been designed which produce other movements, e.g., the source may describe a spiral, but we shall discuss here only circum-axial rotation.

The method used to position a patient in the therapy beam depends upon the treatment technique and type of unit being used. In rotation therapy, the distance from the source to the axis of rotation remains constant and the patient is positioned so that the axis of rotation passes through or near the centre of the region to be treated. Thus the distance from the source to a point in the treatment region remains constant but the distance from the source to the skin surface varies, depending on the patient's contour. In stationary field treatments, there are two alternative methods; either the distance from the source to a point in the treatment region is kept constant as in rotation therapy, or the distance from the source to the patient's skin is kept constant. We shall describe the former as the constant source-axis distance (S.A.D.) method, and the latter as the constant source-skin distance (S.S.D.) method. In constant S.A.D. techniques, a given setting of the diaphragms in the head of the therapy set will produce a treatment field of specified area at the axis of rotation, but the size of the field at the skin surface will vary according to the distance of the skin from the source. In constant S.S.D. techniques, a given diaphragm setting or choice of "cone" (see below) produces a specified field size at the skin surface but the area at the treatment region depends upon the depth of the latter below the surface.

In stationary field treatments with constant S.S.D., cones or applicators are often attached to the head of the therapy set. The cones give a visual indication of the direction of the radiation beam and of the size and position of the field at the skin surface. They also help to maintain the source-skin distance and can be of assistance in keeping bolus in place. Modern cones are usually made of transparent plastic (see fig. 11.39(*a*)). For energies below about 400 keV., the area of the radiation beam is limited by a diaphragm at the tube end of the cone and the distal end of the cone may be either open or closed. (In some older designs, the cone walls were made of metal and were used to help limit the beam.) For megavoltage units, the weight of diaphragm required if the cones were used to limit the beam, would make the cones excessively heavy and the area of the beam is determined by the setting of an adjustable diaphragm in the treatment head. The cones are also always open-ended. An adjustable diaphragm is always used to determine the beam area for constant S.A.D. techniques, since cones cannot be used because of the changing skin distance. When the beam area is determined by a diaphragm in the head, a " visual localiser " is commonly used to indicate the size and position of the field at the skin surface. The localiser usually consists of a lamp and mirror placed behind the diaphragm and at such a distance that the light beam has the same dimensions as the radiation beam. These devices have the disadvantage that constant care is necessary to ensure correct alignment.

11.02. The determination of dose in teletherapy

In day-to-day radiotherapy, the absorbed dose delivered at any point in an individual patient by a particular X- or γ-ray unit, is calculated from a knowledge of the absorbed dose which would be delivered by the same beam at some convenient reference point under specified conditions.

The position of the reference point and the conditions under which the reference dose is determined are selected so that the reference dose is independent of the location of the treatment region in individual cases, but the dose at any point in a particular patient can be readily calculated from the reference dose.

The position used for the reference point depends upon the technique being considered. For fixed field techniques with constant S.S.D., the reference point is normally the point on the central axis of the radiation beam at which the absorbed dose is a maximum. For radiation generated below 400 kVp., this means the reference point is at the skin surface (the point where the axis intersects the surface), whereas for more energetic radiation, the reference point is below the surface. For rotation techniques and fixed field techniques with constant source-axis distance, the reference point is the point at which the axis of the radiation beam intersects the axis of rotation. (This is usually called the centre of rotation.)

In stationary field techniques with constant S.S.D., it is assumed that the patient (or phantom material) is present when the absorbed dose at the reference point is determined. The dose at any other specified point is then obtained by multiplying the reference dose by a factor, called the percentage depth dose, which depends upon the location of the particular point considered. The percentage depth dose (P say) is the ratio (expressed as a percentage) of the absorbed dose (D) at any point to the absorbed dose (D_R) at the reference point under identical conditions. Thus

$$P = \frac{D}{D_R} \times 100 \text{ per cent.}$$

$$\text{or } D = D_R \times P/100. \qquad \dots \dots (1)$$

For constant S.A.D. techniques, the point of interest in the patient is usually at the centre of rotation, but the reference dose is determined in the absence of the patient. (The reference dose is measured at the centre of rotation in free air within a volume of phantom material just sufficient to produce full electronic build-up, see section 11.09.) The dose at the centre of rotation in the presence of a particular patient is obtained by multiplying this reference dose by a factor called the tissue air ratio (T.A.R.), which depends upon the thickness of tissue overlying the reference point in the individual case. Thus for constant S.A.D. techniques

$$D = D_R \times (\text{T.A.R.})$$

The absorbed dose at the reference point during any particular treatment, is itself usually derived by multiplying the absorbed dose-rate by the treatment time.

Because the methods of dose estimation differ, it is simpler to consider constant S.S.D. techniques and constant S.A.D. techniques separately. We shall start by considering constant S.S.D. techniques and we shall discuss firstly the various factors which determine the magnitude of the absorbed dose-rate at the reference point and the methods which are used to measure this dose-rate (sections 11.03 to 11.06) and secondly the factors which determine percentage depth doses (sections 11.07, 11.08).

11.03. Stationary field therapy with constant source-skin distance: output measurements

Although it is possible to measure the absorbed dose-rate at the selected reference point directly, in practice this is not the usual procedure. Partly for historical reasons, measurements are usually made with thimble ionisation chambers designed and calibrated for the measurement of exposure. These chambers may be used in one of two ways.

(1) The chamber is placed at the position of the reference point *in air*. From the exposure-rate measured at this position, the absorbed dose-rate at the reference point in the presence of the patient (or phantom material) is calculated, using the appropriate data upon (back) scatter factors and the rad per roentgen conversion factor as described in section 11.04 and 11.05.

(2) The chamber is placed in a tissue equivalent phantom at a depth of 5 cm. or more, i.e. at a position other than the selected reference point. From the chamber reading, the absorbed dose-rate at the chamber position is calculated and the absorbed dose-rate at the reference point is derived from this, using the appropriate percentage depth dose tables.

The absorbed dose-rate at any point can be easily calculated from the exposure-rate if there is absolute electronic equilibrium at the point considered (see section 7.04). This is normally the case for radiation energies below about 400 keV. but not for more energetic radiation. In the past, radiation with energy above 400 keV. was seldom encountered and therefore the first method was the standard calibration procedure. The second method was originally developed for the calibration of high energy equipment, but it has recently been suggested

377

that this method of calibration be adopted at all energies (I.C.R.U., 1962).[1,2] However, exposure measurements in free air are still frequently used as the basis for dosimetry. Moreover even when exposure measurements are made in a phantom, it is convenient to consider separately the effect upon the exposure-rate of those factors which are determined by the output of the therapy machine and those factors which depend upon absorption and scattering of the radiation in the phantom. We therefore discuss first, the calibration procedures when the exposure measurements are made in air at the reference point. The alternative technique, using measurements in a phantom, and the reasons for preferring this method are discussed in section 11.06.

The instruments which may be used to measure exposure have already been discussed in Chapter VII. It may be useful to summarise here the corrections which are usually necessary to derive the " true " exposure-rate from the instrument reading. (1) Corrections are usually necessary for the effect of temperature and pressure on the mass of gas in the ionisation chamber. (If t denotes the temperature in degrees Centigrade, at which the measurement is made, and p the pressure in millimetres of mercury, while t_s and p_s denote the values of temperature and pressure at which the instrument was calibrated, then the instrument reading should be multiplied by $\dfrac{273+t}{273+t_s} \cdot \dfrac{p_s}{p}$. Commercial instruments are usually provided with tables of correction factors for temperature and pressure.) (2) To allow for differences between the response of the measuring instrument actually used and that of a free air chamber, it is usually necessary to apply a correction which depends upon the quality of the radiation which is being measured. (It is desirable that this correction factor be small. This was discussed in Chapter VII.) (3) In the case of X-ray sets, if the kilovoltage or current fluctuates during the exposure, a correction may be necessary for the difference between the mean kilovoltage or current and the pre-selected values. (See below.) (4) When the reference point is at the surface and closed ended cones are used, the centre of the chamber cannot be placed in the position of the end of the cone and it is necessary to correct for the difference in the distance of the source from the centre of the chamber and from the end of the cone.

Some precautions to be observed when measuring the exposure are as follows: (1) It is necessary to avoid any stray scattered radiation reaching the measuring instrument, so the beam should be pointed in such a direction that no objects other than the measuring instrument are in the direct beam. (2) In some units, the shutter opening and/or closing time is appreciable and is included in the nominal exposure time. If a condenser ionisation chamber is used for the exposure measurement, it is desirable to determine the exposure-rate by determining the difference between exposures of long and short duration to eliminate the shutter opening/closing time. (3) It is usually necessary to measure the exposure-rate for each field size. This is because, although the exposure-rate in air depends mainly upon the intensity of the radiation coming directly from the source of radiation, it may also depend in part upon radiation scattered from inside the treatment head and perhaps also from the treatment cone if one is used. The amount of scattered radiation depends upon the area of the field, since the region within the head from which scattered radiation can come depends upon the size of the diaphragm which determines the field area, so even the air exposure-rate may vary with field size.

For isotope teletherapy units, the exposure-rate at a particular distance depends upon the nature and activity of the source at the time of measurement. For X-ray units, the exposure-rate at a given distance depends upon the accelerating voltage, the filtration and the tube current. The exposure is directly proportional to the tube current, increases with increased kilovoltage, and decreases with increased filtration. The variation with kilovoltage depends upon the voltage and filtration that are being considered. The intensity of the continuous X-ray spectrum generated at the target is proportional to the square of the accelerating voltage but because increase in kilovoltage also increases the penetrating power of the radiation, the intensity of the X-rays emerging from the unit varies as a higher power of the voltage than the square. For deep therapy sets the exposure-rate is often assumed to be proportional to V^3. It is therefore necessary to measure the variation of exposure-rate with kilovoltage experimentally for each particular X-ray unit. (The experimentally determined relation should be used in calculating the correction factor for fluctuation in KV. mentioned above.)

11.04. Surface backscatter and scatter factors

Having measured the exposure-rate in free air at the selected reference point on the central axis of the radiation beam for each field size, the next step is to determine the exposure-rate in the presence of the patient or a phantom.

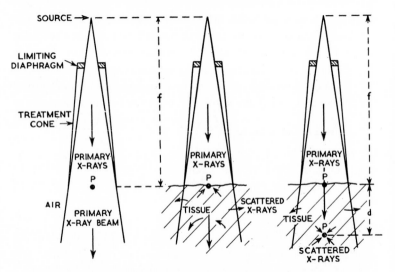

FIG. 11.02. Diagram illustrating the contribution of scattered radiation to the exposure-rate at points in tissue.

We are considering stationary field techniques using a constant source-skin distance. Suppose first that radiation below 400 keV. in energy is being used, so that the exposure-rate in free air was measured at the source-surface distance. Then in the presence of a patient there will be tissue in front of (but not behind) the reference point. Since tissue scatters more radiation backwards than the air which it displaces, the exposure-rate at the surface is increased by the "backscatter", i.e. by the radiation scattered back to the surface from the

380

tissue (see fig. 11.02). This may be measured experimentally using a suitable phantom material to simulate tissue or it may be determined from tables which have been compiled from the experimental results of other workers using similar conditions. (Phantom materials should differ as little as possible from tissue in electron density and in effective atomic number for the radiation quality which is being measured. The most widely used materials are water and a mixture of waxes known as Mix D.[3])

Information concerning the amount of back-scatter present under given conditions is commonly given by specifying either the backscatter as a percentage of the incident radiation or by specifying the " backscatter factor ". The latter is defined as the ratio of the exposure (X_{tissue}) at the surface in the presence of tissue or phantom material to the exposure at the position of the surface in free air (X_{air}) for similar irradiation conditions. If we denote the backscatter factor for field of area A by $B(A)$ then

$$\text{(Surface) Backscatter factor} = B(A) = \left(\frac{X_{tissue}}{X_{air}}\right)_{surface.}$$

For radiation of greater energy, when the reference point used for the measurement of exposure lies below the tissue surface, the exposure-rate in the presence of tissue differs from that in free air, not only on account of backscatter from tissue in front of the reference point, but also on account of both absorption and scattering in tissue between the reference point and the surface. In this case, the ratio of the exposure at the reference point in the presence of the patient or phantom to the exposure at the same position in free air is called the " scatter factor " ($S(A)$ say), i.e.

$$\text{Scatter factor} = S(A) = \left(\frac{X_{tissue}}{X_{air}}\right)_{reference\ depth}$$

This name arises naturally from extending the idea of back-scatter factor as used in connection with measurements made at the surface but it must be noted that (1) the scatter factor defined as above includes the effect of attenuation in the tissue above the reference point and (2) the term scatter factor has also been used with other meanings in the older literature.

(The ratio of the exposure at the tissue surface to the exposure in air at the same position can be measured for megavoltage radiation, but is less useful than the corresponding ratio at the reference point. For Co^{60} radiation, it so happens that for small field sizes the attenuation of the primary radiation is compensated by the production of (forward) scatter in the tissue overlying the reference point so that "backscatter factors" measured at the surface are approximately equal to scatter factors at the reference depth, but this equality does not hold in general.[4])

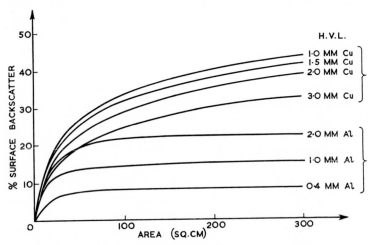

FIG. 11.03.   Variation of percentage surface backscatter with field area.

The amount by which scatter from the patient or phantom material increases the exposure-rate at the reference point depends upon both the quality of the radiation and upon the volume and (to a lesser extent) the shape of the block of tissue which scatters the radiation. When the depth of tissue is greater than the range of the scattered radiation, then for a particular source-skin distance and for a particular shape of field, the volume of tissue which scatters radiation back to the skin is proportional to the field area. In this case it is sufficient to know the field area instead of the tissue volume. Fig. 11.03, based mainly on results obtained in a survey carried out in Great Britain by the Hospital Physicists' Association in 1953,[5] shows how the amount of radiation scattered back to the skin varies with the quality of the radiation and the area of the radiation field for (*a*) fairly penetrating radiations such as are commonly used in deep therapy, and (*b*) for soft radiations such as are used for superficial therapy. The figures refer to the scatter received at a point at the centre of a circular or square field on the surface of a block of tissue of depth greater than the range of the scattered radiation. (The experimental measurements were made with " open " fields, the field size being determined by lead diaphragms, but the use of applicators with closed ends to define the treatment area does not increase the backscatter significantly, provided the applicator is of the modern design with an end cover of plastic less than ⅛ inch thickness.)

If the area irradiated is an ellipse or rectangle, the backscatter is less than from a circle or square of equal area because of the greater distance of the extremities of the long axis. Results obtained for circular or square fields may be used to determine the backscatter in these cases, if an " equivalent " circular or square area is used instead of the actual area. The " equivalent area " is that circular or square area which has been found by experiment to produce the same scatter (and the same percentage depth doses), as the actual area considered. Tables relating actual and equivalent areas have been prepared by a number of physicists.[6,7,8,9] Somewhat surprisingly it is found that the same equivalent areas can be used over the entire range of radiation qualities normally used in therapy.

It can be seen from fig. 11.03 that the scatter for a given radiation quality increases with increasing field size but for large fields approaches an upper limit. It can also be seen from fig. 11.03 and (more clearly) from fig. 11.04 that for a given field size the scatter increases with increase in half-value layer to a maximum between 0·5 and 1·0 mm. Cu and then decreases again. The initial increase is due to the increasing penetration of the scattered radiation, scatter from greater distances being able to reach the reference point. For soft radiation this effect predominates but for more penetrating radiation as the half-value layer increases, the total scatter decreases, and also more of the scattering is in a forward direction. This results in a decrease in the amount of scatter at the reference point.

If the thickness of tissue being irradiated does not exceed the range of the scattered radiation, then the amount of

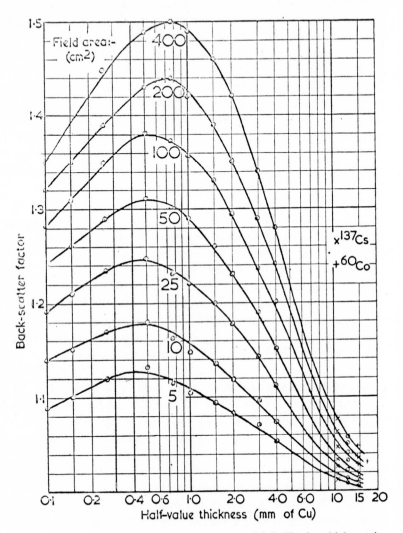

FIG. 11.04. Variation of back-scatter factor with half-value thickness in the range 0·1-14·8 mm. of Cu. " Field area " denotes the actual area for circular fields and the equivalent circular area for other shapes. (See text.)[9]

By permission from the *British Journal of Radiology, Supplement* 10.

back-scatter decreases with decrease in thickness and a correction must be made to the usual scatter data to allow for this (fig. 11.05).[10, 19]

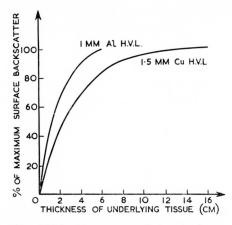

FIG. 11.05. Percentage of the maximum surface back-scatter obtained when the depth of tissue irradiated does not exceed the range of the scattered radiation; for radiation of half-value layers of 1·5 mm. of copper and 1 mm. of aluminium.[10]

11.05. Conversion of exposure to absorbed dose

If there is absolute electronic equilibrium at the position at which the exposure is measured, then the absorbed dose D in rads is related to the exposure X in roentgens at the same point by the equation

$$D = f \cdot X$$

where f is the rad per roentgen conversion factor for the radiation quality and medium considered. (See section 7.04 of Chapter VII.)

For radiation energies below about 400 keV., this relation can be applied even within a fraction of a millimetre of the surface (see below). Thus for constant S.S.D. techniques at these energies the absorbed dose at the surface D_0 may be calculated from the equation

$$D_0 = f \cdot X_{\text{surface}}$$

i.e.
$$D_0 = f \cdot (X_0)_{\text{air}} \cdot B(A_0)$$

385

where $(X_0)_\text{air}$ is the exposure measured at the surface in free air and $B(A_0)$ is the backscatter factor for area A_0 on the surface, i.e.

Surface dose = air exposure at reference point $\times$
backscatter factor $\times$ rad./R. factor   (2)

For constant S.S.D. techniques with radiation energies of a few MeV. although there is not strictly absolute electronic equilibrium at the reference point (the position of the peak absorbed dose), because this point is within the range of secondary electrons from the surface (see following discussion) conditions are such that there is an energy balance and the absorbed dose at the reference point can be calculated from the exposure at the reference point using a similar equation, i.e.

$$D_\delta = f \cdot (X_\delta)_\text{air} \cdot S(A_0)_\delta \tag{3}$$

where δ denotes the depth of the reference point below the surface and $S(A_0)_\delta$ denotes the scatter factor at the depth δ for an area A_0 measured at the surface.   Thus

Absorbed dose at reference point =
air exposure at reference point $\times$ scatter factor $\times$ rad./R. factor.

The evaluation of the rad per roentgen factor f was discussed in section 7.04.   For muscle, f varies only slowly with the radiation quality, passing through a shallow minimum at an equivalent energy of about 30 keV., and a shallow maximum at about 200 keV., then decreasing slowly with increasing energy.   In the usual deep therapy range f is of the order of 0·95 or 0·96 rad per roentgen.   (See fig. 11.06.)

For megavoltage radiation, the general relationship between exposure and absorbed dose at any depth is complicated by the fact that the secondary electrons produced in tissue have an appreciable range and consequently absolute electronic equilibrium is not attained.   Electronic equilibrium was discussed in Chapter VII (in section 7.04 and in connection with thimble chamber measurements in section 7.08) but we consider it again here in order to explain the variation of absorbed dose with depth and the conditions at the reference point for megavoltage radiation.   Recapitulating, therefore, in part, the discussion in Chapter VII, for radiation of moderate energy, the secondary electron range is so short that all the energy transferred from the radiation beam to an electron is given up by the electron to the medium within a fraction of a millimetre of its point of origin. Over this distance the attenuation of the radiation is negligible. Thus the energy removed from the radiation beam in a small volume element can be regarded as given up to the medium in essentially the same volume element. This means the absorbed dose at any depth below the surface of a homogeneous region of water or soft tissue is in a constant ratio to the exposure at the same depth. The absorbed

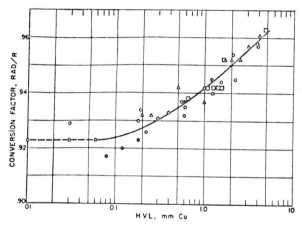

Fig. 11.06. Rad per roentgen conversion factor (f) in muscle.[1]
Courtesy United States National Bureau of Standards

dose is therefore a maximum at the surface and decreases with increasing depth below the surface. For more energetic radiation, the secondary electrons travel a greater distance. For Co[60] radiation, for example, the maximum secondary electron range in water is about 5 mm. and for 10 MeV. radiation it is about 5 cm. Also most of the electrons travel in the forward direction. The energy removed from the radiation beam at the point of origin of the electron is dissipated along the electron tracks, and some of this energy is therefore given up to the medium at points an appreciable distance in front of the point of origin of the electron. Consequently the absorbed dose at any point depends in part upon the energy transferred to secondary electrons in a region nearer the

387

radiation source than the point considered. In particular the absorbed dose within the secondary electron range of the surface of a region of homogeneous soft tissue depends in part upon the electron flux in the air above the surface. With the field sizes and source-surface distances normally used in therapy, the electron flux in air for megavoltage radiation is always less than the flux corresponding to electronic equilibrium. (The secondary electron range in air is at least several metres for megavoltage radiation, and for regions closer to the source than this, or within the secondary electron range of the beam edges, there will be fewer electrons per cc. than under equilibrium conditions.) Consequently there are fewer electrons traversing the surface layers immediately below the air-tissue interface than at greater depths, where all the electrons originate in tissue, and the absorbed dose does not reach its maximum value until an appreciable depth below the surface. If there were no attenuation of the incident radiation, the absorbed dose in tissue would attain a maximum value at a depth equal to the secondary electron range and would be constant at all greater depths (see fig. 11.07). Because there is, in fact, appreciable attenuation of the incident radiation, fewer electrons per cc. are generated in the absorber as the depth below the surface increases. The secondary electron flux (and the absorbed dose) therefore initially increases with increasing depth below the surface (as the flux of electrons originating in air is gradually replaced by the flux of electrons originating in tissue) but a maximum is reached at a depth less than the secondary electron range and thereafter the electron flux and absorbed dose decrease with increasing depth on account of the attenuation of the incident radiation (fig. 11.07(b)). The position at which the absorbed dose is a maximum is determined by the competition between these processes.

At depths (greater than that of the peak absorbed dose), where all the electrons originate in tissue the energy carried by electrons entering any volume element exceeds that of the electrons leaving the volume element (so there is not absolute electronic equilibrium), and the dose is determined by the average exposure at somewhat lesser depths. However, if the attenuation of the radiation is exponential and there is no change in the radiation quality, the ratio of the absorbed dose to the exposure at the same point is a constant. In these circumstances, (called relative or transient equilibrium) the absorbed dose can be calculated from the reading of a suitably calibrated exposure-meter as described in the last part of section 7.09 (Chapter VII). The overall dose conversion factor includes a

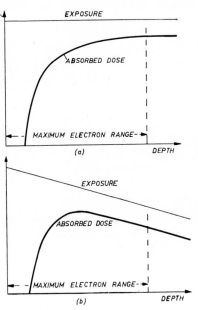

FIG. 11.07. Graphs illustrating the variation of absorbed dose with depth within the secondary electron range of the tissue surface
(a) if there were no attenuation of the primary radiation;
(b) when attenuation of the primary occurs.

correction for the fact that the dose is determined by the exposure at somewhat lesser depths. It must be emphasised, however, that for depths within the secondary electron range of the surface (which includes the reference point), the dose cannot be estimated from the exposure in this way. The absorbed dose at the peak of the dose curve is unique and is related to the exposure at the same point by means of the equation $D_\delta = f.X_\delta$. Thus below 400 keV. percentage depth doses represent the variation with depth of both exposure and dose, but at high energies apply to dose only.

11.06. Alternative method of calibration

The alternative method of determining the absorbed dose at the reference point, already outlined in section 11.03, can be

389

used equally well for high energy radiation and in the ortho-voltage range, the only difference being that instrument readings have to be converted directly into values of absorbed dose at high energies whereas either exposure or dose measurements may be recorded at low energies. The procedure suggested by the International Commission on Radiological Units and Measurements [2] may be summarised as follows:

(1) In a tissue-equivalent phantom, either the absorbed dose-rate or (below 400 keV.) the exposure rate is measured for a selected field size at a depth of 5 cm. (or at a depth greater than the peak of the absorbed dose curve if this exceeds 5 cm.).

(2) Using percentage depth dose tables, from the measured exposure-rate or dose-rate and the percentage depth dose at the point of measurement, the 100 per cent. exposure-rate or dose-rate is calculated.

If dose has been measured this gives the absorbed dose-rate at the reference point directly. If exposure has been measured, the absorbed dose-rate at the reference point can be obtained by multiplication by the rad per roentgen factor. Doses at other points in the same field can then be calculated by multiplication by the percentage depth dose in the usual way.

The absorbed dose-rate at the reference point for other field sizes is probably best determined in separate experiments but if the exposure-rate in air is known to be independent of field size, it may be calculated by multiplying the value obtained for one field size by the ratio of the scatter factor for the field in question to the scatter factor for the measurement field. The exposure-rate in free air can be calculated if desired by dividing the exposure-rate at the reference point by the appropriate scatter factor.

The reason why the International Commission on Radio-logical Units has recommended that this method of calibration be adopted in preference to measurements in air, is as follows. A number of different centres have made measurements of percentage depth doses on the central axis of radiation beams in the 200-400 kVp. range, using the air exposure method.

When the values obtained by the different centres for nominally identical treatment conditions are compared, there is not as close agreement as might be expected. If, however, the values from the different centres instead of all being referred to 100 per cent. at the surface, are all referred to the same percentage depth dose at 5 cm. depth, although the values for the surface dose now vary from centre to centre, there is much better agreement for depth doses from 5 to 15 cm. It is suggested that the surface values are more strongly influenced by the contribution of scattered radiation (which is quite likely to vary from centre to centre) than are the doses at a depth. Consequently, if dose estimates are to be based upon published tables of percentage depth doses (and have not been measured for the particular conditions of use at the centre where they are required) it is suggested, it is better to make the calibration measurements under conditions where low energy scattered radiation and electron contamination should be less important. If there are unusual scattering conditions, doses near the surface may be in error, using this method, but it is argued that this is generally of less importance clinically.

These arguments apply equally to high energy radiation, although differences between centres have been less obvious at high energies, presumably because measurements at the peak of the absorbed dose curve are influenced rather less by unusual scattering conditions and electron contamination than are doses at the surface. Calibration at a depth of 5 cm. or " well beyond the peak of the depth dose curve " is therefore now recommended at all energies.

The construction and use of a suitable phantom is not difficult. Either water or " Mix D " wax are suitable substitutes for soft tissue. The phantom must be of sufficient size to allow an adequate amount of scattering material around the largest fields which are to be used (a cross-sectional area of at least 30×30 cm.² is normally required) and of sufficient depth to obtain full backscatter beyond the measurement point, for the particular quality of radiation which is being measured. The volume required makes a phantom of Mix D rather expensive. If water is used, a water-proof, tissue-equivalent sheath must, of course, be provided around the measuring instrument. A close-fitting tube of polymethylmethacrylate (perspex, lucite, or plexiglas) can be used to support the ionisation chamber as well as to protect it from the water and has been recommended by the I.C.R.U. (This material has a greater electron density but somewhat lower effective atomic number than water and a thin sheath appears to make little difference to the instrument reading.)

It should be noted that compared with measurements in air (1) the chamber size affects the estimate of the exposure-rate in a phantom more than in air, since the radiation intensity changes more rapidly with distance, and (2) because of the presence of scattered radiation, the quality of the radiation at a depth in tissue is not the same as that of the primary radiation. This may introduce error if the response of the chamber is energy dependent.

TABLE 11.01

CENTRAL AXIS PERCENTAGE DEPTH DOSES [9]

H.V.T. 2·0 mm. of Cu., closed applicators, 50 cm. F.S.D.

Field size (cm.) B.S.F.	4×4 $1 \cdot 14_9$	6×6 $1 \cdot 20_7$	8×8 $1 \cdot 25_2$	10×10 $1 \cdot 29_3$	12×12 $1 \cdot 32_9$	15×15 $1 \cdot 36_9$	20×20 $1 \cdot 41_5$
Depth in cm.							
0	100·0	100·0	100·0	100·0	100·0	100·0	100·0
0·5	96·7	97·4	97·9	98·6	98·9	99·3	99·8
1	91·7	93·1	94·3	95·4	96·2	97·2	98·0
2	80·6	83·5	86·0	88·3	89·8	91·4	93·0
3	69·2	73·9	77·4	80·0	82·1	84·5	86·5
4	58·6	63·9	67·9	71·2	73·8	76·7	79·5
5	49·5	55·0	59·7	63·3	65·9	68·9	72·0
6	42·0	47·4	52·0	56·0	58·7	61·9	65·8
7	35·7	40·9	45·3	49·1	51·9	55·0	59·3
8	29·9	34·8	38·9	42·7	45·7	49·2	53·8
9	25·1	29·6	33·6	37·3	40·3	43·7	48·2
10	21·2	25·2	29·2	32·4	35·2	38·5	43·3
12	15·0	18·3	21·4	24·3	26·8	29·9	34·3
14	10·6	13·2	15·8	18·2	20·2	23·1	27·0
16	7·4	9·6	11·7	13·7	15·5	17·8	21·4
18	5·2	6·9	8·7	10·3	11·9	13·8	16·7
20	3·7	5·0	6·4	7·8	9·0	10·6	13·2

11.07. Central axis percentage depth doses

Experimental measurements of percentage depth doses for radiation energies from a few keV. to a few MeV. have been made by many investigators. A few measurements have been made with radiation generated at voltages up to 100 MV. The measurements have usually been made in phantoms consisting of either water or Mix D wax. For measurements made on the central axis, the results are usually presented in the form of sets of tables, each table showing the percentage depth dose as a function of depth and field size for given operating conditions. Useful collections of such tables have been prepared by the British Hospital Physicists' Association.[9] Typical examples are shown in Table 11.01. The data apply strictly only to the field size specified, but depth doses for squares and circles of

TABLE 11.01.—*Continued.*

Cobalt 60 γ rays, 80 cm. S.S.D.

Field size (cm.) S.F.	4×4 $1 \cdot 01_4$	6×6 $1 \cdot 02_1$	8×8 $1 \cdot 02_9$	10×10 $1 \cdot 03_6$	12×12 $1 \cdot 04_3$	15×15 $1 \cdot 05_2$	20×20 $1 \cdot 06_1$
Depth in cm.							
0·5	100·0	100·0	100·0	100·0	100·0	100·0	100·0
1	96·8	97·4	97·8	98·2	98·0	98·4	98·4
2	90·6	91·9	92·7	93·3	93·6	93·9	94·0
3	84·7	86·5	87·6	88·3	88·8	89·3	89·6
4	79·0	81·1	82·5	83·4	84·0	84·7	85·2
5	73·5	75·9	77·4	78·5	79·3	80·1	80·8
6	68·1	70·7	72·4	73·6	74·4	75·4	76·4
7	62·9	65·7	67·5	68·8	69·8	70·8	72·1
8	58·0	60·8	62·7	64·1	65·3	66·5	68·0
9	53·5	56·2	58·2	59·7	60·8	62·3	64·0
10	49·3	52·0	54·0	55·6	56·9	58·4	60·2
12	41·9	44·5	46·5	48·1	49·5	51·2	53·2
14	35·6	38·0	40·1	41·8	43·2	44·9	47·0
16	30·4	32·6	34·5	36·2	37·6	39·3	41·5
18	26.0	28·0	29·8	31·4	32·8	34·5	36·7
20	22·1	24·0	25·7	27·?	28·5	30·3	32·6

Scatter factors from Cunningham *et al*,[4]

equal area are almost identical. For rectangles, it is necessary to determine the dimensions of an "equivalent" square or circular field. Tables of equivalent field sizes are included with the depth dose tables.

The effect upon the central axis depth doses of changes in operating conditions such as field area, source-skin distance (S.S.D.), and half-value layer (H.V.L.) are illustrated in figs. 11.09, 11.10, and 11.11. To understand these figures it is necessary to know under what conditions scattered radiation makes a major contribution to the absorbed dose. This depends upon the depth considered. The variation with radiation quality and field area is generally similar to that already discussed in connection with backscatter to the surface. For very soft radiation, the scatter does not travel far and therefore makes a relatively small contribution. For penetrating radiation the scatter, although penetrating, is a small fraction only of the primary radiation. In the usual deep therapy range, however, the scattered radiation may contribute more to the dose absorbed at a depth than the primary radiation. This is illustrated in fig. 11.08.

Notice that the depth at which the scattered contribution is a maximum increases with increasing half-value layer.

Fig. 11.09 shows the effect of changes in half-value layer upon the percentage depth dose for depths of 5, 10 and 15 cm. for a number of field sizes. An increase in half-value layer is accompanied by an increase in the penetrating power of the primary radiation and hence in increased percentage depth doses for small fields, but for medium and large fields in the usual deep therapy range there is an accompanying decrease in the amount of scattered radiation. This tends to counteract the effect of the increased dose from the primary radiation and for the larger fields there is very little change in depth dose with quality between about 1·5 mm. and 6 mm. Cu. H.V.L. (at 5 cm. depth, the percentage depth dose may actually decrease with increase in H.V.L. in this range). The effect of changes in field area upon the percentage depth doses is also illustrated by fig. 11.09. For soft radiation, where the scattered radiation from near the axis only can contribute, the variation with area is small. For penetrating radiation also, where there is little

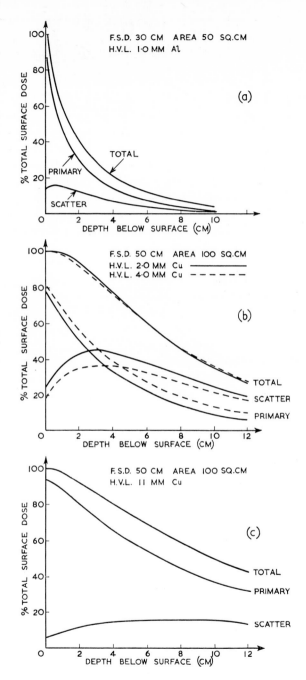

Fig. 11.08. Graphs showing the contribution to the total dose at a depth made by (1) primary and (2) scattered radiation, for radiation of half-value layers (a) 1·0 mm. Al, (b) 2·0 and 4·0 mm. Cu., (c) 11 mm. Pb. (Co⁶⁰ γ-rays).

395

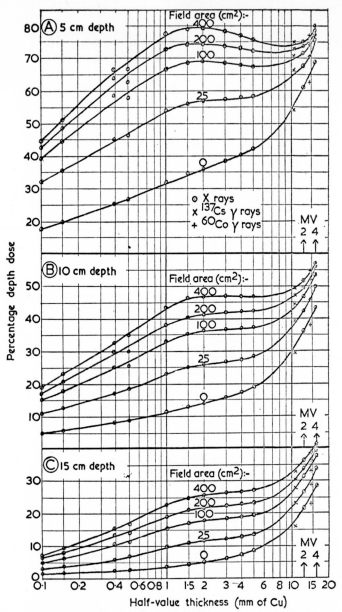

FIG. 11.09. Variation of percentage depth dose with half-value thickness in the range 0·1 to 15·6 mm. of Cu. Source-skin distance = 50 cm. The curves are drawn through the X-ray points. " Field area " denotes the actual area for circular fields and the equivalent circular area for other shapes.[9]

By permission from the *British Journal of Radiology, Supplement No.* 10.

scatter, the change with area is also small. The most marked variation with area is obtained in the conventional deep therapy range where scatter makes a large contribution to the depth dose.

The data of fig. 11.09 all refer to an S.S.D. of 50 cm. To illustrate the effect of changing the source-skin distance, in fig. 11.10, the half-value depth, i.e. the depth at which the dose is 50 per cent. of the maximum, is plotted against S.S.D. for fields of 100 cm.² in area and various qualities. For very soft

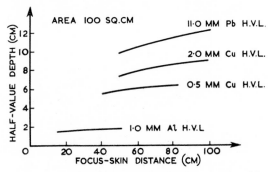

FIG. 11.10. Variation of half-value depth with focus-skin distance.

radiation, which is absorbed in a distance short compared with the usual source-skin distances, changes in the latter do not appreciably alter the half-value depth. The more penetrating the radiation, the greater the half-value depth and (above about 2·0 mm. Cu. H.V.L.) the less the contribution from scattered radiation, so the more marked is the effect of a change in the source-skin distance. When the depth dose is mainly due to primary radiation (i.e. for small fields or very penetrating radiation), the ratio of the dose at a depth d with source-skin distance f_2 to that at the same depth with source-skin distance f_1 varies on account of the inverse square effect

as $\qquad \left(\dfrac{f_2}{f_2 + d}\right)^2 \Big/ \left(\dfrac{f_1}{f_1 + d}\right)^2$ i.e. as $\left(\dfrac{f_2(f_1+d)}{f_1(f_2+d)}\right)^2 .$

When scatter makes an appreciable contribution to the dose, as for large fields in the deep therapy range, Mayneord and

Lamerton [11] found that the variation with focus-skin distance was approximately

$$\frac{1}{2}\left\{1 + \left[\frac{f_2(f_1+d)}{f_1(f_2+d)}\right]^2\right\}.$$

This formula is empirical only and a more accurate method of converting percentage depth doses for one S.S.D. for use at another is discussed in section 11.11.

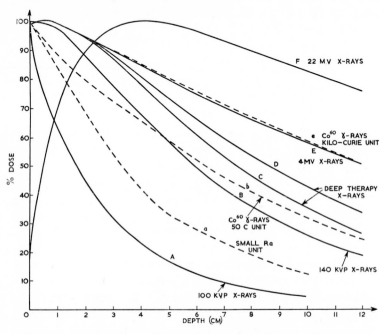

FIG. 11.11.   Graphs showing the variation of dose with depth for some typical therapy beams.   Field area = 100 cm.^{2} except curve a = 10 cm.^{2} S.S.D in cm., a = 8; A,b = 20; B,C = 50; D,E,e,F = 100.

It should be remembered that depth dose data apply to regions of tissue of large extent.   When an X-ray beam passes through a limited depth of tissue, the dose on the surface from which the beam emerges (the " exit " dose) is less than the corresponding depth dose because of the absence of back-scatter from tissue at greater depths.[19]

Another point to be borne in mind is that the energy of the scattered radiation is less than that of the primary radiation, so that whenever there is an appreciable amount of scattered radiation, the effective energy of the beam as a whole is considerably less than the effective energy of the primary beam.

11.08. Isodose charts

The preceding discussion has been confined to the doses absorbed on the central axis of a X- or γ-ray beam which enters a homogeneous block of soft tissue. We now consider the dose absorbed at points off the central axis.

The dose-rate near the edges of the beam is less than on the central axis at the same depth. This is partly due to the slightly greater distance from the X-ray focus or isotope source and the oblique filtration of the filters and intervening tissue, but mainly due to the smaller contribution from scattered radiation. The distribution of dose-rate has been determined experimentally and isodose charts showing the distribution in one or more planes through the central axis, such as those shown in figs. 11.12, 11.13 and 11.14, have been prepared for a great many of the X- and γ-ray beams which are commonly used in radiotherapy. The decrease in the dose-rate near the beam edge is less for megavoltage radiation than for a beam generated at about 200 to 400 kVp. where scatter makes a large contribution to the dose-rate, while the scatter outside the beam is greater for 200 kVp. radiation. Compare figs. 11.12 and 11.13.

Isodose charts for X-radiation of very high energy (greater than 10 MeV. say) show special features which are not observed at lower energies. For these radiations (1) the entrance surface dose-rate is a relatively small fraction of the maximum (as already explained), and (2) the distribution of dose across the beam is not uniform unless special " beam flattening filters " are used. At high energies, X-rays are emitted from the target in a narrow cone in the forward direction (see Chapter III). To obtain a uniform dose distribution across the field sizes required in therapy it is necessary (*a*) to use large source-skin distances (100 cm. or more is usual) and (*b*) to attenuate the radiation on the beam axis to whatever intensity is attainable at the edges of the fields required.

It should be noted that standard isodose charts assume the radiation beam enters a region of homogeneous soft tissue at right angles to a plane surface. When this is not the case corrections are necessary which are discussed in section 11.12.

The accurate experimental determination of isodose contours requires special equipment, e.g. small ionisation chambers so designed that the presence of the chamber does not modify

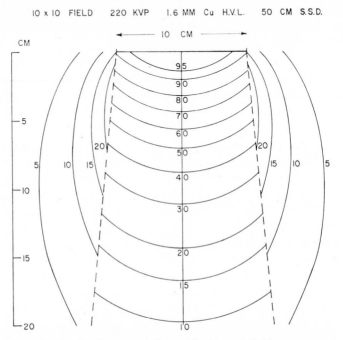

FIG. 11.12. Isodose curves for a 10×10 cm.^{2} field at source-skin distance of 50 cm. for 220 kVp. X-radiation (H.V.L. 1·75 mm. Cu.)

the scattered radiation and preferably a means of moving the chamber from point to point automatically. Methods have therefore been devised of calculating doses at points off the axis from central axis depth dose data. In these calculations the contribution made by the primary and by the scattered radiation to the absorbed dose at each point is usually determined separately. The dose due to the primary radiation can be most conveniently obtained from published tables giving central axis depth doses extrapolated to zero field area, the error in neglecting the slight decrease in the primary radiation near the edges of an X-ray beam due to the increased oblique focus-skin distance and filtration being small. Methods of calculating the contribution from scattered radiation have been

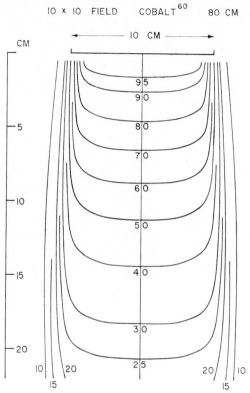

FIG. 11.13.   Isodose curves for a 10×10 cm.² field at a source-skin distance of 80 cm. for Co⁶⁰ γ-radiation (H.V.L. 11 mm. Pb.)

suggested by several physicists. The most widely used are probably those of Clarkson[13] and of Meredith and Neary[14] which are described below.

Clarkson's method can be used to obtain the dose at any point in a field of any shape. The procedure is as follows : Firstly it is necessary to prepare depth dose tables for circular fields giving the total dose for each depth and field size for a constant primary exposure at the reference point (100 R. say, measured in free air), i.e. percentage depth doses are multiplied by the appropriate 'back'-scatter factor for each field size. Then the central axis dose for a circular field of zero area at the depth considered is subtracted from the central axis doses at

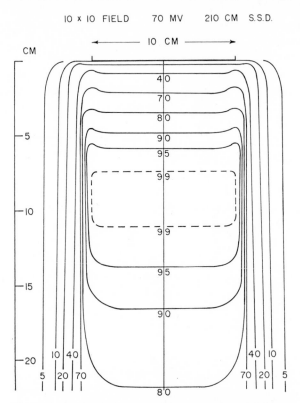

10 × 10 FIELD   70 MV   210 CM S.S.D.

FIG. 11.14.   Isodose curves for a 10×10 cm.^{2} field at a source skin distance of 210 cm. for 70 MV. X-rays (after Adams[12]).

that depth for circular fields of increasing radius.   The difference is the contribution from scattered radiation to the central axis dose and is plotted as a function of the radius r.   Suppose that ΔD_r denotes the contribution from scattered radiation to the central dose for a field of radius r.   Then the contribution from a sector subtending an angle $\Delta\theta$ at the centre is $\Delta\theta\Delta D_r/2\pi$. The cross-section of the actual field in which the dose is required, is now drawn to scale and divided into sectors, each

402

sector subtending an angle $\Delta\theta$ at the point P. (Values of $\Delta\theta$ of the order of 20° are usually convenient.) The mean radius of each sector is measured. The total scatter at P is the sum of terms $\Delta\theta\Delta D_r/2\pi$ for each sector. This is added to the primary dose to obtain the total dose at P.

The summations required in Clarkson's method are a disadvantage. If the contribution to the depth dose due to scatter from an elementary area at a distance r can be expressed as an analytical function of the radius r, then the total scatter at any point in fields of simple shape can be obtained by integration instead of by summation. Meredith and Neary found that the contribution from an element of area δA at a distance r could be represented by $f(r) \cdot \delta A/2\pi r$ where $f(r) = M[1 - \lambda r K_1(\lambda r)]$. M and λ are arbitrary constants determined for each set of irradiation conditions (S.S.D. and H.V.L.) and for each depth. K_n is the modified Bessel function of second kind of order n. Values of the constants and scatter integrals required for circular and for rectangular fields (rectangular fields have to be treated as the sum of triangular fields) were tabulated by Meredith and Neary for different values of λr for radiations of half-value layer between 1·0 and 5·0 mm. Cu. Revised values of the constants have been published by Horsley and Aspin.[15] Mechanical and optical methods of integrating the scatter have also been devised.[16]

A modification of Clarkson's method (suggested by Lamerton and Winsborough[17] and used by Tranter[18]) consists in representing the scatter-radius curve by a series of annuli, such that each annulus contributes an equal amount of scatter to the central axis at the depth considered. Radial lines can be used to subdivide the annuli into iso-contribution elements and the number of such elements within any field shape can then be counted to determine the scatter contribution.

For points off the axis of rectangular fields, the following method due to Day[7] (which does not involve calculating the scatter separately) can be used. The field is divided into four rectangles by lines intersecting in the point at which the dose is required. If the length of each side of each of these rectangles is then doubled (so that P is at the centre of each of the large rectangles) then the dose at P can be calculated as one-quarter of the sum or difference of the central axis doses for the four large rectangles.

Although sufficient information for most X-ray planning can usually be obtained from isodose charts in a principal plane of an X-ray field, it is sometimes desirable to be able to show the distribution either in a paraxial plane (i.e. a plane parallel to a principal plane but displaced from the central axis) or in a plane inclined at an angle to a principal plane. The distribution may be calculated by one of the preceding methods but for circular fields may usually be obtained more conveniently by projection of the isodose contours of the appropriate principal plane. The isodose contours can be projected geometrically or by the aid of mechanical or optical projectors of which that due to Mayneord [20] is probably the best known. It should be noted that this technique is only suitable for circular fields. There is no analogous method of obtaining charts showing the distribution in paraxial or inclined planes for rectangular fields.

11.09. Determination of absorbed dose in techniques using a constant source-axis distance

In rotation therapy it is necessary to maintain a point within the region to be treated (usually the centre of the treatment volume) on the axis of rotation and at a constant distance from the radiation source. In this case the source-skin distance varies both as the beam moves around any one patient and also from one patient to another. As already explained, the technique of using a constant source-axis distance is not restricted to moving field treatments but is frequently used when stationary field treatments are given on a rotation or " isocentric " unit.

For this type of treatment the reference point used in dose calculations is the point where the central axis of the radiation beam intersects the axis of rotation (the centre of rotation) and the reference absorbed dose is the absorbed dose which would be measured at this point in free air within a volume of phantom material just sufficient to provide the maximum electronic build-up.

In order to determine the reference dose, the usual procedure at low energies is to measure first the exposure-rate in free air at the centre of rotation. This exposure-rate multiplied by the rad per roentgen conversion factor gives the reference absorbed dose-rate.

The exposure-rate at the centre of rotation in the presence of a patient or phantom material differs from the exposure-rate in free air, partly on account of radiation scattered from underlying tissue but mainly on account of absorption and scattering in tissue between the source and the centre of rotation. The ratio of the exposure at the centre of rotation in the presence of tissue or phantom material to the exposure at the centre of rotation in free air was originally given the name " tumour-air ratio " and tables giving values of this ratio as a function of the depth of overlying tissue and field area (measured at the axis of rotation) for various radiation qualities were published by Johns et al.[21, 22] (The ratio is independent of S.S.D., see below.) However, for high energy radiation, a ratio analogous to John's tumour-air ratio but in terms of absorbed dose not exposure, is more useful. The International Commission on Radiological Units and Measurements have therefore defined " tissue-air ratio " in such a way that it may be applied at all energies. The definition is as follows.[2]

The tissue-air ratio is the ratio of the absorbed dose at a given point in a phantom to the absorbed dose which would be measured at the same point in free air within a volume of the phantom material just large enough to provide the maximum electronic build-up at the point of measurement.

If the attenuation of the radiation in the thickness of phantom required for electronic build-up is negligible, i.e. for radiation energies below (say) 400 keV., the tissue-air ratio defined in this way is equal to the ratio defined in terms of exposure. It should be noted that the tissue-air ratio (usually abbreviated to T.A.R.) is a pure number and is *not* the ratio of an absorbed dose to an exposure.

From the I.C.R.U. definition of T.A.R., the absorbed dose in the patient at the centre of rotation (D say) is given by the equation

$$D = D_\mathrm{R} \times \text{T.A.R.} \qquad . \qquad . \qquad . \qquad (4)$$

14
405

where D_R denotes the reference absorbed dose at the centre of rotation in the absence of the patient. In S.A.D. techniques, T.A.R. therefore play a part similar to the part played by percentage depth doses in constant S.S.D. techniques. In each case a knowledge of the appropriate ratio or percentage enables the dose absorbed at a point of interest in the patient to be calculated from an absorbed dose at a reference point, which is independent of the particular patient. Tables of T.A.R. are now usually included in compilations of depth dose data. Each table shows the T.A.R. as a function of overlying tissue depth and field size for given operating conditions. Examples are shown in Table 11.02.[9] To avoid confusion with percentage depth doses, tissue-air ratios are conventionally expressed as fractions.

We have assumed above that, for each field size, the reference absorbed dose is obtained by a direct measurement in

TABLE 11.02

TISSUE AIR RATIOS [9]

H.V.T. 2·0 mm. of Cu (diaphragm limited)

Field size (cm.)	0	4×4	6×6	8×8	10×10	12×12	15×15	20×20
Depth in cm.								
0	1·00	1·14	1·20	1·25	1·29	1·32	1·36	1·42
1	0·847	1·11	1·21	1·28	1·33	1·38	1·43	1·50
2	0·720	1·02	1·14	1·22	1·29	1·35	1·42	1·50
3	0·607	0·906	1·02	1·12	1·20	1·27	1·37	1·47
4	0·515	0·800	0·918	1·02	1·10	1·18	1·28	1·40
5	0·438	0·705	0·822	0·927	1·02	1·09	1·19	1·32
6	0·371	0·612	0·735	0·839	0·927	1·00	1·10	1·22
7	0·316	0·529	0·648	0·750	0·837	0·910	1·01	1·14
8	0·268	0·461	0·567	0·663	0·748	0·822	0·919	1·04
9	0·228	0·402	0·494	0·585	0·665	0·737	0·834	0·957
10	0·193	0·345	0·430	0·513	0·590	0·659	0·753	0·865
12	0·140	0·256	0·322	0·394	0·460	0·521	0·605	0·709
14	0·102	0·192	0·243	0·300	0·354	0·408	0·483	0·577
16	0·073	0·143	0·184	0·228	0·273	0·320	0·387	0·465
18	0·054	0·107	0·140	0·174	0·210	0·252	0·309	0·378
20	0·040	0·081	0·106	0·132	0·163	0·199	0·249	0·302

TABLE 11.02—*Continued*

Cobalt 60 γ rays

Field size (cm.)	0	4×4	6×6	8×8	10×10	12×12	15×15	20×20
Depth in cm.								
0·5	1·00	1·011	1·016	1·021	1·026	1·030	1·037	1·046
1	0·965	0·989	1·000	1·009	1·018	1·024	1·031	1·042
2	0·905	0·950	0·967	0·981	0·992	1·001	1·009	1·020
3	0·845	0·910	0·932	0·948	0·961	0·970	0·982	0·995
4	0·792	0·868	0·894	0·914	0·929	0·940	0·953	0·968
5	0·742	0·824	0·854	0·877	0·893	0·906	0·922	0·939
6	0·694	0·781	0·813	0·855	0·855	0·870	0·887	0·908
7	0·650	0·736	0·772	0·798	0·817	0·833	0·850	0·875
8	0·608	0·694	0·728	0·756	0·777	0·794	0·815	0·841
9	0·570	0·652	0·688	0·716	0·739	0·756	0·778	0·808
10	0·534	0·615	0·648	0·676	0·700	0·719	0·745	0·776
12	0·469	0·542	0·577	0·605	0·629	0·650	0·677	0·712
14	0·412	0·478	0·512	0·540	0·564	0·587	0·615	0·650
16	0·361	0·425	0·454	0·481	0·506	0·528	0·556	0·593
18	0·317	0·375	0·405	0·431	0·454	0·474	0·503	0·542
20	0·278	0·330	0·358	0·383	0·405	0·425	0·454	0·494

air at the centre of rotation. For the reasons discussed in section 11.06 in connection with constant S.S.D. techniques, an alternative method, which may be preferable if published tables of tissue air ratios are to be used, is to take the measurements in a phantom with 5 cm. or more of tissue-equivalent material overlying the centre of rotation. The reference absorbed dose may then be calculated using the published T.A.R. for the thickness of phantom used. If the exposure-rate in air is known to be independent of field size (but not otherwise) measurements for one field size only are sufficient.

If the radiation beam is stationary during treatment, then the depth of tissue between the surface and the centre of rotation (and hence the T.A.R.) will have a single value. However, if the beam is moving, the depth of tissue will vary with the position of the beam in the rotation cycle. In this case it is necessary to determine an average value of the T.A.R. for the whole cycle. For 360° rotation, the moving field is usually represented by 18 or 24 fields at 20° or 15° angles to one another. The overlying depth of tissue in each position is measured and the corresponding T.A.R. read from the tables for the appropriate radiation quality and field area. The average value of the T.A.R. is then obtained by dividing the sum of the individual values by the number of fields considered.

11.10. Isodose curves for techniques using a constant source-axis distance

In constant source-surface distance techniques, there are a limited number of possible field sizes at the surface and it is therefore possible to plot isodose curves in at least the two principal planes for all field sizes which will be used. In constant source-axis distance techniques, although there are a limited number of possible field sizes as measured at the axis, the depth of overlying tissue and, hence, the surface field size are continuously variable. However, the *relative* value of the doses at two points which are both remote from the surface, depends primarily upon the thickness of tissue by which they are separated and to a much lesser extent upon the actual depth of tissue overlying each point. It is therefore possible to plot isodose charts for a given field size at the axis and for an arbitrary thickness of tissue overlying the axis which can be used for a wide range of S.S.D., provided doses are not required at points near the surface. Such isodose charts are commonly plotted with the 100 per cent. value at the centre of rotation. The dose at any point P in the field is then given by the equation

Dose at P = dose (in patient) at centre of rotation ×

percentage depth dose at P

The error introduced by using an isodose chart for an incorrect S.S.D. is much less when megavoltage radiation is being employed (where scatter makes a relatively small contribution to the total dose) than at lower energies where the scattered contribution to the dose is large. The error is also less for points within the geometrical edge of the beam than for points outside.

When a moving field is represented by n stationary fields, the total dose at P is obtained as the sum of the contributions from each of the n fields. Since for each field, the dose at the centre of rotation is given by the product of the appropriate T.A.R. and the reference absorbed dose (D_R) at the centre, the total dose at $P(D_P)$ may be written

$$D_P = \frac{1}{n} \sum_{j=1}^{n} (\text{per cent depth dose at } P \text{ in field } j \times \text{T.A.R. for field } j) \times D_R.$$

Where the central ray is incident obliquely on the skin, correction must be made for the oblique incidence. This problem also arises with stationary field techniques. The methods of making the correction are essentially the same for the two techniques and are discussed in section 11.12.

11.11. The relationship between percentage depth doses and T.A.R. and conversion of percentage depth doses from one S.S.D. to another

Consider a homogeneous absorber of large extent and let the energy fluence due to the primary photon flux at a reference depth δ below the surface be F_δ. It will be assumed that for a given quality of radiation the energy fluence due to scattered radiation at the point considered depends upon the primary fluence and the area of the field (A_δ) at the depth δ but is independent of the direction of the primary radiation, and therefore independent of the divergence of the beam. (This assumption introduces an error of less than 1 or 2 per cent. into the estimate of the scattered radiation.)[24] Then the total energy fluence at the depth δ may be written $F_\delta . \psi(A_\delta)$ where $\psi(A_\delta)$ will be called the scatter function for area A_δ at depth δ. (Note, $\psi(A_\delta)$ has been called by some authors, the scatter factor for area A_δ but it is *not* the same as the scatter factor as defined by the International Commission on Radiological Units (and denoted above by $S(A)_s$ so we have preferred to use a different name). For any other depth d, similarly, the total energy fluence is given by $F_d . \psi(A_d)$.

For a divergent radiation beam, if the source-surface distance is f, then

$$F_d = F_\delta . \left(\frac{f+\delta}{f+d}\right)^2 . e^{-\mu(d-\delta)}$$

where μ denotes an effective attenuation coefficient for the primary radiation considered (μ is constant for monochromatic radiation).

If there is absolute electronic equilibrium at the depths considered, the ratio of absorbed doses D_d/D_δ is given by

$$\frac{D_d}{D_\delta} = \frac{F_d . \psi(A_d)}{F_\delta . \psi(A_\delta)}$$

or

$$D_d = \left(\frac{f+\delta}{f+d}\right)^2 . e^{-\mu(d-\delta)} . \frac{\psi(A_d)}{\psi(A_\delta)} . D_\delta \qquad (5)$$

For constant source-surface distance techniques with radiation generated below 400 kVp., the absorbed dose at the surface is taken as 100 per cent.

For such radiation, therefore, substituting $\delta = 0$ and $D_\delta = 100$ per cent. in equation (5), the percentage depth dose at depth d, for a field of area A_0 (measured at the surface) is given by

$$P(A_0,d) = \left(\frac{f}{f+d}\right)^2 . e^{-\mu d} . \frac{\psi(A_d)}{\psi(A_0)} . 100 \text{ per cent.}$$

Since in this case the scatter at the surface is all backscatter, $\psi(A_0) = B(A_0)$ where $B(A_0)$ denotes the backscatter factor

$$\therefore \qquad P(A_0,d) = \left(\frac{f}{f+d}\right)^2 . e^{-\mu d} . \frac{\psi(A_d)}{B(A_0)} . 100 \text{ per cent.} \qquad (6)$$

For constant source surface distance techniques using radiation with energy of a few MeV. where the peak absorbed dose at the reference depth δ is taken as 100 per cent.,

$$P(A_0,d) = \left(\frac{f+\delta}{f+d}\right)^2 . e^{-\mu(d-\triangle-\delta)} . \frac{\psi(A_d)}{\psi(A_\delta)} . 100 \text{ per cent.} \qquad (7)$$

In this equation the attentuation of the primary radiation which produces the absorbed dose at the depth d has been written as $e^{-\mu(d-\triangle-\delta)}$ (not $e^{-\mu(d-\delta)}$). $\triangle$ has been introduced because where there is transient electronic equilibrium the absorbed dose is determined by the exposure at a somewhat lesser depth. $\triangle$ is small, so the difference between $\psi(A_d)$ and $\psi(A_{d-\triangle})$ has been assumed negligible.

For high energy radiation, the scatter factor at the reference depth δ is given by $e^{-\mu\delta} . \psi(A_\delta)$

$$\therefore \qquad P(A_0,d) = \left(\frac{f+\delta}{f+d}\right)^2 . e^{-\mu(d-\triangle)} . \frac{\psi(A_d)}{S(A_0)_\delta} . 100 \text{ per cent.} \qquad (8)$$

$S(A_0)_\delta$ has been used in this equation to denote the scatter factor since although it refers to the scatter at the depth δ, the scatter factor is conventionally tabulated by reference to the area of the field at the surface.

For constant source-axis distance techniques, let A_r denote the field area at the centre of rotation. Then using the same notation as above, let the energy fluence due to the primary radiation at the centre of rotation in the absence of the patient be F_r. Then in the presence of a patient or phantom with tissue depth d above the centre of rotation, the energy fluence which determines the absorbed dose at the centre of rotation becomes $F_r \, e^{-\mu(d-\triangle)} . \psi(A_r)_d$ where $\psi(A_r)_d$ denotes the scatter function for the area A_r when the overlying tissue depth is d. If a thickness of material δ is required to produce maximum electronic build-up at the centre of rotation, the energy fluence in the presence of this amount of material is $F_r . e^{-\mu\delta} . \psi(\delta^2)$ where $\psi(\delta^2)$ denotes the scatter from the build-up material. (The area of the radiation beam intercepting build-up material is denoted by δ^2.) For any area A as $A{\rightarrow}0$, $\psi(A){\rightarrow}1$, so $\psi(\delta^2)$

410

will be close to 1, since the volume of build-up material will usually be small.

The T.A.R. may then be written as

$$T(A_r,d) = \frac{F_r \cdot e^{-\mu(d-\Delta)} \cdot \psi(A_r)_d}{F_r \cdot e^{-\mu\delta} \cdot \psi(\delta^2)}$$

$$= e^{-\mu(d-\Delta-\delta)} \cdot \psi(A_r)_d/\psi(\delta^2) \qquad (9)$$

When $d = \delta$,

$$T(A_r,\delta) = e^{\mu\Delta} \cdot \psi(A_r)_\delta/\psi(\delta^2)$$

$$= e^{\mu(\Delta+\delta)} \cdot S(A_r)_\delta/\psi(\delta^2)$$

where $S(A_r)_\delta$ denotes the scatter factor at the equilibrium depth δ. For radiation below 400 keV. in energy, $\delta = \Delta = 0$

$\therefore$
$$T(A_r, 0) = \psi(A_r)_0 = B(A_r)_0$$

where $B(A_r)_0$ denotes the back-scatter factor at the surface. Thus for low energy radiation, the tissue-air ratio for zero depth is equal to the back-scatter factor for the field of area A_r.

Comparing equations (8) and (9), if fields are considered such that A_r in equation (9) (the area measured at the centre of rotation) is equal to A_d in equation (8) (the area measured at the depth d), so that $\psi(A_r)_d = \psi(A_d)$, i.e.

if
$$A_0\left(\frac{f+d}{f}\right)^2 = A_r,$$

then
$$T(A_r,d) = \left(\frac{f+d}{f+\delta}\right)^2 \cdot P(A_0 d) \cdot S(A_0)_\delta \cdot e^{\mu\delta}/\psi(\delta^2) \qquad (10)$$

For radiation generated below 400 kVp., this reduces to

$$T(A_r,d) = \left(\frac{f+d}{f}\right)^2 \cdot P(A_0 \cdot d) \cdot B(A_0) \qquad (11)$$

Conversely

$$P(A_0,d) = \frac{T(A_r,d)}{e^{\mu\delta} \cdot S(A_0)_\delta} \cdot \left(\frac{f+\delta}{f+d}\right)^2 \cdot \psi(\delta^2)$$

$$= \frac{T(A_r,d)}{T(A_\delta,\delta)} \cdot \left(\frac{f+\delta}{f+d}\right)^2 \cdot e^{\mu\Delta}$$

or for radiation generated below 400 kVp.

$$P(A_0,d) = \frac{T(A_r,d)}{T(A_0,0)} \left(\frac{f}{f+d}\right)^2$$

This provides a convenient method of calculating percentage depth doses for any source skin distance, when tables of T.A.R. are available.

In order to obtain percentage depth doses for some unusual S.S.D. (f_2 say) when T.A.R. are not available, percentage depth doses for some other S.S.D. (f_1 say) and backscatter factors may be used as follows:

Consider an area $A_0{}^1$ at S.S.D. f_1 such that

$$A_0{}^1\left(\frac{f_1+d}{f_1}\right)^2 = A_0\left(\frac{f_2+d}{f_2}\right)^2$$

411

where A_0 is the field area for which the percentage depth dose for depth d and S.S.D. f_2 is required. Then for each S.S.D., the field area A_d at the depth d is the same and so also is the secondary flux function $\psi(A_d)$.

Then from equation (8)

At S.S.D. f_1

$$P(f_1,A_0{}^1,d) = \left(\frac{f_1+\delta}{f_1+d}\right)^2 . e^{-\mu(d-\triangle)} . \frac{\psi(A_d)}{S(A_0{}^1)_\delta} . 100 \text{ per cent.}$$

At S.S.D. f_2

$$P(f_2,A_0,d) = \left(\frac{f_2+\delta}{f_2+d}\right)^2 . e^{-\mu(d-\triangle)} . \frac{\psi(A_d)}{S(A_0)_\delta}. 100 \text{ per cent.}$$

$$\therefore \qquad P(f_2,A_0,d) = P(f_1,A_0{}^1,d) . \frac{S(A_0{}^1)_\delta}{S(A_0)_\delta} . \left(\frac{f_2+\delta}{f_1+\delta} \cdot \frac{f_1+d}{f_2+d}\right)^2$$

where

$$A_0{}^1 = \left(\frac{f_1}{f_2} \cdot \frac{f_2+d}{f_1+d}\right)^2 . A_0$$

For radiation of moderate energy when $\delta = 0$, this reduces to

$$P(f_2,A_0,d) = P(f_1,A_0{}^1,d) . \frac{B(A^1{}_0)}{B(A_0)} . \left(\frac{f_2}{f_1} \cdot \frac{f_1+d}{f_2+d}\right)^2$$

11.12. Corrections for air spaces and oblique incidence

Conventional isodose charts are drawn on the assumption that the tissue surface is a plane at right angles to the beam axis and there is homogeneous soft tissue everywhere below the surface. In practice this is frequently not the case. For fixed field techniques with radiation below about 400 keV. in energy, any spaces between the skin and the applicator may be filled with tissue equivalent bolus but when megavoltage radiation is used, this is undesirable since the advantage of a low skin dose is lost. With megavoltage radiation, a " compensating filter " [25] is sometimes used. This is a filter designed to produce absorption similar to that which would be produced by the missing tissue, which is introduced into the treatment beam at a sufficient distance from the skin for the electron contribution to the skin to be small. The construction of large numbers of compensating filters is not always practicable, however, and in moving field therapy, their use is in any case impossible. It is therefore necessary to consider methods of estimating the effect of air spaces and oblique incidence upon depth doses.

Consider the dose at a point such as Q fig. 11.15, d cm. below the surface. The percentage depth dose as read from a conventional isodose chart will be in error because of tissue missing in the shaded region.   Let the depth of missing tissue measured along a ray though the point of interest Q, be denoted by σ.   As a first approximation, it is usually assumed that the dose at Q does not depend upon the obliquity of the surface,

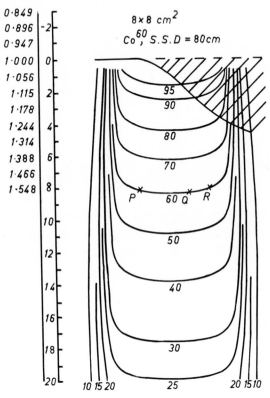

FIG. 11.15.   Diagram to illustrate the use of an isodose chart, with correction factors included on the chart for changes in S.S.D.

except in so far as this determines the depth of missing tissue σ. With this assumption the dose at Q is related to the nominal dose read from the isodose chart by the equation

$$\frac{\text{Dose at } Q}{\text{Nominal dose at } Q} = \frac{\text{T.A.R. for area } A_d \text{ and depth } (d-\sigma)}{\text{T.A.R. for area } A_d \text{ and depth } d}$$

A correction factor to the nominal dose can therefore be

413

determined using tissue-air ratios. This correction factor is of course a function of the depth d and field area A_d at the position

TABLE 11.03

Co^{60} γ-rays, S.S.D. = 80 cm.

Field size at surface	5×5 cm.^{2}	10×10 cm.^{2}	15×15 cm.^{2}
Depth (d)	10 cm.	10 cm.	10 cm.
Area at depth d	$5 \cdot 63 \times 5 \cdot 63$ cm.^{2}	$11 \cdot 25 \times 11 \cdot 25$ cm.^{2}	$16 \cdot 88 \times 16 \cdot 88$ cm.^{2}
T.A.R. at d	0·644	0·713	0·758
T.A.R. at $d-5$	0·849	0·901	0·928
Correction for 5 cm. deficit, at 10 cm. depth	1·318	1·264	1·224
Depth (d)	15 cm.	15 cm.	15 cm.
Area at depth d	$5 \cdot 94 \times 5 \cdot 94$ cm.^{2}	$11 \cdot 88 \times 11 \cdot 88$ cm.^{2}	$17 \cdot 81 \times 17 \cdot 81$ cm.^{2}
T.A.R. at d	0·481	0·556	0·606
T.A.R. at $d-5$	0·647	0·719	0·764
Correction for 5 cm. deficit at 15 cm. depth	1·345	1·293	1·260
Depth (d)	20 cm.	20 cm.	20 cm.
Area at depth d	$6 \cdot 25 \times 6 \cdot 25$ cm.^{2}	$12 \cdot 5 \times 12 \cdot 5$ cm.^{2}	$18 \cdot 75 \times 18 \cdot 75$ cm.^{2}
T.A.R. at d	0·361	0·430	0·484
T.A.R. at $d-5$	0·485	0·561	0·611
T.A.R. at $d-10$	0·653	0·725	0·771
Correction for 5 cm. deficit at 20 cm. depth	1·343	1·305	1·262
K (from 5 cm. deficit at 20 cm.)	0·0592	0·0536	0·0464

considered. However, for radiation with equivalent photon energy of 1 or 2 MeV., the ratio $\dfrac{T(A_d,d-\sigma)}{T(A_d,d)}$ becomes nearly independent of the depth d when $d-\sigma$ is greater than about 5 cm. This is illustrated in Table 11.03 where it can be seen that the correction for a 5 cm. tissue deficit at 20 cm. depth is almost the same as at 15 cm. depth.

Thus when $(d-\sigma)$ is fairly large, for 1 or 2 MeV. radiation, it is possible to use a single correction factor for any given tissue deficit, regardless of the depth of the point considered. Furthermore it is found that the correction factor for any given field size can be satisfactorily represented by an exponential function of the tissue deficit σ, i.e. we can write the correction factor as $e^{K\sigma}$ (say) where K is a constant for a given field size.

When K has been determined, the correction factor for any given tissue deficit is then readily calculated. The best value for K for each field size can be determined by constructing a more extended table of the type of Table 11.03. Alternatively if percentage depth doses for infinite S.S.D. $\left\{ \text{i.e.} \left(\frac{f+d}{f+\delta} \right)^2 P(A_d)_d \right\}$, are plotted on a logarithmic scale against depth on a linear scale, the gradient of the linear portion of the graph enables a function (usually denoted by $\bar{\mu}$) to be determined [26] which is very nearly equal to K. $\bar{\mu}$ is actually given by

$$e^{\bar{\mu}\sigma} = e^{\mu\sigma} \cdot \psi(A_{d-\sigma})_{d-\sigma} / \psi(A_d)_d.$$

whereas $\qquad e^{K\sigma} = e^{\mu\sigma} \cdot \psi(A_d)_{d-\sigma} / \psi(A_d)_d$

The tissue deficit correction factor can be tabulated as a function of field size and thickness of missing tissue or it may be included on isodose charts as shown in fig. 11.15. A chart of this type is used as follows. Consider the points P and Q. The isodose chart indicates that at P the percentage depth dose is 60 per cent. Since the space between P and the nominal surface is in fact completely filled by tissue, this is correct. At Q, the same percentage depth dose is read from the chart, but there is in fact an air space of 2 cm. between the end of the applicator and the tissue surface. The figure 1·115 opposite the 2 cm. depth means that the percentage depth dose must be multiplied by 1·115 to correct for a 2 cm. tissue deficit. Similarly at R where the tissue deficit is 3 cm. the correction is 1·178 and so on. These factors apply strictly only to points near the central axis, but can be used in practice over most of the beam width. Outside the geometrical edge of the beam where the isodose curves (for megavoltage radiation) run approximately parallel to the beam axis, no correction is required.

An alternative method of correcting for an oblique surface is as follows. The isodose chart is moved towards or away from the source, so that the surface as marked on the chart coincides with the surface on the ray through the point (Q) at which the dose is required. The percentage depth dose as read from the chart at Q is then multiplied by $\left(\dfrac{f+d-\sigma}{f+d}\right)^2$. (The percentage depth dose from the chart without correction would give the dose at a point Q^1 distance $(f+d-\sigma)$ from the target with no tissue missing. Q is actually a distance $(f+d)$ not $(f+d-\sigma)$ from the target, and using a simple inverse square law to correct for this change in distance gives the correction factor $\left(\dfrac{f+d-\sigma}{f+d}\right)^2$. This is an approximate correction only since the area of the field and hence the scatter contribution at distance $(f+d)$ is not the same as it would be at distance $(f+d-\sigma)$, but for megavoltage radiation where the scatter contribution to the dose is small, the error is small.) The method is convenient if precalculated correction factors or tissue-air ratios are not available. It is also particularly useful when the dose is required at points close to the surface when the use of a correction factor based on $e^{K\sigma}$ is not correct.

A third method,[27] which has been found empirically to give dose estimates, which are in fair agreement with those measured experimentally, consists in merely shifting the isodose curve from the nominal surface position, a distance either 0.5σ (for 200-400 kVp. radiation) or 0.6σ (for Co^{60} or 4 MV. radiation) towards the actual surface. The dose is then read directly from the chart and no further correction is required. This method is therefore very rapid and convenient to use in practice, although lacking theoretical justification.

11.13. The effects of bone, fat and air cavities upon depth doses

Standard depth dose data and isodose curves assume the radiation traverses a homogeneous region of muscle or muscle-equivalent material. There are three ways in which the presence of inhomogeneities such as air cavities or regions of bone or fat can alter the radiation dose. Firstly, since the absorbing and scattering properties of the inhomogeneity differ from the absorbing and scattering properties of muscle, the exposure is changed at any point which is exposed to radiation which has passed through or been scattered from an inhomogeneity instead of muscle. Secondly, at points within the inhomogeneity itself, the energy absorbed from the radiation for a given exposure is not the same as in muscle, i.e. the rad per roentgen factor (f) depends upon the absorbing material. Thirdly, the absorbed dose within the range of secondary

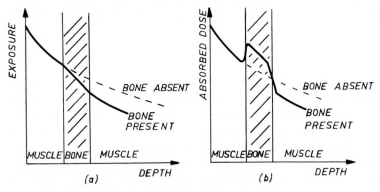

Fig. 11.16. Diagrammatic illustration of the changes produced by the presence of bone, in (a) the exposure at different depths (b) in the absorbed dose.

electrons from an interface depends in part upon energy given up by electrons which originate on the opposite side of the interface. There is therefore a transition region extending on each side of the surface of an inhomogeneity in which the absorbed dose depends upon the distance from the interface. These effects are illustrated diagrammatically in fig. 11.16.

In this section, we consider the first of these effects, namely the changes in depth doses resulting from a change in exposure produced by the presence of media other than soft tissue, particularly bone and lung tissue. Suppose that a medium other than soft tissue, of thickness x, lies in the path of the primary radiation reaching a point Q at a depth d below the surface. If μ_m and μ_x denote the linear attenuation coefficients of the primary radiation in muscle and the medium respectively, the dose at Q will be altered because of the following factors:

417

(1) the intensity of the primary radiation and of the scattered radiation originating below the inhomogeneity will vary as $e^{-[\mu_m(d-x)+\mu_x x]}$ instead of as $e^{-\mu_m d}$, (2) scatter from above the inhomogeneity will vary as $e^{-[\mu'_m(d'-x)+\mu'_x d']}$ instead of as $e^{-\mu'_m d'}$ where d' refers to the distance traversed by the scattered radiation before reaching Q and μ'_m and μ_x differ from μ_m and μ_x because in general the scattered radiation will be of lower energy than the primary, (3) the inhomogeneity itself will scatter a different amount of radiation from soft tissue. In order to assess precisely the relative importance of these effects, particularly if the inhomogeneity covers only part of the irradiation beam, it is necessary to know not only the relative contribution of primary and scattered radiation to the dose at the point considered, but also what fraction of the contribution from scattered radiation is due to radiation coming from a particular direction. This information is rarely available and makes the assessment of the effect of inhomogeneities very difficult, particularly in the conventional deep therapy range. For megavoltage radiation where there is less scatter and this mainly in the forward direction, however, it is possible to make reasonable simplifying assumptions that enable approximate correction factors to be calculated.

Thus consider a beam of radiation of such quality that in the inhomogeneity considered as well as in soft tissue, attenuation is due almost entirely to the Compton process. Then the absorption and scattering produced in the inhomogeneity compared with that produced in soft tissue may be expected to be in the same ratio as the electron density in the inhomogeneity to the electron density in soft tissue. Now the effect of a certain thickness of soft tissue upon the dose at points below may be determined from tissue air ratios. Consider a point P at a constant distance from the radiation source, with overlying tissue of depth either d_1 or d_2 as shown in fig. 11.17. When the overlying tissue depth is d_1 the dose at P = Reference dose × T.A.R. for depth d_1. When the overlying tissue depth is d_2, the dose at P = Reference dose × T.A.R. for depth d_2, i.e. the effect upon the dose at P of introducing the slab of soft tissue thickness (d_2-d_1) is to reduce the dose by the factor $\dfrac{\text{T.A.R. } (d_2)}{\text{T.A.R. } (d_1)}$.

If now the slab of thickness (d_2-d_1) contains $\rho_e n_e$ electrons per cc. instead of the n_e electrons per cc. (say) in soft tissue, the effect of the slab might be expected to be given by $\left(\dfrac{\text{T.A.R. } (d_2)}{\text{T.A.R. } (d_1)}\right)^{\rho_e}$. Thus replacing soft tissue by another material with electron density ρ_e times that of soft tissue, changes the dose-rate at P by the factor $\left(\dfrac{\text{T.A.R. } (d_2)}{\text{T.A.R. } (d_1)}\right)^{\rho_e-1}$. Therefore taking the electron density of bone, for example, as 1·67 times that of soft tissue,

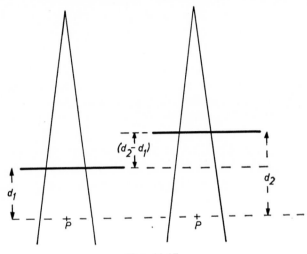

FIG. 11.17.

the dose at P as determined from ordinary depth dose tables, should be multiplied by $\left(\dfrac{\text{T.A.R. } (d_2)}{\text{T.A.R. } (d_1)}\right)^{0\cdot67}$ if bone replaces soft tissue in a slab of thickness (d_2-d_1) at a distance d_1 above P. Similarly, if lung tissue has a density 0·35 times that of soft tissue, the correction factor for the effect of (d_2-d_1) cm. of lung tissue, d_1 cm. above P is given by

$$\left(\frac{\text{T.A.R. } (d_2)}{\text{T.A.R. } (d_1)}\right)^{-0.65} \quad \text{or} \quad \left(\frac{\text{T.A.R. } (d_1)}{\text{T.A.R. } (d_2)}\right)^{0.65}$$

Assuming that we are considering radiation qualities at which the scatter is mainly in the forward direction, these correction factors might reasonably be expected to apply at least at points within the " shadow " of an inhomogeneity. These factors are, of course, a function of field size, but do not vary very rapidly with field size. For Co^{60} radiation, a table of mean correction factors for lung tissue, calculated as above, has been published by Batho.[28]

At points more than a few centimetres from the inhomogeneity, the effect of the scatter from the inhomogeneity is small, and the correction factor for a given inhomogeneity thickness (d_2-d_1), becomes nearly independent of the distance of the point P from the inhomogeneity (i.e. independent of d_1). For

TABLE 11.04

Inhomogeneity	Direction of movement of isodose curves	Distance moved as a fraction of thickness of inhomogeneity	
		Conventional (2·5 mm. Cu. H.V.L.)	Co^{60} and 4 MV.
Air	Distal	0·5	0·6
Lung	Distal	0·5	0·4
Spongy bone	Proximal	—	0·25
Hard bone	Proximal	0·5	0·5

Co^{60} radiation, lung tissue then produces an increase in dose of the order of 3·5 per cent. per cm. while bone decreases the dose by about the same amount.

An empirical method of correcting for the effect of inhomogeneities, which is often very convenient in practice, consists in merely displacing isodose curves when reading the dose at points shadowed by the inhomogeneity. Greene and Stewart have [29] reported that for Co^{60} and 4 MV. radiation, doses within 2 per cent. of those measured experimentally and for conventional X-radiation (with H.V.L. 2·5 mm. Cu.) doses within 5 per cent. of those measured experimentally were obtained within the shadow if the rules given in Table 11.04 were observed.

Changes in dose-rate just outside the " shadow " cannot be simply predicted and are more wide-spread with conventional than with megavoltage radiation. Greene and Stewart state that dosimetric errors of as much as 10 per cent. may arise when these effects are ignored.

An alternative approach to the question of correcting for tissue inhomogeneity, which is perhaps more useful in rotation than in fixed field therapy, is to measure experimentally the equivalent tissue thickness of any body section by means of a transit dosemeter. The latter usually consists of an ionisation chamber provided with a collimator which prevents most of the scattered radiation from entering the chamber (see fig. 11.18).

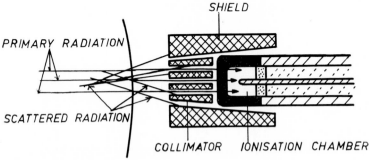

FIG. 11.18. Diagrammatic illustration of a transit dosemeter. The collimator allows only radiation travelling in the direction of the primary beam to reach the ionisation chamber and excludes most of the scattered radiation.

If it can be assumed that only primary radiation enters the chamber (so that the linear attenuation coefficient of the radiation is known), then, from the attenuation of the radiation in the patient, an equivalent thickness of muscle may be calculated. In fixed field therapy such measurements provide a useful check upon whether reasonable assumptions have been made, for example, as to the total amount of lung tissue traversed by a particular field, but can provide no information as to how much of the lung tissue lies in front and how much behind the treatment region. Similarly where bone and air spaces are both traversed, the transit dosemeter measures only the net result on the attenuation of the beam. These limitations are of less importance in rotation therapy where the treatment region is usually fairly centrally placed and is irradiated from many directions. If the treatment region can be regarded as irradiated

421

by many parallel opposed pairs of fields, and the contributions for each member of a pair are nearly equal, it makes comparatively little difference to the dose estimate how the total tissue deficit (say) is distributed between the two members of a pair.

11.14. The dose absorbed in soft tissue elements in bone [2, 30]

Because bone contains calcium and phosphorus, its effective atomic number is greater than that of muscle or air. Consequently at low energies at which photo-electric absorption is appreciable, or at very high energies where pair production

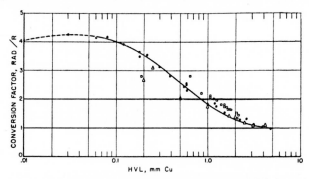

FIG. 11.19.   Rad per roentgen conversion factor (f) in bone.[1]
Courtesy of United States National Bureau of Standards.

is appreciable, the energy absorption per gram of bone is greater than in muscle or air. (See Chapter VI.)   Thus while the rad per roentgen factor (f) for muscle remains constant within a few per cent. regardless of photon energy, the rad per roentgen factor for compact bone increases rapidly below about 300 keV. and it also rises (although more slowly) above 6 MeV.   The variation of f for bone was discussed in Chapter VII and fig. 7.03 of that chapter shows values of f_{bone} as a function of photon energy.   For X-ray beams, it is necessary to calculate a value of f averaged over the appropriate energy spectrum.   Fig. 11.19 gives such values as a function of half-value-layer.

For those radiation energies at which bone absorbs more energy per unit mass than soft tissue, the dose received by any tissue elements within the range of secondary electrons from bone is greater than the dose received by tissue elements remote

422

from bone. It is important to calculate the magnitude of this effect, since radiation damage to bone is believed to be due to harmful effects on the soft tissue elements, particularly the blood capillaries which are carried in the Haversian canals.

Consider soft tissue in a cavity within bone. If the dimensions of the cavity are much less than the average range of the secondary electrons (about $2\,\mu$ for 200 kVp. radiation), the

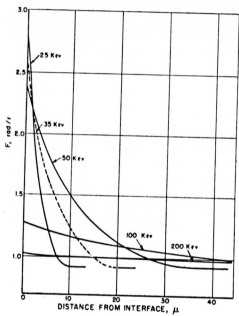

Fig. 11.20. The variation of the rad per roentgen factor (f) with distance from a bone/ muscle interface.[2]
Courtesy of United States National Bureau of Standards.

number of electrons crossing the cavity, and, therefore, the ionisation produced in the cavity is determined mainly by the number of electrons generated, and, therefore, by the energy absorbed in the bone. The ionisation in such a cavity can be calculated using the theory developed in connection with thimble ionisation chambers. In larger cavities, the ionisation produced in the soft tissue varies from a value at the edges partly determined by the energy absorption in bone, to a value at the centre which becomes equal to that which would be produced in a large region of soft tissue, when the radius of the cavity exceeds the range of the most energetic secondary electrons (about 100 μ for 200 kVp. radiation).

Thus the absorbed dose per roentgen exposure (or the rad per roentgen factor f) in soft tissue near bone is a function of the distance from the interface. The variation of f with this distance for different energy radiations is shown in fig. 11.20. The soft tissue elements in bone vary considerably in size, but mean values of the rad per roentgen factor averaged over cavities of specified size, which are believed to be typical of different soft tissue components, are given in Table 11.05. The

TABLE 11.05

RAD PER ROENTGEN FACTOR FOR MEAN DOSES TO SOFT TISSUE
COMPONENTS IN BONE [2]

Photon Energy keV.	Approximately Equivalent Half-value layer	Osteocyte (5 μ diam.)	" Average soft tissue "	10 μ lining of 50 μ Haversian canal	Marrow
25	1 mm. Al.	2·80	1·73	1·50	1·05
35	4 mm. Al.	3·12	2·05	1·76	—
50	{ 7 mm. Al. 0·3 mm. Cu.	3·25	2·27	1·89	1·13
75	1·0 mm. Cu.	2·40	1·85	1·60	—
100	1·8 mm. Cu.	1·52	1·36	1·26	1·07
200	5·0 mm. Cu.	1·05	1·03₅	1·02	1·01

values given in the column headed " average soft tissue " were calculated assuming one-half of the soft tissue is contained within Haversian canals of diameter 50 μ and the remainder in lacunae and canaliculi of 10 μ diameter. The spaces in trabecular bone which contain red marrow are on the average considerably larger than the Haversian canals, so the mean marrow dose is not greatly increased by electrons originating in the bone. The values in the last column of Table 11.05 were calculated assuming the average diameter of a marrow interspace to be 400 μ.

It will be noted in Table 11.05 that the maximum value for the absorbed dose occurs at a photon energy of 50 keV. (corresponding to a half-value thickness for X-rays of the order of

7 mm. Al. or 0·3 mm. Cu.). The energy absorption in compact bone relative to that in a large region of soft tissue is actually a maximum at a lower energy than this (about 30 keV., see fig. 7.03) but for the cavity sizes considered, the decreasing range of the secondary electrons between 50 and 30 keV. results in a net decrease in the average dose. In the energy range 200 keV. to 10 MeV. the energy absorption per gramme in bone and hence also the absorbed dose in soft tissue elements within or near bone, does not differ from that in soft tissue by more than a few per cent. This is one of the principal advantages of using radiation with photon energy greater than 200 keV. for therapy. Above 10 MeV. the energy absorption in bone relative to that in soft tissue increases appreciably on account of pair production, but the secondary electron range is then several centimetres, so bone thicknesses are not normally sufficient to produce full electronic build-up.

11.15. Treatment planning in X- and γ-ray teletherapy

Before considering the planning of teletherapy treatments, it may be useful to summarise the data which the preceding discussion show to be necessary if a reliable estimate of the dose absorbed in any treatment is to be obtained.

It is necessary firstly to specify fully the radiation beams to be used. This specification should include

(1) the quality of the radiation (for X-rays, the half-value thickness should be measured experimentally);

(2) the source-skin distance or source-axis distance;

(3) the field size and the type of applicator if any.

From this information the following tables or charts can be prepared for each set of operating conditions.

(1) A table showing either the absorbed dose-rate at the reference point or the time or monitor setting required to deliver a given dose (e.g. 100 rads) to the reference point, for each field size, for each set of operating conditions.

(2) Tables of central axis, soft tissue, depth dose data and isodose charts in at least one principal plane (for

425

rectangular fields isodose charts for both major and minor axes are necessary) for each treatment field. It is convenient if the isodose charts are drawn on a transparent base so that they may be superimposed on anatomical sections in treatment planning.

(3) A table of correction factors to be applied to the standard data for absorption in different media.

Charts showing anatomical details are also useful.

To obtain uniform dose distributions (and incidentally to facilitate calculations), when X-radiation generated below about 400 kVp. is used, irregular air spaces may be filled with " bolus ", that is a material having the same X-ray absorbing and scattering properties as tissue. For example, when stationary fields are applied obliquely at the skin surface, the space between the skin and the end of the treatment cone is normally so filled. It is also sometimes advantageous to use bolus where an X-ray beam emerges to build up the scatter at the exit surface. A mixture of 50 per cent. sodium bicarbonate and 50 per cent. magnesium carbonate was at one time widely used, but since the properties of any powder form of bolus depend quite considerably upon how tightly the powder is packed, this has been largely replaced by a bolus material in the form of small spheres consisting of 87 per cent. sucrose and 13 per cent. magnesium carbonate (wt./wt.).[31] The mixture of solid spheres and air interstices provides a material which is tissue equivalent and does not vary with packing conditions as does a powder bolus. With high energy radiation, bolus is normally only used when it is desired to bring the treatment region up to the skin surface. For the treatment of tissues at a depth, one of the principal advantages of high energy radiation is that the skin dose is low. If bolus is used, the initial electron build-up occurs in the bolus and the advantage of a low skin dose is lost.

Now let us consider the problem of delivering a lethal dose of radiation throughout a particular region, without at the same time delivering a harmful dose to adjacent normal tissue.

The simplest case is that in which the region to be treated is situated at the skin surface and is not very deep. In this case, a single field of fairly soft radiation directed normally to the skin surface will deliver a greater dose at the surface than to underlying tissues. The cross-section of the radiation field is selected so that it just covers the region to be treated. The quality of the radiation used is chosen so that the lower limit of the treatment region receives a predetermined percentage of the skin dose. With one field the lower layers of the treatment region inevitably receive a smaller dose than the superficial layers. To obtain a more uniform dose throughout the region and also when the underlying tissues are particularly radio-sensitive, it may be preferable to use two or more radiation beams of greater penetrating power, directed approximately tangentially to the skin surface. (See fig. 11.21.)

If the region to be treated lies below the skin surface, then, unless very high energy radiation is available, it is essential to use at least two beams in order to deliver a dose to the treatment region greater than that delivered elsewhere. The precise number of the beams depends upon the radiation available and the size and shape of the block of tissue in which the treatment region is situated.

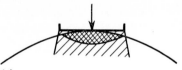

(a) SINGLE FIELD—SOFT RADIATION

Multi-field treatments

In planning multi-field treatments, the following points should be observed:

(1) The area of the fields is selected so that at the depth of the tumour each field just covers the region to be treated.

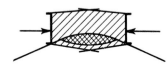

(b) OPPOSED "TANGENTIAL" FIELDS

FIG. 11.21.   Irradiation of superficial region.

(2) Adjacent fields must not overlap at or near the skin surface and the beam edges should preferably be separated by several centimetres.

(3) The greater the number of fields used the greater is the ratio tumour dose/given dose per field. (The term

427

" given dose " is used to describe the dose delivered by a single field at the usual reference point, i.e. at the skin surface or at the peak of the dose curve for constant S.S.D. techniques and at the centre of rotation for constant S.A.D. techniques.)

(4) Dose calculations are simplified if coplanar fields are used.

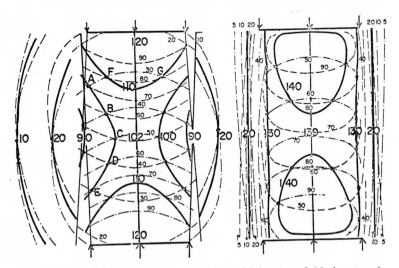

FIG. 11.22. Distributions obtained by combining two fields in opposition.[2] The diagrams show 6×6 cm.[2] fields, 12 cm. apart. *Left:* H.V.L. = 3·0 mm. Cu, S.S.D. = 50 cm. *Right:* Co[60]. S.S.D. = 80 cm.

Courtesy of United States National Bureau of Standards.

(5) It is usually considered desirable to obtain a uniform distribution of dose throughout the treatment region. This is most easily obtained if a symmetrical arrangement of fields is used, e.g. three coplanar fields inclined at 120° to one another, two pairs of opposing fields, etc. If the fields in a symmetrical arrangement are equidistant from the centre of the treatment region, then equal doses can be given on each field. It is not always anatomically possible to use equidistant symmetrically arranged fields, however, and it is then necessary to give unequal doses on the various fields to obtain a reasonably uniform distribution. (Examples are given below.)

428

It is necessary to exercise discretion in deciding to what extent the dose delivered by distant fields shall be increased relative to that delivered by " near " fields in order to obtain a uniform distribution, since it is not desirable to irradiate large volumes of tissue to a high level to obtain a slight improvement in the distribution. (See section 11.17.)

Dose distributions are usually calculated as follows. If only two fields are to be used, the isodose curves of the resultant distribution can be obtained by joining the points of intersection of the appropriate isodose curves for the separate fields as shown in fig. 11.22. When more than two fields are to be used, it is usually easiest to place a transparent isodose chart representing one field only over the appropriate anatomical section and to tabulate the contribution from this field to the dose at each of a set of lattice points covering the region of interest. This process is repeated for each field in turn and the total dose at each point is then calculated. This may be recorded directly or isodose contours may be interpolated.

Combination of two co-planar fields

With two directly opposed fields irradiating a homogeneous block of soft tissue, the entire block of tissue between the fields is irradiated and the dose does not vary very greatly from point to point. As the separation of the fields increases, the dose on the central axis at the mid-point may at first increase slightly relative to that at either surface, but as the separation is further increased the dose at the mid-point falls relative to that near the surface. It can be seen from fig. 11.23 that if the dose at the mid-point is not to be less than (say) 95 per cent. of the dose near the surface, then (for 10×10 cm.^{2} fields) the field separation must be restricted to values less than 12·5 cm. for radiation with H.V.L. 1·5 mm. Cu (50 cm. S.S.D.) to 15 cm. with Co^{60} radiation (80 cm. S.S.D.) to 17·5 cm. with 4 MV. radiation (100 cm. S.S.D.) and 21·5 cm. with 8 MV. radiation (100 cm. S.S.D.). The above separations represent approximately the maximum thicknesses of tissue which can be irradiated homogeneously by two parallel opposed fields of the radiation quality specified. The dose received at the lateral edges of the

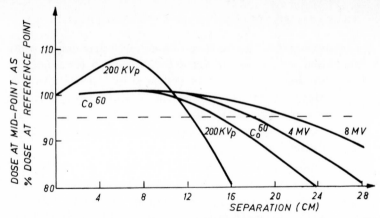

FIG. 11.23. The variation of the dose at the mid-point between two parallel opposed fields with the separation of the fields. The dose at the mid-point is expressed as a percentage of the (total) dose at the reference depth from either surface. 10 × 10 cm.² fields, in each case. 200 kVp., 50 cm. S.S.D.; Co⁶⁰, 80 cm. S.S.D.; 4 MV. and 8 MV., 100 cm. S.S.D.

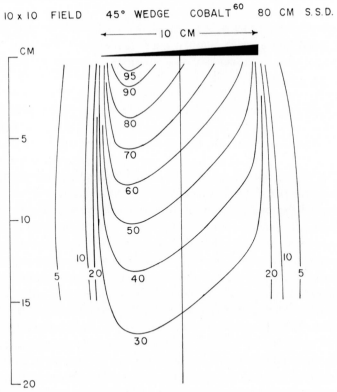

FIG. 11.24. Isodose curves for a wedged field. Co⁶⁰. 80 cm. S.S.D.

430

fields is less than on the central axis, the difference being greater at the lower energies (see fig. 11.22).

For the treatment of a fairly small region lying within a few centimetres of the surface, two inclined coplanar fields with wedge filters may be used to produce a uniform dose distribution. Wedge filters,[32] as their name implies, are filters which introduce more absorbing material at one side of the radiation beam than at the other. They are usually constructed

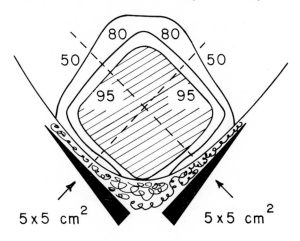

ANTERIOR

Fig. 11.25. Dose distribution obtained by combining two wedged fields at right angles, for treatment of the larynx. Co[60] radiation. S.S.D. = 80 cm. 5 × 5 cm.[2] fields with 45° wedges. Full bolus. Equal given doses on each field = 66 per cent. of treatment dose.

from plates of metal, each successive plate being narrower than the one below it.[33] The metal which is used depends upon the quality of the radiation. The relative widths of the different sections are chosen so that the isodose surfaces of a beam with which the filter is used, instead of lying approximately at right angles to the central axis, lie at some selected angle to the axis, e.g. 30°, 45°, 60°. (See fig. 11.24.) In general it is not possible to design a wedge filter so that all the isodose curves make the selected angle with the axis of the beam, but for megavoltage radiation the differences are quite small. In the 200-400 kVp.

431

range, there is a continuous change in angle in going from low to high values of the percentage depth dose and this makes wedge filter combinations less satisfactory at these energies. If two wedge fields are suitably combined, a region of uniform dose is produced. For example, two " 45° fields " combined at right angles produce a region of uniform dose within a square. (See fig. 11.25.)

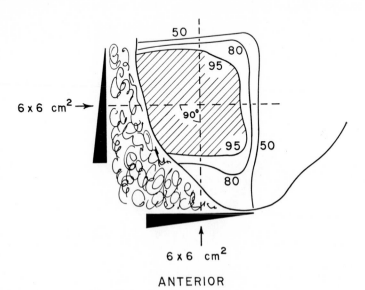

ANTERIOR

FIG. 11.26. Dose distribution obtained by combining two wedged fields at right angles, for treatment of right posterior alveolus. Co^{60} radiation. S.S.D. = 80 cm. 6×6 cm.² fields with 45° wedges. Full bolus. Equal given doses on each field = 78 per cent. of treatment dose.

Wedge fields are particularly useful in treating limited regions of the head and neck and some typical examples using 45° wedges with Co^{60} radiation are illustrated in figs. 11.25, 11.26 and 11.27. Fig. 11.25 shows a treatment plan for the larynx and figs. 11.26 and 11.27 show two plans covering approximately the same region for treatment of the right posterior alveolus. In these and the subsequent figures, the shaded area represents the region throughout which the dose is within ±5 per cent. of the prescribed treatment dose.

432

In fig. 11.27, in order to maintain a low dose-rate on the anterior skin surface, bolus has been omitted anteriorly. The missing absorber partially counteracts the effect of the wedge

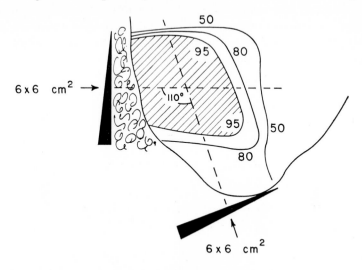

ANTERIOR

FIG. 11.27. Dose distribution obtained by combining two wedged fields as shown for treatment of right posterior alveolus. Co⁶⁰ radiation. S.S.D. = 80 cm. 6×6 cm.² fields with 45° wedges. Wedge angle 110°. Full bolus on lateral field. No bolus on anterior field. Equal given doses on each field = 75 per cent. of treatment dose.

on the anterior field and to maintain a uniform dose distribution, the angle between the fields has been increased from 90° to 110°. Alternative methods would be to employ a wedge of greater angle with the anterior field, or to use a compensating filter.

Combinations of three or more co-planar fields

For the treatment of small volumes at somewhat greater depths, it is necessary to use at least three treatment fields. Three fields at 120° to one another or a parallel opposed wedged pair balancing a third field (unwedged) at right angles, are frequently used. A typical treatment plan of the latter type

433

(again using Co⁶⁰ radiation) for the treatment of the pituitary is shown in fig. 11.28. In this case, the given dose is not the same on all fields. In order to obtain a uniform distribution throughout the treatment volume, the contribution from the anterior field has been adjusted so that the dose gradient along the anterior-posterior axis due to the anterior field, just balances the gradient in this direction due to the two lateral fields. The

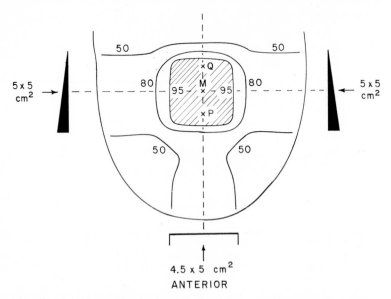

Fig. 11.28. Dose distribution obtained by combining a pair of opposed wedged fields with a third field at right angles, for treatment of the pituitary. Co⁶⁰ radiation. S.S.D. = 80 cm. Lateral fields 5×5 cm.² with 45° wedges. Anterior field 4·5×5 cm.² Given dose on each lateral field = 56·5 per cent. of treatment dose. Given dose on anterior field = 64·5 per cent. of treatment dose.

calculation of the given dose required per field is as follows. The dose is balanced about the two points P and Q shown in fig. 11.28. The percentage depth dose at P from the anterior field is 64 per cent. and at Q it is 50 per cent. The percentage depth doses for each of the wedged lateral fields are 52 per cent. at P and 60 per cent. at Q. Let D_A denote the given dose on the anterior field and D_L the given dose on each lateral field (the given doses on the two lateral fields will be equal in this particular case because the treatment volume is equidistant from each lateral field). Then

$$\text{dose at } P = \frac{64}{100} D_A + \left(2 \times \frac{52}{100}\right) D_L$$

$$\text{dose at } Q = \frac{50}{100} D_A + \left(2 \times \frac{60}{100}\right) D_L$$

Equating these doses

$$(64-50)D_A = 2(60-52)D_L$$

$$\therefore \qquad \frac{D_A}{D_L} = \frac{16}{14} = 1{\cdot}15,$$

i.e. for every 100 rads given on the lateral fields, 115 rads should be given on the anterior field to obtain a balanced distribution. If this is done, the dose at P becomes $= 177{\cdot}6$ per cent. D_L. The dose at other points can be obtained similarly, e.g. at M the percentage depth dose from the anterior field is 57 per cent. and from each lateral field 58 per cent. Therefore the total dose at M

$$= \left(1{\cdot}15 \times \frac{57}{100} + 2 \times \frac{58}{100}\right) D_L$$

$$= \left(\frac{65{\cdot}5 + 116}{100}\right) D_L = \frac{181{\cdot}5}{100} D_L.$$

In this particular case, the prescribed treatment dose was 5,500 rads and the mean dose throughout the treatment volume was estimated as 178 per cent. D_L. The given doses were therefore 3,100 rads on each lateral field and 3,550 rads on the anterior field.

In this example, the lateral fields were equidistant from the centre of the treatment region. When this is not the case, then an exactly similar balancing procedure may be used to determine the required dose ratio between the lateral fields.

As an illustration of the use of three fields inclined at 120° to one another, figs. 11.29 and 11.30 show two plans for treating the bladder and the oesophagus respectively. In fig. 11.29 the region to be treated is symmetrically placed with respect to the mid-sagittal plane, in fig. 11.30 it is slightly displaced laterally. In the latter case, the relative values of the given doses per field required for uniform irradiation of the treatment volume could be calculated by first balancing the contributions of the two posterior-oblique fields at two points such as *L* and *M*, and then balancing the combined doses from the posterior fields at *P* and *Q* by the contributions from the anterior field. However, when fields of approximately equal area are arranged symmetrically about the treatment centre, the dose distribution

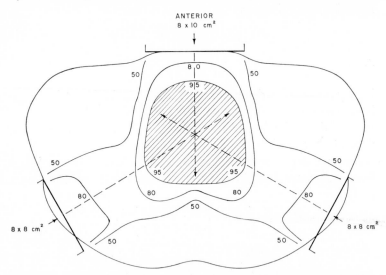

Fig. 11.29. Dose distribution obtained by combining three fields inclined at 120° for treatment of the bladder. Co⁶⁰ radiation. S.S.D. = 80 cm. Anterior field 8×10 cm.² Given dose = 58 per cent. of treatment dose. Posterior-lateral oblique fields 8×8 cm.² Given dose = 89 per cent. of treatment dose.

is balanced more simply by adjusting the given dose per field so that each field makes the same contribution to the dose at the treatment centre. (This results from the fact that the dose gradient due to a single field is proportional to the percentage depth dose if the dose varies exponentially with depth.)

In the example shown in 11.30, the anterior field delivers 40·5 per cent. of the given dose to the treatment centre. For the left posterior oblique field, the percentage depth dose as read from the isodose curve (allowing for oblique incidence) is 36·5 per cent. When this is corrected to allow for the fact that the beam traverses 9 cm. of lung tissue, the dose delivered

436

becomes 46·5 per cent. of the given dose. Similarly the right posterior oblique field (after allowing for passage through 8 cm. of lung) contributes 40·9 per cent. In this particular case

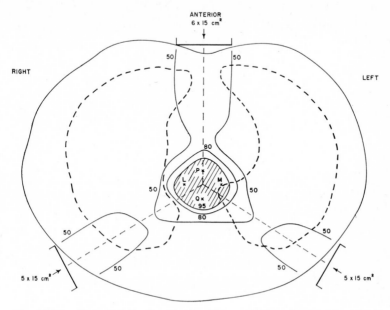

FIG. 11.30. Dose distribution obtained by combining three fields at 120° for treatment of the oesophagus. Co⁶⁰ radiation. S.S.D. = 80 cm. Anterior field 6×15 cm.², given dose = 82·5 per cent. of treatment dose. Right lateral posterior oblique field 5×15 cm.² given dose = 81·5 per cent. of treatment dose. Left lateral posterior oblique field 5×15 cm.² given dose = 72 per cent. of treatment dose. The distribution shown has been corrected for surface obliquity and the presence of lung tissue.

the total dose at the treatment centre was to be 5,500 rads, so each field must contribute 1,833 rads at the centre, i.e.

$$\frac{40\cdot5}{100}D_A = 1,833 \qquad \therefore \quad D_A = 4,526 \text{ rads}$$

$$\frac{46\cdot5}{100}D_L = 1,833 \qquad \therefore \quad D_L = 3,942 \text{ rads}$$

$$\frac{40\cdot9}{100}D_R = 1,833 \qquad \therefore \quad D_R = 4,482 \text{ rads.}$$

For most patients, the bladder may be adequately treated with three fields using Co⁶⁰ radiation, as shown in fig. 11.29, but

15

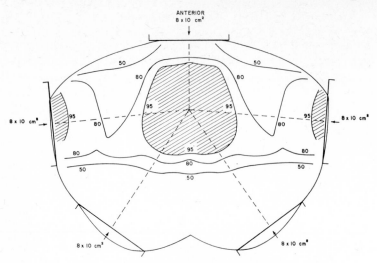

FIG. 11.31. Dose distribution obtained by combining five fields (10×8 cm.²) as shown for treatment of the bladder in a large patient. Co⁶⁰ radiation. S.S.D. = 80 cm. Given doses: anterior field = 35 per cent., lateral fields = 90 per cent., posterior oblique fields 37 per cent. of the treatment dose.

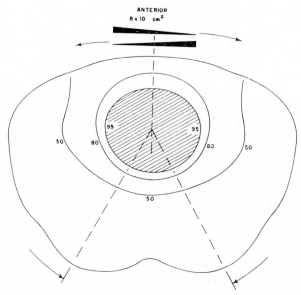

FIG. 11.32. Dose distribution obtained by combination of two arcs of 150° using 8×10 cm.² fields with 45° wedges as shown, for treatment of the bladder in a large patient. Co⁶⁰ radiation. S.A.D. = 90 cm.

438

for the largest patients, it may not be possible to deliver a balanced dose at the tumour centre without exceeding the maximum permissible given dose on one of the posterior oblique fields. Hence, in the larger patients either five stationary fields (fig. 11.31) or a rotation technique (fig. 11.32) are commonly employed.

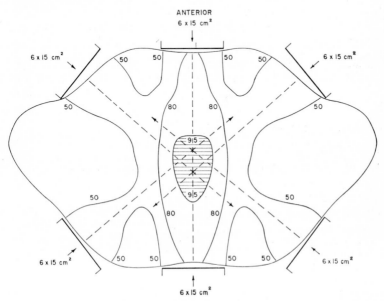

FIG. 11.33. Dose distribution obtained by combination of six fields for treatment of the oesophagus. 250 kVp. X-radiation. H.V.L. 1·75 mm. Cu. S.S.D. = 50 cm. Fields 6 × 15 cm.²

One of the main difficulties in treating the bladder is to deliver an adequate dose to the posterior bladder wall without delivering an undesirably high dose to the rectum. The treatments shown here have been planned to keep the rectal dose low. The rotation plan, using wedges, produces a distribution comparable with that obtained using a single anterior field and a parallel opposed wedged pair (as illustrated in the case of the pituitary). This is superior to rotation without wedges since the penumbra region posterior to the high dose zone is reduced.[34]

The plans illustrated above all use Co[60] radiation. For 1 to 10 MV. X-radiation treatment plans are essentially similar, although for the more energetic radiation (generated at 6 MV. or above say) it is probably possible to treat all sites in all patients without using more than three fields. If only radiation generated in the 200 to 400 kVp. range is available, treatment plans for the deeper sites necessarily become more complicated than with megavoltage radiation, since more fields are required to deliver the same total dose to the treatment region without exceeding the maximum permissible given dose per field. Thus many regions in the head and neck which can be treated by two megavoltage fields require a three-field plan with 200-400 kVp. X-rays, and for the treatment of a deep-seated lesion in the trunk six or more fields may be necessary. Fig. 11.33 shows a typical six-field plan for treatment of the oesophagus using 250 kVp. radiation.

11.16. Practical aspects of treatment planning

Beam direction devices and tumour location

If treatment plans of the type discussed in the preceding section are to be carried out in practice, it is essential that the radiation beams be accurately located and directed with respect to the region to be treated. The point at which the central axis of a radiation beam is incident upon the patient's skin is usually referred to as the " entrance point " of the particular field. This point is marked either directly on the skin or, if the treatment region lies beneath mobile tissues or in a part of the body which is not readily immobilised, upon a treatment " shell ". Treatment shells are usually made from thin sheets of cellulose acetate which can be moulded upon a plaster cast of the patient (see figs. 11.38 and 11.39). These shells are worn during treatments to reduce errors that may arise from relative movement between the skin and underlying tissues or from movement of the patient relative to the treatment beam and are discussed further below.

In addition to the entrance point, it is necessary to fix the direction of each treatment beam. This may be done either by marking the position at which the central axis shall emerge (the " exit point ") or by specifying the angle at which the beam shall be directed. The former method is preferable when the exit point is in such a position that it is accessible during the treatment. A " back pointer " may then be used to ensure that the central axis of the beam is correctly directed. The back pointer consists of a rigid metal hook which can be attached to the master cone of the therapy machine and which will carry a pointer constrained to lie along the central axis of the beam (see figs. 11.34 and 11.39(a)). In some models, the pointer is calibrated so that it may also be used to measure the separation of the entrance and exit points. If the radiation beam is adjusted so that the centre of the treatment cone and the back pointer are accurately placed on the entrance and exit point

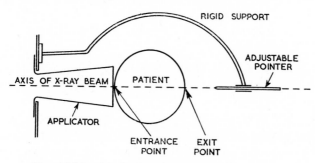

FIG. 11.34. A " back pointer " for beam direction.

respectively, the direction of the beam through the patient is fixed. If cones are not used, the position of the central axis of the beam on the incident surface is normally indicated by a light beam and the mechanical back-pointer may also be replaced by an optical pointer. In rotation units provided with a primary beam shield and counterweight, the light source for the optical back pointer can be mounted in the beam shield and the rather cumbersome metal hook is then unnecessary.

When a patient is lying upon a couch, so that the exit point cannot be reached, the beam direction can be fixed, instead, by specifying the angle at which the beam enters the skin (in addition to the entrance point). The determination of the correct angle is facilitated by the use of a specially designed protractor [35] (see fig. 11.35) which is large enough to be set over the patient's body and can be adjusted so that the horizontal base line lies in the plane of the tumour and the vertical 0° line is vertically above the tumour. If the X-ray beam is set up so that the central axis points in the direction of any line on the protractor, then the beam is directed at the tumour centre. Crossmarks on the protractor at a known distance from the centre enable the distance of the applicator from the centre to be determined. Such protractors are necessarily large and cumbersome and are not very often used in practice. A more compact device which may be considered as a partial protractor and fulfils essentially the same function is the pin and arc. This consists of an arc carried on a metal bar from the head of the

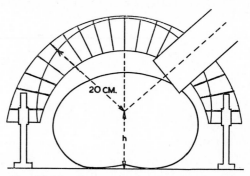

FIG. 11.35. A protractor for beam direction.

treatment machine, as illustrated in fig. 11.36. The arc can be moved along the bar in the direction of the central axis. The centre of the arc is in the central axis of the beam. A pin is mounted on the arc in such a way as to lie in the plane of the arc and to be directed towards the centre. In order to use this instrument the pin is first withdrawn from the centre of the arc a depth (H) equal to the depth of the treatment centre below the skin surface. It is then moved to the selected angle (A) from the central axis and the head of the therapy set is adjusted so that the beam axis is at the same angle to the vertical. This brings the pin into a vertical position and the applicator is then lowered and the arc moved in or out on the bar until the pin rests on the surface vertically above the tumour. The X-ray beam is then automatically directed at the tumour centre.

We have assumed above that the location of the treatment region and the position of entrance and exit points have already been determined. Except for a limited number of sites which can be accurately located by reference to external anatomical landmarks, the determination of the location and extent of the treatment region is usually carried out radiographically. Two radiographs taken at right angles are generally required although other methods such as tomography may also be employed. It is necessary when taking localising radiographs to place

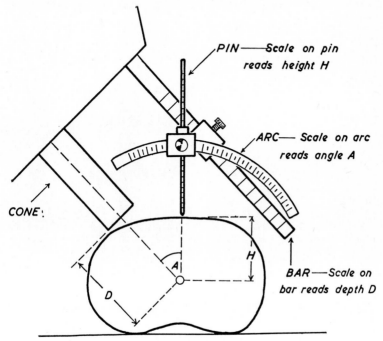

FIG. 11.36. " Pin and arc " for beam direction.

suitable markers on the patient's skin or on the treatment shell if one is to be used. These markers provide reference points for the location of the treatment fields and also enable the magnification of the radiographs (in the plane of the marker) to be determined. The placing of markers and the particular marker construction which is most useful varies from one site to another. Some examples are shown in fig. 11.37.

As a typical example of a localisation procedure, we consider the determination of the required entrance and exit points for implementing a three-field plan for treatment of the pituitary (as shown in fig. 11.28) in a particular case. The patient will

wear a shell for this treatment, so the first stage is to make a
plaster bandage shell which will act as a mould for a plaster

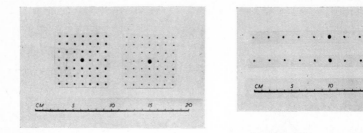

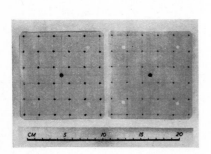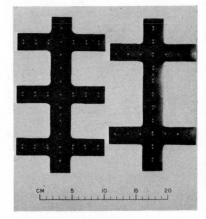

FIG. 11.37. Typical " markers " (consisting of lead inserts in plastic
sheet) used when taking localising radiographs.

cast (fig. 11.38(a)). The treatment shell of cellulose acetate is
then shaped upon the plaster cast (fig. 11.38(b)). Radiographs

FIG. 11.38. Steps in the preparation of a cellulose acetate treatment shell:
(a) making a plaster bandage shell;
(b) the cellulose acetate shell is moulded on the plaster cast;
(c) a localising radiograph is taken with markers attached to the shell;
(d) the location of the central axis of the anterior field, and any other
convenient line which passes through the treatment centre are marked
on the radiograph;
(e) steel rods are inserted in the shell to locate the central axis of the
anterior field and the position of the treatment centre;
(f) the patient's contour in the proposed treatment plane is transferred to
paper.

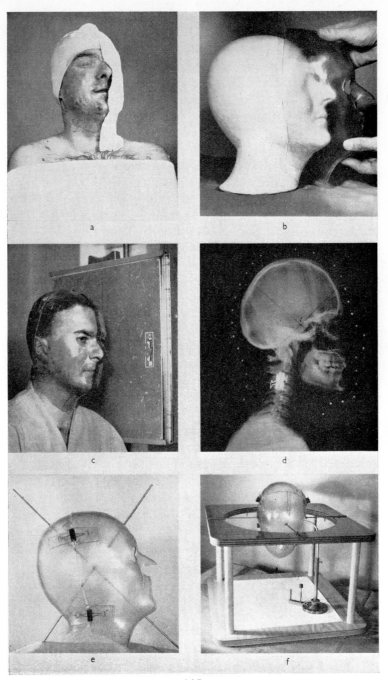

are taken with the patient wearing the cellulose acetate shell, with marker strips attached. In this case, since the treatment region lies in the mid-sagittal plane, a lateral radiograph is taken with markers placed anteriorly and posteriorly along the mid-line (fig. 11.38(c)). The treatment region is noted on the radiograph and a convenient axis for the anterior field is selected and marked. The entrance and exit points for the anterior field are thus fixed and can be located on the shell by reference to the markers. The position of the centre of the treatment region can be located as a certain fraction of the distance between entrance and exit points from (say) the entrance point for the anterior field, or by selecting a second axis passing through the treatment centre. The latter method has been adopted in the example shown (fig. 11.38(d)). Steel rods representing the axes drawn on the radiograph are passed through the treatment shell and enable the treatment centre to be located within the shell (fig. 11.38(e)). A steel rod passing through the treatment centre at right angles to the axis of the anterior field then locates the entrance and exit points for the parallel opposed lateral fields. The magnification of the radiograph is known from the markers so the required field sizes can also be determined. The contour in the treatment plane which is used in the dose estimation is determined from the shell (fig. 11.38(f)). With megavoltage radiation, the appropriate sized windows are cut in the treatment shell and some type of frame is usually affixed to the shell to aid in the accurate placement of the treatment beams (see fig. 11.39(a) and (c)). Fig. 11.39(b) shows a radiograph taken with the therapy machine to verify that the (lateral) fields are correctly located and directed.

The location of the treatment region has been simplified in this case because the centre was located on the mid-sagittal plane. In general a second radiograph is taken at right angles to the first to locate the treatment region completely. If the treatment region is to be extended to the skin surface, or low energy radiation is to be employed, then the appropriate regions of the shell are built up with wax (fig. 11.40(a)). In cases in which shells are not used, markers of the grid type (shown in fig. 11.37 and 11.40(b)) are useful, since any two markers, one on the anterior grid and one on the posterior grid which appear

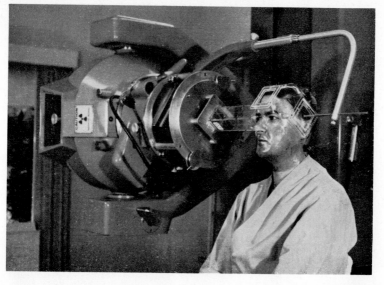

(a)

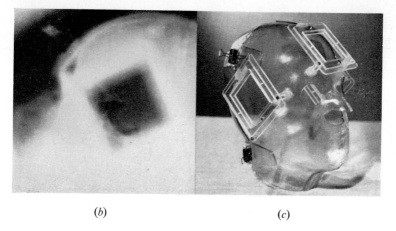

(b)   (c)

FIG. 11.39. (a) The patient wearing the completed shell, being positioned for treatment. The treatment cone of the therapy machine is located in the appropriate frame of the shell and the back pointer is in contact with the exit point.

(b) A radiograph taken with the therapy machine to confirm that the beam is correctly located and directed.

(c) Detail of the completed shell, showing removal of the cellulose acetate in the path of the treatment beams and the addition of frames which fit around the treatment cone of the therapy machine.

447

on a radiograph to coincide with one another and with the centre of the treatment region, will define a line passing through the treatment centre.

As a second typical example, we consider the location of the appropriate reference points required for treating a bladder by the plan illustrated in fig. 11.29. The region to be treated in this case was determined by taking radiographs with a small amount of contrast medium in the bladder. (An olive-tip

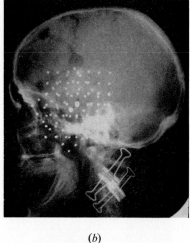

(a)   (b)

FIG. 11.40. (a) A treatment shell with frames for a wedged pair of fields in which the angle between the two fields has been filled by wax. The cylinder projecting from the shell on the right side of the photograph will hold the back pointer.

(b) Radiograph illustrating the use of the grid type of marker in locating a treatment area. (The lines on the grid on the left side run horizontally and vertically, the lines on the grid on the right side are at 45° to the horizontal and vertical.)

Foley catheter with 5 cc. bulb is used to introduce about 20 cc. of dye. A small piece of lead inserted in the olive tip is sometimes of assistance in delimiting the bladder.) Plastic strips carrying distinctive patterns of lead markers are taped to the patient's skin on the mid line, anterior and posterior to the bladder (see fig. 11.41). It is convenient to take an A.P. radiograph first, to determine whether the treatment centre shall be in the midsagittal plane or displaced laterally. If it is to be displaced considerably then the markers shown are moved laterally to lie over the estimated position of the treatment centre (and a second A.P. radiograph obtained before their position is marked with carbofushin or silver nitrate). Lateral radiographs are then taken with the patient prone and with the patient supine. The limits of the region to be treated are outlined on the radiographs (see fig. 11.41(c) and (d)). From the supine lateral radiograph, the position of a point on the anterior skin which lies vertically above the selected treatment centre (C) can be determined relative to the marker strip and also the depth (d_A say) below the surface of the treatment centre. Similarly from the prone lateral radiograph, the position of a similar point on the posterior surface and the distance (d_P) of this point from the treatment centre can be determined. (The bladder may move relative to the skin surfaces when the patient turns over, so the sum of the distances $d_A + d_P$ is not necessarily equal to the thickness of the patient. The distances d_A and d_P may be calculated as a fraction of the measured thickness in the appropriate position or by direct measurement on the radiograph using the magnification factor indicated by the markers.) When the depth of the treatment centre below the anterior surface is determined, the magnification on the A.P. film at this depth is calculated in order to determine the dimensions of the treatment area marked on the A.P. radiograph. When the patient is to be treated, the anterior field is centred on the selected point on the anterior surface and is directed vertically. For the posterior oblique fields, the pin of the pin and arc is placed directly over the selected point on the posterior surface and the pin withdrawn to the depth d_P. With the arc set at 60° and the central axis of the treatment beam also inclined at 60° to the vertical, the oblique fields then pass through the selected treatment centre. The distance of the skin surface from the treatment centre measured along the axis of each oblique field is obtained from the bar reading. These distances together with the distances d_A and d_P (and perhaps one or two measurements of skin to cone distance to determine the obliquity of the skin surface under the posterior fields) are transferred to paper, for the dose calculation, as indicated in the preceding section.

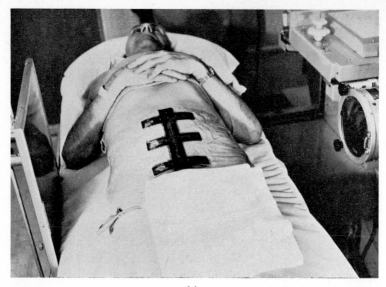

(*a*)

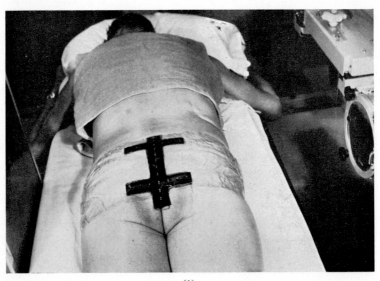

(*b*)

FIG. 11.41.   Determination of the location of the treatment region in a case of bladder cancer

(*a*) and (*b*) The patient wearing marker strips while the localising radiographs are taken.

(*c*) Typical A.P. radiograph with limits of treatment volume outlined. The treatment centre in this case is in the mid-sagittal plane.

(*d*) Typical lateral radiograph (patient supine).

Courtesy of G. B. Goodman, British Columbia Cancer Institute.

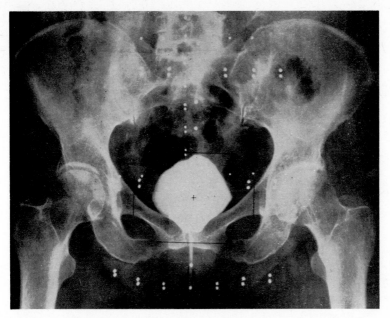

(c)

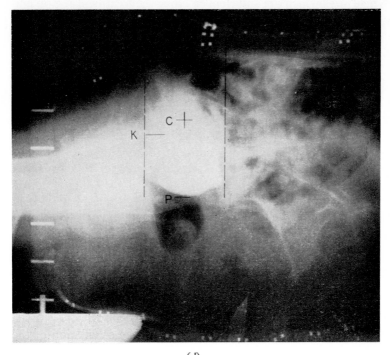

(d)

451

11.17. Integral dose

The aim in radiotherapy is to deliver a lethal dose to a particular region without at the same time harming adjacent normal tissue. The ideal would be to irradiate the selected region only without delivering any radiation elsewhere. It may be possible in some cases to approach this ideal by the use of radioactive material localised in the treatment region but it is not possible with external sources of radiation. It is interesting to compare the total energy absorption in different treatments with the energy delivered to the local treatment region. Mayneord[36] first suggested that the total energy absorption during an X-ray treatment should be called the " integral dose " and devised approximate methods of estimating this quantity. The unit in which integral dose is measured is the gram-rad (g.-rad). One g.-rad represents the energy absorbed by one gram of tissue when the dose is 1 rad. 1 g.-rad $=$ 100 ergs.

In external beam therapy, the integral dose for a given tumour dose is made as small as possible by (1) using the smallest field sizes which are sufficient to cover the treatment region and (2) by directing the fields through skin surfaces near to the treatment region. Increases in the ratio of the tumour dose to the given dose per field, or in the homogeneity of a distribution, which are brought about by adding fields directed through skin surfaces remote from the tumour, result in an increased integral dose and this must be borne in mind in treatment planning. In rotation therapy, for example, the value of the tumour dose/skin dose ratio is normally greater than in fixed field therapy with the same radiation, but this is attained at the cost of giving greater integral doses. If radiation up to about 100 MeV. in energy were generally available, integral doses could be kept to a minimum by selecting for each treatment the radiation quality for which the maximum depth dose occurred at the depth of the tumour. However, most centres have only a limited choice of radiation which is such that the maximum depth dose occurs near the surface. In this case, for tumours at a depth, the integral dose is less, the more penetrating the radiation.

A precise estimate of the total energy absorbed by tissue exposed to a beam of radiation involves the calculation of the volume enclosed between successive isodose surfaces, followed by the summation of the contribution from successive sections. For the calculation of the energy absorbed within the geometrical limits of the radiation beam, the following approximate method of calculation is often adequate. Suppose the isodose surfaces are planes normal to the beam axis and that the dose at the central axis decreases with depth according to an exponential law. Then the dose D at a depth x may be written

$$D_x = D_0 e^{-\mu x}$$

and the integral dose to a depth d is given by

$$\int_0^d D_0 e^{-\mu x} A \, . \, dx$$

(where A denotes the cross-sectional area which is assumed to be constant).

Further if $d_{\frac{1}{2}}$ represents the half-value depth, then $\frac{1}{2} = e^{-\mu d_{\frac{1}{2}}}$ or $\mu = 0 \cdot 693 / d_{\frac{1}{2}}$.

$$\int_0^d D_0 e^{-0 \cdot 693 x / d_{\frac{1}{2}}} \, . \, A \, . \, dx$$

$$= \frac{D_0 A d_{\frac{1}{2}}}{0 \cdot 693} (1 - e^{-0 \cdot 693 d / d_{\frac{1}{2}}})$$

$$= 1 \cdot 44 D_0 A d_{\frac{1}{2}} (1 - e^{-0 \cdot 693 d / d_{\frac{1}{2}}})$$

Allowing for the divergence of the radiation beam (instead of assuming a constant cross-sectional area A) gives as a better approximation

$$1 \cdot 44 D_0 A d_{\frac{1}{2}} (1 - e^{-0 \cdot 693 d / d_{\frac{1}{2}}})(1 + 2 \cdot 88 d_{\frac{1}{2}} / f) \, . \qquad . \quad (12)$$

where f is the source-skin distance.

If d is large compared with $d_{\frac{1}{2}}$, so that the beam is completely absorbed within the thickness d, $e^{-0 \cdot 693 d / d_{\frac{1}{2}}} = 0$ and the integral dose becomes $1 \cdot 44 D_0 A d_{\frac{1}{2}} (1 + 2 \cdot 88 d_{\frac{1}{2}} / f)$.

The assumptions made in deriving these formulae are more nearly fulfilled in practice by beams of radiation of a few MeV. in energy than by either lower or higher energy radiation. (At low energies, where lateral scatter is appreciable and at high energies where the electron build-up region is extensive, a single exponential function is not a satisfactory representation of the variation of percentage depth dose with depth.) It should be noted, also, that as already mentioned, energy scattered out of the direct beam has been neglected and therefore the above equations give the energy absorption within the geometrical limits of the beam only.

An approximate estimate of the energy absorption within a phantom of infinite area but limited depth may, however, be obtained using the above formulae, if the half-value depth for a very large field is used for $d_{\frac{1}{2}}$ instead of the value for the particular field area A.[46] (If the energy which is scattered out of the geometrical limits of the beam had been absorbed within the beam, conditions on the central axis would be the same as if the energy scattered out had been compensated by

TABLE 11.06

DISTRIBUTION OF INTEGRAL DOSE FOR A 10 cm. DIAMETER FIELD,
H.V.L. 1·5 mm. Cu. F.S.D. 50 cm.[14]

Depth	Diameter (cm.)			
	10	20	40	∞
20 cm.	34·8 %	51·8 %	64·3 %	66·3 %
∞	39·5 %	63·5 %	93·1 %	100 %

energy scattered in.   This latter condition exists on the central axis of fields which are so large that further increase in area does not change the central axis depth doses.)   Unfortunately, percentage depth dose data for sufficiently large fields are not always available.

A method of calculating integral doses which involves fewer approximations is due to Meredith and Neary.[14]   These authors used the same analytical expression for scattered radiation as they employed in calculating depth doses (see section 11.07). In this method the integral dose in the direct beam may be calculated if desired, but the method also enables the integral dose out to any desired distance to be obtained.   Table 11.06 shows the results obtained by Meredith and Neary for the percentage of the total integral dose absorbed within (a) the geometrical beam (10 cm. diameter), and (b) confocal cones of the diameters specified for radiation of half-value layer 1·5 mm. Cu.

It is interesting to compare these values with estimates of the percentage of the energy in the direct beam calculated by another method. In Table 11.07, the energy within the direct beam has been calculated from equation 12, using $A = 78 \cdot 5$ cm.^{2} and $d_{\frac{1}{2}} = 7 \cdot 0$ cm. for the X-radiation and $d_{\frac{1}{2}} = 11 \cdot 2$ cm. for the Co^{60} radiation. The total energy delivered by the radiation beams has been calculated from the values of the energy transfer per cm.^{2} per roentgen using a backscatter factor of $1 \cdot 30$ and rad per roentgen factor of $0 \cdot 95$ for the X-radiation, and scatter factor $1 \cdot 023$ and rad per roentgen factor $0 \cdot 96$ for the Co^{60}

TABLE 11.07

	X-radiation, 1·5 mm. Cu. H.V.L., 50 cm. S.S.D. 10 cm. diameter		Co^{60} γ-radiation, 80 cm. S.S.D., 10 cm. diameter	
Incident beam energy for given dose D_0	2,350 D_0 g.-rad.		2,590 D_0 g.-rad.	
Energy absorbed within direct beam	Integral dose (g.-rad.)	% incident energy	Integral dose (g.-rad.)	% incident energy
(a) to 20 cm. depth	950 D_0	40	1220 D_0	47
(b) to ∞ depth	1100 D_0	47	1700 D_0	66

radiation. For example, for the X-radiation, from fig. 7.02, the energy transfer $= 3,720$ ergs/cm.^{2}/R. For an exposure X and area $78 \cdot 5$ cm.^{2}

$$\therefore \quad \text{energy transfer} = 3,720 \times 78 \cdot 5 \times X \text{ ergs.}$$

The given dose (D_0) is related to the exposure (X) by the equation

$$D_0 = 1 \cdot 30 \times 0 \cdot 95 \times X$$

$$\therefore \quad \text{incident energy} = \frac{3,720}{1 \cdot 30} \frac{78 \cdot 5}{0 \cdot 95} D_0 \text{ ergs} = 2,350 . D_0 \text{ g.-rad.}$$

It will be noticed that the values for the percentage of the energy in the direct beam in Table 11.07 are somewhat greater than those given by Meredith and Neary (Table 11.06). This is to be expected since equation 12, assumes the isodose curves

455

continue to the beam edges at the same depth as on the central axis.

To obtain a rough estimate (of the order of magnitude only) of the integral dose delivered in typical therapy treatments, it can be assumed that the integral dose lies between 1 and 2 mega-gram-rads per 1,000 rads given dose per field, for beams of the order of 80 cm.^{2} in area. (The integral dose is, of course, directly proportional to the field area.) Thus an approximate estimate of the integral dose in the six-field plan for treating the oesophagus (fig. 11.33) would be between 24 and 48 mega-g.-rad (assuming a given dose per field of 4,000 rads) whereas in the

TABLE 11.08

INTEGRAL DOSES DURING WHOLE TRUNK IRRADIATION WITH
Co^{60} γ-RAYS, S.S.D. = 200 cm.

Patent thickness	Mean depth dose	Integral dose for given dose D_0	
		Field 60 × 30 cm.^{2}	Field 80 × 40 cm.^{2}
(cm.)	%	(g.-rad.)	(g.-rad.)
14	81	16,000 D_0	28,000 D_0
18	75	19,000 D_0	34,000 D_0
22	70	22,000 D_0	39,000 D_0
26	64	24,000 D_0	42,000 D_0
30	59	25,000 D_0	44,000 D_0

three field plan of fig. 11.29 using Co^{60} radiation, the integral dose might be expected to lie in the range 13 to 26 mega-g.-rad.

If a large region of tissue is irradiated approximately homogeneously (as in irradiation " baths " for the treatment of leukemia, etc.), then it is only necessary to multiply the mass of the region by the mean dose to obtain the integral dose. Treatments of this type are commonly given at a source-skin distance of about 200 cm. to obtain a sufficiently large field, so depth dose data for this distance (or the S.S.D. chosen) and the appropriate field area must be calculated to estimate the mean dose. The figures given in Table 11.08 indicate the order of magnitude of the integral dose delivered in this type of treatment using Co^{60} radiation.

11.18. A comparison of orthovoltage and megavoltage X- and γ-radiation and a discussion of the use of high energy electron beams in radiotherapy

For the treatment of all except the most superficial regions, X- and γ-radiation with energy of a few MeV. has a number of

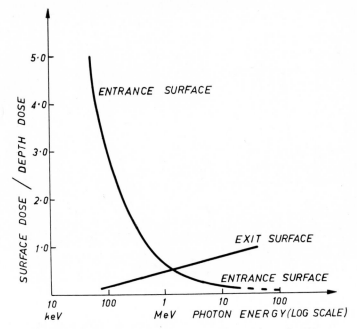

FIG. 11.42. The variation of (*a*) entrance surface dose/dose at 10 cm. depth and (*b*) exit surface dose/dose at 10 cm. depth with radiation energy.

advantages compared with X- or γ-radiation of lower energy. It may be useful to summarise these advantages:

(1) The percentage depth dose at typical treatment depths increases as the radiation energy increases. Therefore the number of treatment fields or the given dose per field can be reduced.

(2) The percentage depth dose at the entrance surface decreases as the radiation energy increases, resulting in less skin damage on the entrance surface.

(3) There is less scatter outside the geometrical beam, and

457

consequently less irradiation of tissues outside the treatment region.

(4) Photoelectric absorption in bone decreases as the radiation energy increases and hence both the shielding effect of bone and the absorbed dose received by soft tissue elements in bone is less for the higher energy radiation.

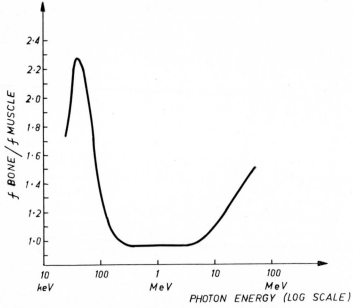

Fig. 11.43.   The variation of the energy absorption in bone compared with that in muscle with radiation energy.

It should be noted that we have described the megavoltage radiation considered as having an energy of a few MeV.   If the radiation energy is increased considerably above this, although the percentage depth dose at (say) 10 cm. depth continues to increase and the dose at the entrance surface continues to fall, the dose on the exit surface may increase to an extent where the possibility of damage to skin must be considered.   Also pair production results in an increased energy absorption in bone relative to muscle and hence there is again some bone shielding and a higher dose to soft tissue elements in bone. (See figs. 11.42 and 11.43.)

458

Electron beam therapy

Electron beams of sufficient energy and intensity to deliver clinically useful radiation doses can be obtained from many linear accelerators and most betatrons. The manner in which these beams are absorbed in tissue results in a distribution of dose with depth which differs significantly from the distribution obtained with X- and γ-ray beams. The principal differences are (1) there is a relatively homogeneous dose region extending from close to the tissue surface to a depth which depends upon the electron energy, (2) at greater depths the dose decreases rapidly with increasing depth and a curve of percentage depth dose

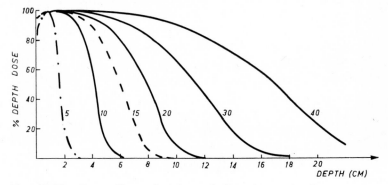

FIG. 11.44. Curves illustrating the variation of central axis percentage depth dose with depth for electron beams of energy 5, 10, 15, 20, 30 and 40 MeV. Field size 10 × 10 cm.²

against depth is convex instead of concave as with X- and γ-radiation. Fig. 11.44 shows central axis depth dose curves for a field area of 10 × 10 cm.²

It will be noticed that for the lower energy electrons the dose decreases from 90 to 20 per cent. of the maximum within a depth of about 1 cm. For 10 MeV. electrons, the dose decreases from 90 per cent. at 3·0 cm. to 20 per cent. at 4·5 cm. Thus for the treatment of regions up to about 3 cm. from the surface, a direct electron beam (of appropriate energy for the depth to be treated) provides a simple method of obtaining homogeneous irradiation, and the dose to underlying tissues is low. As the electron energy increases, however, the dose beyond the homogeneous region decreases less rapidly and if the electron energy exceeds about 10 MeV., the dose to under-lying tissue may not be acceptable. As with X- and γ-ray beams, it then becomes necessary to combine two or more fields to deliver an adequate dose to the treatment region without undue irradiation of normal tissue.

The convex form of the electron isodose curves, means that when two parallel opposed electron beams irradiate a uniform block of tissue, it is possible by suitable choice of the energy of each beam in relation to the thickness of tissue to produce a maximum in the absorbed dose at any selected position in the section. This provides a convenient method of treating regions which are eccentric but overlap the mid-line in the head and neck but the entire block of tissue is irradiated to a fairly high level.[39] When two or more fields are combined at an angle, the rapidity with which the dose decreases outside the treatment region, is determined primarily by the width of the penumbra region in the individual beams and in this respect electron beams appear to be inferior to megavoltage X- and γ-radiation.[37, 38, 40, 41] With the present methods of beam flattening and collimation both the variation of dose-rate from the central axis to the beam edge and also the scatter outside the geometrical limits of the electron beams are large by mega-voltage standards, but it is possible that better methods of collimating and focusing electron beams may yet be devised.

Recent studies of skin reactions produced by electron beams suggest that for most energies there is some skin-sparing in comparison with orthovoltage X-rays, but not as much as with megavoltage X- or γ-rays.[42, 43] Many authors have pointed out that because the electron dose-rate changes rapidly with the mass of absorbing material traversed, tissue inhomogeneities in the path of an electron beam may have a pronounced effect upon the dose-rate in the regions which they shadow. Methods of making approximate corrections for the effects of tissue inhomogeneities have been reported,[44, 45] but omitting the correction or misjudging the thickness of a bone (say), will usually result in a greater error in the dose estimate in the case of electron beams than with photon beams. The distribution of the electron dose in the immediate vicinity of inhomogeneities is presently being investigated at a number of centres.

REFERENCES

1. The International Commission on Radiological Units and Measurements (1962). Report 10b. U.S. National Bureau of Standards Handbook, No. 85.
2. The International Commission on Radiological Units and Measurements (1962). Report 10d. U.S. National Bureau of Standards Handbook No. 87.
3. JONES, D. E. A. and RAINE, H. C. (1949). *Brit. J. Radiol.* **22,** 549.
4. CUNNINGHAM, J. R., JOHNS, H. E. and GUPTA, S. K. (1965). *Brit. J. Radiol.* **38,** 637.
5. GREENING, J. R. (1954). *Brit. J. Radiol.* **27,** 534.
6. JONES, D. E. A. (1949). *Brit. J. Radiol.* **22,** 342.
7. DAY, M. J. (1950). *Brit. J. Radiol.* **23,** 368.
8. BATHO, H. F., THEIMER, O. and THEIMER, R. (1956). *J. Canad. Ass. Radiol.* **7,** 51.
9. Hospital Physicists' Association Scientific Sub-Committee (1961). *Brit. J. Radiol.* Suppl. 10.
10. QUIMBY, E. H. and LAWRENCE, G. C. (1940). *Radiology,* **35,** 138.
11. MAYNEORD, W. V. and LAMERTON, L. F. (1941). *Brit. J. Radiol.* **14,** 255.
12. ADAMS, G. D. (1964). *Radiology,* **83,** 785.
13. CLARKSON, J. R. (1941). *Brit. J. Radiol.* **14,** 265.
14. MEREDITH, W. Y. and NEARY, G. J. (1944). *Brit. J. Radiol.* **17,** 75.
15. HORSLEY, C. and ASPIN, N. (1956). *Brit. J. Radiol.* **29,** 625.
16. WHEATLEY, B. M. (1953). *Brit. J. Radiol.* **24,** 388.
17. LAMERTON, L. F. and WINSBOROUGH, M. (1950). *Brit. J. Radiol.* **23,** 236.
18. TRANTER, F. W. (1956). *Brit. J. Radiol.* **29,** 92.
19. LÉGARÉ, J. M. (1964). *Radiology.* **82,** 272.
20. MAYNEORD, W. V. (1939). *Brit. J. Radiol.* **12,** 262.
21. JOHNS, H. E., WHITMORE, G. F., WATSON, T. A. and UMBERG, F. H. (1953). *J. Canad. Ass. Radiol.* **4,** 1.
22. JOHNS, H. E., MORRISON, M. T. and WHITMORE, G. F. (1956). *Amer. J. Roentg.* **75,** 1105.
23. BRAESTRUP, C. B. and MOONEY, R. T. (1955). *Radiology,* **64,** 17.
24. JOHNS, H. E., BRUCE, W. R. and REID, W. B. (1958). *Brit. J. Radiol.* **31,** 254.
25. ELLIS, F., HALL, E. J. and OLIVER, R. (1959). *Brit. J. Radiol.* **32,** 421.
26. JONES, D. E. A., GREGORY, C. and BIRCHALL, I. (1956). *Brit. J. Radiol.* **29,** 196.
27. GARRETT, J. H. and JONES, D. E. A. (1962). *Brit. J. Radiol.* **35,** 739.
28. BATHO, H. F. (1964). *J. Canad. Ass. Radiol.* **15,** 79.
29. GREENE, D. and STEWART, J. G. (1965). *Brit. J. Radiol.* **38,** 378.
30. SPIERS, F. W. (1946). *Brit. J. Radiol.* **19,** 52 ; (1949) *Brit. J. Radiol.* **22,** 521 ; (1952) *Brit. J. Radiol.* **24,** 283.

31. LINDSAY, D. D. and STERN, B. E. (1952). *Radiology*, **60**, 355.
32. ELLIS, F., SHANKS, W., KEMP, L. A. W. and OLIVER, R. (1950). *J. Fac. Radiol.* **1**, 231.
33. HUBERT, M. H. E. and GROOM, A. C. (1950). *Brit. J. Radiol.* **23**, 649.
34. SUTHERLAND, W. H. (1962). *Brit. J. Radiol.* **35**, 478.
35. DOBBIE, J. L. (1943). *Brit. J. Radiol.* **16**, 36.
36. MAYNEORD, W. V. (1940). *Brit. J. Radiol.* **13**, 235.
37. LOEVINGER, R., KARZMARK, C. J. and WEISSBLUTH, M. (1961). *Radiology*, **77**, 906.
38. BEATTIE, J. W., TSIEN, K. C., OVADIA, J. and LAUGHLIN, J. S. (1962). *Amer. J. Roentg.* **88**, 235.
39. PERRY, H., TSIEN, K. C., NICKSON, J. J. and LAUGHLIN, J. S. (1962). *Amer. J. Roentg.* **88**, 251.
40. SHIRA, J., BOTSTEIN, C., EISENBERG, B. and BERDON, W. (1962). *Amer. J. Roentg.* **88**, 262.
41. GREENE, D. (1964). *Brit. J. Radiol.* **37**, 231.
42. ZATZ, L. M., VON ESSEN, C. F. and KAPLAN, H. S. (1961). *Radiology*, **77**, 928.
43. TAPLEY, N. DUV. and FLETCHER, G. H. (1965). *Radiology*, **84**, 812.
44. LAUGHLIN, J. S., LUNDY, A., PHILLIPS, M. D., CHU, F. and SATTAR, A. (1965). *Radiology*, **85**, 524.
45. BOONE, M. L. M., CROSBY, E. H. and SHALEK, R. J. (1965). *Radiology*, **84**, 817.
46. HAPPEY, F. (1941). *Brit. J. Radiol.* **14**, 235.

GENERAL REFERENCES

PATERSON, R. (1963). *The Treatment of Malignant Disease by Radiotherapy*. 2nd. edn. London, Arnold.
CARLING, E. R., WINDEYER, B. W. and SMITHERS, D. W. (1955). *British Practice in Radiotherapy*. London, Butterworth.

EXAMINATION QUESTIONS

1. What are the criteria by which a phantom material is chosen? Why is the dose measured at the surface of a phantom different from the dose measured in air? In what way is this difference influenced by beam quality, area and shape of field and thickness of the phantom?

M.S.R. (T.), 1965.

2. Upon what factors does the percentage depth dose of X-rays at any point in a water phantom depend? Would the value necessarily be the same for the corresponding point in a patient? Give reasons for your answer.

M.S.R. (T.), 1954.

3. What is an isodose curve and how may isodose curves from an X-ray beam in water be measured? What are the main features of isodose curves from

> (a) a 250 kV. unit
> (b) a telecurie therapy unit
> (c) a 4 MeV. linear accelerator
> (d) a radium needle.

Illustrate by diagrams.

M.S.R. (T.), 1964.

4. What are the advantages and disadvantages of using wedges in X-ray therapy? When are wedged beams generally used?

M.S.R. (T.), 1964.

5. Give a list of beam direction devices in common use in radiotherapy departments. Describe one in detail.

M.S.R. (T.), 1964.

6. Describe and discuss the calibration procedures for (a) a 250 kV. X-ray therapy machine and (b) a megavoltage machine.

F.S.R. (T.), 1965.

7. Give a general account of moving beam therapy, with examples of its clinical applications.

F.S.R. (T.), 1963.

8. A new kilocurie, fixed head, cobalt 60 beam unit is installed in a radiotherapy department and the relevant dosimetry is unknown. Outline the physical measurements you would consider necessary before the apparatus is put into routine clinical use and describe how you would carry these out.

D.M.R. (T.), 1961.

9. Discuss in detail the factors which affect either (a) the average film dose in radiography or (b) the average tumour dose in X-ray therapy. In either case state which factors are used in practice to increase the ratio of this dose to that on the skin through which the beam passes.

D.M.R. (R. and T.), 1963.

10. Describe the purposes, construction and clinical use of beam flattening filters, wedge filters and compensators.

D.M.R. (T.), 1963.

11. What are the main advantages of megavoltage radiotherapy (including Cobalt 60 gamma rays) compared with orthovoltage therapy? Are there any disadvantages and limitations in the use of megavoltage radiations in the treatment of malignant disease?

D.M.R. (T.), 1964.

463

12. A patient has a mid-line carcinoma of the floor of the mouth extending to the jaw. The treatment plan is to use two opposed fields 5 × 10 cm. with a separation of 12 cm., which is the lateral thickness of the patient. Calculate the daily dose at the surface necessary to deliver at the tumour (a) 4,500 r. with a 250 kV. X-ray set, and (b) 6,000 r. with a cobalt-60 unit, when treating 5 days per week over a period of 5 weeks.

Show graphically the distributions of the dose on the beam axes. Which of the two sources of radiation would you use in this case? Justify your answer.

Depth (cm.)		0	0·5	1·0	2·0	3·0	4·0	6·0	8·0	10·0	12·0
Percentage	250 kV.	100	100	97·9	90·3	81·3	71·8	54·5	40·8	30·3	22·3
Depth dose	Cobalt-60	50	100	97·7	92·5	87·2	82·0	71·8	62·1	53·3	45·8

D.M.R. (T.), 1957.

13. Write a brief essay on the principles of moving field therapy and compare its advantages and disadvantages with those of multiple field therapy.

Describe in detail one form of moving field treatment and outline the methods for measuring the dose delivered.

D.M.R. (T.), 1957.

14. Describe the physical properties of high energy electron beams which make them of use in radiotherapy.

Part question D.M.R. (T.), 1964.

CHAPTER XII

THE THERAPEUTIC USE OF IONISING RADIATIONS (*contd.*), BRACHYTHERAPY

12.01. Cavitary and superficial γ-ray therapy

For the treatment of superficial tissues, the radiation intensity must decrease quickly with depth so that underlying normal tissue is not exposed to a harmful dose. There are two principal methods of achieving this:

(1) by the use of radiation of such quality that the radiation is strongly absorbed in the depth to be treated;

(2) by placing the radiation source close to the surface so that the source-skin distance is comparable with the depth to be treated.

The first method includes the use of β-radiation which penetrates only a few millimeteres in tissue and the use of high energy electrons from accelerators or long wavelength X-radiation which penetrate to rather greater depths.

In the second method, γ-emitting isotopes are usually employed and the decrease of dose with depth is determined by geometrical factors, absorption usually being negligible for the depths treated. It is these γ-ray treatments, with short source-skin distances which will be discussed in this section (β-ray treatments are considered in 12.04).

In γ-ray brachytherapy, the exposure rate or absorbed dose-rate at the region of interest is usually calculated from the known activity of the sources. It is not calculated from a measured exposure-rate or dose-rate in a reference position (as in teletherapy) since direct measurements are difficult to make with sufficient accuracy. (The exposure rate varies rapidly from point to point requiring a small measuring instrument and the exposure-rate is usually much less than in teletherapy.) Therefore we consider first the relationship between activity and exposure-rate.

465

Suppose, for simplicity, that the radioactive source emits a single photon of energy E MeV. per disintegration. Then the intensity of the radiation at 1 cm. from a point source of strength 1 mCi. will be

$$\frac{1}{4\pi}\left(\underset{\substack{\text{No. of disintegra-}\\\text{tions per hr.}}}{3\cdot70\times10^7\times3{,}600}\times\underset{\substack{\text{Energy per disintegra-}\\\text{tion in ergs}}}{E\times1\cdot6\times10^{-6}}\right)\text{ergs/cm.}^2\text{/hr.}$$

$$= 1\cdot69\times10^4 \,.\, E \,.\, \text{ergs/cm.}^2\text{/hr.}$$

To convert this expression into an exposure-rate, it is necessary to know either the energy fluence per roentgen or the (real) mass-energy absorption coefficient of air $\left(\frac{\mu_{en}}{\rho}\right)$ for radiation of energy E. (The energy-fluence per roentgen $= 86\cdot9/\left(\frac{\mu_{en}}{\rho}\right)_{\text{air}}$; see section 7.03.)

Then the exposure rate at 1 cm. from a source of 1 mCi. is given by

$$1\cdot69\times10^4 \,.\, E \,.\, \left(\frac{\mu_{en}}{\rho}\right)_{\text{air}}\Big/86\cdot9 \ \text{R/hr.}$$

This is numerically equal to the specific gamma-ray constant (Γ) (formerly called the k-factor), which is defined as the quotient of $l^2\,\dfrac{\Delta X}{\Delta t}$ by A, where $\dfrac{\Delta X}{\Delta t}$ is the exposure rate at a distance l from a point source of the nuclide considered having an activity A. The variation of Γ with photon energy is shown in fig. 12.01. Values of Γ for some common isotopes (which have been calculated and/or measured experimentally) are given in Table 12.01. In the case of isotopes with complex decay schemes, it is necessary to calculate a mean value for Γ allowing for the relative number of quanta of each energy. In general, the specific gamma ray constant gives the exposure-rate which would be produced if there were no attenuation of the γ-radiation either in the source itself or in any intervening material. In the case of radium, however, the constant is by convention, usually specified for a source filtered by 0·5 mm. platinum. For radium we shall therefore use the symbol Γ_0 or $\Gamma_{0\cdot5}$, as appropriate, to indicate zero filtration or 0·5 mm. Pt. filter.

466

In the description of the techniques of surface and interstitial γ-ray therapy which follows, we shall usually refer to radium or radon, since the methods were developed when these were the only radioactive sources available, although now other artificial γ-emitters are also employed. The same techniques may be used when artificial radioactive isotopes are substituted for radium, and by use of the appropriate value for the specific

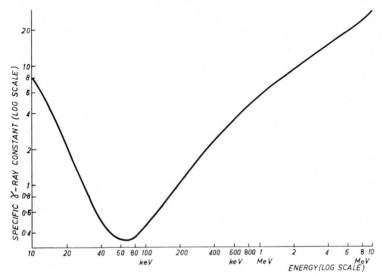

FIG. 12.01.   The variation of the specific γ-ray constant (Γ) (formerly called k-factor) with photon energy.

γ-ray constant, exposure-rates around artificial isotope sources may often be derived from data already available for radium sources.

In superficial and interstitial γ-ray therapy, because small sources are used, it is usually necessary to employ several sources to irradiate the treatment area.   The physical problem is to arrange the sources in such a way that the treatment area is irradiated uniformly and at a specified rate.   It is therefore necessary to know how the exposure-rate varies around the sources which are used.   Radium tubes and needles cannot be regarded as point sources, for which the inverse square law applies, but can usually be regarded as linear sources each element of which acts as a point source.   The variation of the

467

exposure-rate with distance from a linear source of radiation may be obtained as follows:

Suppose that there are ρ mCi. of radioactive material per cm. of the source and assume initially that there is neither absorption nor scattering of the radiation. Then the exposure-rate at any point P (fig. 12.02) due to an element of radioactive material of

TABLE 12.01

THE SPECIFIC γ-RAY CONSTANT (Γ) FOR
SOME COMMON ISOTOPES *

Element	Isotope	Γ (R-cm.^{2}/mCi.-hr.)
Arsenic	As^{72}	10·1
	As^{74}	4·4
Caesium	Cs^{137}	3·1
Chromium	Cr^{51}	0·15
Cobalt	Co^{60}	13·2
Gold	Au^{198}	2·3
Iodine	I^{131}	2·2
	I^{132}	11·8
Iridium	Ir^{192}	4·8
Iron	Fe^{59}	6·4
Mercury	Hg^{203}	1·3
Potassium	K^{42}	1·4
Radium	Ra^{226}	8·25 (0·5 mm. Pt. filter)
Selenium	Se^{75}	2·0
Sodium	Na^{22}	12·0
	Na^{24}	18·4
Tantalum	Ta^{182}	6·2

* Values from the *Radio-chemical Manual* (1962). The Radiochemical Centre, Amersham.

length dl is $\Gamma_0 \rho dl / r^2$. The total exposure at P (X_p) due to all such elements is $\int_0^L \Gamma_0 \rho dl / r^2$ where L is the total length of radioactive material. (L is referred to as the " active length " of the source.)

But $\quad\quad dl = r \sec \theta \, d\theta$ and $r = y \sec \theta$

$\therefore \quad\quad X_p = \int_{\theta_1}^{\theta_2} \Gamma_0 \rho \, d\theta / y = \Gamma_0 \rho (\theta_2 - \theta_1) / y$

If the radioactive material is enclosed in a cylinder of wall thickness d, then the radiation is attenuated by the wall of the container. For the element dl and for points P such that the radiation passes through the lateral wall of the container, the path length of the radiation in the wall is $d \sec \theta$. Suppose that

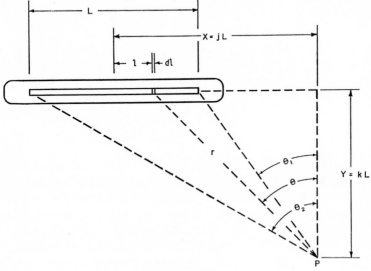

FIG. 12.02.

the wall reduces the exposure by the factor $e^{-\mu d \sec \theta}$. In this case

$$X_p = \int_{\theta_1}^{\theta_2} \frac{\Gamma_0 \rho}{y} e^{-\mu d \sec \theta} \, d\theta$$

$$= \frac{\Gamma_0 \rho}{y} \int_{\theta_1}^{\theta_2} e^{-\mu d \sec \theta} \, d\theta$$

$$= \frac{\Gamma_0 \rho}{y} \left[U(\theta_2) - U(\theta_1) \right] \tag{1}$$

Values of the integral $U(\theta) = \int_0^{\theta} e^{-\mu d \sec \theta} \, d\theta$ have been tabulated by Sievert [1] and others for selected values of μd, assuming μ to be independent of θ. For radium sources, the effective absorption coefficient μ is a function of the path length $d \sec \theta$. This is mainly because the radiation from radium consists of many energies. Values of the integral $U(\theta)$

16   469

allowing for this effect have been calculated by Young and Batho.[2]

It is convenient to rewrite equation (1) with the co-ordinates of P (x and y) expressed as multiples of the active length L of the source. Thus writing $x = jL$ and $y = kL$, equation (1) becomes

$$X_p = \frac{\rho}{L}\left[\frac{\Gamma_0}{k}\int_{\theta_1}^{\theta_2} e^{-\mu d \sec \theta}\, d\theta\right]$$

$$= \frac{\rho}{L}\left[\frac{\Gamma_0}{k}\left\{U(\theta_2)-U(\theta_1)\right\}\right]$$

$$= \frac{A}{L^2}\left[\frac{\Gamma_0}{k}\left\{U(\theta_2)-U(\theta_1)\right\}\right]$$

where A denotes the total activity of the source. If the absorption and scattering of the radiation in any tissue between P and the source is neglected and if it is also assumed there is absolute electronic equilibrium, the absorbed dose-rate in soft tissue at P is given by

$$D_p = \frac{A}{L^2}\left[\frac{\Gamma_0 . f.}{k}\left\{U(\theta_2)-U(\theta_1)\right\}\right] \qquad (2)$$

where f denotes the rad per roentgen conversion factor.

The useful feature of expression (2) is the fact that the quantity in the square bracket is independent of the activity and length of the source. Radium sources are commonly enclosed in containers of standard wall thickness but individual sources differ in activity and active length. The values of the square bracket can be calculated for a specified wall thickness for an array of values of the " reduced " co-ordinates j and k. The resulting table of " dose factors " is then applicable to any radium source with the given filtration. The actual dose-rate at any point P for a given source is obtained by multiplying the dose factor (in the square bracket) from the table by the value of A/L^2 for the particular source. Tables of dose factors for the wall thicknesses commonly used have been published.[2] Alternatively[3] if an isodose chart for a needle of active length L' and radium content A' is available, but the dose-rate is required at a point P'' ($x''y''$) in the vicinity of a needle having the same

filtration but length L'' and total activity A'', then the dose at
$$P'' = \frac{A''}{(L'')^2} \cdot \frac{(L')^2}{A'} \times \text{dose at } P'$$ where the reduced co-ordinates
$(j'k')$ of P' (in the vicinity of the first needle) are equal to the reduced co-ordinates (j'',k'') of P'', i.e. P is at $x'y'$ where $\dfrac{x'}{L'} = \dfrac{x''}{L''}$ and $\dfrac{y'}{L'} = \dfrac{y''}{L''}$.

In the preceding discussion, self-absorption in the radio-active material itself has been neglected. For brachytherapy sources, for radiation which emerges through the lateral wall of the container, absorption in the radium salt is small compared with absorption in the wall and can be adequately represented by increasing the effective wall thickness slightly. For points on the long-axis of the source, where some radiation travels through the entire length of the radioactive material before emerging through the end of the container, salt absorption is more important. For points remote from the source, the dose-rate at a point Q on the axis is given approximately by

$$D_Q = \Gamma_0 \cdot f \cdot A \cdot e^{-(\mu t + \mu' L/2)} / x_Q^2$$

where t denotes the thickness of the end wall and μ' is an effective absorption coefficient for the radioactive salt (for the γ-rays from radium μ' like μ is a function of the path length). For points close to the source, it is necessary to use the more accurate equation

$$D_Q = \Gamma_0 \cdot f \cdot \int_{-L/2}^{+L/2} [e^{-\mu t} e^{-\mu'(L/2-l)} \rho / (x-l)^2] \, dl$$

$$= \Gamma_0 f \cdot \rho \cdot e^{-(\mu t + \mu' L/2)} \int_{-L/2}^{+L/2} [e^{-\mu' l} / (x-l)^2] \, dl$$

This expression can be evaluated to any desired accuracy by expanding $e^{\mu' l}$ as a series and then integrating.

It will be appreciated that there is a region close to but not actually on the long axis of a cylindrical source where some radiation reaching the point considered travels through the end wall and some through the lateral wall of the container. The dose-rate in this region depends on the way in which the ends of the particular container are shaped, but is normally less than that at adjacent points on the axis since there is more absorption in the lateral wall than in the radioactive source. (See fig. 12.03.)

When a radium source is completely surrounded by soft tissue, the presence of tissue instead of air, reduces the exposure-rate by about 1 or 2 per cent. per cm. When the regions to be treated are within 1 or 2 cm. of the radioactive sources (as is frequently the case), the error introduced by neglecting the apparent absorption is small. In some intra-cavitary treatments, however (particularly the treatment of the cervix), the

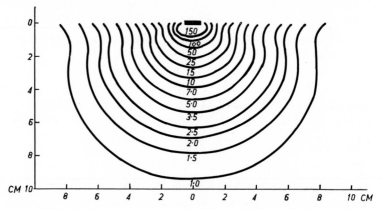

FIG. 12.03.   Isodose curves around a 10 mg. radium tube (active length 1 cm., Pt. filter 1·0 mm.) in soft tissue.

dose-rate at more distant points may be of interest and a correction is then necessary for tissue absorption. See Table 12.02. If the radium is at or near the tissue surface, less scattered radiation reaches the point than when the source is completely surrounded by tissue, and the apparent absorption in this case is therefore somewhat greater.

Since (1) the exposure-rate near small γ-emitting radioactive sources is determined primarily by geometrical factors and (2) the mean energy of the γ-rays from radium is not very different from the energy of the γ-rays emitted by Cs^{137}, the distribution of exposure-rate or dose-rate around caesium sources (which are now usually enclosed in platinum containers of the same design as are used for radium sources) is very similar to that around radium sources of similar dimensions. The dose-rate distribution around Co^{60} sources is also quite similar, although the encapsulation of the cobalt sources is somewhat different. The distributions in the equatorial plane where most of the radiation travels normally through the container wall are almost identical, but there are some differences in dose-rate for points near the axis where the radiation travels obliquely through the container wall. The specific γ-ray constant for

TABLE 12.02 [4]

ATTENUATION OF RADIUM γ-RAYS IN SOFT TISSUE

Tissue thickness between source and point (cm.)	% Apparent absorption	
	in infinite phantom	*when radium at surface of semi-infinite phantom*
1	1	
2	2	3
3	3·5	
4	5	6
5	7	
6	9	10
7	11	
8	13	15
9	15	
10	17·5	20

Co^{60} is 13·2 and for Cs^{137} is 3·1, but as already mentioned in Chapter V, cobalt and caesium sources are usually described *not* by the activity of the cobalt or caesium, but in terms of the millicuries or milligrammes of radium which would produce an " equivalent " source, i.e. would give equal exposure rates in the equatorial plane.

Fig. 12.03 shows a typical dose-rate distribution around a 10 mg. radium tube. (In this figure, the dose-rates shown have been corrected for the effects of absorption in tissue, assuming the tube is surrounded on all sides by soft tissue or tissue equivalent material.) It will be noted that the isodose contours in the central region run approximately parallel to the source. Hence if the area to be treated approximates to the inner surface of a cylinder (e.g. the oesophagus or rectum or uterine

473

canal), radium uniformly distributed along the axis of the cylinder will give uniform irradiation over the surface except for a drop at the extreme ends, provided some device is used to keep the surface at a uniform distance from the radium. The surface dose-rate may be obtained from isodose contours such as fig. 12.03 if these are available, or may be obtained from tables

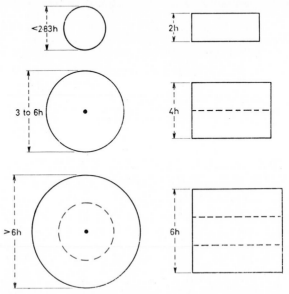

Fig. 12.04. Diagram illustrating the Paterson-Parker method of distributing radium on surface applicators.

which have been prepared by a number of authors. If it is desired to avoid a drop in dose-rate opposite the ends of the source, a composite source can be used with a greater density of radium in the end than in the centre sections.[5]

The treatment area which is the inner surface of a cylinder happens to be rather simple to irradiate uniformly, and has, therefore, been considered first. In superficial, as opposed to cavitary treatments, however, it is more usual for the treatment area to be approximately planar. For this type of treatment a system of rules for distributing radium over areas of various shapes and sizes to obtain a homogeneous distribution of dose over the surface was devised in the 1930s by Paterson and Parker [6, 7] at Manchester. (In this system, a distribution is regarded as homogeneous if the variations from the mean dose do not exceed $\pm$ 10 per cent.) The arrangement of the radium depends upon the shape of the area to be treated and upon the ratio of the linear dimensions of the area to the distance (h) between the plane carrying the radium and the treatment area. In general, the rules suggest distributing the radium around the periphery of an area equal to the treatment area, using a constant linear intensity. The inevitable gaps due to the inactive ends of needles and tubes, should not exceed h. For small areas (e.g. circles in which the diameter is less than $3h$, squares of sides less than $2h$) this alone is sufficient. For larger areas

TABLE 12.03

DISTRIBUTION RULES FOR SURFACE APPLICATORS

Circles					
Ratio diameter/h. . .	< 2·83	3-6	6	7·5	10
Per cent. Ra on periphery	100	95	80	75	70
Per cent. Ra. in inner circle	0	0	17	22	27
Per cent. Ra. at centre .	0	5	3	3	3
Squares and rectangles					
Ratio shorter side/h. .	2	4	6	8	10
No. of additional lines parallel to longer side .	0	1	2	3	4
Linear intensity of added lines compared with periphery . . .		$\frac{1}{2}$	$\frac{2}{3}$	$\frac{3}{4}$	$\frac{4}{5}$

it is necessary to add radium within the periphery (e.g. a central spot or concentric circle within circles, and extra lines within squares and rectangles) to maintain a uniform dose. See table 12.03. The rules apply strictly only to plane areas, but they can be extended to convex or concave surfaces. The radium is spread over a parallel curved surface, the amount being determined by the treatment area for convex surfaces but by the applicator area for concave surfaces. The rules were deduced by a mathematical analysis of the distribution of intensity resulting from combinations of linear sources of radiation. The distance h between the plane carrying the radium and the treatment area is determined primarily by the percentage of the surface dose which it is desired to deliver at (say) 0·5 cm. or 1 cm. below the surface. In practice, a separation of 0·5 cm. is usually the minimum distance employed, since if h is less than this small variations in h produce large variations in dose-rate. The maximum distance used is 3 to 4 cm. since distances greater than this require an excessive amount of radium to obtain an adequate dose-rate.

In order to obtain the desired value of h, the radium may be attached to the upper surface of a material such as felt or sorbo-rubber, which is available in sheets of specified thickness and may be fitted accurately to the patient. Alternatively and more usually the radium is mounted on or in applicators made from dental compound, cellulose acetate or perspex sheet. It is desirable that the substances used to carry the radium should not differ greatly in absorbing and scattering properties from tissue. When applicators are made it is necessary to take an impression of the region to be treated. If this is done in dental compound or similar material it may itself form the basis of the applicator. In other cases, a plaster cast is made from the impression, and the applicator constructed to fit the cast.

In addition to determining the optimum distribution of radium to produce a homogeneous dose, Paterson and Parker also prepared tables giving the number of milligram hours required to deliver 1,000 R. for different areas and treatment distances. Since the original tables were published, the accepted value of the specific gamma ray constant for radium filtered by 0·5 mm. Pt. has been decreased (from 8·4 R.-cm.²/mCi.-hr. to 8·25 R.-cm.²/mCi.-hr.) and the rad has been introduced as the unit of absorbed dose. Table 12.04 corresponds with part of a table given by Paterson and Parker, but the values have been recalculated using $\Gamma_{0.5} = 8.25$ R.-cm.²/mCi.-hr. and have been divided by 0·956 to obtain the absorbed dose in rads in muscle instead of the exposure in roentgens. No allowance is made in the table for the effects of absorption and scattering in tissue or in applicator materials. An approximate correction for the apparent absorption in soft tissue can be made using Table 12.02 and tables of correction factors for different applicator materials have been published by Cook.[8] Table 12.04 also assumes the radium is filtered by 0·5 mm. Pt., but approximate corrections

476

for radium containers of differing wall thicknesses are given in the table. An example of the way in which the Paterson-Parker tables are used in planning a superficial treatment is given below.

TABLE 12.04

SURFACE APPLICATORS AND PLANAR IMPLANTS
THE NUMBER OF MG.-HRS. REQUIRED TO DELIVER 1000 RADS

Area (cm.²)	Treatment distance (h.) (cm.)							
	0·5	1·0	1·5	2·0	2·5	3·0	3·5	4·0
0	32	127	285	507	792	1141	1553	2028
1	72	182						
2	103	227	399	637	921	1275	1699	2176
3	128	263						
4	150	296	492	743	103	1390	1824	2309
5	171	326						
6	188	355	571	833	1135	1496	1940	2436
7	204	382						
8	219	409	638	911	1230	1597	2049	2551
9	235	434						
10	250	461	698	983	1315	1693	2151	2663
12	278	511	756	1054	1397	1782	2249	2772
14	307	558	814	1121	1476	1867	2343	2873
16	335	603	867	1185	1555	1949	2431	2971
18	364	644	919	1246	1624	2029	2517	3066
20	392	683	969	1305	1691	2108	2604	3158
22	418	718	1022	1363	1757	2182	2686	3245
24	444	753	1074	1422	1823	2255	2767	3329
26	471	785	1125	1478	1883	2330	2844	3408
28	496	817	1172	1531	1945	2400	2920	3488
30	522	847	1216	1584	2002	2471	3000	3566
32	546	876	1262	1637	2062	2535	3076	3642
34	572	909	1306	1690	2121	2601	3148	3717
36	594	936	1350	1744	2181	2665	3218	3790
38	619	968	1393	1795	2236	2729	3289	3863
40	642	995	1433	1845	2292	2790	3355	3935
50	751	1142	1621	2085	2558	3085	3690	4279
60	852	1284	1791	2322	2818	3365	3978	4609
70	948	1427	1946	2535	3062	3632	4251	4918
80	1045	1569	2094	2729	3305	3895	4537	5218

| Filtration (mm. Pt.) | | 0·3 | 0·5 | 0·6 | 0·8 | 1·0 | 1·5 | |
| Correction | | −4 % | 0 | +2 % | +6 % | +10 % | +20 % | |

Illustrative example

A rodent ulcer on the back of the hand, approximately elliptical in shape, is to be treated by a superficial applicator to a dose of 5,000 rads in 7 days. The major axis of the ellipse is 3·8 cm., the minor axis is 3·4 cm.

∴ The area to be treated $= \pi \times 3\cdot8 \times 3\cdot4/4 = 10\cdot2$ cm.^{2}

Suppose the treating distance is 1 cm. Then 95 per cent. of the radium must be around the periphery, 5 per cent. at the centre.

Interpolating in table 12.04, 466 mg.-hr. are required per 1,000 rads, i.e. a total of 2330 mg.-hr. are required to deliver 5,000 rads. Eight 5 mg. radium tubes will fit conveniently around the periphery of the ellipse and two 1 mg. needles can be used at the centre, i.e. the applicator can be conveniently loaded with 42 mg. of radium. It would then be worn for $2330/42 = 55\cdot5$ hr. or for just under 8 hr. per day.

Now suppose that in order to reduce somewhat the time for which the applicator must be worn, it is decided to reduce the treating distance to 8 mm. A distribution of 95 per cent. of the radium around the periphery and 5 per cent. at the centre is still satisfactory, but the number of mg.-hr. required will be reduced.

No data are given in table 12.04 for a treating distance of 8 mm. The required number of mg.-hr. could be obtained approximately by interpolation, but it is more accurate to calculate the area A at (say) 5 mm. distance which would be exposed to the same cone of radiation as 10·2 cm.^{2} at 8 mm. To irradiate 10·2 cm.^{2} at 8 mm., it is necessary to irradiate an area of $\dfrac{5^2}{8^2} \times 10\cdot2$ cm.^{2} at 5 mm., i.e. 3·98 cm.^{2}. From table 12.04 to deliver 1,000 rads to this area would require 149·6 mg.-hr. and this would deliver $1,000 \times \dfrac{5^2}{8^2}$ rads to the 10·2 cm.^{2} area at 8 mm., i.e. to deliver 1,000 rads to 10·2 cm.^{2} at 8 mm. requires $149\cdot6 \times \dfrac{8^2}{5^2}$ mg. hr. $= 383\cdot5$ mg.-hr. per 1,000 rads.

Therefore for 5,000 rads, 1917·5 mg. hr. are required. Using the same radium as before, i.e. a total of 42 mg., the applicator must be worn for 1917·5/42 = 45·65 hours or just over 6½ hours per day.

A radiograph showing this applicator in position on the patient's hand is shown in fig. 12.05.

After an applicator is constructed and loaded with radium, some centres like to check the dose-rate at selected points

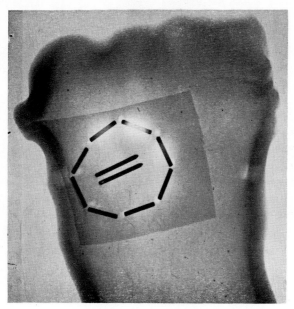

FIG. 12.05. Radiograph of surface applicator on patient's hand.
Courtesy of N. W. Ramsey, Charing Cross Hospital, London.

experimentally. Experimental measurements take into account the effects of absorption, scatter, oblique filtration, etc., which may have been neglected in the calculations. However, to make such measurements a sensitive measuring system is essential, since (1) the dose-rates are low (much less, for example, than in X-ray treatments), and (2) a measuring instrument of small volume must be used because the dose-rate varies rapidly from point to point. Solid state dosimeters are often more convenient for this purpose than ionisation chambers.

Lesions in certain regions such as the floor of the mouth, the lip or the cheek may often be conveniently treated by means of two planar (or nearly planar) applicators between which the lesion is sandwiched. In this way a high degree of

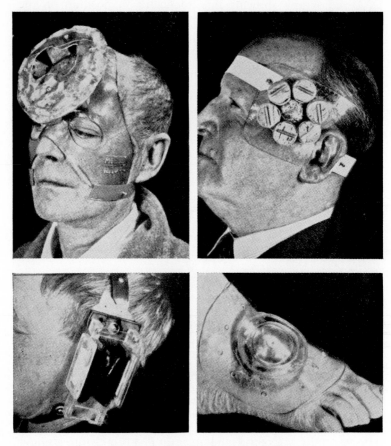

FIG. 12.06. Examples of radium applicators.

(a) Single mould for basal cell carcinoma of the forehead.
(b) Single mould for basal cell carcinoma of the temple.
(c) Sandwich mould for squamous-cell carcinoma of the pinna.
(d) Radioactive tantalum wire applicator for squamous cell carcinoma of the dorsum of the foot.

By permission from *British Practice in Radiotherapy* by Carling *et al.* (Butterworth & Co. Ltd., London.)

uniformity of dose is obtained throughout the block of tissue provided the thickness of the latter does not greatly exceed the distance *h*.

480

Occasionally the area to be treated approximates to the outer surface of a cylinder. In this case uniform irradiation can be obtained by a suitable distribution of radium over an outer coaxial cylinder. Rules for calculating the amount and distribution of radium required to give a specified dose are also given by Paterson and Parker.

Instead of using a " sandwich " mould, it is sometimes more convenient to deliver part of the radiation dose by a local γ-ray source and part by an external beam of X-rays or γ-rays from a teletherapy unit. For example the dose delivered by an intra-oral radium applicator may be supplemented by external irradiation. The supplementing of local γ-ray sources by external radiation is also commonly employed in the radiation treatment of cancer of the cervix uteri. This is probably the site in which intra-cavitary radium applicators are most widely used, and its treatment is therefore discussed below.

Treatment of carcinoma of the cervix uteri

When cancer of the uterine cervix is treated by radiotherapy, the main dose is normally given by local radioactive sources. In most techniques, radium sources are placed both in the uterine canal and in the vagina, but the precise positioning, particularly of the vaginal sources, differs from one radiotherapy centre to another. The volume to be treated is approximately pear-shaped, extending laterally to include tissue at the base of the parametria but flattened from front to back. In Great Britain treatments are usually assessed in terms of the dose delivered at certain points (conventionally designated A and B) which were selected by Tod and Meredith [9] at Manchester as being useful reference points. A was originally defined as a point " 2 cm. lateral to the central canal of the uterus and 2 cm. up from the mucous membrane of the lateral fornix in the plane of the uterus " and B was defined as 5 cm. lateral to the canal and at the same level as A. (See fig. 12.07.) The level of the mucous membrane of the lateral fornix is assumed in practice to be at the level of the lower end of the radium in the uterine canal since this is readily visible on a radiograph. In the original definitions of A and B, the uterus was envisaged as lying centrally in the pelvis with the uterine canal in the

481

mid-sagittal plane. With a symmetrical distribution of radium, the dose at the point A on the left side is then equal to the dose at the point A on the right side. In practice, the uterus may be displaced laterally or lie obliquely in the pelvis and the radium insertion may not be symmetrical, and the definitions of A and B above are then ambiguous. In these circumstances different centres use different conventions in their dose estimations. At Manchester, the dose which is recorded is that which would have been delivered by the actual quantity of radium used, had it been in a centrally and symmetrically sited uterus.[10] Some clinicians, however, prefer dose estimates at points on both the left and right sides. It is then necessary to consider whether A and/or B shall be located relative to the uterine canal or the mid-sagittal plane. Point A was intended to be in a region of paracervical tissue where over-dosage might occur and it is logical to define A so that it remains in a fixed position relative to the uterine canal. Thus the position of A might be defined as 2 cm. from the lower end of the uterine radium (the distance being measured along the axis of the tube) and 2 cm. lateral to the central axis of the tube (the "lateral" distance being measured at right angles to the tube axis). Point B, on the other hand, was intended to be in a position where the radium dose is low and may need to be supplemented by external irradiation. It may therefore be preferable to define B so that it is in a fixed position relative to the pelvis as a whole, e.g. B may be located 5 cm. from the mid-sagittal plane of the patient instead of 5 cm. from the uterine canal. (See fig. 12.08.) If the uterine canal lies in the mid-sagittal plane, the definitions are of course identical but if the uterus is displaced or inclined laterally then the dose at point B on the left side of the pelvis

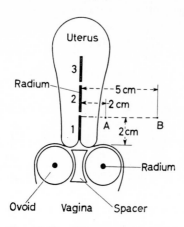

FIG. 12.07. Diagrammatic representation of position of radium in treatment of carcinoma of the uterine cervix by the Manchester method.

may differ appreciably from the dose at point *B* on the right side.

If the dose delivered by the radium at *A* is adequate, tissues in the immediate vicinity of the cervix receive sufficient irradiation to destroy any malignant cells, but with most techniques the dose at *B* is considerably less, and, if the cancer has spread laterally, the dose at *B* must be supplemented by X-irradiation. Neary [11] has shown that a single source placed centrally in the vagina gives a higher dose at *B* for the same dose at *A*, than the usual arrangement of radium in uterine canal and lateral fornices, but since a larger source is necessary,

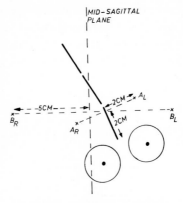

FIG. 12.08. Diagram to illustrate one method of locating points *A* and *B* when the uterine radium is not in the mid-sagittal plane.

an unacceptably high dose is delivered to the bladder and rectum unless very heavy screening is introduced anteriorly and posteriorly. Care is always necessary to ensure that the dose to the anterior rectal wall is not excessive and it is usual to introduce a suitable dosimeter into the rectum during treatments to measure the dose-rate experimentally in each individual case.

A typical method of treatment (based upon that of Tod and Meredith at Manchester) is as follows. The uterine applicator normally consists of either one or two 10 mg. and one 15 mg. radium tubes (active length 1·35 cm., total length 2 cm., diameter 4·05 mm., platinum wall thickness 1 mm.) contained in a thin-walled rubber tube, which is provided with a flange at the lower end. The number of tubes used is selected according to the length of the uterine canal. (Occasionally it may only be possible to insert one radium tube into the uterine canal and in this case a 20 mg. tube is used.) The vaginal applicators are " ovoids " of hard rubber or bakelite 2, 2·5 or 3 cm. in diameter, shaped so that the outer surface is an isodose surface of the radium tube or tubes they contain, and kept apart by a washer or spacer. The smallest ovoids are normally loaded with

17·5 mg. of radium, the medium ovoids with 20 mg. of radium and the large ovoids with 22·5 mg. These loadings produce an approximately constant dose-rate at *A* and in combination with the uterine applicator give isodose contours of suitable shape. The dose-rates produced at *A* and *B* by two typical combinations of sources are given in Table 12.05 and typical dose distributions are shown in fig. 12.09.

TABLE 12.05

Position of tube	Ra. content (mg.)	Dose-rate at A (rads./hr.)		Dose-rate at B (rads./hr.)	
		Uncorrected	Corrected for tissue absorption	Uncorrected	Corrected for tissue absorption
Large patient					
Uterus 1 (Cervix)	10	14·2 ⎫	13·9 ⎫	2·5 ⎫	2·3 ⎫
Uterus 2	10	14·2 ⎬36·1	13·9 ⎬35·2	2·5 ⎬8·1	2·3 ⎬7·4
Uterus 3 (Fundus)	15	7·7 ⎭	7·4 ⎭	3·1 ⎭	2·8 ⎭
Vagina 1 (large ovoid 1 cm. spacer)	22·5	13·1 ⎫18·9	12·6 ⎫18·0	7·8 ⎫10·4	7·3 ⎫9·6
Vagina 2	22·5	5·8 ⎭	5·4 ⎭	2·6 ⎭	2·3 ⎭
Total		55·0	53·2	18·5	17·0
Small patient					
Uterus 1 (Cervix)	10	14·2 ⎫35·5	13·9 ⎫34·8	2·5 ⎫6·2	2·3 ⎫5·7
Uterus 2 (Fundus)	15	21·3 ⎭	20·9 ⎭	3·7 ⎭	3·4 ⎭
Vagina 1 (small ovoid no spacer)	17·5	12·6 ⎫19·7	12·2 ⎫19·0	5·1 ⎫7·9	4·8 ⎫7·3
Vagina 2	17·5	7·1 ⎭	6·8 ⎭	2·8 ⎭	2·5 ⎭
Total		55·2	53·8	14·1	13·0

The radium dose is usually delivered in two or three fractions. After each insertion, the actual radium distribution obtained is determined from radiographs. (Two radiographs at right angles such as those shown in fig. 12.10 or two radiographs taken with a tube shift between exposures are required.)

484

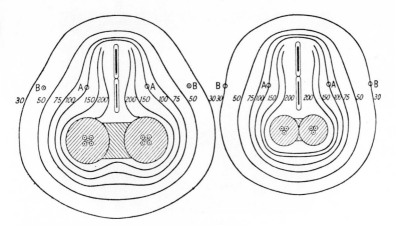

FIG. 12.09. Isodose curves (in the plane of reference for Manchester technique) of radium treatment of cancer of the cervix uter, dose at *A* as 100 per cent.

A standard applicators for large vagina;
B standard applicators for small vagina.

By permission from *The Treatment of Malignant Disease by Radiotherapy*, by R. Paterson. (E. Arnold, London.)

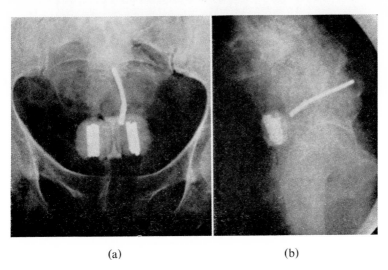

(a)   (b)

FIG. 12.10.   Treatment of carcinoma of the uterine cervix.   Radiographs of Manchester technique.   (*a*) anterior-posterior, (*b*) lateral.

By permission from *British Practice in Radiotherapy*, Carling *et al.* (Butterworth & Co. Ltd., London.)

485

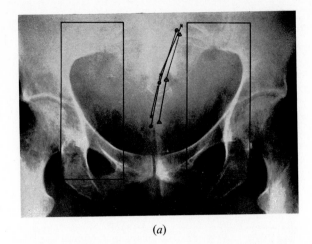

(*a*)

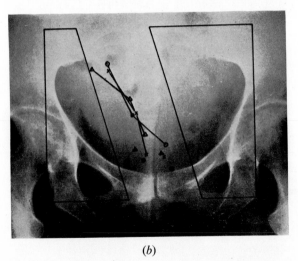

(*b*)

FIG. 12.11. Diagrams illustrating the positioning of an adjustable lead filter (to shield the tissues already adequately treated by radium), during supplementary treament with external radiation. In each of these cases, the radium treatment was given in three fractions. The axes of the radium sources in each of the three insertions (located radiographically) have been superimposed on one A.P. radiograph and the area to be treated by external radiation is drawn in.

(*a*) uterine radium approximately in mid-sagittal plane;

(*b*) uterine radium lying obliquely in the pelvis.

Courtesy of D. A. Boyes, British Columbia Cancer Institute.

486

The actual doses at the points *A* and *B* received in each individual case may then be calculated.

The dose to *B* is normally supplemented by external irradiation which may be delivered either before, between, or after the radium insertions. Using megavoltage radiation, a typical treatment plan is to use anterior and posterior direct fields, 12 or 14 cm. wide but with the central 4 cm. blocked off by a lead filter. The treatment is therefore approximately equivalent to directing two fields 4 cm. or 5 cm. wide towards each parametrium. It is convenient if the position of the lead filter is adjustable so that it can be moved across the X-ray field, to shield the tissues which were in the vicinity of the radium, wherever the radium was actually located in each individual patient. (See fig. 12.11.) With 200 kVp. X-radiation it is necessary to add lateral oblique fields to obtain a sufficient dose at *B*. It should be noted that the lower the energy of the radiation used, the greater is the scattered dose received at *A*, and allowance must be made for the scatter contribution from the external radiation when the size of the dose at *A* to be delivered by the radium is determined.

12.02. Interstitial γ-ray therapy

Instead of using surface applicators, radioactive sources are sometimes introduced directly into the tissues to be irradiated. If long-lived isotopes such as radium, Co^{60}, Cs^{137} or Ta^{182} are used, the sources must be removed after the appropriate treatment time. Hence these materials are used only in the more accessible sites. Isotopes of short-half-life, such as radon or Au^{198}, on the other hand, may be left permanently in the tissues. In this method of treatment it is inevitable that the tissues adjacent to the radioactive sources receive a dose which is high compared with that delivered to more distant tissues. However, if Paterson and Parker's rules for distributing radioactive sources are followed, the minimum dose-rate between sources should be fairly uniform throughout the region treated. If the minimum dose is sufficient to produce the desired clinical result, the value of the higher dose delivered at other points is less important provided that the maximum is not sufficient to produce undesirable results such as necrosis. Paterson considers that in order to avoid excessive local reactions near the source, the following concentrations should not be exceeded :

(1) 1·0 mg. of radium per cm. of needle (0·5 mm. Pt. filtration) for 6 days, or 0·66 mg. per cm. for 10 days.

(2) 1·3 mCi. in a radon seed.

A single planar implant is usually considered to be sufficient for the treatment of regions not exceeding 1 cm. in thickness. For such regions the central plane is implanted. The amount of radium or radon required can be calculated from the same table as is used for surface applicators taking the treatment

TABLE 12.06

DISTRIBUTION RULES FOR PLANAR IMPLANTS

Area (cm.²)	% Radium on periphery	% Radium within periphery
0-25	67	33
25-100	50	50
>100	33	67

distance as 0·5 cm. Tissues within 0·5 cm. of the implant will then receive a dose not less than 10 per cent. less than the prescribed dose. (The dose over the plane at 0·5 cm. distance will be equal to the prescribed dose within ± 10 per cent. and tissues nearer the implant will receive a greater dose.) For other isotopes, the amount of radioactive material required can be readily calculated from the same table, if appropriate corrections are made for the change in specific gamma-ray constant and (for short-lived isotopes) average half-life. An example is given below.

The distribution rules already given for surface applicators should be followed as closely as possible, but since there are in any case considerable variations in dose-rate within the 1 cm. slab of tissue around the implanted plane, it is usually considered permissible to relax these rules somewhat, when the radium supply or the field of implantation require it. Approximate distribution rules for implants are given in Table 12.06, but it

488

should be realised that the dose distribution is better, the more nearly the distribution rules for surface applicators are implemented.

For the treatment of superficial regions where the surface is either concave or very irregular, implants are often more convenient than the use of an external applicator. Sheets of plastic with holes drilled in the position in which seeds are to be implanted, which can be placed over the skin surface to help the surgeon obtain a desired distribution, and plastic jigs by means of which implanted needles can be clamped in position, are sometimes employed. It is customary to take radiographs of the completed implant to determine the distribution actually produced. If an accurately planar implant is attained and a radiograph can be taken with the X-ray film parallel to the plane of the implant, the distribution may be determined from a single film. (It is only necessary to allow for the magnification of the radiograph.) In general, however, it is necessary to calculate the distribution from the images projected on two films at right angles or from two films taken with a film shift between exposures. Typical radiographs (A.P. and lateral) of a single plane implant with radium needles are shown in fig. 12.12.

It will be noticed in these radiographs that there are no radium needles along the lower border of the treatment region. When approximately rectangular areas are implanted it is not unusual to be unable to introduce needles at right angles at either one or both ends of the plane. In such cases, either needles with greater specific activity at the ends are used to compensate for the missing " crossing " needles, or the area which is effectively treated is reduced by 10 per cent. for each " uncrossed " end.

In this particular example, the area to be implanted was estimated beforehand to be a rectangle of area about 3×4 cm.^{2} It was known that it would be impossible to insert radium along the inferior border and that the lines within the periphery would have to be parallel to the short not the long side of the rectangle. The treatment plan suggested was as follows. Single 2 mg. needles (active length 3·0 cm., total length 4·4 cm.) to be used on the anterior and posterior borders and two 1 mg. needles (active length 1·5 cm. total length 2·4 cm.) on the superior edge. (These particular needles were chosen because it was not

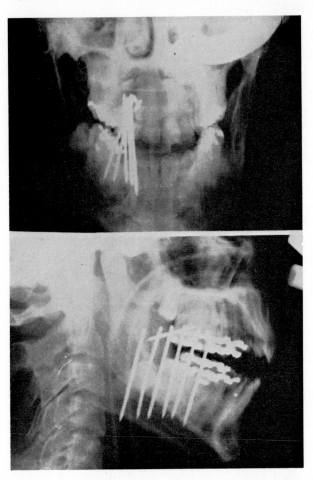

FIG. 12.12.   Radiographs of a single plane implant of the right side of the tongue.

above, A.P. view; *below*, lateral.

Courtesy of J. M. W. Gibson, British Columbia Cancer Institute.

considered practicable to insert longer needles.)   Three needles each containing 1·3 mg. of radium within the periphery, would satisfy the distribution rules but with the radium stock available it was necessary to use four needles each containing 1 mg.

(active length 3·0 cm., total length 4·4 cm.). Thus the treatment plan required the insertion of a total of 10 mg. of radium. From the radiographs of the implant actually achieved, the area fully treated was estimated to be 10·9 cm.² From table 12.04, for this area, 263 mg.-hr. are required to deliver 1,000 rads. The treatment dose desired in this case was 6,500 rads. Therefore the treatment time was 6·5 × 26·3 = 171 hours.

As a typical example of an implant using short-lived radioactive sources consider the treatment of a rodent ulcer or cancer of the inner canthus with radon seeds described by Paterson.

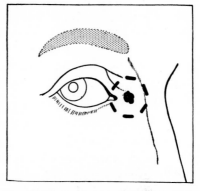

Fig. 12.13. Radon seed implant of the inner canthus.

By permission from *Malignant Disease and its Treatment by Radium and X-rays* by R. Paterson. (Edward Arnold Ltd., London.)

Suppose the treatment area is a circle 2 cm. in diameter and a dose of 6,500 rads is required.

Then the treatment area = 3·14 cm.²

∴ From table 12.04, for 1,000 rads, 130·9 mg.-hr. are required

∴ For 6,500 rads, 851 mg.-hr. are required.

But a permanent implant of 1 mCi. of radon is equivalent to 132·4 mg.-hr. (See Chapter V.) Therefore the number of mCi. of radon required = 851/132·4 = 6·4 mCi. The seeds should be distributed as shown in fig. 12.13, with 0·3 or 0·4 mCi. (approximately 5 per cent.) at the centre and the remainder (say 6 × 1 mCi.) around the periphery.

If radioactive gold grains (Au¹⁹⁸) were to be used instead of radon seeds, the treatment planning would be as follows. Firstly, the effective duration of the treatment with Au¹⁹⁸ (average life 93·5 hours) is less than with radon (average life 132·4 hours). Hence if 6,500 rads is a satisfactory treatment dose with radon, a dose less than 6,500 rads should be required using Au¹⁹⁸ (see Chapter X). There may be differences of opinion as to the equivalent dose in the shorter time, but suppose that the aim is to deliver 6,000 rads with the gold grain implant.

491

(Useful graphs relating (1) the total dose and (2) the dose-rate to the overall treatment time for interstitial implants have been published by Johnson.[12])

The dose calculation would then be as follows: The specific γ-ray constant of Au^{198} is 2·3 R.-cm.²/mCi.-hr. (compared with 8·25 for radon screened by 0·5 mm. Pt. or its equivalent) and the average half-life is 93·5 hours instead of 132·4 hours. Therefore to produce the *same* total exposure, if the activity of the gold grains is denoted by A_{Au} and the activity of the radon seeds by A_{Rn}, then

$$2\cdot3 \times 93\cdot5 \times \alpha \times A_{Au} = 8\cdot25 \times 132\cdot4 \times A_{Rn}$$

The factor α is introduced to allow for the difference between the exposure-rate from an actual platinum-encased gold grain and the exposure-rate from an unscreened point source. ($\alpha . A_{Au}$ is sometimes called the exposure-rate equivalent activity.[15]) Thus

$$\alpha . A_{Au} = \frac{8\cdot25 \times 132\cdot4}{2\cdot3 \times 93\cdot5} \times A_{Rn} = 5\cdot1 \, A_{Rn}.^{*}$$

To deliver 6,000 rads, 5·9 mCi. of radon would be required, so $5\cdot1 \times 5\cdot9 = 30\cdot1$ mCi. equivalents of Au^{198} are required.

In order that the maximum exposure-rate at any point in the gold implant, shall not exceed that produced in the radon implant, it is necessary to restrict the activity of the individual gold grains. In this case 1 mCi. radon seeds were used. 3.6 mCi. equivalent gold grains would produce an equal exposure-rate initially ($\Gamma_{Rn}/\Gamma_{Au} = 8\cdot25/2\cdot3 = 3\cdot6$). Eight gold grains of initial equivalent activity 3·6 mCi. around the periphery and one grain of 1·3 mCi. initial equivalent activity at the centre might therefore be used.

Tumours rather greater than 1 cm. in thickness can sometimes be treated by being " sandwiched " between two planar implants, although if the separation of the implants is greater than 1·5 cm. there will be a region of lower dose midway between the planes. When the three dimensions of a tumour are of the same order of magnitude, multiplanar or volume implants are necessary. Cuboidal volumes are probably most

* If Γ_0 for Au^{198} is taken as 2·4 (instead of 2·3) R.-cm.²/mCi.-hr., then $\alpha A_{Au} = 4\cdot9 \, A_{Rn}$.

easily treated by a multiplanar implant, the planes being separated by 1·0 to 1·5 cm. and the outer planes being loaded with three parts of radium to two parts on the inner planes, the total amount of radium being determined by the total volume to be implanted. For volumes which approximate to a sphere or cylinder, Paterson and Parker suggest distributing three-quarters of the radium over the surface and one-quarter as uniformly as possible throughout the " core ", i.e. the volume to be treated. In the case of cylindrical volumes, the surface radium should be distributed in the ratio of one part over each flat end to four parts around the curved surface. If the end radium is omitted, the effective volume which is treated is reduced by 7·5 per cent. for each open end. In all cases the separation of needles or seeds should not exceed 1 cm. Paterson and Parker prepared tables similar to table 12.04 showing the number of mg.-hr. required to produce a given minimum dose throughout different treatment volumes. Their system has been extended to other geometrical figures by Oddie.[13]

12.03. Superficial and intra-cavitary β-ray therapy

Within a large volume containing a uniformly distributed β-emitter, the dose-rate is constant throughout the volume up to a distance of the order of the range of the β-particles from the surface. All the energy emitted by the isotope is absorbed. Let E denote the *average* energy of the β-particles (in MeV.) and let C denote the concentration of the isotope (in mCi./g.). Then the energy emitted by the isotope

$$= 3 \cdot 7 \times 10^7 C \times E \times 1 \cdot 6 \times 10^{-6} \text{ ergs/g./sec.}$$

No. of disintegra- energy per disintegrations per g per sec. tion in ergs

$$= 59 \cdot 2 \cdot C \cdot E \cdot \text{ergs/g./sec.}$$

Hence the absorbed dose-rate is given by

$$D_\beta/t = 0 \cdot 592 \cdot C \cdot E \cdot \text{rads/sec.}$$
$$= 35 \cdot 5 \cdot C \cdot E \cdot \text{rads/min.}$$
$$= 2131 \cdot C \cdot E \cdot \text{rads/hr.} \qquad (3)$$

At the surface of a large volume containing a β-emitter, conditions of symmetry require that the dose-rate be one-half that in the interior, i.e. $0 \cdot 296 \, C \cdot E \cdot$ rads/sec. or 1055 $C \cdot E \cdot$ rad s/hr.

To calculate the dose-rate within or near β-emitting regions which are not infinitely large in comparison with the range of the particles, it is necessary to make certain assumptions about the variation of dose-rate with distance in absorbing media near

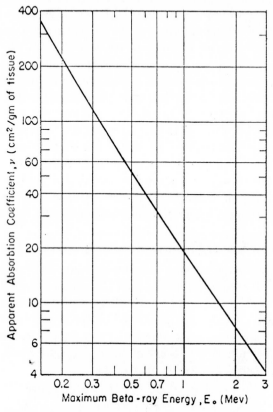

FIG. 12.14.   The apparent absorption coefficient v for β particles as a function of the β-ray energy.

By permission from *Radiation Dosimetry*, ed. by Hine and Boswell. (Academic Press, London.)

point sources.   A simple inverse square law is not adequate (except very close to the source) because the effects of absorption and scattering cannot be neglected for β-radiation.

It has been found [14] that a law of the form e^{1-vr}/vr, (where r is the distance from the source and v is an absorption co-efficient) represents the observed variation of dose-rate with distance for distances greater than $1/\nu$ from the source. The absorption coefficient ν varies almost inversely as the energy (E) of the β-particles so that νE is approximately constant (see fig. 12.14). At distances less than $1/\nu$, a simple inverse square law can be used for the more energetic β-emitters (with

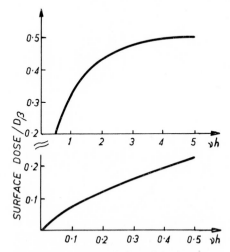

FIG. 12.15.   The variation of the dose at the surface of a plane β-emitting source of infinite area but finite thickness with the thickness of the plane.   Ordinates, surface dose expressed as a fraction of the dose within an infinite volume.   Abscissae, the dimensionless product of the apparent absorption coefficient (ν) and the thickness (h).   The graph applies to β-emitters with $E_{max} > 1\cdot5$ MeV.   (After Loevinger, Japha and Brownell[14].)

$E_{max} \geqslant 1\cdot5$ MeV.), so for these isotopes the dose-rate may be written as $\dfrac{k}{(\nu r)^2}$ for $r < 1/\nu$ and $\dfrac{k}{\nu r} e^{1-\nu r}$ for $r \geqslant 1/\nu$ (where k is a constant).   For low energy β-emitters, rather more complicated functions are required to represent the variation of dose-rate near the source adequately.   An expression which has been found generally applicable is

$$\frac{k}{(\nu r)^2}\left\{ c\left[1-\frac{\nu r}{c}\,e^{1-(\nu r/c)}\right]+\nu r\,e^{1-\nu r}\right\}$$

495

where $\left[1 - \dfrac{vr}{c}\, e^{1-(vr/c)}\right] \equiv 0$ for $r \geqslant \dfrac{c}{v}$ and c is a constant, which depends on the energy. This expression reduces to those given above for the more energetic β-emitters on substituting $c = 1$ for $E_{max} \geqslant 1\cdot5$ MeV. ($c = 1\cdot5$ for $0\cdot5 \leqslant E_{max} < 1\cdot5$ MeV. and $c = 2$ for $0\cdot17 < E_{max} < 0\cdot5$ MeV.)

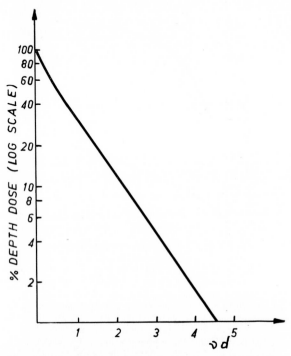

FIG. 12.16. The variation of percentage depth dose outside a plane β-emitting slab of infinite area and thickness with depth (d). Abscissae; the dimensionless produce vd. (After Loevinger Japtha and Brownell.[14])

Using these equations for the dose-rate in the vicinity of a point-source, it becomes possible to calculate the dose-rate within or near limited volumes of β-emitters. Two cases which are of practical interest in therapy are (1) the variation of the dose-rate at the surface of a thin plane of β-emitter with the thickness of the plane, and (2) the variation of the dose-rate with the distance from a β-emitting plane at points outside but close to the plane. The former is required for example, in assessing the dose-rate at the surface of a β-emitting plaque of limited thickness or in estimating the dose delivered to the cavity walls in the treatment of peritoneal or pleural effusions by radioactive gold; the latter is required to determine the dose at a depth using β-applicators or plaques.

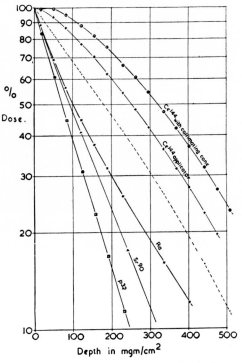

FIG. 12.17.   Graphs showing the depth doses obtained with various β-emitting plaques (P^{32}, Sr^{90}, Ra and Ce^{144}).

By permission from Haybittle (1953), *Brit. J. Radiol.*, **26**, 424.

Fig. 12.15 shows how the surface dose-rate increases with increasing source thickness (h) for a plane slab of large area for the more energetic β-emitters ($E_{max} > 1 \cdot 5$ MeV.).   It is convenient to plot the dose-rate as a function of the (dimensionless) product vh since one graph can then be used for many isotopes.   As an example of the use of this graph, consider a β-ray applicator consisting of a unit density plastic in which

P^{32} is incorporated. If the applicator thickness is large in comparison with the β-particle range (say 1 cm.), the surface dose-rate is that at the surface of an infinitely thick plane and is given by $0.5\, D_\beta/t$, i.e. $0.5\times35.5\,.\,C\,.\,E$. rads/min. For P^{32}, the average β-particle energy $E = 0.69$ MeV., therefore the surface dose-rate $= 0.5\times35.5\times0.69$. C rads/min.

$$= 12.1\ C\ \text{rads/min}.$$

where C is the activity in mCi./g.

If the active layer is only (say) 0.5 mm. thick, however, using figs. 12.14 and 12.15 for P^{32} (max. β-energy 1.7 MeV.), $v = 9.2$ cm.^{2}/g., $vr = 0.46$ and the surface dose-rate is given by $0.215\ (D_\beta/t)$, i.e. for 0.5 mm. active layer, the surface dose-rate

$$= 0.215\times24.2\ C\,.\,\text{rads/min}.$$
$$= 5.2\,.\,C\,.\,\text{rads/min}.$$

where C is the activity in mCi./g.

Fig. 12.16 shows the calculated variation of dose-rate with distance (d) outside a plane β-particle source of infinite area and thickness (the abscissa is the product vd) and fig. 12.17 shows some measured depth doses for typical β-emitting plaques used in therapy. P^{32} and Sr^{90} are pure β-emitters, radium and Ce^{144} emit γ-rays in addition to β-radiation.

12.04. Interstitially distributed radioactivity

When a radioactive isotope is ingested or injected, it may become fairly uniformly distributed throughout the tissues of one or more organs. The dose-rate due to a β-emitting isotope uniformly distributed throughout a large volume of tissue has already been discussed in section 12.03. The expression obtained was $D_\beta/t = 0.592$ $E\,.\,C$. rads/sec. or $2{,}131$ $E\,.\,C$ rads/hr., where E denotes the average β-ray energy in MeV. and C the isotope concentration in mCi./g.

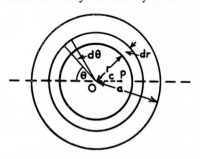

FIG. 12.18.

For γ-emitters which are uniformly distributed throughout a certain volume, the dose-rate can be readily calculated only if the volume through which the isotope is distributed is of simple geometrical form. We shall discuss here only the simplest case, a sphere.

Consider first the dose-rate at the centre of a sphere of radius a due to a thin spherical shell, radius r, thickness dr, in which the absorption of the γ-radiation can be neglected (fig. 12.18). Let C denote the activity per unit volume (mCi./cc.), then the contribution to the dose-rate at the centre from the shell (using the inverse square law)

$$= C.f.\,\Gamma_0 \frac{4\pi r^2 dr}{r^2}\ . \ \text{rad/hr.}$$

where Γ_0 is the specific γ-ray constant of the isotope considered and f is the appropriate rad per roentgen factor. The dose-rate due to all such shells

$$= C.f.\,\Gamma_0 \int_0^a \frac{4\pi r^2}{r^2}\ .\ dr = C.f.\,\Gamma_0\ .\ 4\pi a. \tag{4}$$

If absorption is not negligible, the corresponding expression is

$$C.f.\,\Gamma_0 \int_0^a \frac{4\pi r^2}{r^2}\ e^{-\mu r}\, dr$$

$$= C.f.\,\Gamma_0 \frac{4\pi a}{\mu}\,(1 - e^{-\mu a})$$

At a point displaced by a distance c from the centre the dose-rate (neglecting absorption) is

$$C.f.\,\Gamma_0 \int_{r=0}^{r=a} \int_{\theta=0}^{\theta=\pi} \frac{2\pi r^2 \sin\theta\, dr\, d\theta}{r^2 + c^2 - 2rc\cos\theta}$$

$$= C.f.\,\Gamma_0\ .\ \pi \left\{ 2a + \frac{a^2 - c^2}{c}\ \log \frac{a+c}{a-c} \right\}$$

The variation of the dose-rate with distance from the centre of the active sphere is shown diagrammatically in fig. 12.19. Notice that the dose-rate at the surface is one-half that at the centre. The mean dose-rate throughout the sphere is 0·75 of the dose-rate at the centre.

The integrals in the above expressions are sometimes called geometrical factors and denoted by g. Corresponding integrals for other shapes have been evaluated in a few special cases and tables of g values have been published.[16]

With the exception of P^{32}, most of the isotopes which are administered internally emit both β- and γ-radiation and the total dose includes contributions from both radiations. The isotopes administered internally are also usually of short half-life and therefore the dose-rate changes with time. It is generally assumed that after the initial period of absorption and distribution is completed, the activity present in any organ decreases exponentially with time with a decay constant (λ),

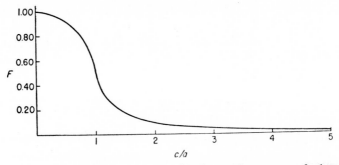

FIG. 12.19. Variation of γ dose-rate with distance from centre of sphere.
By permission from Mayneord (1945), *Brit. J. Radiol.*, 18, 12.

which is determined by the sum of the radioactive decay constant (λ_R) and the biological decay constant (λ_B). The radioactive decay is strictly exponential, the " decay " due to biological elimination can in most cases be represented fairly closely by an exponential function.

Thus, $\lambda = \lambda_R + \lambda_B$

or $1/\tau = 1/\tau_R + 1/\tau_B$

where τ, τ_R, τ_B denote the effective, radioactive and biological half-lives respectively.

The total dose received by an organ

$$= \frac{\tau}{0.693} \times \text{initial dose-rate}$$

$$\simeq \frac{\tau_p}{0.693} \times \text{initial dose-rate}$$

if biological elimination is slow.

As an example, we shall calculate the order of magnitude of the dose delivered to the thyroid gland after administration of I^{131}, assuming that the isotope is uniformly distributed through the gland. The β-dose-rate initially is 2131 $E \cdot C$ rads/hr. (equation 3). For I^{131}, $E = 0\cdot187$ and hence

$$D_\beta/t = 400 \cdot C \cdot \text{rads/hr.}$$

Assuming that the gland can be represented by two spheres in which the absorption of the γ-radiation is negligible, the initial γ dose-rate (equation 4) is given by

$$D/t = 0\cdot75 \cdot 4\pi a \cdot f \cdot \Gamma_0 \cdot C \cdot \text{rads/hr.}$$

For I^{131}, $\Gamma_0 = 2\cdot2$, $f = 0\cdot955$, and assuming $a = 1\cdot54$ cm. (i.e. that the volume of each sphere is 15 cc.)

$$\therefore \quad D_y/t = 30 \cdot C \cdot \text{rads/hr.}$$

$\therefore$ Total dose-rate (assuming it is permissible to add the β and γ doses)

$$= 430 \cdot C \cdot \text{rads/hr.}$$

of which over 90 per cent. is due to the β-radiation (the exact percentage depends upon the gland size). If the effective half-life of iodine in the gland is assumed to be equal to the physical half-life of 8 days the total dose received would be

$$\frac{8 \times 24}{0\cdot693} \times 430 \cdot C \cdot \text{rads}$$

$= 120,000 \cdot C \cdot \text{rads}$

$= 4,000 \cdot A \cdot \text{rads}$, where A is the total initial activity (in mCi.) in the gland.

A tracer dose of 10 μCi., if all the isotope entered the gland, would thus result in a dose of about 40 rads. (In practice, the gland uptake will be less than 100 per cent. and the half-life less than 8 days, and in a euthyroid patient the dose will be of the order of 15 to 20 rad.)

On the other hand, to deliver a therapeutic dose of (say) 6,000 rads, an initial activity of 1·5 mCi. in the gland is required if the half-life is 8 days or 4 mCi. if the half-life is only 3 days.

17

REFERENCES

1. SIEVERT, R. M. (1923). *Acta Radiol.* **2,** 70 ; (1932). *Acta Radiol.* Suppl. XIV.
2. YOUNG, M. E. J. and BATHO, H. (1964). *Brit. J. Radiol.* **37,** 38.
3. LIVERSAGE, W. E. (1959). *Brit. J. Radiol.* **32,** 348.
4. BATHO, H. F., SMOCOVITIS, D. and YOUNG, M. E. J. (1965). Unpublished data.
5. JONES, D. E. A. (1944). *Brit. J. Radiol.* **17,** 46.
6. PATERSON, R. and PARKER, H. M. (1934). *Brit. J. Radiol.* **7,** 592.
7. MEREDITH, W. J. (1947). *Radium Dosage, the Manchester System* Edinburgh, E. & S. Livingstone.
8. COOK, H. F. (1943). *Brit. J. Radiol.* **16,** 115.
9. TOD, M. C. and MEREDITH, J. W. (1938). *Brit. J. Radiol.* **11,** 809 ; (1953). *Brit. J. Radiol.* **26,** 252.
10. PATERSON, R. (1963). *The Treatment of Malignant Disease by Radiotherapy.* London, Arnold. 336.
11. NEARY, G. J. (1943). *Brit. J. Radiol.* **16,** 225, 263 ; (1947). *Brit. J. Radiol.* **20,** 454.
12. JOHNSON, G. C. (1964). *Radiology,* **82,** 831.
13. ODDIE, T. H. (1940). *Brit. J. Radiol.* **13,** 389.
14. LOEVINGER, R., JAPHA, E. M. and BROWNELL, G. L. *Radiation Dosimetry* (1956), ed. by Hine, G. J. and Brownell, G. L. New York, Academic Press.
15. INTERNATIONAL COMMISSION ON RADIOLOGICAL UNITS AND MEASUREMENTS (1962). Report 10e. U.S. National Bureau of Standards. Handbook 86.
16. LOEVINGER, R., HOLT, J. G. and HINE, G. J. *Radiation Dosimetry* (1956), ed. by G. J. Hine and G. L. Brownell. New York, Academic Press.

GENERAL REFERENCES

PATERSON, R. (1963). *The Treatment of Malignant Disease* by *Radiotherapy.* London, Arnold.
WILSON, C. W. (1956). *Radium Therapy, its physical aspects.* 2nd edn. London, Chapman & Hall.
MEREDITH, W. J. (1947). *Radium Dosage,* the Manchester system. Edinburgh, Livingstone.
CARLING, E. R., WINDEYER, B. W. and SMITHERS, D. W. (1955). *British Practice in Radiotherapy.* London, Butterworth.

EXAMINATION QUESTIONS

1. Describe, simply, how the quantity of radium required for an *implant* is determined. Give the basic rules by which radium sources are distributed over the area to achieve " uniform " dose. What does the word " uniform " mean as used here?

M.S.R. (T.), 1964.

2. Describe the use of substitutes for radium in interstitial radiation therapy.

M.S.R. (T.), 1964.

3. Explain the basis for the rules followed in distributing radium or equivalent gamma sources on moulds (surface applicators) with circular treated areas.

Compare the exposure-rates in r per hour at 1 cm. along the central perpendicular from the radioactive plane of a circular applicator of diameter 4 cm. loaded with 30 mg. radium element on the periphery plus a central " point " source of (a) 1·5 mg., (b) 3 mg.

Which of these arrangements conforms to the distribution rules? (specific gamma ray constant $= 8\cdot25$ r./hr. at 1 cm. from a " point " source of 1 mg. Ra. El).

F.S.R. (T.), 1964.

4. It is decided to treat a lesion of the buccal mucosa by means of a radium implant. The lesion is approximately 1 cm. thick and covers an area of 2·5 cm. × 1·5 cm.

Using the Paterson and Parker tables supplied, describe in detail, with diagrams, the implant you would do. State the active lengths, activities, etc., of the individual needles you would use.

D.M.R. (T.), 1964.

5. Discuss the properties of a radioisotope which make it suitable as a radiotherapeutic agent when applied internally.

A thyrotoxic patient is to be treated with iodine-131. A test with a tracer dose has shown that the maximum uptake in the gland was 63 per cent. and the effective half-life of the iodine 4·3 days. The volume of the gland was estimated to be 30 cc. Calculate the amount of I^{131} required to deliver to the gland a β-ray dose of 8,000 rads. State the assumptions which have to be made in this calculation.

Average energy of β-rays from I^{131} is 0·21 MeV., 1 eV. $= 1\cdot6 \times 10^{-12}$ erg.

D.M.R. (T.), 1957.

CHAPTER XIII

THE DIAGNOSTIC USE OF ARTIFICIAL
RADIOACTIVE MATERIALS

13.01. Introduction

Artificial radioactive isotopes * are now widely used in medicine for diagnostic purposes. Because of the radiations they emit, the position and/or concentration of any material containing an artificial nuclide can be readily determined. The method of production and the more important characteristics of the various nuclides to which reference will be made in this chapter have been given in Table 5.04 of Chapter V.

When radio-isotopes are used as diagnostic tracers, the patient is given as small an amount of the material concerned as is practicable, so that the biological effect is minimal. Measuring equipment of high sensitivity is therefore required. The principal measuring instruments and the precautions necessary to obtain statistically significant results have already been described in Chapter VIII. Where the uptake of an isotope in a particular organ is being measured by an external counter, the isotope used will usually be a γ-emitter and the detector a scintillation counter. For measurements of the total activity in an organ such as the thyroid, heart or kidney, a collimator is necessary which permits the crystal to " see " the entire organ but shields it from radiation originating elsewhere. If, however, the local activity in a small region such as a node is to be compared with that elsewhere, a collimator of high resolving power is required (see section 13.09).

Diagnostic tests frequently require the measurement of activity in either blood samples or urine samples. Blood samples are usually of low activity and available only in small volumes, while urine samples may be of low activity but large volume. The activity of a blood sample containing a γ-emitting isotope is normally measured in a well-type scintillation counter

* See footnote, section 5.05.

504

(fig. 8.08(*b*)). A sample containing an isotope which emits β-rays only may be measured by means of the thin-walled Geiger counter specially designed for liquids (fig. 8.02(*c*)), provided a volume of about 10 cc. can be obtained. If the volume available is very much less than this or the isotope emits very low energy β-radiation, it may not be possible to count the sample in liquid form. Low energy β-emitting samples are normally evaporated to dryness and then either counted in front of an end-window Geiger counter (fig. 8.02(*b*)), or introduced into a continuous flow gas counter or a liquid scintillation counter. Urine samples containing γ-emitting isotopes are most conveniently measured in the collecting bottle. This may be inserted in a suitable holder to maintain standard geometry, in front of a scintillation counter or within a ring of Geiger counters. The count-rate will depend upon the volume of liquid present but the dependence of count-rate upon volume is not marked and filling the bottle to some given level is usually adequate. The count-rate from the specimen is normally compared with a standard of comparable activity and volume in a similar bottle. Faeces in a suitable container can be measured in a similar manner.

The diagnostic uses of isotopes which will be discussed in this chapter are as follows:

(1) The investigation of thyroid function and iodine metabolism.

(2) The investigation of iron metabolism and erythropoesis.

(3) Red cell survival and blood volume studies.

(4) Cardiac output measurement and studies of the peripheral circulation.

(5) The investigation of mal-absorption syndromes.

(6) The investigation of renal function.

(7) The determination of local isotope concentrations and the localisation of tumours by " scanning ".

These tests have been selected because they are well established and used routinely in most large medical centres. It must be stressed that in addition there are many other tests which are used in special investigations and an immense number of applications of radioactive tracers in medical research, which cannot be described here.

Although figures will be quoted for the typical response of normal individuals in the various tests, it should be noted that factors such as local differences in diet, as well as differences in measurement techniques may result in somewhat different " normal ranges " being appropriate in different centres.

13.02. The investigation of thyroid function and iodine metabolism

One of the most widely used isotopes for diagnostic purposes is I^{131}, a β- and γ-emitter with an 8-day half-life, which is employed in investigations of thyroid function. It is particularly valuable as an aid in distinguishing thyrotoxicosis from anxiety states which may reproduce many of the clinical signs of thyrotoxicosis. The patient is usually given a drink or an injection of sodium or potassium iodide containing I^{131} and tests are then carried out which enable estimates to be made of either (1) the rate at which inorganic iodine is concentrated by the thyroid, or (2) the rate at which organic (i.e. protein-bound) iodine is produced by the gland and released into the blood stream. In these tests the radioactive tracer is assumed to disperse uniformly through the total iodine " pool ". The concentration of the tracer therefore depends upon the size of the pool and measurements of activity can only be regarded as indicative of total iodine content if the size of the iodine pool is normal. The tracer concentration will be low if the iodine pool is enlarged (as after administration of stable iodine) and high if the pool is reduced (as in cases of endemic goitre) and these possibilities must be considered when interpreting the results of I^{131} tests.

The rate at which inorganic iodine is concentrated in the thyroid is usually estimated from measurements made over the gland with a suitable counter. Occasionally the gland uptake may be inferred from measurements of urinary excretion (the greater the amount of iodine concentrated in the gland, the less is excreted.) If measurements are made at frequent intervals for several days (in patients where the iodine pool is of normal size) graphs showing the increase with time of the amount of I^{131} in the thyroid, or of the amount of I^{131} excreted take the form shown in fig. 13.01.

These curves can be explained fairly adequately [1, 2, 3] if it is assumed (1) that the inorganic iodine is initially uniformly distributed throughout the plasma (this is a simplifying assumption which is not true until one or two hours after the test dose is given, and a more exact analysis [4] makes allowance for the gradual establishment of equilibrium), and (2) that both the thyroid and the kidneys reduce the plasma concentration by a constant fraction per unit time, i.e. that the rate of removal of iodine from the plasma by each organ is proportional to the plasma concentration. Then the rate of decrease of the plasma concentration (c) may be represented by

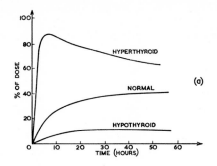

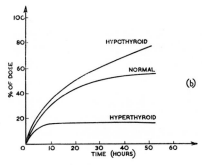

FIG. 13.01.—(a) Graphs showing uptake of radioactive iodine by the thyroid gland in typical cases.

(b) Graphs showing urinary excretion of radioactive iodine in typical cases.

$$-\frac{dc}{dt} = (r_{th} + r_k)c$$

where r_{th} and r_k are constants known as the thyroid and renal accumulation rate constants respectively. Integrating

$$c = c_0 e^{-(r_{th} + r_k)t}$$

where $c = c_0$ when $t = 0$. The quantity of iodine which is concentrated in the thyroid or the kidneys after a time t (denoted by $(q_t)_{th}$ and $(q_t)_k$ respectively) can be obtained from the equations

$$\left(\frac{dq}{dt}\right)_{th} = (vc)r_{th} = vc_0 r_{th} e^{-(r_{th} + r_k)t}$$

$$= q_0 r_{th} e^{-(r_{th} + r_k)t}$$

and

$$\left(\frac{dq}{dt}\right)_k = vcr_k = q_0 r_k e^{-(r_{th} + r_k)t}$$

507

where v denotes plasma volume and q_0 denotes the test dose.

integrating $$\frac{(q_t)_{th}}{q_0} = \frac{r_{th}}{r_{th} + r_k}(1 - e^{-(r_{th} + r_k)t})$$

and $$\frac{(q_t)_k}{q_0} = \frac{r_k}{r_{th} + r_k}(1 - e^{-(r_{th} + r_k)t}).$$

From a semi-logarithmic plot of $(q_t)_{th}/q_0$ or of $(q_t)_k/q_0$ against t, $r_{th} + r_k$ can be evaluated and from the value of $(q_t)_{th}/q_0$ or $(q_t)_k/q_0$ when $t \to \infty$, $r_{th}/(r_{th} + r_k)$ or $r_k/(r_{th} + r_k)$ can be determined. Hence r_{th} can be obtained from a graph showing the accumulation of I^{131} in either the thyroid or the urine.

In this analysis, the conversion of inorganic iodine to protein-bound iodine and the release of the latter into the blood-stream has been neglected. It is therefore a better approximation in the case of normal than of thyrotoxic patients. Nevertheless, the calculation of the thyroid accumulation rate constant on the basis of this analysis gives a useful index of thyroid function. It is important to notice that the amount of iodine in either the thyroid or the urine at a definite time depends upon both r_{th} and r_k, i.e. it depends upon the action of both the thyroid and the kidneys. The advantage of calculating the thyroid accumulation rate constant or the thyroid clearance rate constant is that these constants are independent of fluctuations in the renal function. (The thyroid clearance rate constant represents the volume of plasma cleared of iodine by the thyroid per unit time and is measured by the product $r_{th}v$.)

For routine diagnosis, the determination of uptake curves and rate constants is too time consuming, and a single measurement at a definite time of either (1) the thyroid content, or (2) the ratio of the thyroid content to the plasma content is frequently used as a crude index of thyroid activity. Sometimes measurements are made at two different times; e.g. a common practice is to take one " early " measurement, 2 to 6 hours after the test dose, and a second measurement 24 hours after the dose. These methods are fairly satisfactory provided the renal function is normal.

In 1960, the International Atomic Energy Agency convened a meeting of a group of consultants to recommend an agreed procedure for thyroid uptake measurements. These recommendations were published in 1962 [5] and have been endorsed by the International Commission on Radiological Units and Measurements.[6] A typical uptake determination, which satisfies the I.A.E.A. recommendations is outlined below.

The patient is given a drink of sodium iodide containing 5 to 10 μCi. of I^{131}. At 4 hours, and again at 24 hours after the test dose, a scintillation counter with a suitably designed collimator and some device for maintaining a constant skin-counter distance of about 25 cm. is positioned over the patient's thyroid and the counting rate recorded. (Details of a collimator which satisfies the I.A.E.A. specifications have been published by E. H. Belcher, G. Goruz-Crespo, N. G. Trott and H. Vetter.[7]) To reduce the response of the counter to scattered radiation, the spectrometer or discriminator is set to accept only pulses exceeding (say) 280 keV. in energy, or, alternatively, a lead filter 1·5 mm. in thickness is placed in front of the counter to attenuate the low energy scattered radiation.

A measurement is made under identical conditions with the counter opposite a " neck phantom " containing a dose identical with that given the patient. The " neck phantom " is a cylinder of lucite or perspex 15 cm. in diameter and 15 cm. high containing a cylindrical hole into which a bottle 3 cm. in diameter containing the test dose can be inserted. The distance from the edge of the phantom to the surface of the hole should be 0·5 cm. The test dose should be made up to a total volume equal to that of the thyroid gland of typical test patients (e.g. 30 cc. for adults, less for children). A background count is required in each case and for the 4-hour uptake measurement, it is desirable that this should include the contribution to the observed count made by extra-thyroidal activity in the neck of the patient. (At 24 hours, the plasma activity is sufficiently low for extra-thyroidal activity to introduce only a small error.) It is not easy to make a simple correction for the extra-thyroidal activity. Some centres repeat the measurement over the patient's thyroid with a 2 cm. thick lead filter screening the gland itself, but this does not correct for activity in the blood perfusing the gland and other tissues screened by the filter. Some centres make a measurement over the patient's thigh and use this to estimate the extra-thyroidal activity in the neck but there is appreciable random variation between thigh and athyreotic neck readings. However, assuming that the net count-rate due to activity in the thyroid gland only can be obtained, and assuming that the thyroid gland in the patient lies at the same distance below the skin surface as does the test dose in the phantom, the percentage uptake in the gland can be calculated. In practice, the variation in the position of the effective centre of the gland below the skin surface from patient to patient is probably the main source of error. An increase in gland depth of 1 cm., produces a decrease in counting rate of about 8 per cent. due to the changed source-detector distance (at 25 cm.) and a decrease of about 10 per cent. due to the absorption of primary radiation in the neck tissue. (If the counter responds to scattered radiation, the decrease is somewhat less, since the amount of scatter increases as the depth of the gland below the surface increases up to about 5 cm. depth.) By using a ring of counters around the neck instead of a single detector, the dependence of count-rate on the position of the thyroid can be reduced, but the dependence on extra-thyroidal radio-activity is increased, and for this reason this technique is not recommended.

As an alternative to the determination of the thyroid uptake, some centres determine the so-called " neck-thigh ratio ".[8] This is the actual ratio of observed counts over the neck and over the thigh at a selected time, usually 2 hours after an oral dose. The procedure is similar to that outlined above but no accurate determination of the tracer dose or comparison with a phantom is required. The ratio is increased above normal in cases of hyperthyroidism.

Thyroid uptake tests measure only the first phase of iodine metabolism, namely the concentration of inorganic iodide by the gland. The trapped iodine is incorporated into various organic compounds, two of which, thyroxine (i.e. tetra-iodo-thyronine) and (in lesser amounts) tri-iodo-thyronine are released into the blood stream, where they circulate bound to protein. Some clinicians consider that the rate at which organic iodine is released into the blood-stream is a better index of thyroid function than the rate at which inorganic iodine is accumulated by the gland. If the total radioactivity in the plasma is measured after a test dose of I^{131}, the activity falls initially in all cases as shown in fig. 13.02, but in toxic patients an increase in activity is detectable on the second day due to the release of protein-bound iodine from the gland into the blood-stream. The total activity in the plasma, 48 hours after a test dose is therefore several times greater in toxic than in normal patients, and this may be used as a diagnostic test for thyrotoxicosis.[9] If the protein-bound iodine is separated chemically from the inorganic iodine and estimated separately, a more sensitive index is obtained, which has the important

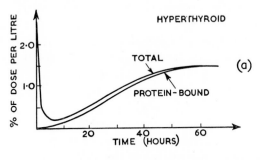

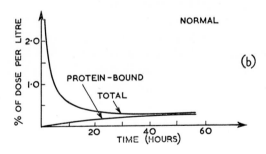

Fig. 13.02.   Graphs showing the amounts of protein-bound iodine and total iodine in the plasma (*a*) in a hyperthyroid case, (*b*) in normal cases.

advantage of being largely independent of renal function.[10] The separation can be made chemically by precipitation of protein-bound iodine with trichlor-acetic acid, or by use of an anion exchange resin which will remove inorganic sodium iodide and leave the protein-bound fraction in the filtrate. The measurement of I^{131} in the plasma also has the advantage, that, provided a blood sample can be obtained, the patient need not attend in person. It has the disadvantage that the concentration in the plasma is low, and therefore in order to be able to measure the activity, it is necessary to give greater

511

doses than are required if only uptake or excretion tests are used.

Some centres determine the ratio of protein-bound I^{131} to the total plasma I^{131} at 24 hours (the so-called " conversion ratio ") [11] but variability in the amount of inorganic I^{131} present (particularly if there is impaired renal function) makes this less reliable than a determination of protein-bound I^{131} only at a later time.

Another test which provides an indirect measure of the output of organically bound iodine by the gland is the determination of the uptake of I^{131} labelled tri-iodo-thyronine by serum constituents *in vitro*. This test has the advantage that no radioactive materials need be administered to the patient and only a blood sample is required from the patient. The result is also independent of the size of the iodine pool and is therefore useful in patients where the pool size may be abnormal. The principle of this test is as follows:

The thyroxine released from the gland is bound to several blood constituents principally thyroxine-binding globulin, and to a lesser extent to albumin and red cells. Tri-iodo-thyronine can be bound to the same sites but less firmly than thyroxine. If tri-iodo-thyronine is added to serum and at the same time a substance to which thyronine can be weakly bound is also added, the tri-iodo-thyronine will be bound first to whatever thyroxine binding globulin sites are available and then to the alternative material. The fraction of the thyronine on the latter can therefore be used as a measure of the extent to which the globulin sites were already occupied by thyroxine. The " alternative materials " first employed were red blood cells[12] but standard polyurethane sponges containing a finely divided anion exchange resin (which are available commercially), are now generally used.[13] The procedure is to add about 0.1 μCi. of I^{131} labelled tri-iodo-thyronine to 1 cc. of serum from the patient in a test-tube. The resin sponge is added immediately and the tube counted in a well counter. After incubation at room temperature for about 1 hour (time and temperature must both be recorded since the results depend to some extent upon the incubation conditions), the fluid is removed from the test-tube by aspiration. After two or three washes the activity remaining on the sponge is counted and the percentage uptake on the sponge determined, correcting if necessary for non-standard conditions of incubation. High values indicate that the globulin binding sites were already filled, i.e. there was a high output of thyroxine by the thyroid gland or hyperthyroidism.

In an alternative test based on the same principle, granular resin already labelled with radioactive tri-iodo-thyronine is incubated simultaneously (a) with the patient's serum and (b) with pooled plasma from normal individuals. The activity in the patient's serum is then compared with that in the control and the ratio used as an index of the relative number of un-saturated binding sites (to which the radioactive thyronine can transfer).

Other methods of using I^{131} to test thyroid function have also been suggested (e.g. by measuring the concentration in the saliva) but the methods described above are those which have been most fully investigated. The radiation dose to the thyroid, using a test dose of 10 μCi. I^{131} is normally less than 30 rads (see chapter XII, section 12.08). The use of I^{132} with a half-life of only 2·33 hours, although less convenient (the I^{132} has to be separated from Te^{132} in the institution using it) reduces the dose to the thyroid by a factor of 50 or more, and to the gonads by a factor of 3 or 4. The use of I^{132} is therefore recommended for studies in children, in pregnant women and in nursing mothers to reduce the dose to the infant thyroid.

It is important to note that any of the thyroid tests mentioned can be invalidated if certain drugs are being administered and the uptake may be depressed for lengthy periods if the patient has received iodine containing materials in any way (e.g. as contrast media in diagnostic radiography). In cases where ambiguous results are obtained, a second test dose after the administration of a drug which modifies the thyroid function in a known manner (e.g. tri-iodo-thyronine, thio-uracil, etc.) is often helpful.

13.03. The investigation of iron metabolism and erythropoiesis

Studies of iron metabolism can be carried out using Fe^{59} or Fe^{55}. Fe^{59} emits β rays (mainly 0·46 MeV. and 0·27 MeV.) and fairly penetrating γ-radiation (1·10 and 1·29 MeV.) and has a half-life of 45 days. This is the isotope normally employed. Fe^{55} decays by electron capture. It can be detected by counting the soft X-radiation emitted in this process, but the X-ray energy is only 5·9 keV. and this presents counting problems. Some workers have, however, used Fe^{55} and Fe^{59} simultaneously to investigate different aspects of iron metabolism.

The absorption of iron from the gastro-intestinal tract is usually investigated by counting the activity in the faeces after an oral dose of ferrous citrate containing 1 to 5 μCi. of Fe^{59} and a known amount of inactive iron (commonly between 50 μg. and 5 mg.).[14, 15] It is important that the amount of carrier be standardised, since the amount of iron absorbed depends on the size of the oral dose. Some centres give ascorbic acid also in the test dose. If facilities for counting Fe^{55} are available, an elegant method of estimating the absorption from gastro-intestinal tract is to give Fe^{59} intravenously and Fe^{55} orally and then compare the amounts of each isotope which appear in the red blood cells.[16]

Iron is transported from the intestinal tract to the plasma in a protein complex known as ferritin and is transported in the blood-stream bound to a β-globulin known as transferrin. The plasma transferrin is in equilibrium with transferrin in the bone marrow (which is used in haemoglobin synthesis) and with ferritin stores in the liver, spleen and lungs. The iron in these organs together with that in the plasma is known as the " labile iron pool ".

A determination of the rate at which iron is removed from the plasma has been found useful in investigating haemato-logical disorders.[17, 18] Since there is an initial rapid loss of unbound iron if inorganic iron is injected intravenously, it was originally considered necessary to withdraw a blood sample, label the globulin by incubation with ferric chloride containing Fe^{59} and then reinject the tagged globulin. Subsequently it was found that if ferrous citrate is injected intravenously, without previous incubation with plasma, it is so rapidly bound *in vivo* that no appreciable loss of unbound iron occurs. The test is therefore now usually carried out by injecting ferrous citrate containing about 10 μCi. of high specific activity $Fe.^{59,19}$ Blood samples are then withdrawn at 15 or 30 minute intervals and the plasma counted after centrifuging. If the logarithm of the plasma activity is plotted versus time, a straight line graph is usually obtained, i.e. the plasma activity appears to decay exponentially. (See fig. 13.03.) If the graph is extrapolated back to zero time, to determine the initial plasma activity, the time for one-half of the activity to leave the plasma can be read off. This time is determined primarily by the rate of iron transfer to red cells but depends also upon the size of the labile iron pool. In

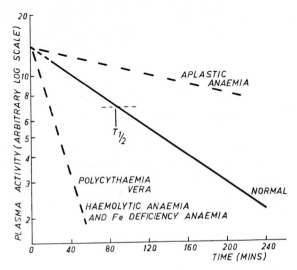

Fig. 13.03. Graphs showing typical rates of disappearance of intravenously injected radioactive iron.

normal individuals, it is 90 ± 30 minutes. The time is reduced markedly in polycythaemia rubra vera and haemolytic anaemia when there is an increased rate of erythropoiesis but it is also reduced, for example, (although usually to a lesser extent), in iron deficiency anaemia, on account of the reduced size of the labile iron pool. Similarly, the time is increased above normal both in aplastic anaemia and in haemochromatosis.

It should be noted that from the plasma activity at zero time, the plasma volume can be determined since

plasma activity per unit volume
$$= \text{injected activity/total plasma volume.}$$

Combining this with a haematocrit determination, enables the total red cell volume to be calculated. (The use of haematocrits and other methods of measuring red cell and plasma volumes are described in the next section.)

If blood samples are withdrawn daily for 10 to 20 days after injection of Fe^{59}, it is possible to follow the rate at which iron is incorporated into the red cells. The most convenient method is usually to count haemolysed whole blood, correcting for the activity in the plasma in the first few days, if necessary, by making a separate measurement of the plasma. In normal individuals, the activity in the red cells increases for 7 to 10 days and then remains constant for about 100 days at a value approaching 100 per cent. of the injected activity.[20]

External counting over the sacrum, liver and spleen, for the first few days after injection of Fe^{59}, is also sometimes used to follow the movement of the iron as it is incorporated into the red cells.[21]

The radiation dose to the circulating blood is of the order of 1·5 rads spread over 10 weeks, after a dose of 10 μCi. of Fe^{59}.

13.04. Red cell survival and blood volume studies

If a representative sample of a patient's red cells can be tagged with a radioactive label which (a) does not modify the cell behaviour, (b) remains firmly attached to the cells throughout the life of the individual cell, but (c) is not reincorporated into other cells after the death of the individual cell, then measurements of the radio-activity of blood samples at intervals, enable the fraction of the red cells surviving for different periods of time to be determined.

The radioactive material most widely used is sodium chromate containing Cr^{51}.[22] Cr^{51} is available with sufficiently high specific activity for the toxicity of chromium not to be a problem, and although there is some loss of the label in the circulation, this is much less than, for example, the loss of P^{32} when cells are labelled with sodium phosphate. There is no re-utilisation of the Cr^{51}. An alternative labelling material is di-iso-propyl-fluoro-phosphonate (DFP) containing P^{32} which binds to esterases.[23] DFP is bound so rapidly *in vivo*

516

that it can be injected directly and it is not necessary to incubate cells and re-inject, but leucocytes, platelets and plasma proteins as well as erythrocytes are " tagged ".

A typical procedure when labelling red cells with Cr^{51} is as follows.[24]   20 cc. of the patient's blood are withdrawn into a sterile bottle containing either standard ACD (acid-citrate-dextrose) solution or Strumia solution (the latter contains more citrate and less glucose than the standard mixture and appears to permit a shorter incubation period).   About $50 \mu Ci.$ of Cr^{51} sodium chromate are added.   After incubation at 37°C for a preselected time, usually of the order of 30 minutes, 50 mg. of ascorbic acid are added to reduce any unused chromate and prevent further binding to red cells.   Over 90 per cent. of the Cr^{51} is normally bound to the red cells.   The cells may be washed and resuspended in plasma but usually 10 cc. of the whole blood is re-injected and a correction made for the Cr^{51} present in the plasma.

In investigations of red cell survival, blood samples are withdrawn at 15 minutes and at 24 hours after the injection and then at 2- or 3-day intervals for 2 to 3 weeks.   It is convenient to store all the samples and count them together at the end of the investigation, since it is then not necessary to correct for physical decay. Measurements are normally carried out on haemolysed whole blood and the readings converted to red cell activity, by dividing by the haematocrit.   After the first 24 hours, a plot of the logarithm of the red cell activity against time is usually linear (see fig. 13.04).   (There is an initial rapid decrease of activity of the order of 6 per cent. in the first 24 hours.)   There is a steady loss of Cr^{51} from the labelled cells, so the activity decreases more rapidly than does the number of red cells surviving, but the rate of elution of Cr^{51} does not appear to vary appreciably from one individual to another, so that the apparent half-life provides a valid means of detecting (say) abnormally rapid cell destruction.   If the true erythrocyte life-span is required, measured activities can be corrected for the early loss and for chromium elution.   In normal individuals the amount of chromium remaining in the circulation decreases to one-half after 25 ± 3 days.   When a significantly shorter half-life is observed, it may be of interest to count externally over organs such as the liver and spleen to determine where the removal of red cells is occurring.

There is some uncertainty in estimating which organs will receive the maximum dose of radiation after tests in which Cr^{51} is employed, but with a test dose of 100 μCi., the liver and spleen may receive a dose of the order of 100 mrad per week.

DFP[32] labelling has the advantage that the label appears to be more permanent than Cr^{51}, so that the decrease of activity in samples follows closely the decrease in the number of labelled cells (normal $T_{\frac{1}{2}} = 42$ days). As already noted DFP is bound

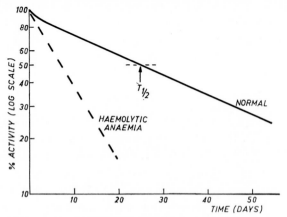

FIG. 13.04. Graphs showing typical Cr^{51} labelled red cell survival curves.

to platelets and leukocytes (and plasma proteins) as well as red cells, so it is possible to determine survival times for any of these cells with this material, but very careful separation and washing of the appropriate cell fraction before counting is necessary. Since P^{32} is a β-emitter only, appropriate counting methods are necessary. When 10 cc. or so of liquid are available, a liquid Geiger counter is convenient (e.g. for counting haemolysed red cells) but when the volume available is restricted (as in platelet survival determinations), a continuous flow gas counter or liquid scintillation counter may be required.

Determination of red cell volume

When red cell survival is studied, measurements of the red cell volume are usually made on the first and last days of the study. The red cell volume is often required apart from the erythrocyte survival test, however.

The most usual method is to label the red cells with Cr^{51} using sodium chromate as described above. After incubation, the red cells may be separated by centrifuging (at not more than 1000 r.p.m. to avoid damaging the cells) and resuspended in a plasma-saline solution, but it is usually simpler to reinject whole blood and correct for activity in the plasma. A small amount of the tagged blood is used to prepare a standard, and the activity in the plasma and the haemolysed whole blood is counted separately. The haematocrit of the blood is also determined. After 10 or 15 minutes, when it can be assumed that mixing of the injected blood is complete, a blood sample is withdrawn. Sufficient blood is set aside for duplicate haematocrit determinations, one half of the sample is used to determine the plasma activity, the remainder haemolysed and counted. The elution of Cr^{51} from the red cells is sufficiently small to be neglected, so only one sample is required (with some other labels such as P^{32}, it is necessary to take a series of samples and extrapolate back to zero time). The red blood cell volume is calculated from the formula which applies to any dilution technique, viz.

$$\text{Volume} = \frac{\text{Total injected activity}}{\text{Sample activity per cc.}}$$

In this case we require the ratio

$$\frac{\text{Total activity of injected red cells}}{\text{Activity per cc. of red cells in sample}}$$

The total activity of injected red cells

$$= \left\{ B_s - P_s \left(\frac{100 - H_s}{100} \right) \right\} D.V.$$

where

B_s = net count per cc. of whole blood standard
P_s = net count per cc. of plasma
H_s = haematocrit of standard
V = volume injected
D = dilution factor of standard

519

The activity per cc. of red cells in the sample

$$= \frac{1}{H_{Pt}} \left\{ B_{Pt} - P_{Pt} \left(\frac{100 - H_{Pt}}{100} \right) \right\}$$

where

B_{Pt} = net count per cc. of whole blood sample from patient
P_{Pt} = net count per cc. of plasma sample from patient
H_{Pt} = haematocrit of blood sample from patient.

It should be noted that H_s and H_{Pt} should be venous haematocrit values corrected for plasma trapped with the red blood cells. The correction factor depends upon the conditions of centrifuging, but is about 0·96 for tubes spun for 30 minutes at 3,000 r.p.m. in a 15 cm. radius.

Determination of plasma volume [25, 26]

The plasma volume can be readily determined by the dilution method by injecting human serum albumin labelled with I^{131} or I^{125} (this material is available commercially and is usually referred to by the abbreviations I.H.S.A. or R.I.S.A.). Typically 10 cc. of tagged albumin containing about 10 μCi. of I^{131} are injected intravenously and blood samples are withdrawn at (say) 10, 20 and 30 minutes after injection. There is some escape of the albumin from the circulation so it is necessary to take a series of samples and extrapolate back to determine the activity per cc. at zero time. The samples are centrifuged and the plasma activity compared with that of a diluted standard using a well-type scintillation counter. When preparing the standard, the protein concentration should be kept above 1 per cent. to avoid absorption on glass-ware or alternatively the protein may be hydrolysed by sodium hydroxide and carrier sodium iodide added. Possible thyroid uptake of I^{131} liberated from the albumin is usually blocked by premedication with stable iodine.

Whole blood volume

An accurate measurement of the whole blood volume may be obtained by simultaneous determinations of the red cell volume using Cr^{51} and the plasma volume using albumin labelled with either I^{131} or I^{125}. Since the energy of the principal γ-ray from I^{131} (360 keV.) is rather close to the γ-ray energy of Cr^{51} (323 keV.), if I^{131} albumin is used, it is necessary to separate the

520

plasma and red cells in the sample, wash the red cells free of plasma and count the plasma and cells separately. If I^{125} albumin is available, the I^{125} and Cr^{51} may be counted in the same sample, since the X- and γ-rays emitted by I^{125} have energies of 27 keV. and 35 keV. respectively.

A somewhat less accurate estimate of the whole blood volume may be calculated from a knowledge of either the red cell volume or the plasma volume only if a value is assumed for the whole body haematocrit. The latter differs from the venous haematocrit because the capillaries contain proportionately more plasma than do the larger vessels. It is generally accepted, however, that the whole body haematocrit $(H_{wb}) = 0.91$ venous haematocrit (H_v) (corrected for trapped plasma) in the majority of cases. (The principle exceptions are some cases of spleno-megaly.)

$$\text{The blood volume} = \text{red cell volume} \times 100/H_{wb}$$
$$= \text{plasma volume} \times 100/(100-H_{wb})$$

In cases of emergency when an estimate of the total blood volume is required as quickly as possible and an error of 5 to 10 per cent. can be tolerated, 10 minutes after injection of I^{131} labelled albumin, a haemolysed whole blood sample may be counted. The " apparent " blood volume is obtained by dividing the count rate of the standard solution by the activity per cc. of the sample and multiplying by 0.95 (the latter is an approximate estimate of the ratio $(100\text{-}H_v)/(100\text{-}H_{wb})$. Equipment in which the syringe used for injection can be counted before and after injection to determine the activity injected, the value so obtained " stored ", and then compared with the activity of the sample withdrawn after mixing, so that the apparent blood volume can be read directly from a calibrated meter, is available commercially. The apparent blood volume determined in this manner can be subsequently corrected for the actual value of the venous haematocrit (H_v) when this is obtained (although it is not possible to correct accurately for plasma loss from the circulation or to detect incomplete mixing unless a second blood sample is taken).

$$\text{True blood volume} = \text{" Apparent " blood volume} \times$$
$$(100-H_v)/(100-0.91\ H_v)$$

It should be noted that the most sensitive method of detecting blood loss due to gastro-intestinal haemorrhage, is a measurement of the activity in the faeces after injection of Cr^{51} labelled red cells.

13.05. The measurement of cardiac output and detection of cardiac shunts

A procedure which is considerably simplified by the use of radioactive isotopes is the determination of cardiac output (i.e. the volume of blood ejected by the heart per minute). When dye is used to determine cardiac output, it is necessary to take arterial samples, but when the tracer is radioactive, the required information can be obtained by external counting over the heart, combined with a venous blood sample. A typical procedure is as follows: [27], [28], [29]

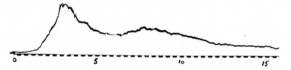

FIG. 13.05. Typical ratemeter record of single passage of I^{131} albumin through the heart. The time scale is in seconds.

A well-collimated scintillation counter is located over the heart. For cardiac output determinations the positioning is not critical but if the pulmonary circulation time or pulmonary blood volume is required the counter must be directed along the axis right ventricle to left auricle. The counter is connected to a ratemeter and chart recorder. About 1 cc. of human serum albumin containing about 50 to 100 μCi. of I^{131} is injected smoothly, but as rapidly as possible, into an arm vein and the time of injection indicated on the chart. The ratemeter should be operated with a time constant of 0·5 sec. and on a range of about 1,000 c./sec. A peak in the counting rate is recorded as the isotope passes through the right side of the heart and 4 or 5 seconds later a second smaller peak as it passes through the left heart (fig. 13.05). The counter is left in position for 10 minutes or more until mixing is complete and the count-rate

522

corresponding to the equilibrium activity is recorded. A blood sample is withdrawn from the opposite arm and used to determine both the haematocrit and the equilibrium activity per cc. (C_{eq}). By comparing the latter with the activity injected, the plasma volume is obtained and from this the total blood volume can be calculated if desired. To determine the cardiac output, the area under the concentration-time graph corresponding to a single passage of the tracer through the heart is measured (the decrease of activity after the peak is usually assumed to be

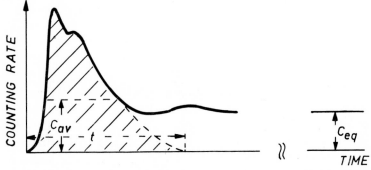

FIG. 13.06. Diagram to illustration method of determining cardiac output.

exponential). Let this area be denoted by $C_{av} \times t$ where C_{av} is the activity per cc. corresponding to the net average count-rate during the time t, (fig. 13.06).

Then the injected activity $= C_{av} \times$
$\qquad\qquad$ plasma output of heart per unit time $\times t$

$\therefore$ Plasma output of heart $= C_{eq} \times$ plasma volume$/C_{av} \times t$.

Assuming that the plasma/red-cell ratio is the same in the heart as in the blood sample withdrawn from a vein, then if H_v denotes the venous haematocrit corrected for trapped plasma

$$\text{Plasma output} = \text{cardiac output} \frac{(100-H_v)}{100}$$

$\therefore$ $\quad$ Cardiac output $= \dfrac{C_{eq}}{(C_{av} \times t)} \times \dfrac{\text{plasma volume (100)}}{(100-H_v)}$

If the blood sample withdrawn from the patient is haemolysed

523

and the activity in the whole blood counted (i.e. without separating red cells and plasma), then

$$\text{Plasma volume} = \frac{V \cdot C_s \cdot D}{C_{Pt} \cdot (100)} (100 - H_v)$$

where V denotes the volume injected

$\quad\quad D =$ dilution factor of standard

$\quad\quad C_s =$ net counts per cc. of standard

$\quad\quad C_{Pt} =$ net counts per cc. of patient sample

Hence in this case

$$\text{Cardiac output} = \frac{C_{eq}}{(C_{av} \times t)} \cdot \frac{V \cdot C_s D}{C_{Pt}}$$

$$= \frac{C_{eq}}{\text{Area}} \cdot \frac{V \cdot C_s D}{C_{Pt}}$$

As is usual, whenever compounds labelled with I^{131} are used, prior administration of inactive inorganic iodine to block the uptake of I^{131} by the thyroid gland is desirable. Provided this precaution is observed the maximum radiation dose during a cardiac output determination is delivered to the trunk and is of the order of 200 mrad spread over 10 days.

If a suitable double-peaked curve is obtained, it is possible to analyse this into two components and hence determine the pulmonary circulation time, and thus the pulmonary blood volume. A third peak corresponding to myocardial blood flow can sometimes be distinguished and the time for myocardial circulation and the myocardial blood volume can then be calculated. (If the primary object of the investigation is the determination of myocardial flow, a second detector over the carotid artery, is useful to indicate the time when the radioactive tracer enters the periphereal circulation.) In cases where there are abnormal connections between the right and left sides of the heart, the radioactive tracer will arrive in the left heart prematurely and this can be used, to detect right to left shunts.[30] An alternative method of detecting shunts uses the radioactive isotope of an inert gas. Isotopes of both krypton (Kr^{85}) and xenon (Xe^{133}) have been employed. When the gas is administered intravenously in solution, over 95 per cent. is normally removed from the blood by one passage through the lungs. A detector located over the femoral artery will give an abnormally high (and early) count when a shunt is present.[31] Left to right shunts can be detected by allowing the patient to inhale Kr^{85} or Xe^{133} for 30 seconds and simultaneously, withdrawing blood samples from (a) a cardiac catheter with the tip in the pulmonary artery, and (b) from the femoral artery.[32] This, however, is a more complicated procedure.

13.06. Studies of the peripheral circulation

Both saline containing Na^{24} and human serum albumin tagged with I^{131} have been widely used in studies of the peripheral circulation. Recently the radioactive gases Kr^{85} and Xe^{133}, dissolved in saline have also been used to study regional blood flow. When I^{131} tagged albumin is employed, the albu-

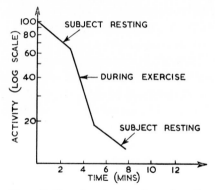

FIG. 13.07. Graph showing the disappearance of radioactive sodium from the gastrocnemius muscle in a normal case.

min leaves the vascular system relatively slowly, whereas Na^{24} tagged saline diffuses quite rapidly into the extra-vascular space. The radioactive gases are evolved into the alveolae on passing through the pulmonary circulation, and therefore have a very short half-life in the body. There are three alternative methods of measurement. (1) The time taken for the isotope to travel between two selected points is measured (the presence of the isotope being detected by an external counter), e.g. the time taken for the isotope to reach a counter held over the axilla or groin after injection in the hand or foot respectively has been used in investigations of the circulation in cases of pregnancy, thrombosis, etc. (2) The rate of build-up of activity in a particular tissue after the isotope is injected into the blood-stream, or (3) the rate of disappearance of activity in a particular tissue after injection into the tissue, may be used to measure the blood supply to particular regions. For example, a comparison of the rate of disappearance of activity from the gastro-cnemius muscle in the calf with the subject either at rest or exercising has been used in investigations of claudication,[33, 34] (fig. 13.07) and the rate of disappearance of activity from tubed skin pedicles has been used to determine when the circulation is established across a new graft.[35]

Any measurement of the circulation is complicated by the marked effect of environment, position, exercise and so on and it is therefore necessary in these tests either to use fully controlled conditions of temperature, humidity, position, etc., or to make the tests comparative, e.g. by comparing a " good " with a " bad " limb. The " disappearance " test (3) appears to give more reproducible results than the " build-up " test (2) and requires the injection of less material. It is therefore generally preferred. The activity in the tissue which is injected, normally decreases exponentially with time.[36] Thus the quantity (Q_t) present at time t is given by $Q_t = Q_0 e^{-kt}$ and results are usually expressed in terms of the clearance constant (k), (which can be readily obtained from a semi-logarithmic plot of activity against time) or in terms of the half-life of the isotope in the tissue.

13.07. The investigation of malabsorption syndromes

Radio-isotopes are widely used to detect impaired absorption from the gastro-intestinal tract. The principal materials used are vitamin B_{12} labelled with a radioactive isotope of cobalt, to detect pernicious anaemia and I^{131} labelled fat or I^{131} labelled oleic acid to investigate incomplete utilisation of fat.

Vitamin B_{12} is absorbed from the gastro-intestinal tract in the presence of an intrinsic factor produced by the gastric mucosa. Lack of the intrinsic factor in pernicious anaemia, prevents normal absorption, which can be restored if intrinsic factor is administered. The vitamin is normally stored in the liver but if the liver is already saturated with vitamin, then further vitamin absorbed from the gastro-intestinal tract is excreted in the urine. The usual procedure in diagnosing pernicious anaemia is therefore to saturate the liver with non-radioactive vitamin, then give radioactive vitamin and measure the urinary excretion of the latter. In the early work, the isotope used was Co^{60}, but now that shorter lived isotopes are available, these are preferred, and either Co^{57} or Co^{58} labelled vitamin B_{12} is commonly employed.[37, 38, 39, 40] A typical test procedure is as follows: 0·5 μCi. of Co^{57} labelled vitamin B_{12} are administered orally to the patient, who has fasted overnight. 1 mg. of non-radioactive vitamin B_{12} is injected subcutaneously or intramuscularly within about an hour of the oral dose to saturate the liver. The urine is collected for 24 hours and the activity excreted is measured and compared with the test dose. Normal individuals excrete more than 10 per cent. of the administered dose in 24 hours. If the excretion is low, a second test dose given together with intrinsic factor, enables pernicious anaemia to be distinguished from conditions such as sprue. The radiation dose to the liver is of the order of 100 mrad with this technique.

The incomplete utilisation of fat may be due to either improper digestion or malabsorption. This can be investigated by determining the amount of activity appearing in the blood after oral administration of I^{131} labelled tri-olein.[41] The absorption of fat is strongly dependent upon the manner in which it is fed, so it is important that this be standardised. Capsules containing 25 μCi. of I^{131} labelled triolein in peanut oil are available commercially and are given after 6 hours fasting. Barium sulphate capsules are usually given at the same time as it is customary to make a fluoroscopic examination 3 hours after the test dose, and inorganic inactive iodine is also administered to block uptake by the thyroid of radio-iodine released from the fat. Blood samples are withdrawn at 4, 5 and 6 hours after the test dose and measured by comparison with a suitable fraction of the test dose using a well counter. It is necessary to estimate the total blood volume from the patient's weight unless the blood volume is separately determined. In the normal individual, the total blood volume usually contains more than 8 per cent. of the administered dose after 6 hours. If the activity is low, the test may be repeated after a few days, using I^{131} labelled oleic acid (a product of the digestion of tri-olein) to distinguish between improper digestion and mal-absorption. A 48-hour collection of faeces is sometimes made since the faecal excretion increases markedly in cases of impaired fat absorption. The normal excretion is less than 2 per cent. in 48 hours.

Tests for impaired absorption of iron from the gastro-intestinal tract using Fe^{59} or Fe^{55} have already been discussed in section 13.03.

13.08. Studies of renal function

By labelling with a γ-emitting isotope, a substance which is cleared by the kidneys, it is possible to study the function of these organs.[42] After intravenous injection, sodium ortho-iodo-hippurate (" Hippuran ") is cleared by the kidneys in about half-an-hour, and is not appreciably taken up by the liver. This material labelled with I^{131} is therefore widely used in the investigation of renal function.[43] (It is advantageous to use a material which is not taken up by the liver for this test, as it is difficult to distinguish activity in the kidneys from activity in the liver with an external counter.) A typical procedure is as follows. Two scintillation counters are required. It is convenient (but not essential) if the counters are identical. The counters are first " balanced " by adjusting the photomultiplier gain of one counter so that when observing the same source under the same conditions, the counts from the two detectors are equal. The counters are then positioned one over each kidney of the patient. The latter may be sitting upright or lying prone and the positions of the kidneys are established either by means of a previous diagnostic radiograph or by administration of a preliminary tracer dose of I^{131} hippurate. For the kidney function test, about 0.5μCi. of I^{131} per kilogram of body-weight are required. It is desirable to use a discriminator or pulse height analyser so that counts due to scattered radiation (particularly that from the other kidney) can be rejected, and the most convenient method of presenting the results is probably to use the ratemeter output to drive a pen recorder. A typical " renogram " can be resolved into three phases. (See fig. 13.08.) A rapid initial rise (*A*) corresponding to the distribution of the isotope through the blood vessels of the kidney (the vascular phase) is followed by a slower rise (*B*) lasting several minutes, as the isotope passes from the blood into the kidney (the secretory phase), and finally

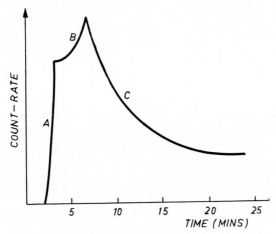

Fig. 13.08. Diagrammatic illustration of ratemeter record of the passage of I^{131} labelled " hippuran " through the kidneys. *A* = vascular phase, *B* = secretory phase, *C* = excretory phase.

a slow decline (*C*) in activity marks the excretory phase. Most centres count for a period of about 30 minutes and some centres collect and measure the urine after 1 hour.

Non-functioning or contracted kidneys, ureteral obstruction and other causes of renal failure cause characteristic alterations in the normal pattern.

13.09. The determination of local isotope concentrations by scanning and the localisation of tumours

If a counter is moved in a regular manner across a patient and the counts recorded in successive positions, regions in which γ-emitting isotopes are concentrated, can be localised. The precision of the localisation will depend upon the manner in which the counter is collimated. Scintillation counters are invariably used for this work because the greater the sensitivity of the detector, the greater the resolving power that can be used for a given isotope concentration.

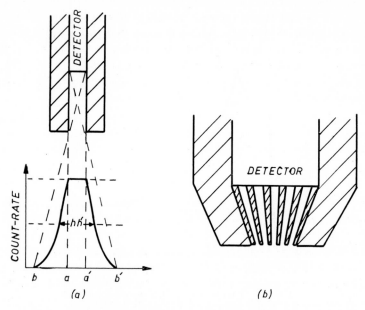

FIG. 13.09. Diagrams illustrating methods of collimating scintillation detectors. (*a*) Cylindrical collimator. The resolving power is usually measured by the distance hh^1 separating points at which the count-rate is one-half the maximum value. (*b*) Multichannel focused collimator.

The resolving power of a collimator determines the distance which must separate two sources of activity in order that they may be recognised as separate sources. It is normally measured by recording the count-rate as a " point " source is moved along a line perpendicular to the axis of the counter. Consider first a cylindrical collimator as shown in fig. 13.09(*a*) and for simplicity let us assume initially that the walls are completely opaque to the radiation being measured. Then a graph of count-rate versus source position will take the form shown. The distance (hh') separating the two points at which the count-rate has fallen to one-half of the maximum value is usually regarded as the minimum distance apart at which two point

530

sources could be distinguished. This minimum distance is inversely proportional to the resolving power of the collimator, i.e. in order to distinguish two sources which are close together, a collimator of high resolving power is required. For a cylindrical collimator, the resolving power is increased by (1) a decrease in the diameter of the crystal and the aperture (which decreases both the width of the region of maximum count-rate, *aa'*, and also the width of the penumbra, *ab* and *b'a'*), and (2) by an increase in the collimator length or a decrease in the source-collimator distance (both of which decrease the width of the penumbra).

For the detection of small localised regions of high activity a single hole cylindrical collimator has two disadvantages. Firstly, if the crystal and collimator aperture are increased in area to obtain greater sensitivity, the resolving power is reduced. Secondly, for small sources, the peak counting rate varies inversely as the square of the source-crystal distance, so the assembly is much more sensitive to deposits near the detector than to those at a depth. If a large volume of uniformly distributed activity is being examined, however, the volume from which radiation can be detected increases as the source-crystal distance increases and this reduces the inverse square effect. To obtain both adequate sensitivity and sufficient resolving power, particularly for sources which may be situated deep in tissue, large crystals are normally used with multichannel, focused (or convergent) collimators. In these collimators, (1) the single hole is divided by septa into a number (*n* say) of smaller channels, (2) the individual channels are tapered and converge towards a common focus at a selected distance in front of the collimator. (See fig. 13.09(*b*).) This means that in the vicinity of the focus, the resolving power is determined by the cross-section of the small apertures, but since radiation can reach the crystal through all *n* channels, the sensitivity is approximately *n* times that which would be obtained from a single small aperture. The field of view of a single tapered hole is illustrated in fig. 13.10. In the focal plane the region of maximum count-rate is reduced to a point and the count-rate decreases to one-half of the maximum at a distance from the focus approximately one-half of the radius of the field of view.

In a multichannel collimator, the fields of view of the individual holes are approximately superimposed in the focal plane and the resolving power is therefore the same as for the individual holes. In planes nearer or further away than the focus, the fields of view of the individual holes are only partially super-imposed and the resolving power decreases. For points beyond the focus, since both the count-rate from individual holes and the amount of field overlap decreases as the distance increases,

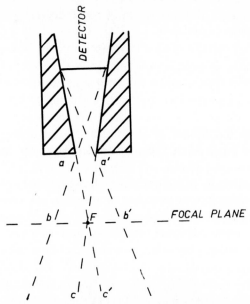

Fig. 13.10. Diagram illustrating the field of view of a single tapered hole collimator.

the count-rate decreases rapidly. For points nearer to the collimator than the focus, the count-rate from the individual holes increases and tends to compensate for the reduced over-lapping of the individual fields. Hence the response of multi-channel focused collimators varies fairly slowly with change in the source distance over an appreciable range of distance within the focal length. (See fig. 13.11(*b*)). This is an im-portant advantage of these collimators. The distance over which the response is nearly constant (and the resolving power is high) is sometimes called the " depth of focus " of the collimator.

The thickness of the septa required between channels depends upon the radiation energy. For any given collimator, the resolving power tends to decrease as the radiation energy increases, due to increased penetration of the septa. In practice, each crystal is usually provided with sets of collimators

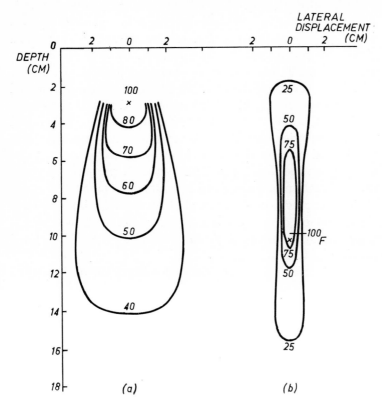

FIG. 13.11.   Isocount curves showing the relative response of the detector to a point source at different positions
(a) single hole cylindrical collimator,
(b) multi-channel focused collimator.

designed (a) for different energy ranges, (b) with different focal lengths, and (c) for either high resolving power and relatively low sensitivity or conversely for high sensitivity and lower resolving power.

The collimated scintillation counter is normally mounted in a carriage which is driven by a motor in such a way that the detector moves at a uniform selected speed in a straight line for a predetermined distance, then returns along a parallel path displaced from the first by a selected constant amount and in this way " scans " any desired area. For particular applications (e.g. brain scanning), counters may travel along circular arcs or other special paths. The output from the counting head is normally fed through a pulse height analyser and scaler to some form of automatic recorder. Although in many clinical situations information of value can be obtained by scanning using a single detector, it is sometimes difficult to obtain adequate " depth of focus ". If two detectors are mounted colinearly on either side of the patient and moved to and fro together, the outputs from the two detectors being added and the sum recorded, then it is possible to obtain a record which is almost independent of the position of the activity along the line joining the detectors. This system is particularly useful in the detection of deep-seated tumours (see below).

The simplest recorder is an electromagnetic printer which is rigidly attached to the counter and therefore moves over a paper in synchronism with the detector. When a selected number of counts is accumulated on the scaler, a relay is energised which causes the printer to make a line or dot on the paper. The spacing of the marks on the paper therefore produces a visual indication of the counting rate in different regions. It is necessary to select the scaling factor (i.e. the number of counts per mark made by the printer) so that in the regions of maximum activity (a) the number of marks per second is within the capacity of the printer (usually about 10 per sec.), and (b) the number of marks per cm. is such that marks do not overlap (this of course depends on the speed of travel of the counter and recorder). To facilitate the recognition of areas of the scan where a given count-rate is obtained, some printers have been designed in which coloured ribbons are moved beneath the printing stylus according to the reading of a count-rate meter, so that changes in count-rate are shown by a change in colour as well as by a change in spacing. By using an uninked ribbon for count-rates less than a selected fraction of the maximum, automatic " back-ground suppression " is produced on the colour-scan, but the back-ground can be retained on a carbon copy. In an alternative method of recording, pulses from the scaler control a light source which is moved across a photographic film in synchronism with the counter. The light source may be a neon lamp or a fluorescent spot produced by a beam of electrons on the screen of a cathode ray tube. (Incandescent lamps are not suitable because their response is much too slow.) The light is diaphragmed so that a small spot is produced on the film after development. A flash of light is normally produced by each pulse from the scaler so that the relative blackening of different regions of the film gives a visual indication of the distribution of activity. In the photographic method, the light spots can be permitted to overlap as this can be registered as an increased density in the developed film. In some equipment, the intensity of the light source is determined by the reading of a count-rate meter, so that the blackening of the individual spots as well as their spacing is proportional to the count-rate. The photographic method has the advantage that it is possible to enhance or diminish the contrast between regions of different activity by changing the recording factors.

In a third method of recording, the intensity of the electron beam in a stationary cathode ray tube is controlled by the count-rate and the electron beam moves across the tube screen in synchronism with the counter. In this system, the cathode-ray tube is not connected mechanically to the counter and may be remote from the detector. A " storage " screen is used in the cathode ray tube so that the picture of the isotope distribution which is gradually built up on the screen is retained. This is photographed on completion of the scan. In some equipment, provision is made to record the count-rate on magnetic tape. This has the advantage that if the first visual recording of the scan is not satisfactory due to incorrect choice of (say) scaling factor, then a satisfactory record may still be produced by replaying the tape with changed recording conditions. Fig. 13.12 illustrates some of the alternative methods of presentation.

Scans are frequently made of the thyroid gland, both to detect abnormalities and to estimate the gland size before giving therapeutic doses of I^{131}. About 25 μCi. of I^{131} are

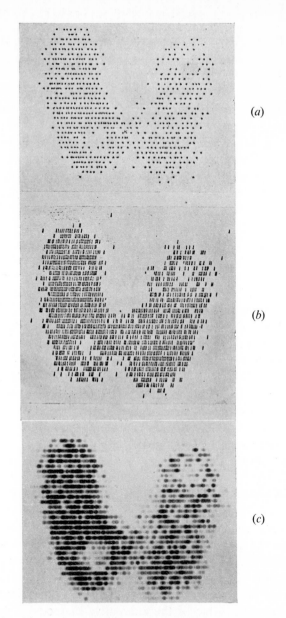

Fig. 13.12. Alternative methods of presenting information obtained by scanning a thyroid phantom.

(a) " dot " scan; (b) " line " scan; (c) photo scan. In each case the mean activity in the left lobe is greater than that in the right. There are regions of " missing " uptake in the lower part of the right and upper part of the left lobe.

536

normally administered 24 hours before scanning, and the dose to the thyroid is of the order of 75 rads.

Functioning kidneys can be visualised by scanning after the administration of chlormerodrin (" neohydrin ") containing either Hg^{203} or Hg^{197}. Hg^{203} has a half-life of 47 days and emits 280 keV. γ-radiation (in addition to β-radiation). Hg ^{197} has a half-life of 65 hours and decays by electron capture, emitting 69 keV. X-rays and 77 keV. γ-rays. Although about 50 per cent. of the chlormerodrin is excreted in 6 to 8 hours, the rate of excretion then decreases. After the initial phase, effective half-lives from about 7 to 28 days have been reported for the Hg^{203} labelled material and about 1 to 2 days for the Hg^{197} material. The shorter half-life and lower energy of the photons from Hg^{197} mean that the radiation dose to the patient is considerably reduced when this isotope is used instead of Hg^{203}. About 50 to 100 μCi. are normally administered intravenously about 1 hour prior to the scan. Depending on the effective half-life the kidney dose is of the order of 20 rads per 100 μCi. for Hg^{203} but probably less than 3 rads per 100 μCi. for Hg^{197}.

For the delineation of the liver, I^{131} labelled rose bengal is probably the material most widely used. About 100 μCi. are administered intravenously and scanning is begun about 15 minutes later. It is usual to scan the lower border of the liver first and proceed superiorly so that the dye has not concentrated in the gall bladder when the region of the latter is examined. The half-life of the dye in the liver is normally only 2 to 3 hours so the radiation dose to the liver is fairly low (1 or 2 rads). The whole body dose can be reduced by giving a cholecystagogue and laxative after the test. Colloidal Au^{198} can be used to obtain satisfactory liver scans but a much greater radiation dose is given to the patient. Recently colloidal Tc^{99M} has been recommended. Tc^{99M} has a half-life of 6 hours so this material has the disadvantage that it must be prepared by the user. The parent material is Mo^{99} which has a half-life of 67 hours. The short half-life, low γ-ray energy (140 keV.) and the absence of β-radiation, however, mean that the dose to the liver is reduced when Tc^{99M} is used.

Other organs which may be studied by scanning include the pancreas, using Se^{75} labelled methionine, the spleen, using heated red cells labelled with Cr^{51}, and the lungs, using macro aggregates of human serum albumin labelled with I^{131}.

The presence of non-differentiated and therefore non-functional tissues in any of the above organs will be indicated by a region of low activity and this can sometimes be used to locate tumours.   In other regions selective absorption of an isotope may indicate the presence of a malignant growth.   Metastases from thyroid carcinoma can sometimes be located by their ability to concentrate I^{131} and skeletal metastases can be detected by their uptake of Sr^{85}.

An increased uptake of P^{32} can be used to detect malignant melanomas and some intra-ocular tumours.   Since there is usually only a small area to be examined and because P^{32} is a β-emitter, manual scanning using a detector in contact with the skin or eye surface is used in these cases.   The detector may be a thin-walled end-window Geiger counter or a scintillation counter.   It is usual to compare the uptake in the region investigated with a similar region on the contra-lateral side or on the other eye.   An uptake of 60 per cent. or more in excess of that in the control area is commonly regarded as significant. The uptake is usually measured 24 hours after administration of the test dose (some workers repeat the measurement at 48 hours), which is of the order of 100 μCi. for skin cases and 500 μCi. for ocular cases.

The scanning of the brain when a neoplastic growth is suspected is now a standard technique in many centres.   In the region of the tumour, the normal blood-brain barrier appears to break down so that substances introduced into the bloodstream can diffuse into the tumour and produce an increased activity in the tumour region relative to normal brain, even if there is not preferential uptake in the neoplastic cells.   Human serum albumin labelled with I^{131} or chlormerodrin (neohydrin) labelled with Hg^{203} are the materials which have been most widely employed, although a number of other isotopes may also be used (see below).   About 300 to 500 μCi. of I^{131} albumin are required and the scan is usually made 24 hours after the test dose.   Using chlormerodrin, about 700 μCi. of Hg^{203} are required.   Since chlormerodrin is rapidly cleared from the bloodstream, scans with this material are usually made about 4 hours after injection. The whole body radiation dose to the patient is decreased by using chlormerodrin rather than albumin. It may be further reduced by using Hg^{197} rather than Hg^{203} (see

TABLE 13.01

CALCULATED RADIATION DOSAGE LEVELS FOR VARIOUS
BRAIN-SCANNING AGENTS

(after McAfee and Fueger.)[44]

Agent	IV dose	Radiation dose *	
		Total body	Critical organ
I^{131} albumin	375 μCi.	0·4 rad	2 rads (blood)
Hg^{203} chlormerodrin	750 μCi.	0·18 rad	165 rads (kidney)
Hg^{197} chlormerodrin	750 μCi.	0·08 rad	13 rads (kidney)
† $Hg^{197}+5$ % Hg^{203} chlormerodrin	750 μCi.	0·09 rad	21 rads (kidney)
Tc^{99m} pertechnetate	10 mCi.	0·13 rad	2 rads (large bowel)

* The assumptions made in radiation dosage calculations are as follows :

I^{131} albumin : $\bar{E}_\beta$ 0·187 MeV., Γ_{gamma} (R.-cm²./mCi.-hr.) 2·18, physical $T\frac{1}{2}$ 8 days. Thyroid blocked with Lugol's solution.
$\begin{cases} 5 \text{ per cent. fast component biological } T\frac{1}{2} \text{ 0·5 days, effective } T\frac{1}{2} \text{ 0·47 days.} \\ 95 \text{ per cent. slow component biological } T\frac{1}{2} \text{ 15 days, effective } T\frac{1}{2} \text{ 5·2 days.} \end{cases}$
At equilibrium time (2·5 days) 40 per cent. of dose in plasma, 60 per cent. extravascular.
Blood volume 7·7 per cent. of body weight of 70 kg or 5·4 litres.

Hg^{203} chlormerodrin : $\bar{E}_\beta$ 0·1 MeV., Γ_{gamma} 1·2, physical $T\frac{1}{2}$ 47 days.
Kidney—Average integrated concentration 22 per cent. of dose during first 6 hours, followed by one effective $T\frac{1}{2}$ of 18 hours, subsequent effective $T\frac{1}{2}$'s 28 days.
Blood—Average integrated concentration during first hour : 10 per cent. of administered dose ; successive effective $T\frac{1}{2}$'s of 2, 2, 4, 6, and 9 hours.

Hg^{197} chlormerodrin : $\bar{E}_\beta$ 0·0773 MeV., Γ_{gamma} 0·35, physical $T\frac{1}{2}$ 2·7 days.

Tc^{99m} pertechnetate : $\bar{E}_\beta$ 0·016 MeV., Γ_{gamma} 0·56, physical $T\frac{1}{2}$ 6 hours. No biological excretion assumed. Thyroid blocked with Lugol's solution (70 kg. man, total body g. factor 125, 150 gm. kidney g. factor 35).

† Hg^{197} chlormerodrin always contains some Hg^{203}.

Table 13.01), but some workers feel that the low energy of the Hg^{197} γ-ray makes the detection of the deeper tumours rather difficult. The use of sodium pertechnate containing Tc^{99M} is presently being investigated at a number of centres. The γ-ray energy (140 keV.) is suitable and the absence of β-radiation and short half-life (6 hours) mean that the patient dose is very low but the scan must be carried out at a time when the isotope concentration in the blood is still high.

Scanning is usually carried out in two planes at right angles (frontal and sagittal) or over a spherical surface concentric with the skull. For plane scans, most centres use a single detector but it is important that the collimator has a sufficient depth of focus and, as already mentioned, greater sensitivity and a response which is almost independent of the tumour depth can be obtained if two detectors are mounted colinearly on either side of the patient's head and used together. A few centres use positron emitting isotopes for the location of brain tumours. Since the annihilation of a positron is accompanied by the simultaneous emission of two photons in opposite directions, counts are recorded simultaneously in two parallel opposed detectors only when a positron is annihilated on the axis between the counters. A printer operated from a co-incidence circuit (which records only pulses received simultaneously in both detectors) therefore indicates the concentration of isotope on the line joining the counters, while a second printer actuated by the difference in counts recorded by the detectors can be used to indicate whether the concentration is on the left or right side. The positron-emitting isotope principally employed is As^{74} as sodium arsenate. About 1 to 1·5 mCi. is required and the scan is usually commenced about 1 hour after injection. Some workers find a repeat scan at 24 hours helpful.

To obtain a complete scan of any region commonly requires anything from about 15 minutes to one or two hours. One method of reducing this time is to use an array of detectors linked together so that each individual detector is required to traverse only a fraction of the total area. An alternative approach (first developed by Anger)[45] is to use a stationary crystal of large area which is viewed by an array of photomultipliers (typically 19 photomultipliers are used to view a crystal 11 inches in diameter and $\frac{1}{2}$ inch in thickness). When a scintillation is produced in the crystal, pulses of different sizes will be produced in the various photomultipliers depending upon the distance of each photomultiplier from the point at which the scintillation is produced in the crystal. These pulses can be fed into electronic circuits arranged to deflect and modulate the electron beam in a cathode-ray tube in such a way that the spot produced on the tube screen corresponds in position and brightness with the position and brightness of the scintillation in the crystal. A picture can be built up on the screen in a few minutes showing the distribution of activity in the region viewed. Such " scintillation cameras " (or " γ cameras ") are now available commercially, but are only just coming into clinical use.

REFERENCES

1. KEATING, E. and ALBERT (1949). *Recent Progress in Hormone Research*, 4.
2. MYANT, N. B. and POCHIN, E. E. *et al.* (1950).   *Clin. Sci.* **9**, 405.
3. MYANT, N. B. (1952).   *Brit. Med. Bull.* **8**, 141.
4. ROLLINSON, E. and ROTBLAT, J. (1955).   *Brit. J. Radiol.* **28**, 191.
5. International Atomic Energy Agency (1962).   *Acta Radiologica*, **58**, 233.
6. International Commission on Radiological Units and Measurements (1962).   Report 10d.   *U.S. National Bureau of Standards Handbook*, No. 87.
7. BELCHER, E. H., GORUZ-GRESPO, G., TROTT, N. G. and VETTER, H. (1964).   *Nuclear Medicine*, **4**, 78.
8. POCHIN, E. E. (1950).   *Lancet*, **259**, 41, 84.
9. BLONDAL, H. (1952).   *Brit. J. Radiol.* **25**, 260.
10. WAYNE, E. J. (1954).   *Brit. Med. Journ.* **1**, 411.
11. CLARK, D. E., MOE, R. H. and ADAMS, E. E. (1949).   *Surgery*, **26**, 331.
12. HAMOLSKY, M. W., STEIN, M. and FREEDBERG, A. S. (1957).   *J. Clin. Endocrinol.* **17**, 33.
13. MITCHELL, M. L., HARDEN, A. B. and O'ROURKE, M. E. (1960).   *J. Clin. Endocrinol.* **20**, 1474.
14. DUBACH, R., CALLENDER, S. T. and MOORE, C. V. (1948). *Blood*, **3**, 526.
15. BONNET, J. D., HAGEDORN, A. B. and OWEN, C. A. (1960). *Blood*, **15**, 36.
16. SAYLOR, L. and FINCH, C. A. (1953).   *Amer. J. Physiol.* **172**, 372.
17. HUFF, R. L., HENNESSY, T. G., AUSTIN, R. E., GARCIA, J. F., ROBERTS, B. M. and LAWRENCE, J. H. (1950).   *J. Clin. Invest.* **29**, 1041.
18. WASSERMAN, L. R., RASHKOFF, I. A., LEAVITT, D., MAYER, J. and PORT, S. (1952).   *J. Clin. Invest.* **31**, 32.

19. LOEFFLER, R. K., RAPPOPORT, D. A. and COLLINS, V. P. (1955). *Proc. Soc. Exp. Biol. Med.* **88**, 441.

20. DUBACH, R., MOORE, C. V. and MINNICH, V. (1946). *J. Lab. Clin. Med.* **31**, 1201.

21. ELMLINGER, P. J., HUFF, R. L., TOBIAS, C. A. and LAURENCE, J. H. (1953). *Acta Haemat.* **9**, 73.

22. GRAY, S. J. and STERLING, K. (1950). *J. Clin. Invest.* **29**, 1604.

23. COHEN, J. A. and WARRINGER, M. G. P. J. (1954). *J. Clin. Invest.* **33**, 459.

24. STRUMIA, M. M., TAYLOR, L., SAMPLE, A. B., COLWELL, L. S. and DAGAN, A. (1955). *Blood*, **10**, 429.

25. STORAASLI, J. P., KRIEGER, H., FRIEDELL, H. L. and HOLDEN, W. D. (1950). *Surg. Gynae. Obst.* **91**, 458.

26. CRISPELL, K. R., PORTER, B. and NIESET, R. T. (1950). *J. Clin. Invest.* **29**, 513.

27. PRINZMETAL, M., CORDAY, E., SPRITZLER, R. and FLEIG, W. (1949). *J. Amer. Med. Ass.* **139**, 617.

28. VEALL, N., PEARSON, J. D., HANLEY, T. and LOWE, A. E. (1954). *Proc. Radioisotope Conference.* Oxford, 183.

29. HUFF, R. L., FELLER, D. D. and BOGARDUS, C. (1954). *J. Clin. Invest.* **33**, 944.

30. GREENSPAN, R. H., LESTER, R. G., MARVIN, J. F. and AMPLATZ, K. (1959). *J. Amer. Med. Ass.* **169**, 667.

31. BRAUNWALD, E., LONG, R. T. L. and MORROW, A. G. (1959). *J. Clin. Invest.* **38**, 990.

32. SANDERS, R. J. and MORROW, A. G. (1959). *Amer. J. Med.* **26**, 508.

33. WALDER, D. N. (1953). *Clin. Sci.* **12**, 153.

34. LASSEN, N. H. (1964). *J. Clin. Invest.* **43**, 1805.

35. BARRON, J. N. and VEALL, N. (1952). *Brit. Med. Bull.* **8**, 197.

36. KETY, S. S. (1948). *Amer. J. Med. Sci.* **215**, 352; (1949). *Amer. Heart J.* **38**, 321.

37. SCHILLING, R. F. (1953). *Lab. Clin. Med.* **42**, 860.

38. BRADLEY, J. E., SMITH, E. L., BAKER, S. J. and MOLLIN, D. L. (1954). *Lancet*, **ii**, 476.

39. HUTCHINSON, J. L., TOWNSEND, S. R. and CAMERON, D. G. (1958). *Canad. Med. Ass. J.* **78**, 685.

40. EBERLE, B. T. and GLEASON, G. I. (1960). *Clin. Res.* **8**, 208.

41. STANLEY, M. M. and THANNHAUSER, S. J. (1949). *J. Lab. Clin. Med.* **34**, 1634.

42. WINTER, C. C. (1956). *J. Urol.* **76**, 182.

43. NORDYKE, R. A., TUBIS, M. and BLAND, W. (1960). *J. Lab. Clin. Med.* **56**, 438.

44. MCAFEE, J. G. and FUEGER, C. F. (1964). *Scintillation Scanning in Clinical Medicine*, ed. by Quinn J. L. Philadelphia and London, Saunders.

45. ANGER, H. O. (1958). *Rev. Sci. Instr.* **29**, 27.

GENERAL REFERENCES

VEAL, N. and VETTER, H. (1958). *Radioisotope Techniques in Clinical Research and Diagnosis.* London, Butterworth.

QUIMBY, E. H., FEITELBERG, S. and SILVER, S. (1963). *Radioactive Isotopes in Medicine and Biology.* Philadelphia, Lea and Febiger.

LATHJA, L. A. (1961). *Isotopes in Haematology.* Oxford, Blackwell.

International Atomic Energy Agency. (1964). *Medical Radioisotope Scanning.* Vienna, Int. At. Energy Agency.

CHAPTER XIV

HEALTH HAZARDS AND RADIOLOGICAL PROTECTION

14.01. Hazards

Soon after the discovery of X-rays and radio-activity, it was realised that X- and γ-rays could cause dermatitis and skin burns. Both Becquerel and Pierre Curie suffered burns from radium sources.[1] Later it was realised that even radiation doses too small to produce observable histological or functional changes immediately following the irradiation, might produce harmful effects which only became apparent after several years had elapsed. Thus many of the early radiologists and radium technicians developed skin cancers and leukemias, which were attributed to the radiation. The above are examples of somatic effects, i.e. effects which are manifest in the exposed individual. In addition to somatic effects, ionising radiations produce genetic effects which only appear in the offspring of the irradiated individual and may not be manifest for many generations. Most of the radiation induced genetic effects will be harmful. The objectives of radiological protection are therefore two-fold: (1) to prevent or minimise injuries in individuals who are necessarily exposed to radiation (either in the course of their work or for any other reason), and (2) to minimise the genetic effects of radiation upon the population as a whole.

One of the major problems in assessing the possible effects of radiation upon individuals who are exposed occupationally is that it is difficult to obtain information upon the long-term effects of chronic irradiation at low dose-rates in man and it is necessary to extrapolate either from animal experiments or from human experience with higher dose-rates. Fig. 14.01 illustrates different ways in which radiation effects may vary with the radiation dose. In fig. 14.01(a) a very low dose of radiation produces no effect in any individual, i.e. there is a threshold dose below which no individual will show the effect.

As the dose increases above the threshold an increasing proportion of individuals show the effect and there is a maximum dose above which all individuals will be affected. Many radiation effects are of this type, e.g. skin erythema, epilation, sterilisation, reduction in leucocyte count, etc. Figs. 14.01(b) and (c) illustrate another type of radiation response. In these cases there is no dose below which there is zero probability of injury being produced. As the dose increases the probability of the effect increases but even at very small doses there is a finite, although small, probability of injury. Most genetic effects of radiation appear to be of this type and it is possible that so are the late somatic effects. At least until the existence of a threshold dose for a given effect has been firmly established, it is prudent to assume that any radiation exposure may entail some probability of deleterious effects.

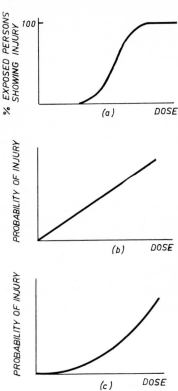

FIG. 14.01. Graphs illustrating different possible relations between radiation injury and radiation dose.

Evidence relating to tumour induction in humans after localised irradiation comes mainly from the following sources.[2]

(1) a limited number of reports of tumours arising after radiotherapy,

(2) skin tumours amongst the early radiologists,

(3) bone tumours in luminous dial painters (who used paints containing radium, mesothorium or radiothorium),

(4) lung tumours in uranium miners.

For tumours arising after radiotherapy, the radiation exposures in adults, when known, have all been in excess of 1000 R.[4] In children, one group studied received irradiation for thymic enlargement in infancy and showed an increased incidence of thyroid tumours. The average latent period between irradiation and the diagnosis of thyroid cancer in this group was 7 years. The skin dose in some of these cases was only 250 rads.[5] However in another series of 1,564 children who received similar treatment prophylactically (although with smaller treatment fields), no malignancies developed.[6] This raises some doubt as to whether the tumours in the first series were solely radiation induced or were related at least in part, to the condition for which the radiation treatment was given. The skin exposures received by the early radiologists and radium technicians are difficult to estimate but a figure of 5 R. per week is perhaps not unreasonable. This would mean that a cumulative exposure of several thousand roentgens was probably received,[7] since in adults a latent period of 15 to 20 years usually elapses between the first exposure to radiation and the clinical appearance of tumours. In the cases of the radium dial painters and the uranium miners also, the total exposures in individuals developing malignancies, although not known with any certainty, are estimated to have probably been several thousand roentgen. (Bone tumours have been produced in cases where the terminal body burden of radium was a few microgrammes.[8] A body burden of 1 μg. of radium, if uniformly distributed throughout the skeleton, delivers a dose to the bone of the order of 0·6 rad per week.[9] However autoradiography has shown that the radium concentration in bone varies markedly (by a factor of up to 15 : 1) [10] so the tumour sites may well have been exposed to over 10 rads/week.)

Evidence relating to the induction in humans of (1) leukaemia, (2) other neoplasms, after irradiation of the whole or a large part of the body comes from the following sources,

(1) survivors of the atomic bombing at Hiroshima and Nagasaki,

(2) patients receiving spinal irradiation for the treatment of ankylosing spondylitis,

(3) children receiving thymic irradiation in infancy or irradiated *in utero*,

(4) radiologists.

In both the Japanese atomic bomb survivors and the spondylitis cases, there is an increased incidence of leukaemia compared with the population at large and the increased incidence is greater, the greater the radiation dose.[11, 12, 13] The order of magnitude of the effect is an increase of one case per 10,000 persons per 100 rads per year at risk. In these groups, the leukaemia incidence appears to reach a peak 4 to 7 years after the exposure. The incidence of all other neoplasms is also increased but less than for leukaemia and the induction period is longer."

The evidence of leukaemia induction by radiation in children is as follows. An increased incidence was reported for those children who received irradiation for thymic enlargement [5] but this series must be regarded with caution since the state of the thymus itself has been found to influence the incidence, timing and cytological type of experimental leukaemias. Amongst children dying of leukaemia, Stewart *et al.*[14, 15] reported that a significantly higher percentage of the mothers had received a diagnostic X-ray examination of the abdomen during pregnancy, than in a control group. In other extensive studies of children irradiated *in utero*, Court-Brown and Doll [16] were unable to detect an increase in the leukaemia incidence whereas MacMahon [17] has confirmed Stewart's observations. (The susceptibility of the foetus to other types of radiation damage is discussed further below.) The only group in whom leukaemia has been reported as a result of *chronic* irradiation is radiologists. Comparative studies of leukaemia incidence amongst American radiologists and amongst physicians not professionally exposed to radiation have shown that the leukaemia incidence between 1929 and 1943 was significantly greater amongst the former, although by 1955 the difference had decreased.[18, 19] Amongst British radiologists starting practice after 1921, there appears to be no significantly increased incidence.[20] Since many of the American radiologists in the 1929-43 group practised at a time when protection procedures were not very rigorous, dose estimates are difficult, but the International Commission on Radiological Protection suggest that chronic exposure at a rate of about 0·3 R./week or an accumulated dose of 750 rads to the blood-forming organs may be sufficient to increase the leukaemia incidence significantly.[21]

Animal studies have shown that chronic exposure to radiation may also cause a shortening of life. In humans, longevity studies of radiologists have not shown any statistically significant life shortening [20, 22] but extrapolating from the animal experiments to humans, a life shortening of the order of 1 day per roentgen of whole body exposure would seem possible.

Animal experiments have also demonstrated that irradiation of the mammalian embryo results in developmental damage which is critically dependent upon the age at which the embryo is exposed.[23] For most of the abnormalities which are recognisable at birth, the crucial period in the mouse corresponds to the second to sixth week of human gestation. Since at this time a pregnancy may not be recognised the International Commission on Radiological Protection have recommended special precautions whenever women of reproductive age may be exposed. (The recommendations are given below.)

The largest genetic effect of radiation appears to be the addition of undesirable mutants. Most experiments upon gene mutations have suggested a linear relationship between the number of mutations and dose, with no threshold dose and no dependence on dose-rate. (However, see Chapter X where some of the experimental work upon radiation induced mutations was described.) Extrapolating from the animal experiments, it appears that doses of the order of 50 rads may well double the normal mutation rate in man. Most geneticists consider that an average genetic dose of 10 rads *per capita* accumulated from conception to the mean age of child-bearing would impose a considerable burden on society due to genetic damage and should certainly not be exceeded.[21]

14.02. Maximum permissible radiation doses

Since there are some radiation effects for which there appears to be no threshold dose, any exposure at a rate higher than the normal background rate of about 125 mR. per year entails some risk of deleterious effects. (The natural background rate is due to cosmic radiation and to naturally occurring radioactive materials, either in the earth and in building materials or within the human body.[25] See Table 14.02.) However for practical purposes it is desirable to determine the maximum doses which can be assumed to constitute a negligibly small hazard. The International Commission on Radiological Protection (I.C.R.P.) define a permissible dose for an individual as " that dose, accumulated over a long period of time or resulting from a single exposure, which, in the light of present knowledge carries a negligible probability of severe somatic or genetic injuries; furthermore, it is such a dose that any effects which ensue more frequently are limited to those of a minor nature that would not be considered unacceptable by the exposed individual or by competent medical authorities ".[21] For a whole population, the individual doses must also be limited in either number or magnitude so that they do not result in an unacceptable burden of genetic defects in future generations. The international Commission on Radiological Protection recommend upper limits for various types of exposure. The current (1966) values of these " maximum permissible doses " or " dose limits " are given below.

Since the biological effect resulting from exposure to ionising radiation depends upon the type of radiation as well as upon the absorbed dose, it is convenient for protection purposes to introduce a quantity which is called the " dose equivalent ", such that equal dose equivalents of different types of radiation produce equal effects. This makes it possible to describe the irradiation incurred by exposed persons on a common scale, regardless of the nature of the particular radiation (i.e. whether X-rays, β-rays, neutrons, etc.). The dose equivalent for any ionising radiation is defined as the product of the absorbed dose (D), the appropriate quality factor (QF), distribution factor (DF) and any other necessary modifying factors. The quality factors are related to the linear energy transfer (L.E.T.) of the radiation considered (see Chapter X) and corresponding values of quality factor and linear energy transfer have been published by the I.C.R.P. However, although the L.E.T. for any radiation depends on the radiation energy, it is usually more convenient in practice to use a single quality factor for each particular type of radiation. This is permissible so long as the approximation does not result in an underestimate of the dose equivalent. Table 14.01 lists values suggested by the I.C.R.P.[21]

TABLE 14.01

Radiation	Quality factor
X- and γ-rays	1
Electrons, energy $\geqslant 0.03$ MeV.	1
< 0.03 MeV.	1.7
Neutrons and α-particles	10 in general
	30 for the lens of the eye
Fission fragments and heavy nuclei	20 in general
	30 for the lens of the eye

TABLE 14.02

TYPICAL YEARLY RADIATION DOSES FROM NATURAL SOURCES [25]

	Gonad dose (mrem)	Bone marrow dose (mrem)
Cosmic rays	50	50
Terrestrial radiation		
(Out of doors from 18-350)	50	50
(Indoors 19-202)		
Internal radiation		
K^{40}	20	15
Ra^{226}	0.5	0.6
Ra^{228}	0.8	1.0
C^{14}	0.7	1.6
Rn^{222} in blood stream	3.0	3.0
	125.0	121.2

Dose distribution factors are not normally required where exposure to external radiation is considered, but when radioactive materials have been inhaled or ingested, there may be gross non-uniformity in the distribution, which requires special consideration in estimating the biological effects. The dose distribution factors are introduced to allow for these cases.

The unit of dose equivalent is the rem. The dose equivalent in rems is numerically equal to the absorbed dose in rads multiplied by the appropriate modifying factors. For exposure to external sources of X- or γ-radiation, the only modifying factor to be considered is the quality factor and this is unity. Thus for external exposures to X- or γ-radiation the dose equivalent in rems is equal to the absorbed dose in rads and for muscle is also almost equal numerically to the exposure in roentgens.

For protection purposes, the I.C.R.P. divide the population as a whole into two categories:

(1) adults exposed in the course of their work,

(2) members of the public.

In some earlier reports of the Commission, a distinction was made between individuals who, in the course of their work, regularly entered " controlled areas " and those who entered such areas only occasionally or worked in the vicinity. These groups are now both included in category 1. (A "controlled area " is an area to which access is controlled and the exposure of personnel is normally supervised and individually monitored. Any area in which persons can receive doses exceeding 1.5 rems/year should be controlled.)

Dose limits for individual exposures recommended by the I.C.R.P. in 1965 are summarised in Table 14.03.[21] For occupational exposure, for organs other than the abdomen in women of reproductive capacity, the maximum dose permitted within any thirteen week period is one-half of the annual dose. If the maximum dose is received in any 13 weeks, subsequent exposure must normally be restricted so that the maximum permissible yearly dose is not exceeded. However, the I.C.R.P. state that for whole body exposures where the gonads and red bone marrow are the critical organs, it may occasionally be justifiable to repeat the thirteen week quota in each quarter of a year provided the total accumulated to age N years does not exceed $5(N-18)$ rems. In special circumstances and subject to certain restrictions, a single exposure up to twice the annual dose

TABLE 14.03
DOSE LIMITS FOR INDIVIDUALS

	In 13 weeks (rems)	In any year (rems)	To age N years (rems)	Equivalent weekly dose-rate continuous exposure (mrem/wk.)
1. Maximum permissible doses for occupational exposure (a) to the abdomen in women of reproductive capacity *	1·3	5	5(N-18)†	100
(b) to the gonads (other than in (a) above) and red bone marrow	3	5	5(N-18)†	100
(c) skin, thyroid, bone	15	30		600
(d) other single organs	8	15		300
(e) extremities	38	75		1500
2. Dose limits for members of the public (a) to the gonads and red bone marrow		0·5		10
(b) to the thyroid in children up to 16 years		1·5		30
(c) other organs		$\frac{1}{10}$ of the corresponding occupational doses		

* In pregnant women, when the pregnancy is confirmed, the dose to the foetus during the remainder of the pregnancy should be restricted to 1 rem.

† If occupational exposure is permitted below the age of 18 years, the dose shall not exceed 5 rems in any one year below the age of 18 and the dose accumulated to age 30 shall not exceed 60 rems.

limit may be permitted to a few workers (not including women of reproductive capacity) if there is no practical alternative.

In addition to the individual exposures, the Commission has recommended that " the genetic dose to the whole population from all sources additional to natural background should not exceed 5 rems plus the lowest practicable contribution from medical exposure ". This means that the *annual* genetically significant dose to the whole population (assuming 30 as the mean age of child-bearing) must not exceed 5/30 rem = 170 mrem. The annual genetically significant dose to a population is the average of the individual gonad doses, each weighted for the expected number of children conceived subsequent to the exposure. The genetic dose from medical exposures differs greatly from country to country but in most countries is considerably less than 170 mrem annually (see table 14.04) so if this recommendation is satisfied the total genetic dose to the population should be considerably less than 10 rems.

TABLE 14.04[3]

MEDICAL PROCEDURES CONTRIBUTING TO THE ANNUAL GENETICALLY SIGNIFICANT RADIATION DOSE IN THE UNITED KINGDOM (EXCLUDING NORTHERN IRELAND)

	Dose in mrem
Diagnostic radiology	14·1
Radiotherapy	
Non-malignant	4·5
Malignant	0·5
Isotopes	0·2
	19·3

In connection with medical exposures, the International Commission have pointed out that in deciding upon radiological examinations of the lower abdomen and pelvis in women of reproductive age, physicians should consider the possibility of an unrecognised pregnancy and bear in mind the reports of extreme sensitivity of the embryo and foetus to ionising radiation. They recommend that examinations which are not of importance in connection with the immediate illness of the patient, be limited to the 10 day interval following the onset of menstruation when it is virtually certain that no pregnancy exists.

It is important to recognise that the doses discussed above are *maximum* values; in the words of the International Commission " every effort (should) be made to reduce exposure to all types of ionising radiation to the lowest possible level " and " any unnecessary exposure (should) be avoided ". It should also be noted that the recommendations described are those made by the *International Commission on Radiological Protection*. Various national authorities have also published recommendations or " codes of practice " for the protection of persons exposed to ionising radiations. At the present time, the permissible doses adopted in most countries are generally similar to those recommended by the I.C.R.P. but in particular instances a national code may differ in detail. For example, in some countries no occupational exposure at all is permitted below the age of 18 years or after a pregnancy is recognised. In other countries such exposure is permitted but only at a lower dose-rate than that accepted by the I.C.R.P. For details of national codes, the publications of the appropriate national authority should be consulted.[30, 31]

14.03. Protection from external radiation

In this section we consider methods of restricting the radiation dose received from X-ray units or from sealed sources of radioactive materials. The additional precautions necessary when handling exposed sources are considered in section 14.05.

The dose received from external radiation may be limited by either restricting the time during which any individual is exposed or by reducing the exposure-rate. The latter can be accomplished by (1) increasing the distance of the source from " occupied space ", (2) by collimating and/or filtering the useful beam, (3) by means of protective barriers. It is convenient to consider separately the precautions required in connection with fixed installations such as X-ray sets and γ-teletherapy units and the problems arising in connection with sources used for local applications, such as radium appliances, β-ray applicators, etc.

Protection for X-ray and tele-isotope installations

Detailed recommendations about the precautions required when radiations up to 3 MeV. are used in medicine have been published by Committee III of the International Commission on Radiological Protection.[26] This report includes specifications for the nature of the tube or source housing; recommendations about the filters, cones and auxiliary equipment to be used in particular techniques, attenuation data for materials used in protective barriers, recommended methods of monitoring and so on. Some of these recommendations are described below but reference should be made to the report itself or to the appropriate national code for full details.

The possible sources of exposure with these units are (1) the useful beam, (2) leakage radiation, i.e. radiation travelling directly from the target through the protective housing, (3) scattered radiation. The area of the useful beam should always be restricted to the minimum that will fulfil the medical requirements and no one but the patient should be exposed to the useful beam. Leakage radiation is usually a fairly small part of the total secondary radiation, the principal part of which is made up of scatter from the patient. (See table 14.05.) However the magnitude of the leakage radiation depends upon the design of the tube or source housing and the user should carry out tests to ensure that the housing is adequate. The International Commission on Radiological Protection recommend that the housing around an X-ray tube be such that, with the tube operated at maximum rating, with the shutter closed, the exposure due to leakage radiation shall not exceed 100 mR. in 1 hour at 1 m. from the focus for diagnostic sets and shall not exceed either 1 R. in 1 hour at 1 m. from the focus nor 30 R. in 1 hour 5 cm. from the surface of the housing at any point accessible to a patient for therapy sets. These recommendations assume that the X-ray tube will not be energised while the patient is being positioned, and that the operator has additional protection when the high tension is switched on, even when the shutter is closed. If the patient is to be positioned with the tube energised, then a higher standard of tube protection is necessary. With teleisotope units, there is no process analogous to switching off the anode voltage in an X-ray set and hence the housing must satisfy more stringent requirements. For these units with the source or shutter in the " off " position, the maximum exposure-rate at 1 m. from the source must be less than 10 mR./hr. and the average exposure-rate at 1 m. from the source must be less than 2 mR./hr. At 5 cm. from the surface of the housing exposure-rates 10 or 20 times the above are permitted, depending on the activity of the source.

In carrying out a survey of the housing of an X-ray installation, the International Commission for Radiological Protection suggest a preliminary examination with a fluorescent screen for voltages up to 200 kVp. For average hardness and after adequate dark adaptation time, the smallest detectable luminescence corresponds to an exposure-rate of about 3 mR./hr. This technique enables radiation escaping through narrow slits to be detected which might be missed by other types of instrument. If ionisation chambers of large volume are used for monitoring, it must be remembered that the exposure-rate in a narrow beam will be under-estimated.

TABLE 14.05

TYPICAL EXPOSURE-RATES IN THE VICINITY OF X-RAY SETS AND TELETHERAPY ISOTOPE UNITS[27, 28]

	Diagnostic per 100 mAs.	Therapy 250 kVp. per min. or per 100 mAs.	Therapy Co^{60} per min.
Primary exposure at patient	2·5 R.	40 R.	100 R.
90° scatter at 1 m. from patient	2·0 mR.	30 mR.	70 mR.
Leakage at same position as scatter	0·06 mR.	0·6 mR.	0·02 mR.

For fluoroscopic equipment, the Commission recommend that a cone should extend from the tube housing as near to the panel or table top as is practicable; that the walls of the cone provide the same degree of protection as the housing and that the cone be connected with the tube and viewing device in such a way that the useful beam cannot fall outside the viewing screen. The target to panel distance should be at least 12 inches (and preferably 18 inches) and the Commission also specify the lead equivalent of the protective glass required on the fluoroscopic screen for different operating conditions.

Table 14·05 shows the order of magnitude of the exposure-rate due to scattered radiation at a distance of 1 m. from the patient during typical radiological procedures.[27, 28] The magnitude of the scattered radiation dose which could be received by anyone remaining in the vicinity of a patient during treatment make it essential that for therapy equipment, the control panel is outside the treatment room and that no one is normally permitted within the room during treatments. An exception is sometimes made for therapy equipment operated at voltages below 60 kVp., but this is not generally considered desirable. The use of interlocking switches on the doors of treatment rooms so that sets are automatically switched off if the door is opened, is recommended for therapy equipment. Although the exposure-rates are lower for diagnostic equipment, the operator requires some protection if maximum permissible exposure levels are not to be exceeded and the control panel for radiography should be behind a protective screen. For those procedures where members of the staff cannot remain behind a permanent structural shield (i.e. principally fluoroscopy and radiography with mobile units) anyone who may be exposed to radiation should wear a protective apron of at least 0·25 mm. lead equivalent. The fluoroscopist should also wear protective gloves. It should be noted that the exposure-rate due to scattered radiation increases with increase in the area of the useful beam so the use of the smallest area which is sufficient to cover the region being investigated not only keeps the patient dose to a minimum but is also of benefit to the radiographer. (See Chapter IX, section 9.09 for other recommended procedures to reduce the dose to the patient.)

The amount of shielding which must be provided by permanent structural elements such as walls, floors, ceilings and control booths depends upon the following factors:

(1) the work-load (W) of the machine considered. This is usually expressed in milliampere-minutes per week for X-ray units and in roentgen per week at one metre for isotope units,

(2) the source-barrier distance,

(3) whether the primary radiation beam can impinge upon the barrier considered or whether it is exposed to leakage and scattered radiation only,

(4) the nature of the " occupancy " of the space which the barrier is to shield. For example a control booth will

TABLE 14.06
THICKNESS OF PROTECTIVE BARRIERS REQUIRED FOR TYPICAL INSTALLATIONS[30]

Type of Installation	WUT	Exposure-rate in occupied area	Distance to occupied area (ft.)	Primary barrier		Secondary barriers*	
				Lead (mm.)	Concrete (in.)	Lead (mm.)	Concrete (in.)
Fluoroscopic	mA-min./wk. 2000 at 100 kVp or 400 at 150 kVp.	100 mR./wk	7 14	Viewing screen		0·7 0·2	2·2 0·8
		10 mR./wk.	7 14			1·2 0·8	3·8 2·8
Radiographic	mA-min./wk. 1000 at 100 kVp. or 200 at 150 kVp.	100 mR./wk.	7 14	1·7 1·2	5·3 3·8	0·4 0	1·4 0
		10 mR./wk.	7 14	2·4 2·0	7·2 6·2	1·0 0·6	3·2 2·1
Therapeutic 100 kVp.	4000 mA-min./wk.	100 mR./wk.	7 14	2·0 1·6	6·3 5·2	1·1 0·7	3·7 2·4
		10 mR./wk.	7 14	2·9 2·4	8·5 7·3	1·8 1·4	5·7 4·6

Equipment	Workload	Weekly dose	Distance				
Therapeutic 250 kVp.	40000 mA.-min./wk.	100 mR./wk.	7	10·4	18·0	5·7	11·5
			14	8·6	15·6	4·2	9·4
		10 mR./wk.	7	13·0	21·6	8·0	14·8
			14	11·2	19·2	6·5	12·7
Therapeutic 2000 kV (constant potential)	2000 mA.-min./wk.	100 mR./wk.	7	235	50	67	15
			14	210	45	43	12
			30	185	40	19	8·2
		10 mR./wk.	7	280	58	107	22
			14	255	53	83	18
			30	230	48	57	14
Therapeutic* Cs137	12000 R./wk. at 1 m.	100 mR./wk.	7	93	30·2	16	13·5
			14	80	26·3	11	10·6
			28	67	22·4	7	7·8
		10 mR./wk.	7	114	36·4	23	18·2
			14	101	32·5	18	15·3
			28	88	28·6	14	12·5
Therapeutic* Co60	40000 R./wk. at 1 m.	100 mR./wk.	7	201	42·7	27	13·2
			14	177	37·8	18·5	9·6
			28	153	32·9	10·0	6·0
		10 mR./wk.	7	241	51·3	41·5	19·4
			14	217	46·4	33·0	15·8
			28	193	41·5	24·5	12·2

* For isotope units secondary barrier assumed exposed to radiation scattered through at least 90° and leakage radiation negligible.

be occupied whenever the machine is operated and it will be occupied by an individual who is occupationally exposed to radiation. In considering the shielding in an outside wall, however, it may be permissible to assume the outside space is occupied only occasionally but if the space is accessible to members of the population at large then this factor must be taken into consideration. When precise occupancy data are not available, nominal " occupancy factors " (T) for different types of space have been suggested by the I.C.R.P.[26]

In calculating the required shielding, the work-load (W) is multiplied by the occupancy factor. (T = 1 for full occupancy, $\frac{1}{4}$ for partial and $\frac{1}{16}$ for occasional occupancy). W may also be multiplied by a " use factor " (U), where a machine is directed for only a limited time at a particular barrier, e.g. where a therapy set is used mainly for fixed field techniques, but occasionally for rotation, the use factor for the ceiling will be less than 1.

Table 14.06 illustrates the amount of shielding required to reduce the exposure-rate to either 100 mR./wk. (i.e. to the maximum permissible level for occupational exposure) or to 10 mR./wk. (the maximum level for the population at large) for some typical installations. In calculating the shielding necessary for scattered radiation, it is usual to assume that the intensity of the radiation scattered through 90°, at 1 m. from the scatterer is not more than 0·1 per cent. of the intensity of the primary radiation at the scatterer. For X-rays generated below 500 kVp., the energy of the scattered radiation is usually equated with that of the primary (so the attenuation in a barrier is the same for the primary and secondary radiation) although in the 200 to 250 kVp. range, the half-value layer of the scattered radiation is about one-half that of the primary.[29] (Equating the scattered and primary energies introduces an error in the " safe " direction.) For megavoltage radiation, both the intensity and the energy of the scattered radiation depend markedly upon the angle of scattering and the difference in the shielding required for radiation scattered through different angles is considerable. The attenuation of the radiation scattered at different angles has been measured experimentally for some sources. [28, 30] (See table 14.07.) For X-rays generated between 1 and 3 MV., a rough guide to shielding requirements can be obtained by assuming the scattered radiation to be attenuated in the same way as X-rays generated at 500 kVp.

" Secondary barriers " must provide sufficient shielding to attenuate both the leakage radiation and the scattered radiation, so that the total radiation transmitted does not exceed the maximum permissible. For megavoltage X-ray units, the leakage radiation may produce a hazard comparable with that due to scattered radiation.

TABLE 14.07

THE ATTENUATION OF RADIATION FROM Co[60] SOURCES [30]

	Lead		Concrete	
	Half-value layer (cm.)	Tenth-value layer (cm.)	Half-value layer (in.)	Tenth-value layer (in.)
Useful beam and leakage radiation	1·20	4·0	2·6	8·6
Scatter at angle of				
30°	1·02	3·40	2·5	8·2
45°	0·87	2·90	2·4	8·0
60°	0·75	2·50	2·3	7·6
90°	0·43	1·45	1·8	6·2
120°	0·20	0·65	1·7	5·8
150°	0·14	0·45	1·5	5·0

Illustrative example

Consider a Co[60] therapy set and assume the data on leakage and scattered radiation given in Table 14.05. Calculate (1) the primary shielding required in a wall 5 metres from the source, and (2) the secondary shielding required in a wall 3 metres from the patient which receives leakage radiation and radiation scattered through an angle of at least 90°. Assume the work load is 20 hours per week, the output is 100 R./min. at 1 m., and the maximum permissible exposure-rate beyond each wall is to be 100 mR./wk.

Primary exposure-rate at 5 m. = 100/25 = 4 R./min.

∴ Weekly exposure in 20 hours = 20×60×4 = 4800 R.

Attenuation required in primary shield to reduce weekly exposure to 0·1 R. = 48,000, i.e. approximately five tenth-value layers less one half-value layer of shielding material is required. From Table 14.07

∴ Thickness of lead = 19 cm.

or thickness of concrete = 40 inches.

For the secondary barrier

Exposure-rate due to leakage radiation at 1 m. = 0·02 mR./min.

$$\text{Exposure-rate at 3 m.} \qquad = \frac{0 \cdot 02}{9} \times 60 \text{ mR./hr.}$$

$$\text{Exposure per week} \qquad = 20 \times 60 \times \frac{0 \cdot 02}{9} \text{ mR.}$$

$$= 3 \text{ mR.}$$

(This can be neglected in comparison with the scatter.)

$$\text{Exposure-rate due to scattered radiation at 3 m.} = \frac{70}{9} \text{ mR./min.}$$

$$\text{Exposure per week} \qquad = 20 \times 60 \times \frac{70}{9} \text{ mR.}$$

$$= 9300 \text{ mR.}$$

Attenuation required   = 93

i.e. approximately two tenth-value layers.

∴ From table 14.07

thickness of lead = 3·0 cm.

thickness of concrete = $12\frac{1}{2}$ inches.

When new equipment is installed or when structural alterations are made which may alter shielding in the vicinity of existing equipment, a radiation survey of all occupied space in the vicinity is necessary to ensure that the barriers, as constructed, are, in fact, adequate.

14.04. Protection from radiation from sealed sources for brachytherapy [26, 30]

In this section we consider the precautions necessary in storing and transporting brachytherapy sources and in preparing and applying devices containing such sources.

Protection from β-radiation is readily achieved by the use of protective barriers, since a centimetre of glass or plastic material is usually sufficient to stop the particles completely. For pure β-emitters, it is preferable to use low atomic number materials to stop the β-particles, since this keeps to a minimum the secondary X-radiation emitted as the electrons are brought to rest (Bremsstrahlung). If very intense sources of high energy β-radiation are employed, however, Bremsstrahlung may constitute a hazard and in this case additional shielding

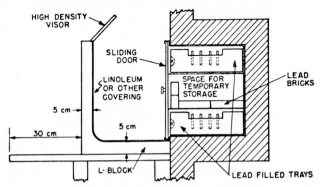

FIG. 14.02. A suggested arrangement of preparation bench for sealed brachytherapy sources, showing L-block and source storage recessed in wall.
Courtesy United States National Bureau of Standards.

will be necessary. For γ-ray sources, it is less easy to provide protection by barriers because of the greater penetration of the radiation. In order to reduce the intensity of the γ-radiation from radium to 1 per cent. of the incident intensity, for example, about 3 inches of lead are required. It is therefore usually necessary to rely upon a combination of distance and barriers to provide protection.

Brachytherapy sources are commonly stored in lead-lined steel safes with separate lead-lined compartments or lead trays holding the individual sources of a given type (fig. 14.02). For storing radioactive sources, it is an advantage if the safe is provided with an exhaust fan, which permits air to be drawn from the safe, through a filter and discharged away from occupied space, since checking the filter for contamination then provides a convenient method of checking for leaking

sources (see below). The shielding required depends upon the
nature and activity of the sources in the store and the nature of

TABLE 14.08

PROTECTION REQUIREMENTS (IN CENTIMETERS OF LEAD) FOR
VARIOUS GAMMA-RAY SOURCES [30]

Millicurie-hours	Radium T.V.L.* = 5·5 cm. lead			Cobalt-60 T.V.L.* = 4·1 cm. lead			Cesium-137 T.V.L.* = 2·2 cm. lead		
	Thickness of lead required to reduce radiation to 100 mR. † at a distance of								
	1 ft.	3·2 ft.	6·5 ft.	1 ft.	3·2 ft.	6·5 ft.	1 ft.	3·2 ft.	6·5 ft.
100	4·0	0	0	5·0	0·7	0	1·1	0	0
300	6·2	1·5	0	7·0	2·8	0	2·1	0	0
1,000	8·9	3·6	1·1	9·1	4·9	2·5	3·3	1·1	0
3,000	11·3	5·8	3·1	11·0	6·8	4·4	4·3	2·1	0·8
10,000	14·1	8·5	5·5	13·1	8·9	6·5	5·4	3·2	1·9
30,000	16·7	11·0	7·8	15·0	10·8	8·4	6·4	4·2	2·9
100,000	19·5	13·7	10·5	17·2	12·9	10·5	7·5	5·3	4·0

Millicurie-hours	Iridium-192 T.V.L.* = 2·0 cm. lead			Gold-198 T.V.L.* = 1·1 cm. lead		
	Thickness of lead required to reduce radiation to 100 mR. † at a distance of					
	1 ft.	3·2 ft.	6·5 ft.	1 ft.	3·2 ft.	6·5 ft.
100	0·8	0	0	0·4	0	0
300	1·4	0·1	0	0·9	0	0
1,000	2·2	0·7	0·1	1·5	0·3	0
3,000	3·1	1·4	0·6	2·1	0·9	0·2
10,000	4·0	2·1	1·2	3·0	1·4	0·8
30,000	5·0	3·0	2·0	3·9	2·0	1·3
100,000	6·2	4·0	2·8	5·3	2·9	1·9

* Approximate value obtained with large attenuation.
† Add one tenth-value layer (T.V.L.) to reduce radiation to 10 mR.
(*U.S. National Bureau of Standards Handbook*, No. 73).

564

the occupancy of nearby space. (See table 14.08.) It is usually convenient if the radioactive store is located adjacent to a shielded work-bench where applicators can be loaded and dismantled. The shielding customarily provided at the work bench is a lead L-block, at least 2 inches in thickness. A sheet of lead glass placed across the top of the L-block, inclined at 45°, gives the eyes protection from β-radiation and will provide some attenuation of γ-radiation. (See fig. 14.02.) Alternatively mirrors may be used for viewing.

A small storage receptacle with additional lead shielding incorporated into the work-bench in which sources can be placed temporarily (for example, while loading an applicator) is convenient. The provision of long-handled forceps of various types and vises and clamps for holding applicators or sources is essential, unless magnetic or pneumatic devices are preferred. The use of remote handling devices which can be operated from outside a protective barrier enables hand doses to be greatly reduced. It may be necessary to practise using such devices, however, if the time required for manipulations is not to be increased. (When manipulations are observed by means of mirrors or prisms practice may also be required.)

As an example of the effects of distance and shielding upon exposure-rate consider the exposure received by an operator loading an applicator with a 25 mg. radium tube. If the tube is held in ordinary forceps with no shielding devices, the hands will be about 10 cm., and the nearest body surface about 30 cm., from the tube. Under these conditions the hands would receive approximately 35 mR./min. and the body 4 mR./min. If long-handled forceps were used so that the hands were about 32 cm. from the source, and the operation was carried out behind a 2-inch lead barrier, the hand exposure would be reduced by a factor of 10 on account of the increased distance to about 3·5 mR./min., and the barrier would reduce the body exposure by a factor of 20 to 0·2 mR./min.

In this particular example, the maximum time a worker could be so occupied per year is determined by the hand exposure as $\frac{75{,}000}{3 \cdot 5 \times 60} = 357$ hrs. Working 89 hours in each thirteen-week period, the whole body exposure in this time would be about

1·1 R and the average exposure-rate to the gonads and blood-forming organs would be slightly less than 100 mR./wk.

Any region which cannot be continuously occupied without exceeding the maximum permissible exposure (whatever the source of radiation) must be clearly indicated. With radio-active sources it is customary to use the conventional sign shown in fig. 14.03.

FIG. 14.03.   Radiation warning sign.
By permission from Recommendations of the International Commission on Radiological Protection (1955), *Brit. J. Radiol.*, Suppl. 6, 12.

While radioactive sources are being stored, or transported, and applicators are being prepared or dismantled, it is usually possible to supply a considerable degree of protection to personnel by shields. (Long-handled lead carriers for small sources and wheeled lead carriages for large sources are normally used for transport.) When the sources are applied or removed from the patient, however, it is usually not practicable to provide shielding, and distance and speed must be relied upon to keep the exposure as low as possible. During the time the patient is being treated, "bed-side" shielding may or may not be practical. The position, within a hospital, where patients shall stay while being treated with radioactive materials, requires careful consideration, in order to reduce as far as possible the exposure of other patients and staff. It is helpful if any individual patient can be confined to a single room, since this usually restricts the exposure of others and reduces the area in which a source can be " lost ". If the removal of anything whatsoever from the room is prohibited until either (*a*) it has been monitored (this would apply to bed-linen, sweepings, etc.), or (*b*) permission for removal has been explicitly received, then it should be impossible for any radioactive source to be removed from the room by accident. (Articles which might be removed without monitoring depend on the anatomical site of the radioactive material in individual cases). Radiation "alarms" in laundries and refuse disposal areas can be used as extra safeguards.

So far we have been considering the hazards from external radiation, but it is important to recognise that the escape of radioactive materials from nominally sealed sources may occur if the containers are damaged. Sources should be examined after use and if there is any suspicion of damage (for example, if a needle is bent during implantation), the source should be tested for leakage immediately. The source may be placed in a suitable container with an absorbent such as charcoal or cotton-wool which can then be tested for contamination. In some cases, wiping the source with an absorbent material may be adequate. While these tests are carried out the source should be treated as a potential source of radioactive contamination and anything with which it is in contact, such as forceps, should be regarded as contaminated until the contrary is established.

Although in normal use, the likelihood of damage to a source sufficient to cause rupture of the container and actual spillage of the contents, might be expected to be remote, such accidents have occurred from time to time in the past and staff should be instructed in the procedures to be followed in such cases. Heat sterilisation of most radioactive sources is probably best avoided (heat sterilisation of radium sources is definitely undesirable) because of the possibility of source rupture. If a major escape of radioactive material from a source is suspected, windows should be closed, fans turned off and everyone should leave the room, closing and locking the doors. If gaseous or powdered sources are involved, the doors should be sealed. Personnel should then remain in any convenient *adjacent* room until they have been monitored, in order to avoid spreading radioactive contamination. The radiation safety officer should be informed of the situation immediately and any necessary steps taken to remove contamination from individuals. No attempts, however, should be made to clean up the spill itself until expert assistance is available.

14.05. Personnel monitoring

The efficacy of the precautions taken to reduce the external exposure of radiation workers is normally checked by personnel monitoring. This is carried out by requiring workers to wear either small wrapped photographic films or pocket meters. The "film badge" method is convenient for recording either β-, X- or γ-exposures accumulated over a week or month in cases where the working conditions are fairly constant. The badges are not suitable for α-particle monitoring since the wrapping needed to exclude visible light absorbs the α-particles. Pocket exposure-meters (see section 7.12) are convenient for measuring X- or γ-exposures received during a particular manipulation or sequence of manipulations. These meters are not normally designed to measure exposure due to β- or very soft X-radiation but can be made relatively independent of radiation quality for the harder electromagnetic radiations.

The photographic film method suffers from two main disadvantages, (1) the delay imposed by the need for processing before an exposure can be determined, and (2) the variation in the response of the film to radiation of different qualities. It has, however, the advantage of providing a small, easily carried, integrating meter with no electrical circuits to get out of adjustment, and it can be used for a wide range of exposures. It is the method usually chosen where fairly routine operations are carried out with radiations of known quality and is thus widely used in hospital radiological departments. When a worker is exposed to several radiations of different type or energy or to radiation of unknown quality, evaluation of the dose received becomes more uncertain. To give some indication of the radiation quality it is usual to cover part of the film either by a single piece of metal (usually lead, but occasionally silver or cadmium) or, less commonly, by a composite shield made up of several metals. β or very soft X-radiation will

568

cause blackening of the unshielded area only, whereas penetrating radiation will cause greater blackening under a dense shield than on the uncovered portion because of the greater energy absorption and consequent electron production in the shield. Film badges must be calibrated against sources of known strength and preferably of the same quality radiation as is to be measured, if this is known. One unexposed and a series of calibrated films from the same batch of film are normally processed with each set of monitoring films. Special types of film are used for workers who may be exposed to neutrons.

Film badges are usually worn on the chest, but in some circumstances additional films may be worn elsewhere, e.g. on the wrist or fingers, if hand exposures are likely to be critical. Pocket ionisation chambers may be carried in addition to film badges, if a high exposure-rate is anticipated in a particular procedure, in order to obtain an immediate indication of the exposure. Most national codes of practice require occupationally exposed individuals to wear film badges at all times while at work, since this is the most convenient method of determining the total exposure received by each individual. Many national authorities also require that a record be kept of the radiation doses received by every worker and that a summary of the radiation dose record be made available when a worker changes employment.

The International Commission on Radiological Protection recommend that every worker in a radiological department shall have a pre-employment medical examination including a complete blood count. Such examinations shall be repeated at regular intervals depending upon the exposure conditions. For persons exposed to neutrons or other penetrating heavy particles, the examination should include ophthalmological tests.

14.06. Precautions to be observed with exposed sources

Workers handling exposed radioactive isotopes must be protected not only from external radiation but also from the danger of taking radioactive materials into the body either by inhalation, ingestion or through a cut or open wound. Thus when any material which is likely to give off active vapour is to be handled, the work should be carried out in a fume cupboard. This is particularly important in the case of α-emitters which in general constitute a severe hazard if inhaled. In some cases it may be necessary to work in respirators. All laboratories handling exposed radioactive isotopes should in any case be adequately ventilated and a forced air flow with the exhaust discharged well away from occupied space is usually considered desirable.

To prevent contamination of the hands with the risk of subsequent ingestion, gloves should be worn whenever radioactive materials are to be handled and it is desirable to reserve special overalls and overshoes for work in " active " laboratories. Such operations as pipetting must be carried out by means of mechanical aids and eating and smoking in the laboratory should be prohibited.

In order to prevent the contamination of working surfaces (and the possibility of such contamination being transferred to the worker) it is usual to carry out manipulations over trays or within outer vessels which are lined with an absorbent material which can be discarded if a spill occurs. The trays and working surfaces beneath the absorbent should be impervious to liquids. Plastic containers for liquids have the advantage of being both unbreakable and more readily cleaned than glass-ware. When glass containers are used and particularly during procedures such as sterilisation, the glass-ware should be placed inside an outer unbreakable vessel. Anyone handling radioactive isotopes should realise that, besides being safer, it is far easier to prevent contamination occurring than it is to remove active material from an ordinary surface. Regular monitoring of all working areas and of the clothing and exposed skin of workers is desirable, not only for health reasons, but to avoid errors of measurement due to contamination. The maximum levels of surface contamination permitted in various countries are given in the report of Committee V of the I.C.R.P.[24]

It is difficult to devise simple methods of testing whether workers have absorbed trace amounts of radioactive materials which can be used generally and routinely. Where work is mainly with a particular γ-emitting isotope which is concentrated in one organ, uptake may be detected by routine external counting over the organ in question, the outstanding example being concentration of I^{131} in the thyroid.[32] Centres which are equipped with whole body counters, can monitor their employees for trace amounts of any γ-emitters, but other centres will normally only send workers for this type of test, when absorption is suspected. Assays of excreta can indicate whether ingestion or the inhalation of soluble material has occurred but are also usually only carried out if accidental intake is suspected. Breath monitoring is useful in some cases.

14.07. Maximum body burdens and maximum permissible concentrations of radioactive isotopes in air and water

The maximum permissible radiation doses listed in Table 14.03 apply to both external and " internal " radiation. The latter cannot be measured directly, so it is convenient to establish a maximum permissible body burden for each isotope. When such permissible body burdens have been determined, it is then possible to estimate the maximum concentrations of radioactive material in air or in water, which, even if the air is breathed continuously or the water is used for drinking for fifty years, will not cause the permissible body burden to be exceeded. Such data are required not only to establish safe working conditions for those handling radioactive materials, but also to protect the population as a whole when methods of disposal of used radioactive material are being considered.

The maximum permissible body burden is usually determined by the dose equivalent in one particular critical organ or tissue. The critical organ is frequently that in which the concentration of radioactive material is greatest, but this is not necessarily so, because of variations in radio-sensitivity.

For α- and β-emitting nuclides which are concentrated in bone, the permitted dose-rate equivalent is 600 mrem per week (Table 14.03). This figure is based upon the dose equivalent delivered to bone by a body burden of 0.1 μg. of radium assuming a quality factor of 10 for α-particles but equating other modifying factors to 1. (In fact radium is not uniformly distributed in bone, see section 14.01, but this introduces an error in the " safe " direction.) The figure of $0 \cdot 1 \mu g$. for the maximum permissible body burden of radium is based on clinical experience with radium dial painters (as described in section 14.01), with patients treated with radium and with persons using water supplies relatively rich in radium.[9] For other bone seeking nuclides if the parent element is not an isotope of radium and if the radiation considered includes α, β^-, β^+, e^- or recoil atoms, a " relative damage factor " (n) equal to 5 is to be used in calculating the dose equivalent. This factor is intended to include the effects of (a) non-uniformity of distribution greater than that of radium, (b) deposition in a more radio-sensitive portion of the bone than in the case of radium, or (c) greater essentialness of damaged tissue.

In general, if the maximum permissible dose-rate equivalent in the critical organ is R. rems/wk., the maximum permissible body burden q (in μCi.) can be calculated from the equation

$$q = \frac{100 \cdot m \cdot R}{(3 \cdot 7 \times 10^4) \times (1 \cdot 6 \times 10^{-6}) \times (6 \cdot 05 \times 10^5) f_2 \epsilon} = \frac{2 \cdot 8 \times 10^{-3} \, m.R.}{f_2 \epsilon}$$

where

m = mass of the organ of reference (in grams)

f_2 = the fraction of the body burden in the organ

ϵ = effective energy absorbed per disintegration of the nuclide considered (in MeV).

$\epsilon = \Sigma E_i F_i (QF)_i \, n_i$ where E_i is the energy in MeV. of radiation of type i, and $(QF)_i$ and n_i denote respectively the quality factor and relative damage or other modifying factors for radiation of type i. F_i is the fraction of the total number of disintegrations producing radiation of type i.

$3 \cdot 7 \times 10^4$ = disintegrations per second per microcurie

$1 \cdot 6 \times 10^{-6}$ = ergs/MeV.

$6 \cdot 05 \times 10^5$ = sec./wk.

100 = ergs/g.-rad

In order to calculate from the maximum permissible body burden of any isotope, the maximum concentration which is permissible in air or in water, it is usually necessary (1) to make certain simplifying assumptions about the manner in which the isotope is absorbed and eliminated, and (2) to assume values for various biological constants, which may not in practice be known at all accurately. For example, it is usually assumed that after a single dose, the amount of isotope present in any organ after the initial period of distribution is completed, decreases exponentially with time on account of the biological processes of elimination. In practice the decrease is not strictly exponential, and other representations have also been used. Assuming the elimination is represented by an exponential function the effective decay constant (λ) and effective half-life (τ) for an isotope in any particular organ are defined by the equations

$$\lambda = \lambda_R + \lambda_B$$

and $$1/\tau = 1/\tau_R + 1/\tau_B$$

where λ_R, λ_B denote the radioactive and biological decay constants respectively and τ_R, τ_B the radioactive and biological half-lives. The actual values to be assigned to λ or τ have in most cases to be based on animal experiments, although human data (for acute exposures) are available for a few of the isotopes now used clinically. Clearly the greater the effective half-life of an isotope, the less must be the permissible daily intake. The maximum concentration of an isotope which may be permitted in air or water will therefore be low if *either* the radiations emitted are of high energy and high biological efficiency (e.g. α-rays) *or* if the effective half-life in a critical organ is very great. The α-emitting isotopes such as radium and plutonium which are deposited in bone are particularly dangerous if taken into the body because they both emit radiations of high biological efficiency and also have a long half-life.

The precise relation between permissible concentration and effective half-life may be deduced as follows :

For those organs, to which the assumption of exponential elimination is applicable, the burden of isotope in the organ will change with time (t) according to the equation

$$\partial(qf_2)/\partial t = cvF - \lambda qf_2$$

where q denotes the body burden in μCi.

f_2 denotes the fraction of the body burden in the organ,

λ denotes the effective decay constant $= 0.693/\tau$,

v denotes the volume of air or water inhaled or ingested, in cc.,

c denotes the concentration of isotope in the air or water in μCi./cc.

F denotes the fraction of the amount inhaled or ingested, per day which reaches the critical organ (the selection of values for F is a matter of some difficulty in practice owing to scarcity of data).

Integrating

$$\therefore \quad \log_e \frac{cvF - \lambda q f_2}{cvF} = -\lambda t$$

or

$$\frac{\lambda q f_2}{cvF} = 1 - e^{-\lambda t}.$$

Assuming that $q = 0$ when $t = 0$, then for an exposure of t days during which q reaches the maximum permissible value q_{max}, the corresponding maximum permissible concentration c_{max} is determined by the equation

$$c_{max} = \frac{0.693}{\tau} \frac{q_{max} f_2}{vF} \frac{1}{(1 - e^{-0.693 t/\tau})}.$$

If t is large compared with τ, $e^{-0.693 t/\tau} \to 0$ and a state of equilibrium is reached after a time depending on τ in which the quantity absorbed just equals that eliminated. In this case

$$c_{max} = \frac{0.693}{\tau} \frac{q_{max} f_2}{vF}.$$

In a 24-hour day, a " standard " man consumes 2.2×10^3 cc. of water and breathes 2×10^7 cc. of air. For continuous exposure therefore

$$(c_{max})_{water} = \frac{3.1 \times 10^{-4}}{\tau} \frac{q_{max} f_2}{F} \frac{1}{(1 - e^{-0.693 t/\tau})} \ \mu\text{Ci./cc}$$

$$(c_{max})_{air} = \frac{3.5 \times 10^{-8}}{\tau} \frac{q_{max} f_2}{F} \frac{1}{(1 - e^{-0.693 t/\tau})} \ \mu\text{Ci./cc.}$$

For persons who are exposed only while at work it is assumed that one-half of the above intake occurs in 8 hours per day, 5 days per week for 50 weeks of the year. The maximum permissible concentrations are then given by

$$(c_{max})_{water} = \frac{9.2 \times 10^{-4}}{\tau} \frac{q_{max} f_2}{F} \frac{1}{(1 - e^{-0.693 t/\tau})} \ \mu\text{Ci./cc.}$$

$$(c_{max})_{air} = \frac{10^{-7}}{\tau} \frac{q_{max} f_2}{F} \frac{1}{(1 - e^{-0.693 t/\tau})} \ \mu\text{Ci./cc.}$$

The dose received by the gastro-intestinal tract is likely to be the limiting factor in determining the maximum permitted concentrations when insoluble substances are inhaled or ingested or when a mixture of isotopes is being used. (In the latter case all the isotopes will irradiate the gastro-intestinal tract whereas other organs will probably concentrate only one isotope.) In the G-I tract, the radioactive material spends a time $(t_2 - t_1)$ say, in contact with, but not absorbed by the tissue and then moves away, so the calculations of permissible concentrations are not the same as for an organ in which the elimination is exponential.

If the radioactive decay is slow so that the tissue can be assumed to be irradiated at a constant dose-rate for the time $(t_2 - t_1)$ each day, then the maximum permissible concentration can be deduced directly by equating the dose delivered in the time (t_2-t_1) to one-seventh of the maximum permissible weekly dose (R). Then

$$R/7 = \tfrac{1}{2}c_{max} \cdot v \cdot F \cdot 3{\cdot}7 \times 10^4 \times 1{\cdot}6 \times 10^{-6} \times 3600 \times 24 \times (t_2-t_1) \times \epsilon/100m'$$

In this equation (t_2-t_1) is expressed as a fraction of a day and the factor $\tfrac{1}{2}$ is introduced since the critical tissue is irradiated from only $\tfrac{1}{2}$ of the solid angle. m' denotes the mass of the section of the G-I tract considered.

Thus
$$c_{max} = \frac{5{\cdot}59 \times 10^{-3} Rm'}{v \cdot F \cdot \epsilon(t_2-t_1)}$$

For continuous exposure, therefore

$$(c_{max})_{water} = \frac{2{\cdot}54 \times 10^{-6} Rm'}{\epsilon \cdot (t_2-t_1)} \ \mu Ci./cc.$$

and
$$(c_{max})_{air} = \frac{2{\cdot}79 \times 10^{-10} Rm'}{F \cdot \epsilon(t_2-t_1)} \ \mu Ci./cc.$$

For exposure during working hours only

$$(c_{max})_{water} = \frac{7{\cdot}4 \times 10^{-6} Rm'}{(t_2-t_1)} \ \mu Ci./cc.$$

and
$$(c_{max})_{air} = \frac{8{\cdot}2 \times 10^{-10} Rm'}{F \cdot \epsilon(t_2-t_1)} \ \mu Ci./cc.$$

For the general case of an isotope decaying with a half-life τ_R which is not long compared with $(t_2 - t_1)$, the dose delivered is given by

$$R/7 = \tfrac{1}{2} \cdot \frac{c_{max} \cdot v \cdot F \cdot 3{\cdot}7 \times 10^4 \times 1{\cdot}6 \times 10^{-6} \times 3600 \times 24 \times \epsilon}{100m'} \int_{t_1}^{t_2} e^{-\lambda_R t} dt$$

and
$$c_{max} = \frac{5{\cdot}59 \times 10^{-3} m'}{v \cdot F\epsilon} \frac{0{\cdot}693}{\tau_R(e^{-0{\cdot}693 t_1/\tau_R} - e^{-0{\cdot}693 t_2/\tau_R})}$$

Values of the maximum permissible concentrations of the various radioactive isotopes, together with the values assumed for the relevant biological constants are given in the report of the International Commission upon Radiological Protection.[9]

Data for a few of the commoner isotopes only are given in Table 14.08 to illustrate the order of magnitude of the permissible concentrations.

TABLE 14.08

Element	Isotope	Critical organ	Maximum permissible body burden (μCi.)	Maximum permissible concentration (μCi./cc.)			
				40-hr. week		168-hr. week	
				water	air	water	air
Caesium	$Cs^{137}+$ Ba^{137}	Total body Lung	30	2×10^{-3}	4×10^{-7} 2×10^{-7}	9×10^{-4}	10^{-7} 6×10^{-7}
Chromium	Cr^{51}	Total body G-I Lung	800	0·6 0·05	10^{-5} 10^{-5} 2×10^{-6}	0·2 0·02	4×10^{-6} 4×10^{-6} 8×10^{-7}
Cobalt	Co^{60}	Total body G-I Lung	10	4×10^{-3}	4×10^{-7} 3×10^{-7}	10^{-3} 5×10^{-4} 9×10^{-9}	10^{-7} 10^{-7} 3×10^{-9}
Gold	Au^{198}	Kidneys G-I Lung	20	0·07 2×10^{-3}	3×10^{-6} 3×10^{-7} 6×10^{-7}	0·02 5×10^{-4}	9×10^{-7} 10^{-7} 2×10^{-7}
Iodine	I^{131}	Thyroid G-I	0·7	6×10^{-5} 2×10^{-3}	9×10^{-9} 3×10^{-7}	2×10^{-5} 6×10^{-4}	3×10^{-9} 10^{-7}
Iron	Fe^{59}	Spleen G-I Lung	20	4×10^{-3} 10^{-4} 2×10^{-3}	10^{-7} 4×10^{-7} 5×10^{-8}	10^{-3} 6×10^{-4}	5×10^{-8} 10^{-7} 2×10^{-8}
Phosphorus	P^{32}	Bone G-I Lung	6	5×10^{-4} 3×10^{-3}	7×10^{-8} 6×10^{-7} 8×10^{-8}	2×10^{-4} 9×10^{-4}	2×10^{-8} 2×10^{-7} 3×10^{-8}
Radium	$Ra^{226}+$ 55 % dr.	Bone G-I	0·1	4×10^{-7} 9×10^{-4}	3×10^{-11} 2×10^{-7}	10^{-7} 3×10^{-4}	10^{-11} 6×10^{-8}
Radon	$Rn^{222}+$ dr.	Lung			3×10^{-8}		10^{-8}
Strontium	Sr^{89}	Bone G-I Lung	4	3×10^{-4} 10^{-4}	3×10^{-8} 10^{-7} 4×10^{-8}	10^{-4} 3×10^{-4}	10^{-8} 5×10^{-8} 10^{-8}
Strontium	$Sr^{90}+$ Y^{90}	Bone G-I Lung	2	4×10^{-6} 10^{-3}	3×10^{-10} 2×10^{-7} 5×10^{-9}	10^{-6} 4×10^{-4}	10^{-10} 6×10^{-8} 2×10^{-9}
Tantalum	Ta^{182}	Liver G-I Lungs	7	0·9	4×10^{-8} 3×10^{-7} 2×10^{-8}	0·3 4×10^{-4}	10^{-8} 9×10^{-8} 7×10^{-9}

Regulations concerning the disposal of radioactive isotopes are made by various national authorities but it is usually accepted that soluble materials may be disposed of in the ordinary sewer system if the daily quantity released by the institution does not result in an average concentration exceeding the maximum permissible concentration in water for an 168-hour week. For hospitals, the daily water flow is usually assumed to be 1000 litres per bed per day or 500 litres per person per day. The daily permissible discharge is therefore $10^6 \times c_{max} \times$ no. of beds or $5 \times 10^5 \times c_{max} \times$ no. of persons. Insoluble waste with activity of the order of 1 μCi can usually be disposed of as ordinary refuse. More active items can be stored until the activity has decayed sufficiently for safe disposal. Highly active waste or material of long half-life is usually transferred to an accepted disposal agent, who will bury it, sink it at sea, or adopt other measures acceptable to the appropriate national authority.

REFERENCES

1. BECQUEREL, H. and CURIE, P. (1901). *C.R. Acad. Sciences, Paris,* **132,** 1289.
2. The Medical Research Council (1956). The Hazards to Man of Nuclear and Allied Radiations. London, H.M.S.O.
3. Ministry of Health and Department of Health for Scotland (1960). Radiological Hazards to Patients. Second report. London, H.M.S.O.
4. GLUCKSMANN, A., LAMERTON, L. F. and MAYNEORD, W. V. (1957). *Cancer,* ed. by R. W. Raven. Butterworth.
5. SIMPSON, E. L. and HEMPELMANN, L. H. (1955). *Radiology,* **64,** 840; (1957). *Cancer,* **10,** 42.
6. CONTI, E. A., PATTON, G. D., CONTI, J. E. and HEMPELMANN, L. H. (1960). *Radiology,* **74,** 386.
7. CILLEY, E. I. L., KIRKLIN, B. R. and LEDDY, E. T. (1935). *Amer. J. Roentg.* **33,** 390, 787; (1936). *ibid.* **34,** 241.
8. EVANS, R. D. (1943). *J. Ind. Hyg. Toxicol.* **25,** 253.
9. International Commission on Radiological Protection (1959). *Report of Committee II,* 12. London, Pergamon.
10. HINDMARSH, M. and VAUGHAN, J. (1957). *Brit. J. Radiol.* Suppl. 7, 71.
11. The International Commission on Radiological Protection (1966). Report of a Task Group of Committee 1. *Health Physics.* **12,** 239.
12. HEYSSEL, R., TOMONOGA, M., BRILL, A. B. and ITOGA, T. (1959). *Atomic Bomb Casualty Commission Technical Report* 11-59.

13. COURT-BROWN, W. M. and DOLL, R. (1957). *Medical Research Council, London*, Report No. 295.
14. STEWART, A., WEBB, J. and HEWITT, D. (1958). *Brit. Med. J.* **1**, 1495.
15. STEWART, A. and HEWITT, D. (1965). *Current Topics in Radiation Research*, ed. by Ebert, M. and Howard, A. Amsterdam, North Holland.
16. COURT-BROWN, W. M., DOLL, R. and HILL, A. B. (1960). *Brit. Med. J.* ii, 1539.
17. MACMAHON, B. (1962). *J. Cancer Nat. Inst.* **28**, 1173.
18. LEWIS, E. P. (1957). *Science*, **125**, 965.
19. SCHWARTZ, E. E. and UPTON, A. C. (1958). *Blood*, **12**, 845.
20. COURT-BROWN, W. M. and DOLL, R. (1958). *Brit. Med. J.*, **21**, 181.
21. International Commission on Radiological Protection. (1964). *Recommendations*, Publication 6; (1966), *Recommendations*, Publication 9. London, Pergamon.
22. SELTSER, R. and SARTWELL, P. E. (1958). *J. Amer. Med. Ass.* **166**, 585.
23. RUSSELL, L. B. and RUSSELL, W. L. (1952). *Radiology*, **58**, 369.
24. International Commission on Radiological Protection. (1964). *Report of Committee V.* London, Pergamon.
25. *United Nations Scientific Committee on the Effects of Atomic Radiation* (1962). Supplement 16 (A/5216).
26. International Commission on Radiological Protection (1960). *Report of Committee III.* London, Pergamon.
27. BATHO, H. F. (1950). *J. Canad. Ass. Radiol.* **1**, 48.
28. DIXON, W. R., GARRETT, C. and MORRISON, A. (1952). *Nucleonics*, **10**, No. 3, 42.
29. HOLLOWAY, A. F. (1961). *Amer. J. Roentg.* **85**, 152.
30. *U.S. National Bureau of Standards*, Handbooks Nos. 59, 65, 69, 73, 76.
31. (BRITISH) MINISTRY OF LABOUR (1964). Code of Practice for the Protection of Persons against Ionising Radiations (i) arising from Medical and Dental Use, (ii) in Research and Teaching. London, H.M.S.O.
32. MALLARD, J. R. (1958). *Brit. J. Radiol.* **31**, 439.

EXAMINATION QUESTIONS

1. Explain the meaning of the term "maximum permissible dose". State the present recommended values for whole body irradiation appropriate to a radiographer working in an X-ray department. State briefly what should be done by

   (a) The architect and radiologist responsible for the design of the department and

   (b) the radiographers in their daily work to ensure that these levels are not exceeded.

   M.S.R. (R. & T.), 1964.

2. What are the advantages and disadvantages of photographic film as compared with an ionisation chamber for the routine measurement of occupational radiation dose? Describe the construction of a film badge suitable for such use, stating the reasons for the presence of the various component parts.

M.S.R. (R. & T.), 1963.

3. Describe the *minimum* requirements for adequate X-ray protection of personnel * in an X-ray room equipped for
>   (*a*) gastro-intestinal examinations,
>   (*b*) angiography of the heart and aorta,
>   (*c*) general radiography.

* Including essential non X-ray department medical and nursing staff.

F.S.R. (R.), 1964.

4. Give an account of the protection recommendations for therapy X-ray installations and gamma-ray beam units. Explain where necessary the reasons for the recommendations.

F.S.R. (T.), 1965.

5. 100 mg. of radium is being prepared for clinical use. Calculate the exposure-rate at 50 cm. from the sources (assume they can be regarded as one " point " source and that the *k*-factor for radium is 8·0 roentgen/ hr./mg. at 1 cm.)

For protection purposes, what dose in rads and dose equivalent in rems would a person receive if irradiated at this exposure-rate? What thickness of lead shielding would be used to reduce the dose equivalent received in one hour to 3·2 millirems? (H.V.T. of lead = 1 cm.)

F.S.R. (T.), 1965.

6. State the maximum permissible doses recommended for radiation workers.

Describe the main requirements to ensure that minimum personal exposure is received by a worker in a radiological department.

D.M.R., 1963.

7. Explain the principles on which two methods of measuring the X-ray doses received by radiological workers are based and describe the important features of the apparatus in each case. What is meant by maximum permissible dose? How does it affect the protection of radiographers?

D.M.R., 1964.

8. What do you consider to be the duties of a Safety Officer in a large Radiotherapy Department?

Describe the precautions taken to avoid unnecessary radiation of others during the treatment of a patient who has carcinoma of the thyroid with 150 millicuries of I^{131}.

D.M.R. (T.), 1963.

APPENDIX I

USEFUL DATA*

1 micron (μ)	10^{-4} cm.
1 Ångstrom unit (Å)	10^{-8} cm.
1 electron volt (eV)	$1\cdot60210 \times 10^{-12}$ ergs.
1 atomic mass unit (a.m.u)	$1\cdot66043 \times 10^{-24}$ g.
	$931\cdot478$ MeV.
Velocity of light	$2\cdot997925 \times 10^{10}$ cm./sec.
Planck's constant	$6\cdot62559 \times 10^{-27}$ ergs-sec.
Mass of the electron	$0\cdot000548597$ a.m.u.
Mass of the proton	$1\cdot007277$ a.m.u.
Mass of the neutron	$1\cdot008665$ a.m.u.
Mass of the hydrogen atom	$1\cdot007825$ a.m.u.
Electronic charge	$4\cdot80298 \times 10^{-10}$ e.s.u.
Avogadro's number	$6\cdot02252 \times 10^{23}$ per mole
1 curie	$3\cdot7 \times 10^{10}$ dis./sec.
1 roentgen	$2\cdot58 \times 10^{-4}$ C./kg.
1 rad	100 ergs/g.

SOME PROPERTIES OF AIR AND BIOLOGICAL MATERIALS.†

Material	Density (gm./cc.)	No. of electrons per gm.	Effective atomic No. for	
			Photoelectric absorption	Pair production
Air	$1\cdot29 \times 10^{-3}$	$3\cdot03 \times 10^{23}$	$7\cdot64$	$7\cdot36$
Water	$1\cdot00$	$3\cdot34 \times 10^{23}$	$7\cdot42$	$6\cdot60$
Muscle	$1\cdot00$	$3\cdot36 \times 10^{23}$	$7\cdot42$	$6\cdot60$
Subcutaneous fat	$0\cdot91$	$3\cdot48 \times 10^{23}$	$5\cdot92$	$5\cdot2$
Bone	$1\cdot85$	$3\cdot00 \times 10^{23}$	$13\cdot8$	$10\cdot0$

* Physical constants from E. R. Cohen and J. W. M. Du Mond (1965), *Rev. Mod. Phys.* **37**, 537.

† Data on Biological Materials from H. E., Johns, *Physics of Radiation Therapy*, Illinois, Thomas.

APPENDIX II

THE CHEMICAL STRUCTURE OF SOME
BIOLOGICAL MOLECULES

Fatty acids have the general formula

$$C_n—H_{2n+1}—COOH$$

Amino acids have the general formula

$$NH_2—CHR—COOH$$

where R denotes a side group,

e.g. glycine $\quad\quad\quad\quad\quad NH_2—CH_2—COOH$

cysteine $\quad\quad\quad\quad NH_2—CH—COOH$
$$\quad\quad\quad\quad\quad\quad\quad\quad | $$
$$\quad\quad\quad\quad\quad\quad\quad CH_2$$
$$\quad\quad\quad\quad\quad\quad\quad | $$
$$\quad\quad\quad\quad\quad\quad\quad SH$$

tyrosine $\quad\quad\quad\quad NH_2—CH—COOH$
$$\quad\quad\quad\quad\quad\quad\quad\quad | $$
$$\quad\quad\quad\quad\quad\quad\quad CH_2$$
$$\quad\quad\quad\quad\quad\quad\quad | $$
$$\quad\quad\quad\quad\quad\quad\quad C_6H_4 . OH$$

Peptides are formed by the combination of two or more amino-acids with the elimination of water,

e.g. glycylglycine $\quad NH_2—CH_2—C—N—CH_2—COOH$
$$\quad\quad\quad\quad\quad\quad\quad\quad\quad\quad || \quad | $$
$$\quad\quad\quad\quad\quad\quad\quad\quad\quad\quad O \quad H$$

peptide linkage

The general formula for a peptide may be written

$$R \quad\quad\quad\quad\quad\quad O \quad\quad R''$$
$$| \quad\quad\quad\quad\quad\quad\quad || \quad\quad\quad | $$
$$NH_2—CH—C—NH—CH—C—NH—CH—C—NH—CH—COOH$$
$$\quad\quad\quad\quad || \quad\quad\quad\quad | \quad\quad\quad\quad\quad\quad || \quad\quad\quad\quad | $$
$$\quad\quad\quad\quad O \quad\quad\quad\quad R' \quad\quad\quad\quad\quad O \quad\quad\quad\quad R'''$$

where R, R', R'', R''' denote side chains.

Proteins may consist of either a single polypeptide chain or alternatively of two or more polypeptide chains which are inter-connected. Disulphide links and hydrogen bonds are common types of interchain connection.

Enzymes have the property of catalysing certain reactions and are usually called after the substrate upon which they react. Some enzymes are pure proteins whereas others consist of a protein in combination with a non-protein constituent.

Nucleic acids are formed by the combination of individual nucleotides. Each nucleotide is composed of a purine or pyrimidine base attached to a sugar (this combination is known as a nucleoside) and the sugar is combined with phosphoric acid. The purine and pyrimidine bases are

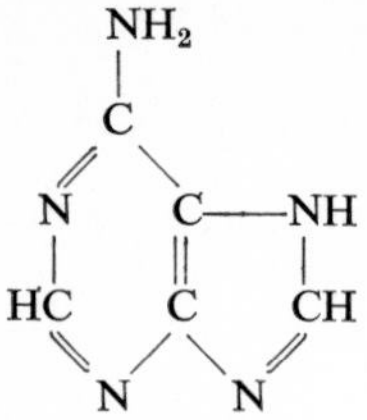

adenine

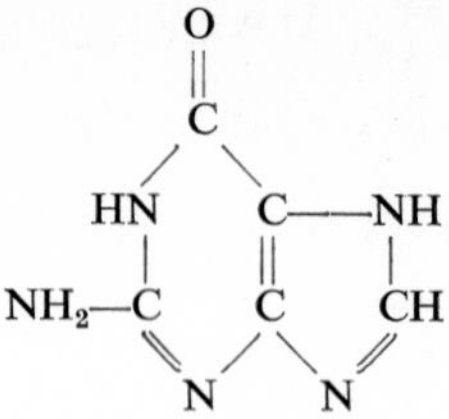

guanine

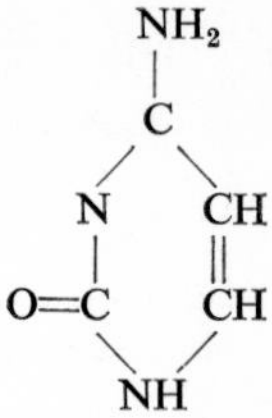

cytosine

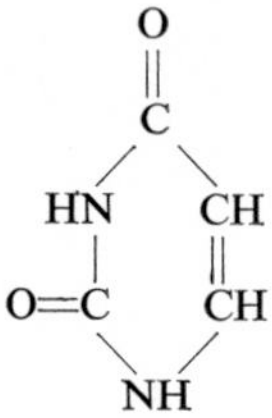

uracil

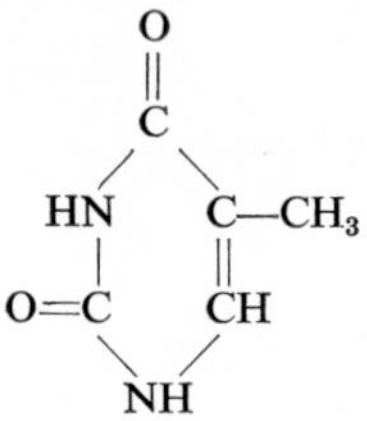

thymine

Adenine, guanine and cytosine are found in both RNA (ribose nucleic acid) and DNA (desoxyribosenucleic acid), uracil in RNA only and thymine in DNA only.

The sugars are

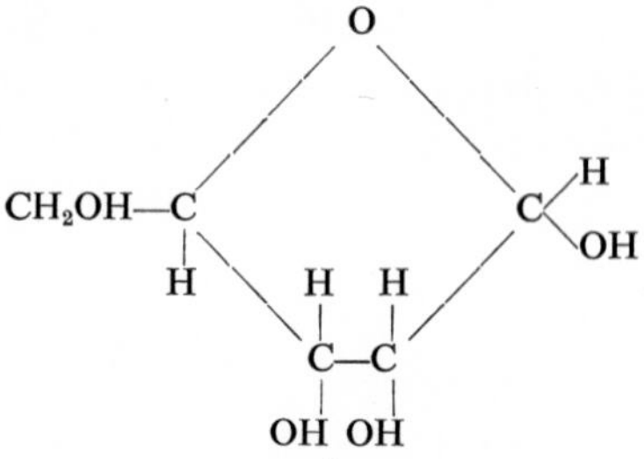

in RNA

ribose

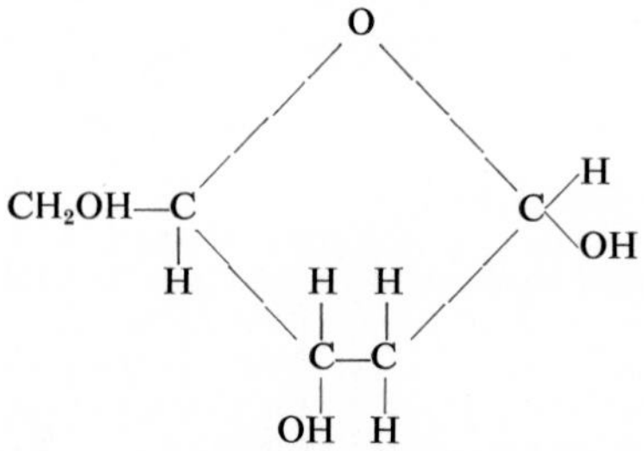

in DNA

desoxyribose

As an example of a nucleotide, the structure of adenine desoxyribonucleotide (thymus adenylic acid) is shown below.

582

In the nucleic acids, the individual nucleotides are linked through the sugar and phosphate groups to form long chains

In the Watson-Crick model of DNA it is postulated that two polynucleotide chains are wound side by side in the form of a double helix about 20 Å in diameter. The two chains are linked by hydrogen bonds between either (1) cytosine and guanine or (2) between adenine and thymine. (In DNA, the amount of cytosine always equals the amount of guanine and the amount of adenine equals the amount of thymine.)

INDEX

When a subject is discussed on consecutive pages, the number of the first page only is given. Italicised names indicate that the author is mentioned in references only.

A

Absorbed dose: 208, 216
  definition of, 209
  in tissue elements in bone, 422
  measurement of, 231
  relation to exposure, 213, 385
  unit of, 210
Absorption coefficients: (*see also* attenuation coefficients), 172
  real, 198
  total apparent, 172
Absorption of alpha (α) rays, 117
Absorption of beta (β) rays, 120
Absorption of X- and gamma (γ) rays: (*see also* attenuation), 171, 175
  real and apparent, 194
  summary, 175, 191
Accelerators:
  cyclic, 103
  linear, 100
  particle, 100
Activity, background equivalent, 289
Activity, of radioactive material:
  definition of, 127
  exposure-rate equivalent, 492
  saturation, 145
  specific, 145
After-loading techniques in therapy, sources for, 164
Air, maximum permissible concentration of radioactive materials in (table), 576
Adams, E. E., 541
Adams, G. D., 111, 461
Air ionisation chamber, 218
Air wall of ionisation chamber, 224
Albert, 541
Allen, 368
Alexander (and Bacq), effect of radiation on synthetic polymers, 346, 370
Allison, 204
Almond, 257
Alper, 368
Alpha (α) particles (alpha rays):
  chemical effects of, in water, 333
  discovery, nature and general properties of, 121

ionising properties of, 117
  range of, 119
Amasono, 329
Ames, 168
Amplatz, 542
Amplification factor:
  of transistor, 33
  of vacuum triode, 23
Anderson, discovery of positron by, 7
Andrade (and Rutherford), determination of wavelengths of γ-rays, 113
Anger, development of scintillation camera, 540, 542
Angstrom unit (Å), 2, 580
Angular distribution:
  of annihilation radiation, 188
  of classically scattered radiation, 177, 184
  of Compton (recoil) electrons, 185
  of Compton scattered radiation, 183, 184
  of pairs, 188
  of photo-electrons, 181
  of X-rays, 55
Annihilation radiation, 188
Anode, of X-ray tube:
  construction of, 40, 44
  cooling of, 44, 54
  hooded, 47
  rotating, 50
Anode circuit of X-ray set, 61
Anode current:
  of diode, 18
  of triode, 22
  of X-ray tube, 57, 63, 67, 78
Anoxia, effect on radiosensitivity, 342, 358
Applicators:
  beta-ray, 138, 165
  dose-rate from beta-ray, 493
  dose-rate from radium (table), 477
  for teletherapy, 374
  intra-cavitary, 481
  ophthalmic, 163
  rules for distributing radium on, 474
  superficial, 476
Aqueous solution, effect of radiation on, 338
Ardran, 329

585